Instructor's Solutions Manual

Volume 1 : Chapters 1 – 10

for Stewart's <u>Calculus</u>

Prepared by James Stewart

Brooks/Cole Publishing Company

Pacific Grove, California

Brooks/Cole Publishing Company
A Division of Wadsworth, Inc.

Printed in the United States of America

10 9 8 7 6 5 4 3 2 1

QA303.S8825   1986   515'.15   86-6078

ISBN 0-534-06693-3

Preface

I have edited this Instructor's Solutions Manual, consisting of solutions to all of the even–numbered exercises in the first ten chapters of <u>Calculus</u>, by carefully comparing those solutions obtained by myself and my colleagues at McMaster, during the seven years that we have class–tested the book, with those obtained by Daniel Anderson, University of Iowa; Daniel Drucker, Wayne State University; and Terry Tiballi, North Harris County College. I have paid particular attention to ensuring consistency of solutions techniques with those used in the text.

Daniel Anderson and Daniel Drucker were invaluable in proofing solutions "one more time." Daniel Drucker supplied much of the artwork for this volume.

I am grateful for the very capable assistance of David Dankort, who proofed and positioned solutions and artwork, and the following solutions checkers: Eric Bosch, Don Callfas, Ron Donaberger, Sara Lee, Marc Riehm, Martin Sarabura, Jeff Schultheiss, and Joe Vetrone. I typed the solutions myself, assisted by Lothar Redlin. I am confident that the accuracy of these solutions is very high.

James Stewart

Additional Solutions

The remaining solutions to the exercises in <u>Calculus</u> are found in three volumes, all of which are available at no cost to the instructor using this text in class.

The solutions to the remaining even–numbered exercises (Chapters 11 –15) are found in <u>Instructor's Solutions Manual, Vol. 2</u>, (ISBN: 0–534–06688–7) by the author.

The solutions to all of the odd–numbered exercises in the first ten chapters of <u>Calculus</u> are found in <u>Student Solutions Manual, Vol. 1</u> (ISBN: 0–534–06691–7) by Daniel Anderson and Daniel Drucker.

Solutions to the odd–numbered exercises in Chapters 11 – 15 are found in <u>Student Solutions Manual, Vol. 2</u>, (ISBN: 0–534–06692–5) by Barbara Frank, Pennsylvania State University.

All of the above manuals are available from your Wadsworth – Brooks/Cole sales representative or from the publisher. Write or call:

Brooks/Cole Publishing Company
511 Forest Lodge Road
Pacific Grove, California
93950

(408) 373–0728

Contents

CHAPTER ONE

Exercises 1.1

2. $3x-11 < 4 \iff 3x < 15 \iff x < 5 \iff x \in (-\infty,5)$

4. $4-3x \geq 6 \iff -3x \geq 2 \iff x \leq -2/3 \iff x \in (-\infty,-2/3]$

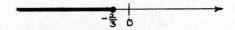

6. $1+5x > 5-3x \iff 8x > 4 \iff x > 1/2 \iff x \in (1/2,\infty)$

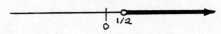

8. $1 < 3x+4 \leq 16 \iff -3 < 3x \leq 12 \iff -1 < x \leq 4 \iff x \in (-1,4]$

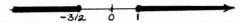

10. $-5 \leq 3-2x \leq 9 \iff -8 \leq -2x \leq 6 \iff 4 \geq x \geq -3 \iff x \in [-3,4]$

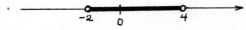

12. $2x+3 < x+4 < 3x-2$. So $2x+3 < x+4 \iff x < 1$, and $x+4 < 3x-2 \iff 6 < 2x \iff 3 < x$. Impossible, so no solution.

14. $x > 1-x \geq 3+2x$. So $x > 1-x \iff 2x > 1 \iff x > 1/2$, and $1-x \geq 3+2x \iff -2 \geq 3x \iff -2/3 \geq x$. Impossible, so no solution.

16. $(2x+3)(x-1) \geq 0$. Case (i): $2x+3 \geq 0 \iff x \geq -3/2$, and $x \geq 1$; so $x \in [1,\infty)$. Case (ii): $2x+3 \leq 0 \iff x \leq -3/2$, and $x \leq 1$; so $x \in (-\infty,-3/2]$. Solution set: $(-\infty,-3/2] \cup [1,\infty)$

18. $x^2 < 2x+8 \iff x^2-2x-8 < 0 \iff (x-4)(x+2) < 0$ Case (i): $x > 4$ and $x < -2$, which is impossible. Case (ii): $x < 4$ and $x > -2$. So solution set is: $(-2,4)$

20. $x^2+x > 1 \iff x^2+x-1 > 0$. Using the quadratic formula we obtain:

$x^2+x-1 = \left[x-\left[\frac{-1-\sqrt{5}}{2}\right]\right]\cdot\left[x-\left[\frac{-1+\sqrt{5}}{2}\right]\right] > 0.$ Case (i): $x-\left[\frac{-1-\sqrt{5}}{2}\right] > 0$ and

$x-\left[\frac{-1+\sqrt{5}}{2}\right] > 0$, so that $x > \frac{-1+\sqrt{5}}{2}$. Case (ii) $x-\left[\frac{-1-\sqrt{5}}{2}\right] < 0$ and

$x-\left[\frac{-1+\sqrt{5}}{2}\right] < 0$, so $x < \frac{-1-\sqrt{5}}{2}$. Solution set: $\left[-\infty, \frac{-1-\sqrt{5}}{2}\right] \cup \left[\frac{-1+\sqrt{5}}{2}, \infty\right]$

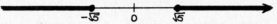

$(-1-\sqrt{5})/2 \qquad 0 \qquad (-1+\sqrt{5})/2$

22. $x^2 \geq 5 \Leftrightarrow x^2-5 \geq 0 \Leftrightarrow (x-\sqrt{5})(x+\sqrt{5}) \geq 0.$ Case (i): $x \geq \sqrt{5}$ and
$x \geq -\sqrt{5}$, so $x \in [\sqrt{5},\infty).$ Case (ii): $x \leq \sqrt{5}$ and $x \leq -\sqrt{5}$, so
$x \in (-\infty,-\sqrt{5}].$ Solution set: $(-\infty,-\sqrt{5}] \cup [\sqrt{5},\infty).$
[Another method: $x^2 \geq 5 \Leftrightarrow |x| \geq \sqrt{5} \Leftrightarrow x \geq \sqrt{5}$ or $x \leq -\sqrt{5}$]

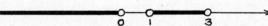

$-\sqrt{5} \qquad 0 \qquad \sqrt{5}$

24. $x^3+3x < 4x^2 \Leftrightarrow x^3-4x^2+3x < 0 \Leftrightarrow x(x^2-4x+3) < 0 \Leftrightarrow$
$x(x-1)(x-3) < 0.$

Interval	x	x-1	x-3	x(x-1)(x-3)
x < 0	−	−	−	−
0 < x < 1	+	−	−	+
1 < x < 3	+	+	−	−
x > 3	+	+	+	+

Solution set: $(-\infty,0) \cup (1,3)$

$0 \qquad 1 \qquad 3$

26. We solve the two inequalities separately and take the intersection
of the solution sets. First, $-3 < 1/x$ is clearly true if $x > 0$.
So suppose $x < 0$. Then $-3 < 1/x \Leftrightarrow -3x > 1 \Leftrightarrow x < -1/3$, so
for this inequality, the solutions set is: $(-\infty,-1/3) \cup (0,\infty)$. Now,
$1/x \leq 1$ is clearly true if $x < 0$. So suppose $x > 0$. Then $1/x \leq 1$
$\Leftrightarrow 1 \leq x$, and the solution set here is: $(-\infty,0) \cup [1,\infty)$. Taking
the intersection gives the final solution set: $(-\infty,-1/3) \cup [1,\infty)$.

$-1/3 \qquad 1$

28. $\frac{x}{x+1} > 3.$ Case (i): if $x+1 > 0$ (i.e. $x > -1$) then $x > 3(x+1) \Leftrightarrow$
$-3 > 2x \Leftrightarrow -3/2 > x$, which is impossible in this case.
Case (ii): if $x+1 < 0$ (i.e. $x < -1$) then $x < 3(x+1) \Leftrightarrow -3 < 2x$

⟺ -3/2 < x, so -3/2 < x < -1. Solution set: (-3/2,-1).

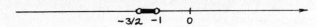

30. $\dfrac{2+x}{3-x} \le 1$. Case (i): if 3-x < 0 (i.e. 3 < x) then 2+x ≥ 3-x ⟺

2x ≥ 1 ⟺ x ≥ 1/2, so x ∈ (3,∞). Case (ii): if 3-x > 0 (i.e.

3 > x) then 2+x ≤ 3-x ⟺ 2x ≤ 1 ⟺ x ≤ 1/2, so x ∈ (-∞,1/2].

Solution set: (-∞,1/2] ∪ (3,∞)

32. $\dfrac{x^2-2x}{x^2-2} > 0$ ⟺ $\dfrac{x(x-2)}{(x-\sqrt{2})(x+\sqrt{2})} > 0$. (Call this quotient Q).

Interval	x	x-2	x-√2	x+√2	Q
x < -√2	−	−	−	−	+
-√2 < x < 0	−	−	−	+	−
0 < x < √2	+	−	−	+	+
√2 < x < 2	+	−	+	+	−
x > 2	+	+	+	+	+

Solution set: (-∞,-√2) ∪ (0,√2) ∪ (2,∞)

34. |3x+5| = 1 ⟺ 3x+5 = 1 or -1. In the first case, 3x = -4 so
x = -4/3, and in the second, 3x = -6 so x = -2.

36. $\left|\dfrac{2x-1}{x+1}\right| = 3$ ⟺ $\dfrac{2x-1}{x+1} = 3$ or -3. In the first case, 2x-1 = 3x+3 so

x = -4, and in the second, 2x-1 = -3x-3 so x = -2/5.

38. By (1.6), |x| ≥ 3 ⟺ x ≤ -3 or x ≥ 3, so x ∈ (-∞,-3] ∪ [3,∞).

40. |x-6| < 0.1 ⟺ -0.1 < x-6 < 0.1 ⟺ 5.9 < x < 6.1 ⟺
x ∈ (5.9,6.1)

42. |x+1| ≥ 3 ⟺ x+1 ≥ 3 or x+1 ≤ -3 ⟺ x ≥ 2 or x ≤ -4 ⟺
x ∈ (-∞,-4] ∪ [2,∞)

44. |5x-2| < 6 ⟺ -6 < 5x-2 < 6 ⟺ -4 < 5x < 8 ⟺ -4/5 < x < 8/5
⟺ x ∈ (-4/5,8/5)

46. 0 < |x-5| < 1/2. Clearly 0 < |x-5| for any x ≠ 5. Now |x-5| < 1/2
⟺ -1/2 < x-5 < 1/2 ⟺ 4.5 < x < 5.5. So solution set is:
(4.5,5) ∪ (5,5.5).

48. $|2x-5| \leq |x+4| \iff |2x-5|^2 \leq |x+4|^2 \iff (2x-5)^2 \leq (x+4)^2 \iff$
$4x^2-20x+25 \leq x^2+8x+16 \iff 3x^2-28x+9 \leq 0 \iff (3x-1)(x-9) \leq 0$.
Case (i): $x-9 \geq 0$ (i.e. $x \geq 9$) and $3x-1 \leq 0 \iff x \leq 1/3$, which is
impossible in this case. Case (ii): $x-9 \leq 0$ (i.e. $x \leq 9$) and
$3x-1 \geq 0 \iff x \geq 1/3$, so $1/3 \leq x \leq 9$. Solution set: $[1/3, 9]$

50. $\left|\frac{2-3x}{1+2x}\right| \leq 4 \iff \left(\frac{2-3x}{1+2x}\right)^2 \leq 16 \iff (2-3x)^2 \leq 16(1+2x)^2$ (for $x \neq -1/2$)
$\iff 4-12x+9x^2 \leq 16+64x+64x^2 \iff 0 \leq 55x^2+76x+12 = (5x+6)(11x+2)$.
Case (i): $5x+6 \geq 0 \iff x \geq -6/5$ and $11x+2 \geq 0 \iff x \geq -2/11$, so $x \in$
$[-2/11, \infty)$. Case (ii): $5x+6 \leq 0 \iff x \leq -6/5$ and $11x+2 \leq 0 \iff$
$x \leq -2/11$, so $x \in (-\infty, -6/5]$. Solution set: $(-\infty, -6/5] \cup [-2/11, \infty)$

52. We consider three cases. Case (i): if $x \geq 2$, then $|x+1| = x+1$ and
$|x-2| = x-2$. So $|x+1| + |x-2| < 7 \iff x+1 + x-2 < 7 \iff 2x < 8$
$\iff x < 4$. So $x \in [2, 4)$. Case (ii): if $-1 \leq x < 2$, then
$|x+1| = x+1$, but $|x-2| = -(x-2)$. So $|x+1| + |x-2| < 7 \iff$
$x+1 - (x-2) < 7 \iff 3 < 7$. Since this is always true, this case
leads to $x \in [-1, 2)$. Case (iii): if $x < -1$, then $|x+1| = -(x+1)$
and $|x-2| = -(x-2)$. So $|x+1| + |x-2| < 7 \iff -(x+1) - (x-2) < 7$
$\iff -2x < 6 \iff x > -3$. Combining the three cases, we obtain the
solution: $x \in (-3, 4)$.

54. $a \leq bx+c < 2a \iff a-c \leq bx < 2a-c \iff \frac{a-c}{b} \leq x < \frac{2a-c}{b}$ (since $b>0$)

56. $\frac{ax+b}{c} \leq b \iff ax+b \geq bc$ (since $c < 0$) $\iff ax \geq bc-b \iff$
$x \leq \frac{b(c-1)}{a}$ (since $a < 0$)

58. If $0 < a < b$, then $\frac{1}{ab} > 0$. So $a < b \iff \frac{1}{ab} \cdot a < \frac{1}{ab} \cdot b \iff \frac{1}{b} < \frac{1}{a}$

60. $|a/b||b| = |(a/b) \cdot b| = |a|$ (using the result of Exercise 59).
Dividing the equation through by $|b|$ gives $|a/b| = |a|/|b|$.

62. Since $|a| \geq 0$, $-|a| \leq 0$, so that $-|a| \leq |a|$. Now from (1.3),
$a = |a|$ or $-|a|$. Thus $-|a| \leq a \leq |a|$.

64. Following the hint, the Triangle Inequality becomes
$|(x-y)+y| \leq |x-y|+|y| \iff |x| \leq |x-y|+|y| \iff |x-y| \geq |x|-|y|$.

Exercises 1.2

2. $\sqrt{(5-1)^2+(7-(-3))^2} = \sqrt{4^2+10^2} = \sqrt{116} = 2\sqrt{29}$

4. $\sqrt{(-1-1)^2+(-3-(-6))^2} = \sqrt{(-2)^2+3^2} = \sqrt{13}$

6. $\sqrt{(b-a)^2+(a-b)^2} = \sqrt{(a-b)^2+(a-b)^2} = \sqrt{2(a-b)^2} = \sqrt{2}\,|a-b|$

8. $|AB| = \sqrt{(11-6)^2+(-3-(-7))^2} = \sqrt{5^2+4^2} = \sqrt{41}$

   $|AC| = \sqrt{(2-6)^2+(-2-(-7))^2} = \sqrt{(-4)^2+5^2} = \sqrt{41}$

   $|BC| = \sqrt{(2-11)^2+(-2-(-3))^2} = \sqrt{(-9)^2+1^2} = \sqrt{82}$ So
   $|AB|^2+|AC|^2 = 41+41 = 82 = |BC|^2$, and so $\triangle ABC$ is a right
   triangle. Its area is $\dfrac{\sqrt{41}\cdot\sqrt{41}}{2} = \dfrac{41}{2}$

10. $|AB| = \sqrt{(3-(-1))^2+(11-3)^2} = \sqrt{4^2+8^2} = \sqrt{80} = 4\sqrt{5}$,

    $|BC| = \sqrt{(5-3)^2+(15-11)^2} = \sqrt{2^2+4^2} = \sqrt{20} = 2\sqrt{5}$, and

    $|AC| = \sqrt{(5-(-1))^2+(15-3)^2} = \sqrt{6^2+12^2} = \sqrt{180} = 6\sqrt{5} = |AB|+|BC|$

12. Let M be the point $\left[\dfrac{x_1+x_2}{2}, \dfrac{y_1+y_2}{2}\right]$. Then

    $|MP_1|^2 = \left[x_1-\left[\dfrac{x_1+x_2}{2}\right]\right]^2 + \left[y_1-\left[\dfrac{y_1+y_2}{2}\right]\right]^2 = \left[\dfrac{x_1-x_2}{2}\right]^2 + \left[\dfrac{y_1-y_2}{2}\right]^2$, and

    $|MP_2|^2 = \left[x_2-\left[\dfrac{x_1+x_2}{2}\right]\right]^2 + \left[y_2-\left[\dfrac{y_1+y_2}{2}\right]\right]^2 = \left[\dfrac{x_2-x_1}{2}\right]^2 + \left[\dfrac{y_2-y_1}{2}\right]^2$.

    Hence $|MP_1| = |MP_2|$.

14. The midpoint M_1 of AB is $\left[\dfrac{1+3}{2}, \dfrac{0+6}{2}\right] = (2,3)$, the midpoint M_2 of BC
    is $\left[\dfrac{3+8}{2}, \dfrac{6+2}{2}\right] = (11/2,4)$, and the midpoint M_3 of CA is $\left[\dfrac{8+1}{2}, \dfrac{2+0}{2}\right] =$
    $(9/2,1)$. The lengths of the medians are

    $|AM_2| = \sqrt{(11/2-1)^2+(4-0)^2} = \sqrt{(9/2)^2+4^2} = \sqrt{145/4} = \sqrt{145}/2$

    $|BM_3| = \sqrt{(9/2-3)^2+(1-6)^2} = \sqrt{(3/2)^2+(-5)^2} = \sqrt{109/4} = \sqrt{109}/2$, and

    $|CM_1| = \sqrt{(2-8)^2+(3-2)^2} = \sqrt{(-6)^2+1^2} = \sqrt{37}$.

16. y = -2

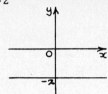

18. |y| = 1 ⟺ y = 1 or y = -1

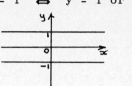

20. y = 2x+5

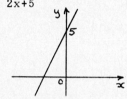

22. y = x³

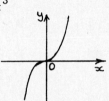

24. x+√y = 4 ⟺ x = 4-√y

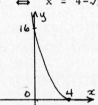

26. {(x,y) | y > 0}

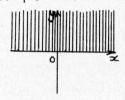

28. {(x,y) | x ≥ 1 and y < 3}

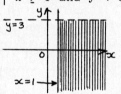

30. {(x,y) | |x| < 3 and |y| < 2}

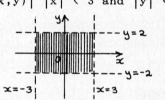

32. {(x,y) | x²+y² > 4}

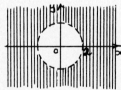

34. (x+2)² + (y+8)² = 100

36. The equation has the form $(x+1)^2 + (y-5)^2 = r^2$. Since $(-4,-6)$ lies on the circle, we have $r^2 = (-4+1)^2 + (-6-5)^2 = 130$. So the required equation is $(x+1)^2 + (y-5)^2 = 130$.

38. $x^2+y^2+6y = -2$ ⟺ $x^2+(y^2+6y+9) = -2+9 = 7$ ⟺ $x^2+(y+3)^2 = 7$.

6

Center: $(0,-3)$, radius: $\sqrt{7}$.

40. $16x^2+8x+16y^2+32y = -1 \iff (16x^2+8x+1) + (16y^2+32y+16) = -1+1+16 =$

$16 \iff (x^2+\frac{1}{2}x+\frac{1}{16}) + (y^2+2y+1) = 1 \iff (x+\frac{1}{4})^2 + (y+1)^2 = 1$

Center: $(-1/4,-1)$, radius: 1.

42. $x^2+ax+y^2+by = -c \iff (x^2+ax+\frac{a^2}{4}) + (y^2+by+\frac{b^2}{4}) = -c + \frac{a^2}{4} + \frac{b^2}{4} \iff$

$(x+\frac{a}{2})^2 + (y+\frac{b}{2})^2 = \frac{a^2+b^2-4c}{4}$. For this to represent a non-degenerate

circle, we must have $\frac{a^2+b^2-4c}{4} > 0$ or $a^2+b^2 > 4c$. If this is the

case, the center of the circle is $\left[-\frac{a}{2}, -\frac{b}{2}\right]$ and the radius is

$\frac{\sqrt{a^2+b^2-4c}}{2}$.

Section 1.3

Exercises 1.3

2. $\frac{-3-6}{4-(-1)} = \frac{-9}{5}$ 4. $\frac{0-(-4)}{6-(-1)} = \frac{4}{7}$

6. $y-4 = -3(x-(-1))$ or $y = -3x+1$

8. $y-(-5) = -(7/2)(x-(-3))$ or $7x+2y+31 = 0$

10. $m = \frac{3-(-2)}{4-(-1)} = 1$. So $y-3 = 1(x-4)$ or $y = x-1$.

12. $y = \frac{2}{5}x + 4$

14. $m = \frac{6-0}{0-(-8)} = \frac{3}{4}$. So $y = \frac{3}{4}x+6$.

16. $m = \tan 135° = -1$. So $y-3 = -1(x-(-5))$ or $x+y+2 = 0$.

18. Vertical line: $x = 4$.

20. $2x+3y+4 = 0 \iff y = -\frac{2}{3}x - \frac{4}{3}$, so $m = -2/3$. So the required line

is $y = -(2/3)x + 6$.

22. $4x-8y = 1 \iff y = \frac{1}{2}x - \frac{1}{8}$. Since this line has slope $1/2$, a line

perpendicular to it would have slope -2, so the required line is

$y-(-\frac{2}{3}) = -2(x-\frac{1}{2}) \iff y = -2x + \frac{1}{3}$ or $6x+3y = 1$.

24. AB has slope $\frac{3-(-1)}{3-(-3)} = \frac{2}{3}$ and AC has slope $\frac{8-(-1)}{-9-(-3)} = -\frac{3}{2}$. So by (1.17), AB is perpendicular to AC, and hence $\triangle ABC$ is a right triangle.

26. (a) The line segment from $(1,1)$ to $(3,9)$ has slope $\frac{9-1}{3-1} = 4$ and the line segment from $(3,9)$ to $(6,21)$ has slope $\frac{21-9}{6-3} = 4$ as well, so the three points are collinear.

    (b) The line segment from $(-1,3)$ to $(1,7)$ has slope $\frac{7-3}{1-(-1)} = 2$, while the line segment from $(1,7)$ to $(4,15)$ has slope $\frac{15-7}{4-1} = \frac{8}{3}$. Thus the points are not collinear.

28. (a) Side PQ has slope $\frac{4-0}{3-1} = 2$ so its equation is $y-0 = 2(x-1)$ ⟺ $y = 2x-2$. Side QR has slope $\frac{6-4}{-1-3} = -\frac{1}{2}$ so its equation is $y-4 = -\frac{1}{2}(x-3)$ ⟺ $y = -\frac{1}{2}x + \frac{11}{2}$. Side RP has slope $\frac{0-6}{1-(-1)} = -3$ so its equation is $y-0 = -3(x-1)$ ⟺ $y = -3x+3$.

    (b) M_1 (the midpoint of PQ) has coordinates $\left[\frac{1+3}{2}, \frac{0+4}{2}\right] = (2, 2)$. M_2 (the midpoint of QR) has coordinates $\left[\frac{3-1}{2}, \frac{4+6}{2}\right] = (1, 5)$. M_3 (the midpoint of RP) has coordinates $\left[\frac{1-1}{2}, \frac{0+6}{2}\right] = (0, 3)$. RM_1 has slope $\frac{2-6}{2-(-1)} = -\frac{4}{3}$ and hence equation $y-2 = -\frac{4}{3}(x-2)$ ⟺ $y = -\frac{4}{3}x+\frac{14}{3}$. PM_2 is a vertical line with equation $x = 1$. QM_3 has slope $\frac{3-4}{0-3} = \frac{1}{3}$ and hence equation $y-3 = \frac{1}{3}(x-0)$ ⟺ $y = \frac{1}{3}x + 3$. PM_2 and RM_1 intersect where $x = 1$ and $y = -\frac{4}{3}\cdot(1) + \frac{14}{3} = \frac{10}{3}$, or at $(1,10/3)$. PM_2 and QM_3 intersect where $x = 1$ and $y = \frac{1}{3}(1)+3 = \frac{10}{3}$, or at $(1,10/3)$, so this is the point where all three medians intersect.

30. $2x-5y = 0$ ⟺ $y = \frac{2}{5}x$, so the slope is 2/5 and the y-intercept 0.

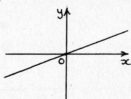

32. $2x-3y+6 = 0 \iff y = \frac{2}{3}x+2$, so the slope is $\frac{2}{3}$ and the y-intercept 2.

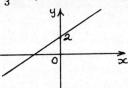

34. $4x+5y = 10 \iff y = -\frac{4}{5}x+2$, so the slope is $-\frac{4}{5}$ and the y-intercept 2

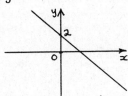

36. $\sqrt{3}x-y = 1 \iff y = \sqrt{3}x-1$, so the slope m is $\sqrt{3} = \tan\theta$ and $\theta = 60°$.

38. $3x-4y+5 = 0 \iff y = \frac{3}{4}x+\frac{5}{4}$, so m = 3/4 = $\tan\theta$ and $\theta \approx 37°$.

40. $y = 2x+3$, $y = 3x+2$. Setting $2x+3 = 3x+2$ gives $x = 1$, so $y = 2(1)+3 = 5$, and the point of intersection is $(1,5)$. Since $m_1 = 2$ and $m_2 = 3$, $\tan\theta = \frac{3-2}{1+2\cdot3} = \frac{1}{7}$, and so $\theta \approx 8°$ (or 172°).

42. In slope-intercept form the lines are $y = 2x+1$ and $y = \frac{1}{2}x+\frac{5}{2}$. Setting $2x+1 = \frac{1}{2}x+\frac{5}{2}$ gives $x = 1$ and $y = 2(1)+1 = 3$, so the lines intersect at $(1,3)$. Since $m_1 = 2$ and $m_2 = 1/2$, $\tan\theta = \frac{(1/2) - 2}{1 + (1/2)\cdot2} = -\frac{3}{4}$, and so $\theta \approx 143°$ (or 37°).

44. $\{(x,y) \mid y > 2x-1\}$

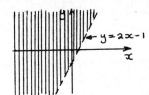

46. $\{(x,y) \mid -x \le y < \frac{x+3}{2}\}$

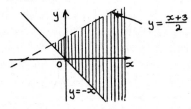

48. $\{(x,y) \mid |x-y|+|x|-|y| \leq 2\}$. Case (i): $x > y \geq 0$. Then
$|x-y|+|x|-|y| \leq 2$ ⟺ $x-y + x - y \leq 2$ ⟺ $2x-2y \leq 2$ ⟺ $x-y \leq 1$
⟺ $y \geq x-1$. Case (ii): $y \geq x \geq 0$. Then $|x-y|+|x|-|y| \leq 2$ ⟺
$-x+y +x - y \leq 2$ ⟺ $0 \leq 2$, so in this case the inequality is
always true. Case (iii): $x \geq 0$, $y < 0$. Then $|x-y|+|x|-|y| \leq 2$ ⟺
$x-y + x + y \leq 2$ ⟺ $2x \leq 2$ ⟺ $x \leq 1$. Combining cases (i) to
(iii), we get the portion of the graph below that lies in the first
and fourth quadrants (i.e. the right half of the coordinate plane).
Now note that the inequality that defines the set is unchanged if
we replace x by -x and y by -y and simplify. Thus the set is
symmetric about the origin, and we obtain the left half of the
graph below from the right half by symmetry.

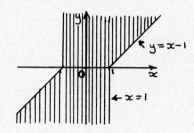

Section 1.4

Exercises 1.4

2. $y^2-x^2 = 1$. Hyperbola.

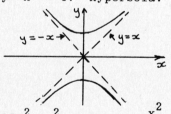

4. $x = -2y^2$. Parabola.

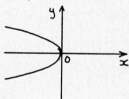

6. $25x^2+4y^2 = 100$ ⟺ $\dfrac{x^2}{4} + \dfrac{y^2}{25} = 1$. Ellipse.

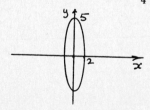

10

8. $y = x^2+2$. Parabola with vertex at $(0,2)$.

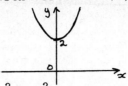

10. $9x^2-25y^2 = 225 \iff \dfrac{x^2}{25} - \dfrac{y^2}{9} = 1$. Hyperbola.

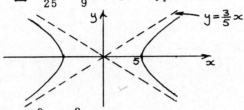

12. $2x^2+5y^2 = 10 \iff \dfrac{x^2}{5} + \dfrac{y^2}{2} = 1$. Ellipse.

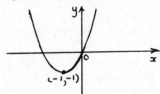

14. $y = x^2+2x = (x^2+2x+1)-1 = (x+1)^2-1$. Parabola with vertex at $(-1,-1)$.

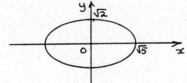

16. $16x^2+9y^2-36y = 108 \iff 16x^2+9(y^2-4y+4) = 108+36 = 144 \iff$
$\dfrac{x^2}{9} + \dfrac{(y-2)^2}{16} = 1$. Ellipse centered at $(0,2)$.

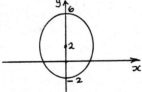

18. $x^2-y^2-4x+3 = 0 \iff (x^2-4x+4)-y^2 = -3+4 = 1 \iff (x-2)^2-y^2 = 1.$
Hyperbola centered at $(2,0)$.

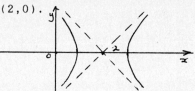

20. $y^2-2x+6y+5 = 0 \iff y^2+6y+9 = 2x-5+9 = 2x+4 \iff (y+3)^2 = 2(x+2).$
Parabola with vertex at $(-2,-3)$.

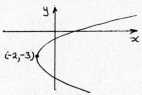

22. $4x^2+9y^2-16x+54y+61 = 0 \iff 4(x^2-4x+4) + 9(y^2+6y+9) = -61+16+81 = 36$
$\iff \dfrac{(x-2)^2}{9} + \dfrac{(y+3)^2}{4} = 1.$ Ellipse centered at $(2,-3)$.

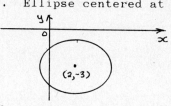

24. $y = 4-x^2$, $x-2y = 2$. Substitute y from first equation into second:
$x-2(4-x^2) = 2 \iff 2x^2+x-10 = 0 \iff (2x+5)(x-2) = 0 \iff x = -5/2$
or 2. So the points of intersection are $(-5/2, -9/4)$ and $(2,0)$.

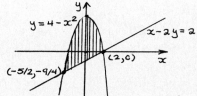

26. The ellipse has an equation of the form $\dfrac{x^2}{a^2} + \dfrac{y^2}{b^2} = 1$. Substituting

$x = 1$, $y = -10\sqrt{2}/3$ gives $\dfrac{1^2}{a^2} + \dfrac{(-10\sqrt{2}/3)^2}{b^2} = \dfrac{1}{a^2} + \dfrac{200}{9b^2} = 1.$

Substituting $x = -2$ and $y = 5\sqrt{5}/3$ gives $\dfrac{(-2)^2}{a^2} + \dfrac{(5\sqrt{5}/3)^2}{b^2} =$

$\dfrac{4}{a^2} + \dfrac{125}{9b^2} = 1.$ From the first equation, $\dfrac{1}{a^2} = 1 - \dfrac{200}{9b^2}.$ Putting this

12

into the second equation gives $4\left[1 - \dfrac{200}{9b^2}\right] + \dfrac{125}{9b^2} = 1 \iff 3 = \dfrac{675}{9b^2}$

$\iff b^2 = \dfrac{675}{27} = 25$, so b = 5. Hence $\dfrac{1}{a^2} = 1 - \dfrac{200}{9(5)^2} = \dfrac{1}{9}$ and so

a = 3. The equation of the ellipse is $\dfrac{x^2}{9} + \dfrac{y^2}{25} = 1$.

28. $\{(x,y) \mid x^2 + 4y^2 \leq 4\}$

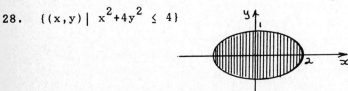

Section 1.5

Exercises 1.5

2. $f(x) = x^3 + 2x^2 - 3$, so $f(0) = 0^3 + 2(0)^2 - 3 = -3$, $f(3) = 3^3 + 2(3)^2 - 3 = 42$,

$f(-3) = (-3)^3 + 2(-3)^2 - 3 = -12$, $f(-x) = (-x)^3 + 2(-x)^2 - 3 = -x^3 + 2x^2 - 3$,

$f(1/a) = (1/a)^3 + 2(1/a)^2 - 3 = (1 + 2a - 3a^3)/a^3$

4. $h(t) = t + (1/t)$, so $h(1) = 1 + (1/1) = 2$, $h(\pi) = \pi + (1/\pi) = (\pi^2 + 1)/\pi$

$h(t+1) = (t+1) + \dfrac{1}{t+1} = \dfrac{t^2 + 2t + 2}{t+1}$, $h(t) + h(1) = t + (1/t) + 2 = \dfrac{t^2 + 2t + 1}{t}$,

$h(x) = x + (1/x)$

6. $f(x) = 2/x$, $1 \leq x \leq 4$

Machine diagram   Arrow diagram   Graph

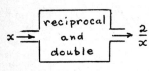 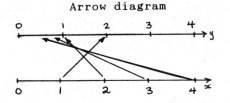 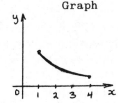

8. $f(x) = 2x + 7$, $-1 \leq x \leq 6$. The domain is $[-1, 6]$. If $-1 \leq x \leq 6$,

then $5 = 2(-1) + 7 \leq 2x + 7 \leq 2(6) + 7 = 19$, so the range is $[5, 19]$.

10. $g(x) = \dfrac{1}{x+4}$. Since division by 0 is undefined, the domain is

$\{x \mid x \neq -4\} = (-\infty, -4) \cup (-4, \infty)$, and the range is

$\{y \mid y \neq 0\} = (-\infty, 0) \cup (0, \infty)$.

12. $h(x) = \sqrt[4]{7-3x}$. This is defined when $7-3x \geq 0$ or $x \leq 7/3$, so the domain is $(-\infty, 7/3]$. The range is $[0,\infty)$ since every non-negative real number is the fourth root of some non-negative real.

14. $F(x) = 1-\sqrt{x}$ is defined when $x \geq 0$, so the domain is $[0,\infty)$. Now $\sqrt{x}$ takes on all values ≥ 0, so $-\sqrt{x}$ takes on all values ≤ 0 and $1-\sqrt{x}$ takes on all values ≤ 1, so the range is $(-\infty, 1]$.

16. $G(x) = \sqrt{x^2-9}$ is defined when $x^2-9 \geq 0 \iff x^2 \geq 9 \iff |x| \geq 3 \iff x \leq -3$ or $x \geq 3$, so the domain is $(-\infty, -3] \cup [3,\infty)$, and the range is $[0,\infty)$.

18. $f(x) = x^4/(x^2+x-6)$ is defined for all x except when $0 = x^2+x-6 = (x+3)(x-2) \iff x = -3$ or 2, so the domain is $\{x \in R \mid x \neq -3, 2\}$.

20. $g(x) = \sqrt{x^2-2x-8}$ is defined when $0 \leq x^2-2x-8 = (x-4)(x+2) \iff x \geq 4$ or $x \leq -2$, so the domain is $(-\infty, -2] \cup [4,\infty)$.

22. $\phi(x) = \left[\dfrac{x^2-2x}{x-1}\right]^{1/2}$ is defined when $0 \leq \dfrac{x^2-2x}{x-1} = \dfrac{x(x-2)}{x-1}$.

Interval	x	x-1	x-2	x(x-2)/(x-1)
x < 0	-	-	-	-
0 < x < 1	+	-	-	+
1 < x < 2	+	+	-	-
x > 2	+	+	+	+

So the domain is $[0,1) \cup [2,\infty)$.

24. $f(t) = \sqrt{t^2+1}$ is defined for every t, since t^2+1 is always positive. The domain is the set of all real numbers.

26. $f(x) = -3$. Domain is R.

28. $f(x) = \dfrac{x+3}{2}$, $-2 \leq x \leq 2$.

    Domain is $[-2,2]$.

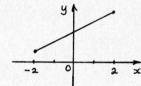

30. $f(x) = x^2-4$. Domain is R.

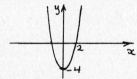

32. $f(x) = -x^2+6x-7 = -(x^2-6x+9)+2$
$= -(x-3)^2+2$, so the graph is a
parabola with vertex at $(3,2)$.
The domain is R.

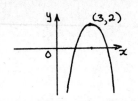

34. $g(x) = x^5$. Domain is R.

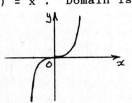

36. $g(x) = \sqrt{6-2x}$. Domain is
$\{x \mid 6-2x \geq 0\} = (-\infty, 3]$.

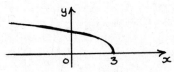

38. $h(x) = \sqrt{x^2-4}$. Now $y = \sqrt{x^2-4}$ $\Rightarrow$
$y^2 = x^2-4$ $\iff$ $x^2-y^2 = 4$, so the
graph is the top half of a
hyperbola. The domain is
$\{x \mid x^2-4 \geq 0\} = (-\infty, -2] \cup [2, \infty)$.

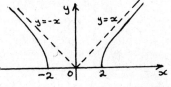
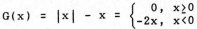

40. $F(x) = \dfrac{2}{x+4}$. Domain is
$\{x \mid x \neq -4\}$.

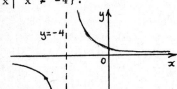

42. $G(x) = |x| - x = \begin{cases} 0, & x \geq 0 \\ -2x, & x < 0 \end{cases}$
Domain is R.

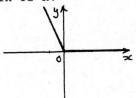

44. $H(x) = |2x-3| = \begin{cases} 2x-3, & x \geq 3/2 \\ 3-2x, & x < 3/2 \end{cases}$ Domain is R.

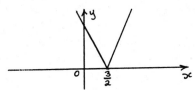

46. $f(x) = |x^2-1| = \begin{cases} x^2-1, & x \geq 1 \text{ or } \leq -1 \\ -x^2+1, & -1 \leq x \leq 1 \end{cases}$ Domain is R.

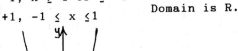
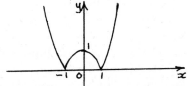

15

48. $f(x) = \dfrac{x^2+5x+6}{x+2} = \dfrac{(x+3)(x+2)}{x+2}$, so

for $x \neq -2$, $f(x) = x+3$. Domain
is $\{x \mid x \neq -2\}$.

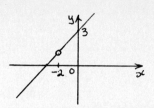

NOTE: In each of Problems 50-60, the domain is all of R.

50. $f(x) = \begin{cases} x+3, & x \neq -2 \\ 4, & x=-2 \end{cases}$

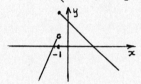

52. $f(x) = \begin{cases} 1, & -1 \leq x \leq 1 \\ -1, & x > 1 \text{ or } x < -1 \end{cases}$

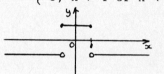

54. $f(x) = \begin{cases} 2x+3, & x < -1 \\ 3-x, & x \geq -1 \end{cases}$

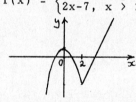

56. $f(x) = \begin{cases} |x|, & -1 \leq x \leq 1 \\ 1, & x > 1 \text{ or } x < -1 \end{cases}$

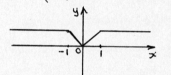

58. $f(x) = \begin{cases} 1-x^2, & x \leq 2 \\ 2x-7, & x > 2 \end{cases}$

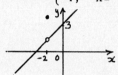

60. $f(x) = \begin{cases} \sqrt{-x}, & x < 0 \\ x, & 0 \leq x \leq 2 \\ \sqrt{x-2}, & x > 2 \end{cases}$

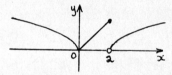

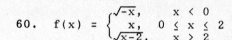

62. No, this is not the graph of a function by (1.24).

64. Yes, this is the graph of a function with domain $[-3,2]$ and range $\{-2\} \cup (0,3]$.

66. The slope of this line segment is $\dfrac{3-(-2)}{6-(-3)} = \dfrac{5}{9}$, so its equation is $y+2 = \dfrac{5}{9}(x+3)$ The function is $f(x) = \dfrac{5}{9}x - \dfrac{1}{3}$, $-3 \leq x \leq 6$.

68. $(x-1)^2+y^2 = 1 \Rightarrow y = \pm\sqrt{1-(x-1)^2} = \pm\sqrt{2x-x^2}$. The top half is given by by the function $f(x) = \sqrt{2x-x^2}$, $0 \leq x \leq 2$.

70. Let the length and width of the rectangle be ℓ and w respectively. Then the area is $\ell w = 16$, so that $w = 16/\ell$. The perimeter is $P = 2\ell + 2w$, so $P(\ell) = 2\ell + 2(16/\ell) = 2\ell + 32/\ell$, and the domain of P is $\ell > 0$, since lengths must be positive quantities.

72. Let the volume of the cube be V and the length of an edge be ℓ.
Then $V = \ell^3$ so $\ell = \sqrt[3]{V}$, and the surface area will be
$S(V) = 6(\sqrt[3]{V})^2 = 6V^{2/3}$, with domain $V > 0$.

74. $C(x) = \begin{cases} \$2.00 & 0.0 < x \le 1.0 \\ 2.20 & 1.0 < x \le 1.1 \\ 2.40 & 1.1 < x \le 1.2 \\ 2.60 & 1.2 < x \le 1.3 \\ 2.80 & 1.3 < x \le 1.4 \\ 3.00 & 1.4 < x \le 1.5 \\ 3.20 & 1.5 < x \le 1.6 \\ 3.40 & 1.6 < x \le 1.7 \\ 3.60 & 1.7 < x \le 1.8 \\ 3.80 & 1.8 < x \le 1.9 \\ 4.00 & 1.9 < x < 2.0 \end{cases}$

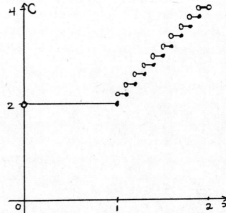

76. $f(-x) = (-x)^{-3} = -(x^{-3}) = -f(x)$, so f is odd.

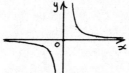

78. $f(-x) = (-x)^4 - 4(-x)^2 = x^4 - 4x^2 = f(x)$, so f is even.

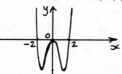

80. $f(-x) = 3(-x)^3 + 2(-x)^2 + 1 = -3x^3 + 2x^2 + 1$. Since this is neither $f(x)$ nor $-f(x)$, the function f is neither even nor odd.

Section 1.6

Exercises 1.6

In this problem set, "D =" stands for "the domain of the function is".

2. $f(x) = x^3+2x^2$, $g(x) = 3x^2-1$. $(f+g)(x) = x^3+2x^2+3x^2-1 = x^3+5x^2-1$,
    $D = R$, $(f-g)(x) = x^3+2x^2-(3x^2-1) = x^3-x^2+1$, $D = R$
    $(fg)(x) = (x^3+2x^2)(3x^2-1) = 3x^5+6x^4-x^3-2x^2$, $D = R$
    $(f/g)(x) = (x^3+2x^2)/(3x^2-1)$, $D = \{x \in R \mid x \neq \pm 1/\sqrt{3}\}$

4. $f(x) = \sqrt{9-x^2}$, $D = [-3,3]$; $g(x) = \sqrt{x^2-1}$, $D = (-\infty,-1] \cup [1,\infty)$
    $(f+g)(x) = \sqrt{9-x^2} + \sqrt{x^2-1}$, $D = [-3,-1] \cup [1,3]$
    $(f-g)(x) = \sqrt{9-x^2} - \sqrt{x^2-1}$, $D = [-3,-1] \cup [1,3]$
    $(fg)(x) = \sqrt{9-x^2} \cdot \sqrt{x^2-1} = \sqrt{-x^4+10x^2-9}$, $D = [-3,-1] \cup [1,3]$
    $(f/g)(x) = \sqrt{9-x^2}/\sqrt{x^2-1}$. $D = [-3,-1) \cup (1,3]$

6. $f(x) = \sqrt[4]{x+1}$, $D = [-1,\infty)$; $g(x) = \sqrt{x+2}$, $D = [-2,\infty)$;
    $(f+g)(x) = \sqrt[4]{x+1} + \sqrt{x+2}$, $D = [-1,\infty) \cap [-2,\infty) = [-1,\infty)$;
    $(f-g)(x) = \sqrt[4]{x+1} - \sqrt{x+2}$, $D = [-1,\infty)$; $(fg)(x) = \sqrt[4]{x+1} \cdot \sqrt{x+2}$,
    $D = [-1,\infty)$; $(f/g)(x) = \sqrt[4]{x+1}/\sqrt{x+2}$, $D = [-1,\infty)$

8. $F(x) = \sqrt{1-x} + \sqrt{x-2}$. $D = (-\infty,1] \cap [2,\infty) = \{\}$ (empty set).

10. $f(x) = \sqrt{x}$, $g(x) = 3$ 12. $f(x) = x^3$, $g(x) = -x^2$

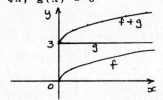   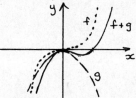

14. $f(x) = 6x-5$, $g(x) = x/2$. Domain and range is R for all composites.
    $(f \circ g)(x) = f(g(x)) = f(x/2) = 6(x/2)-5 = 3x-5$.
    $(g \circ f)(x) = g(f(x)) = g(6x-5) = (6x-5)/2 = 3x - 5/2$.
    $(f \circ f)(x) = f(f(x)) = f(6x-5) = 6(6x-5)-5 = 36x-35$.
    $(g \circ g)(x) = g(g(x)) = g(x/2) = x/4$.

16. $f(x) = \sqrt{x-1}$, $D = [1,\infty)$; $g(x) = x^2$, $D = R$. $(f \circ g)(x) = f(g(x))$
    $= f(x^2) = \sqrt{x^2-1}$. $D = \{x \in R \mid g(x) \in [1,\infty)\} = (-\infty,-1] \cup [1,\infty)$
    $(g \circ f)(x) = g(f(x)) = g(\sqrt{x-1}) = (\sqrt{x-1})^2 = x-1$. $D = [1,\infty)$
    $(f \circ f)(x) = f(f(x)) = f(\sqrt{x-1}) = \sqrt{\sqrt{x-1}-1}$. $D = \{x \in [1,\infty) \mid \sqrt{x-1} \geq 1\}$

$= [2,\infty)$. $(g \circ g)(x) = g(g(x)) = g(x^2) = (x^2)^2 = x^4$. $D = R$

18. $f(x) = \dfrac{1}{x-1}$, $D = \{x \mid x \neq 1\}$; $g(x) = \dfrac{x-1}{x+1}$, $D = \{x \mid x \neq -1\}$.

$(f \circ g)(x) = f\left[\dfrac{x-1}{x+1}\right] = \left[\dfrac{x-1}{x+1} - 1\right]^{-1} = \left[\dfrac{-2}{x+1}\right]^{-1} = \dfrac{-x-1}{2}$ $\qquad D = \{x \mid x \neq -1\}$

$(g \circ f)(x) = g\left[\dfrac{1}{x-1}\right] = \dfrac{1/(x-1) - 1}{1/(x-1) + 1} = \dfrac{2-x}{x}$ $\qquad D = \{x \mid x \neq 0,1\}$

$(f \circ f)(x) = f\left[\dfrac{1}{x-1}\right] = \dfrac{1}{1/(x-1) - 1} = \dfrac{x-1}{2-x}$ $\qquad D = \{x \mid x \neq 1,2\}$

$(g \circ g)(x) = g\left[\dfrac{x-1}{x+1}\right] = \dfrac{(x-1)/(x+1) - 1}{(x-1)/(x+1) + 1} = -\dfrac{1}{x}$ $\qquad D = \{x \mid x \neq 0,-1\}$

20. $f(x) = \sqrt{x^2-1}$, $D = (-\infty,-1] \cup [1,\infty)$; $g(x) = \sqrt{1-x}$, $D = (-\infty,1]$.

$(f \circ g)(x) = f(g(x)) = f(\sqrt{1-x}) = \sqrt{(\sqrt{1-x})^2-1} = \sqrt{-x}$

$D = \{x \leq 1 \mid \sqrt{1-x} \in (-\infty,-1] \cup [1,\infty)\} = (-\infty,0]$

$(g \circ f)(x) = g(f(x)) = g(\sqrt{x^2-1}) = \sqrt{1-(x^2-1)^{1/2}}$

$D = \{x \in (-\infty,-1] \cup [1,\infty) \mid \sqrt{x^2-1} \in (-\infty,1]\} = [-\sqrt{2},-1] \cup [1,\sqrt{2}]$

$(f \circ f)(x) = f(f(x)) = f(\sqrt{x^2-1}) = \sqrt{x^2-2}$ $\qquad D = (-\infty,-\sqrt{2}] \cup [\sqrt{2},\infty)$

$(g \circ g)(x) = g(g(x)) = g(\sqrt{1-x}) = \sqrt{1-\sqrt{1-x}}$ $\qquad D = [0,1]$

22. $f(x) = 1/\sqrt{x}$, $D = (0,\infty)$; $g(x) = x^2-4x$, $D = R$.

$(f \circ g)(x) = f(g(x)) = f(x^2-4x) = 1/\sqrt{x^2-4x}$

$D = \{x \mid x^2-4x > 0\} = (-\infty,0) \cup (4,\infty)$

$(g \circ f)(x) = g(f(x)) = g(1/\sqrt{x}) = 1/x - 4/\sqrt{x}$ $\qquad D = (0,\infty)$

$(f \circ f)(x) = f(f(x)) = f(1/\sqrt{x}) = \dfrac{1}{\sqrt{1/\sqrt{x}}} = x^{1/4}$ $\qquad D = (0,\infty)$

$(g \circ g)(x) = g(g(x)) = g(x^2-4x) = (x^2-4x)^2-4(x^2-4x) = x^4-8x^3+12x^2+16x$

$D = R$.

24. $(f \circ g \circ h)(x) = f(g(h(x))) = f(g(x^2+2)) = f((x^2+2)^3) = \dfrac{1}{(x^2+2)^3}$

26. $(f \circ g \circ h)(x) = f(g(h(x))) = f(g(\sqrt[3]{x})) = f\left[\dfrac{\sqrt[3]{x}}{\sqrt[3]{x} - 1}\right] = \left[\dfrac{\sqrt[3]{x}}{\sqrt[3]{x} - 1}\right]^{1/2}$

28. Let $g(x) = \sqrt{x}$ and $f(x) = x+1$. Then $(f \circ g)(x) = \sqrt{x} + 1 = F(x)$.

30. Let $g(x) = x+3$ and $f(x) = 1/x$. Then $(f \circ g)(x) = \dfrac{1}{x+3} = G(x)$.

32. Let $h(x) = \sqrt{x}$, $g(x) = x-1$ and $f(x) = \sqrt[3]{x}$. Then $(f \circ g \circ h)(x) = \sqrt[3]{\sqrt{x}-1}$.

34. We need a function g so that $g(f(x)) = g(x+4) = h(x) = 4x-1 = 4(x+4)-17$. So we see that the function g must be $g(x) = 4x-17$.

Exercises 1.7

2. $y = \sqrt[4]{x}$

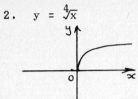

4. $y = -x^3$

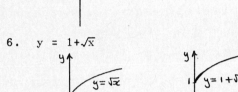

6. $y = 1 + \sqrt{x}$

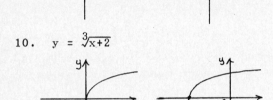

8. $y = -\cos x$

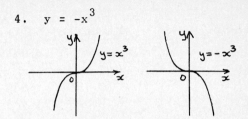

10. $y = \sqrt[3]{x+2}$

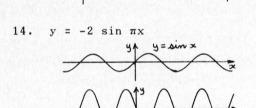

12. $y = x^2 + x + 1 = \left[x + \frac{1}{2}\right]^2 + \frac{3}{4}$

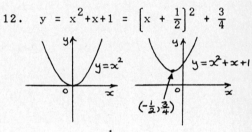

14. $y = -2 \sin \pi x$

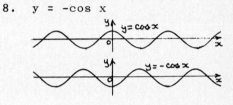

16. $y = 2 + \frac{1}{x+1}$

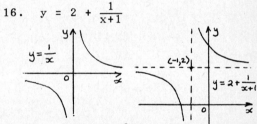

18. $y = \frac{1}{2}\sqrt{x+4} - 3$

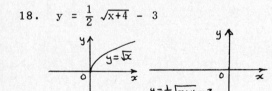

20. $y = 1 - (x-8)^6$

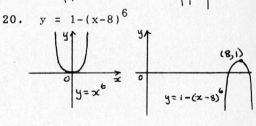

Review Exercises for Chapter 1

2. $-5 \leq 1-2x \leq 3 \iff -6 \leq -2x \leq 2 \iff 3 \geq x \geq -1 \iff x \in [-1,3]$

4. $|2x-7| > 1$. Case (i): $2x-7 > 1 \iff 2x > 8 \iff x > 4$. Case (ii): $2x-7 < -1 \iff 2x < 6 \iff x < 3$. Solution set: $(-\infty,3) \cup (4,\infty)$.

6. Since $x^2+2 > 0$ for all x, $\dfrac{2x^2+x}{x^2+2} \leq 1 \iff 2x^2+x \leq x^2+2 \iff$

   $x^2+x-2 \leq 0 \iff (x+2)(x-1) \leq 0$ Case (i): $x+2 \geq 0$ (so $x \geq -2$) and $x-1 \leq 0$ (so $x \leq 1$); $-2 \leq x \leq 1$.   Case (ii): $x+2 \leq 0$ (so $x \leq -2$) and $x-1 \geq 0$ (so $x \geq 1$); impossible.   Solution set: $[-2,1]$.

8. $\{(x,y) \mid |x| \leq 2,\ |y| > 1\}$

10. The equation must have the form $(x+6)^2 + (y-4)^2 = r^2$. Since the origin lies on the circle, we substitute $x=0$, $y=0$ in the equation to find r: $6^2+(-4)^2 = 52 = r^2$, so $(x+6)^2 + (y-4)^2 = 52$.

12. $y-1 = -3(x-2)$ or $3x+y = 7$

14. $y = -\frac{1}{3}x + 2$ or $x+3y = 6$

16. $3x-4y = 6 \iff y = \frac{3}{4}x - \frac{3}{2}$; slope is $\frac{3}{4}$ so perpendicular line has slope $-\frac{4}{3}$. So $y-1 = -\frac{4}{3}(x-(-1))$ or $4x+3y+1 = 0$.

18. (a) Substitute y from first equation into second: $2x + (3x+1) = 9 \iff 5x = 8 \iff x = 8/5$, so $y = 3(8/5) + 1 = 29/5$. $(8/5, 29/5)$.

    (b) First line has slope $m_1 = 3$. Second line $\iff y = -2x +9$, so $m_2 = -2$. So $\tan\theta = \dfrac{-2-3}{1+3(-2)} = 1 \Rightarrow \theta = 45°$ exactly (or $135°$).

20. $x^2+4y^2 =16 \iff \dfrac{x^2}{16} + \dfrac{y^2}{4} = 1$,   22. $x+4y^2 = 0 \iff x = -4y^2$,

    an ellipse   a parabola

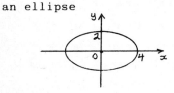
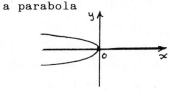

24. $y^2 - x^2 = 4 \iff \dfrac{y^2}{4} - \dfrac{x^2}{4} = 1$,

hyperbola.

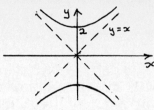

26. $f(x)$ is defined unless the denominator is 0. $\sqrt[3]{2x} + 2 = 0 \iff$
$\sqrt[3]{2x} = -2 \iff 2x = -8 \iff x = -4$. Domain is $\{x \mid x \neq -4\}$.

28. $h(x)$ is defined whenever $5 - 4x - x^2 \geq 0 \iff (5+x)(1-x) \geq 0$. Case
(i): $5+x \geq 0$ (so $x \geq -5$) and $1-x \geq 0$ (so $1 \geq x$), so $-5 \leq x \leq 1$.
Case (ii): $5+x \leq 0$ (so $x \leq -5$) and $1-x \leq 0$ (so $1 \leq x$), which is
impossible. So the domain is $[-5,1]$.

30. $f(x) = 2 + 3x$

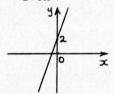

32. $g(x) = 4x - x^2 = -(x-2)^2 + 4$

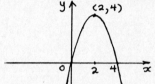

34. $h(x) = 1 - x^5$

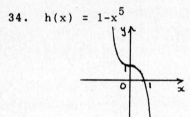

36. $F(x) = \begin{cases} 1 - x/2, & x < 2 \\ x - 3, & x \geq 2 \end{cases}$

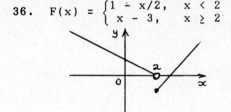

38. $f(x) = x^2 + 3x$, domain is R; $g(x) = \sqrt{x+2}$, domain is $[-2,\infty)$.
 (a) $(f+g)(x) = x^2 + 3x + \sqrt{x+2}$. $D = [-2,\infty)$
 (b) $(f/g)(x) = (x^2 + 3x)/\sqrt{x+2}$. $D = (-2,\infty)$
 (c) $(f \circ g)(x) = f(g(x)) = f(\sqrt{x+2}) = (\sqrt{x+2})^2 + 3(\sqrt{x+2}) = x + 2 + 3\sqrt{x+2}$.
      $D = [-2,\infty)$

 (d) $(g \circ f)(x) = g(f(x)) = g(x^2 + 3x) = \sqrt{x^2 + 3x + 2}$. $D = \{x \mid x^2 + 3x + 2 \geq 0\}$
      $= (-\infty, -2] \cup [-1, \infty)$

40. Let $f(x) = 1/x$, $g(x) = \sqrt[3]{x}$ and $h(x) = x^2 + 3$. Then
$f(g(h(x))) = 1/\sqrt[3]{x^2 + 3} = F(x)$, so $F = f \circ g \circ h$.

CHAPTER TWO

Exercises 2.1

2. $y = x^2 - 2x$, $(4,8)$

(a) $m_{PQ} = \dfrac{f(x)-f(4)}{x-4} = \dfrac{x^2-2x-8}{x-4} = \dfrac{(x-4)(x+2)}{x-4} = x+2$ if $x \neq 4$.

(b)

.x-4.	..x..	m_{PQ}
0.5	4.5	6.5
-0.5	3.5	5.5
0.1	4.1	6.1
-0.1	3.9	5.9
0.01	4.01	6.01
-0.01	3.99	5.99
0.001	4.001	6.001
-0.001	3.999	5.999

(c) 6

(d) $y-8 = 6(x-4)$ or $y = 6x-16$

4. $y = x^3 + x^2$, $(1,2)$

(a) $m_{PQ} = \dfrac{f(x)-f(1)}{x-1} = \dfrac{x^3+x^2-2}{x-1} = \dfrac{(x-1)(x^2+2x+2)}{x-1} = x^2+2x+2$ if $x \neq 1$

(b)

.x-1.	..x..	m_{PQ}
0.5	1.5	7.25
-0.5	0.5	3.25
0.1	1.1	5.41
-0.1	0.9	4.61
0.01	1.01	5.0401
-0.01	0.99	4.9601
0.001	1.001	5.004001
-0.001	0.999	4.996001

(c) 5

(d) $y-2 = 5(x-1)$ or $y = 5x-3$

6. $y = 1 - 2x^3$, $(-1,3)$

(a) $m_{PQ} = \dfrac{f(x)-f(-1)}{x-(-1)} = \dfrac{1-2x^3-3}{x+1} = \dfrac{-2(x+1)(x^2-x+1)}{x+1} = -2(x^2-x+1)$ if

$x \neq -1$.

(b)

x-(-1)	..x..	m_{PQ}
0.5	-0.5	-3.5
-0.5	-1.5	-9.5
0.1	-0.9	-5.42
-0.1	-1.1	-6.62
0.01	-0.99	-5.9402
-0.01	-1.01	-6.0602
0.001	-0.999	-5.994002
-0.001	-1.001	-6.006002

(c) -6

(d) $y-3 = -6(x+1)$
    or $6x+y+3 = 0$

8. $y = \dfrac{x}{1-x}$, $(0,0)$.

(a) $m_{PQ} = \dfrac{f(x)-f(0)}{x-0} = \dfrac{x/(1-x)}{x} = \dfrac{1}{1-x}$ if $x \neq 0,\ 1$.

(b)

.x-0.	...x..	^{m}PQ.....
0.5	0.5	2
-0.5	-0.5	2/3
0.1	0.1	1.11111
-0.1	-0.1	0.90909
0.01	0.01	1.010101
-0.01	-0.01	0.990099
0.001	0.001	1.001001
-0.001	-0.001	0.999001

(c) 1

(d) y-0 = 1(x-0) or y = x

10. $y = \cos x$, $(\pi/6, \sqrt{3}/2)$

(a) $m_{PQ} = \dfrac{f(x)-f(\pi/6)}{x - \pi/6} = \dfrac{\cos x - \sqrt{3}/2}{x - \pi/6}$ if $x \neq \pi/6$

(b)

.x-π/6	...x...	^{m}PQ....
0.5	1.02360	-0.69146
-0.5	0.02360	-0.26739
0.1	0.62360	-0.54243
-0.1	0.42360	-0.45590
0.01	0.53360	-0.50432
-0.01	0.51360	-0.49566
0.001	0.52460	-0.50043
-0.001	0.52260	-0.49957

(c) -1/2

(d) $y-\dfrac{\sqrt{3}}{2} = -\dfrac{1}{2}(x-\dfrac{\pi}{6})$

or $6x+12y = \pi+6\sqrt{3}$

12. Average velocity between t and t+h seconds is

$$\frac{58(t+h)-0.83(t+h)^2-(58t-0.83t^2)}{h} = \frac{58h-1.66th-0.83h^2}{h} =$$

$58-1.66t-0.83h$ if $h \neq 0$.

(a) Here t = 1, so the average velocity is

$\quad$ 58-1.66-0.83h = 56.34-0.83h

$\quad$ [1,2]: h = 1 so 55.51 m/s $\quad$ [1,1.5]: h = 0.5 so 55.925 m/s

$\quad$ [1,1.1]: 56.257 m/s $\quad\quad\quad$ [1,1.01]: 56.3317 m/s

$\quad$ [1,1.001]: 56.33917 m/s

(b) 56.34 m/s

(c) From the formula for average velocity, we see that as h approaches 0, the velocity approaches 58 - 1.66t.

(d) When the height is 0, i.e. $58t - 0.83t^2 = 0 \iff$

$t(58 - 0.83t) = 0 \iff t = \dfrac{58}{0.83} \approx 69.88$ s (since t can't be 0).

(e) $58- 1.66(69.88) \approx -58$ m/s

14. Average velocity between times 1 and 1+h is $\dfrac{s(1+h)-s(1)}{h} =$

$\dfrac{(1+h)^3/6 - 1/6}{h} = \dfrac{h^3+3h^2+3h}{6h} = \dfrac{h^2+3h+3}{6}$ if $h \neq 0$.

(a)   **(i)** $\frac{2^2+3(2)+3}{6} = \frac{13}{6}$ ft/s   **(ii)** $\frac{1^2+3(1)+3}{6} = \frac{7}{6}$ ft/s

(iii) $\frac{(0.5)^2+3(0.5)+3}{6} = \frac{19}{24}$ ft/s   **(iv)** $\frac{(0.1)^2+3(0.1)+3}{6} = \frac{331}{600}$ ft/s

(b) As h approaches 0, the velocity approaches 1/2 ft/s.

(c) & (d)

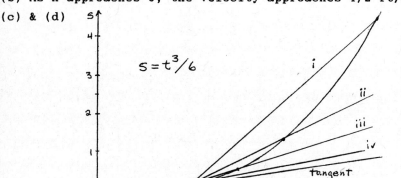

16.   **(a) (i)** $\frac{164-117}{4} = 11.75$ **(ii)** $\frac{150-117}{3} = 11$ **(iii)** $\frac{137-117}{2} = 10$

   (iv) $\frac{126-117}{1} = 9$

(b)

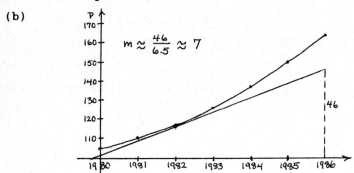

Tangent line at 1982 has approximate slope 7 (thousand people per year).

18.   Rate of change between 20 and 20+h minutes is

$$\frac{V(20+h) - V(20)}{h} = \frac{100000\left[1 - \frac{(20+h)}{60}\right]^2 - 100000\left[1 - \frac{20}{60}\right]^2}{h} =$$

$-\frac{20,000}{9} + \frac{2500h}{9}$.   As h approaches 0, the rate of flow approaches

$-\frac{20,000}{9} \approx -2222.2$ gal/min.

Exercises 2.2

2. -1   4. 1   6. Does not exist

8. Does not exist   10. 0   12. Does not exist

14. $\lim\limits_{x \to -1} (5-x^2) = 5-(-1)^2 = 4$

16. $\lim\limits_{x \to 3} \dfrac{6+x}{9-x} = \dfrac{6+3}{9-3} = \dfrac{3}{2}$

18. $\lim\limits_{x \to 4} \dfrac{\sqrt{x}}{1+2x-x^2} = \dfrac{\sqrt{4}}{1+2\cdot 4-4^2} = -\dfrac{2}{7}$

20. $\lim\limits_{x \to 3} \dfrac{x^2-9}{x-3} = \lim\limits_{x \to 3} \dfrac{(x-3)(x+3)}{x-3} = \lim\limits_{x \to 3} (x+3) = 6$

22. $\lim\limits_{x \to -1} \dfrac{x^2-x-2}{x+1} = \lim\limits_{x \to -1} \dfrac{(x+1)(x-2)}{x+1} = \lim\limits_{x \to -1} (x-2) = -3$

24. $\lim\limits_{x \to 1} \dfrac{x^3-1}{x^2-1} = \lim\limits_{x \to 1} \dfrac{(x-1)(x^2+x+1)}{(x-1)(x+1)} = \lim\limits_{x \to 1} \dfrac{x^2+x+1}{x+1} = \dfrac{1^2+1+1}{1+1} = \dfrac{3}{2}$

26. $\lim\limits_{h \to 0} \dfrac{(h-5)^2-25}{h} = \lim\limits_{h \to 0} \dfrac{(h^2-10h+25)-25}{h} = \lim\limits_{h \to 0} \dfrac{h^2-10h}{h} = \lim\limits_{h \to 0} (h-10) = -10$

28. $\lim\limits_{h \to 0} \dfrac{(a+h)^3-a^3}{h} = \lim\limits_{h \to 0} \dfrac{(a^3+3a^2h+3ah^2+h^3)-a^3}{h} = \lim\limits_{h \to 0} \dfrac{3a^2h+3ah^2+h^3}{h}$

$= \lim\limits_{h \to 0} (3a^2+3ah+h^2) = 3a^2$

30. $\lim\limits_{x \to 1} \dfrac{x^2+x-2}{x^2-3x+2} = \lim\limits_{x \to 1} \dfrac{(x+2)(x-1)}{(x-2)(x-1)} = \lim\limits_{x \to 1} \dfrac{x+2}{x-2} = \dfrac{1+2}{1-2} = -3$

32. $\lim\limits_{t \to 2} \dfrac{t^2+t-6}{t^2-4} = \lim\limits_{t \to 2} \dfrac{(t+3)(t-2)}{(t+2)(t-2)} = \lim\limits_{t \to 2} \dfrac{t+3}{t+2} = \dfrac{5}{4}$

34. $\lim\limits_{x \to 0} \dfrac{1}{x^4}$ does not exist since $x^4 \to 0$ as $x \to 0$.

36. $\lim\limits_{x \to -3} \dfrac{1}{x+3}$ does not exist since $x+3 \to 0$ as $x \to 0$.

38. $\lim\limits_{x \to 5^-} \sqrt[4]{5-x} = \sqrt[4]{5-5} = 0$

40. Since $g(x) = x+2$ for $x \neq 1$, $\lim\limits_{x \to 1} g(x) = \lim\limits_{x \to 1} (x+2) = 1+2 = 3$

     Therefore $\lim\limits_{x \to 1^-} f(x) = 3 = \lim\limits_{x \to 1^+} f(x)$.

42. (a) $\lim_{x\to 1^-} p(x) = \lim_{x\to 1^-} (x+2) = 3$ (b) $\lim_{x\to 1^+} p(x) = \lim_{x\to 1^+} (4-x) = 3$

(c) $\lim_{x\to 1} p(x) = 3$

44. $\lim_{x\to 0^+} \frac{|x|}{x} = \lim_{x\to 0^+} \frac{x}{x} = \lim_{x\to 0^+} 1 = 1$ and $\lim_{x\to 0^-} \frac{|x|}{x} = \lim_{x\to 0^-} \frac{-x}{x} = \lim_{x\to 0^-} -1 = -1$

Since the one-sided limits differ, $\lim_{x\to 0} \frac{|x|}{x}$ does not exist.

46. $g(x) = \frac{\cos x - 1}{\sin x}$ (a)

..x..	....g(x).
1	-0.546302
0.5	-0.255342
0.4	-0.202710
0.3	-0.151135
0.2	-0.100335
0.1	-0.050042
0.05	-0.025005
0.01	-0.005000

(b) It appears that $\lim_{x\to 0} g(x) = 0$.

48. $h(x) = \frac{\tan x - x}{x^3}$.

(a)

x	h(x)
1	0.55740773
0.5	0.37041992
0.1	0.33467210
0.05	0.33366704
0.01	0.33335000
0.005	0.33333600

(b) It seems that $\lim_{x\to 0} h(x) = \frac{1}{3}$

(c)

x	h(x)
0.001	0.33300000
0.0005	0.33360000
0.0004	0.33281250
0.0003	0.33333333
0.0002	0.33750000
0.0001	0.30000000
0.00005	0.32000000
0.00001	0.00000000
0.000001	0.00000000
0.0000001	0.00000000

Here the values will vary from one calculator to another. Every calculator will eventually give false values. (See Appendix D.) Later, in Example 6.10.4, we'll see that the limit is indeed 1/3.

Exercises 2.3

2. (a) $|(8x - 5) - 11| < 0.01 \iff |8x - 16| < 0.01 \iff$
$8|x - 2| < 0.01 \iff |x - 2| < (0.01)/8 = 1/800$

(b) $|(8x - 5) - 11| < 0.01 \iff |x - 2| < (0.001)/8 = 1/8000$

(c) $|x - 2| < (0.0001)/8 = 1/80000$

4. Given $\epsilon > 0$, we need $\delta > 0$ so
that if $|x-2| < \delta$, then
$|(5-2x) - (-3)| < \epsilon \iff$
$|-2x+8| < \epsilon \iff 2|x-4| < \epsilon \iff$
$|x-4| < \epsilon/2$. So choose $\delta = \epsilon/2$,
then $|x-4| < \delta \Rightarrow$
$|(5-2x) - (-3)| < \epsilon$.

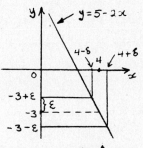

6. Given $\epsilon > 0$, we need $\delta > 0$ so
that if $|x-(-1)| < \delta$, then
$|(3-4x) - 7| < \epsilon \iff$
$|-4x-4| < \epsilon \iff 4|x+1| < \epsilon \iff$
$|x-(-1)| < \epsilon/4$. So if we choose
$\delta = \epsilon/4$, then $|x-(-1)| < \delta \Rightarrow$
$|(3-4x) - 7| < \epsilon$.

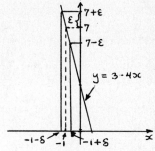

8. Given $\epsilon > 0$, we need $\delta > 0$ so that if $|x - 4| < \delta$ then
$\left|(\frac{x}{3}+1) - \frac{7}{3}\right| < \epsilon \iff \frac{1}{3}|x - 4| < \epsilon \iff |x - 4| < 3\epsilon$. So take
$\delta = 3\epsilon$. Then $|x - 4| < \delta \Rightarrow \left|(\frac{x}{3}+1) - \frac{7}{3}\right| < \epsilon$.

10. Given $\epsilon > 0$, we need $\delta > 0$ so that if $|x - 3| < \delta$ then $|x - 3| < \epsilon$.
So obviously $\delta = \epsilon$ will work.

12. Given $\epsilon > 0$, we need $\delta > 0$ so that if $|x - 1| < \delta$ then $|\pi - \pi| < \epsilon$.
But $|\pi - \pi| = 0$, so this will be true no matter what δ we pick.

14. Given $\epsilon > 0$, we need $\delta > 0$ so that if $|x - a| < \delta$ then $|c - c| < \epsilon$.
But $|c - c| = 0$, so this will be true no matter what δ we pick.

16. Given $\epsilon > 0$, we need $\delta > 0$ so that if $|x| < \delta$ then $|x^3-0| < \epsilon \iff$
$|x|^3 < \epsilon \iff |x| < \sqrt[3]{\epsilon}$. Take $\delta = \sqrt[3]{\epsilon}$. Then $|x-0| < \delta \Rightarrow |x^3-0| < \delta$.

18. Given $\epsilon > 0$, we need $\delta > 0$ so that if $9 - \delta < x < 9$, then

$|\sqrt[4]{9-x} - 0| < \epsilon \iff \sqrt[4]{9-x} < \epsilon \iff 9 - x < \epsilon^4 \iff 9 - \epsilon^4 < x < 9.$

So take $\delta = \epsilon^4$. Then $9 - \delta < x < 9 \Rightarrow |\sqrt[4]{9-x} - 0| < \epsilon.$

20. $\lim\limits_{x \to 3} x^2 = 9$

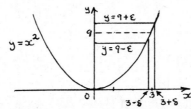

22. Suppose that $\lim_{t \to 0} H(t) = L$. Given $\epsilon = 1/2$, there exists $\delta > 0$

such that $0 < |t| < \delta \Rightarrow |H(t) - L| < 1/2 \iff$

$L - \frac{1}{2} < H(t) < L + \frac{1}{2}$. For $0 < t < \delta$, $H(t) = 1$, so $1 < L + \frac{1}{2} \Rightarrow$

$L > \frac{1}{2}$. For $-\delta < t < 0$, $H(t) = 0$, so $L - \frac{1}{2} < 0 \Rightarrow L < \frac{1}{2}$. This

contradicts $L > \frac{1}{2}$. Therefore $\lim_{t \to 0} H(t)$ does not exist.

24. First suppose that $\lim_{x \to a} f(x) = L$. Then, given $\epsilon > 0$ there exists

$\delta > 0$ so that $0 < |x - a| < \delta \Rightarrow |f(x) - L| < \epsilon$. Then

$a - \delta < x < a \Rightarrow 0 < |x - a| < \delta$ so $|f(x) - L| < \epsilon$. Thus

$\lim_{x \to a-} f(x) = L$. Also $a < x < a + \delta \Rightarrow 0 < |x - a| < \delta$ so

$|f(x) - L| < \epsilon$. Hence $\lim_{x \to a+} f(x) = L$.

Now suppose $\lim_{x \to a-} f(x) = L = \lim_{x \to a+} f(x)$. Let $\epsilon > 0$ be given.

Since $\lim_{x \to a-} f(x) = L$, there exists $\delta_1 > 0$ so that $a - \delta_1 < x < a$

$\Rightarrow |f(x) - L| < \epsilon$. Since $\lim_{x \to a+} f(x) = L$, there exists $\delta_2 > 0$ such

that $a < x < a + \delta_2 \Rightarrow |f(x) - L| < \epsilon$. Let δ be the smaller of δ_1

and δ_2. Then $0 < |x - a| < \delta \Rightarrow a - \delta_1 < x < a$ or $a < x < a + \delta_2$

so $|f(x) - L| < \epsilon$. Hence $\lim_{x \to a} f(x) = L$.

Exercises 2.4

2. $\lim\limits_{x\to-3}(x^3+2x^2+6) = \lim\limits_{x\to-3}x^3 + \lim\limits_{x\to-3}2x^2 + \lim\limits_{x\to-3}6$ (1)

$\qquad\qquad\qquad = (-3)^3 + 2\lim\limits_{x\to-3}x^2 + 6$ (9, 3, & 7)

$\qquad\qquad\qquad = -27 + 2(-3)^2 + 6 = -3$ (9)

4. $\lim\limits_{x\to-2}(x^2+x+1)^5 = \left[\lim\limits_{x\to-2}(x^2+x+1)\right]^5$ (6)

$\qquad\qquad\qquad = \left[\lim\limits_{x\to-2}x^2 + \lim\limits_{x\to-2}x + \lim\limits_{x\to-2}1\right]^5$ (1)

$\qquad\qquad\qquad = [(-2)^2 + (-2) + 1]^5 = 243$ (9,8,& 7)

6. $\lim\limits_{t\to-2}\dfrac{t^3-t^2-t+10}{t^2+3t+2} = \lim\limits_{t\to-2}\dfrac{(t+2)(t^2-3t+5)}{(t+2)(t+1)} = \lim\limits_{t\to-2}\dfrac{t^2-3t+5}{t+1}$

$\qquad\qquad = \dfrac{\lim\limits_{t\to-2}(t^2-3t+5)}{\lim\limits_{t\to-2}(t+1)}$ (5)

$\qquad\qquad = \dfrac{\lim\limits_{t\to-2}t^2 - 3\lim\limits_{t\to-2}t + \lim\limits_{t\to-2}5}{\lim\limits_{t\to-2}t + \lim\limits_{t\to-2}1}$ (1,2,& 3)

$\qquad\qquad = \dfrac{(-2)^2 - 3(-2) + 5}{(-2) + 1} = -15$ (9,8,& 7)

8. $\lim\limits_{x\to64}(\sqrt[3]{x} + 3\sqrt{x}) = \lim\limits_{x\to64}\sqrt[3]{x} + 3\lim\limits_{x\to64}\sqrt{x}$ (1 & 3)

$\qquad\qquad\qquad = \sqrt[3]{64} + 3\sqrt{64} = 28$ (10 & 8)

10. $\lim\limits_{r\to3}(r^4-7r+4)^{2/3} = \left[\lim\limits_{r\to3}(r^4-7r+4)\right]^{2/3}$ (6 & 11)

$\qquad\qquad\qquad = \left[\lim\limits_{r\to3}r^4 - 7\lim\limits_{r\to3}r + \lim\limits_{r\to3}4\right]^{2/3}$ (2,1,& 3)

$\qquad\qquad\qquad = [(3)^4 - 7(3) + 4]^{2/3} = 16$ (9,8,& 7)

12. $\displaystyle\lim_{y\to3} \frac{3(8y^2-1)}{2y^2(y-1)^4} = \frac{\displaystyle\lim_{y\to3} 3(8y^2-1)}{\displaystyle\lim_{y\to3} 2y^2(y-1)^4}$ (5)

$\displaystyle = \frac{3(8 \lim_{y\to3} y^2 - \lim_{y\to3} 1)}{2 \lim_{y\to3} y^2 \lim_{y\to3} (y-1)^4}$ (2,3,& 4)

$\displaystyle = \frac{3[8(3)^2 - 1]}{2(3)^2(3-1)^4} = \frac{71}{96}$ (9,7,& 6)

14. $\displaystyle\lim_{t\to16} t^{-1/2}(t^2-14t)^{3/5} = \lim_{t\to16} t^{-1/2} \lim_{t\to16} (t^2-14t)^{3/5}$ (4)

$\displaystyle = \left[\lim_{t\to16} t\right]^{-1/2} \left[\lim_{t\to16} (t^2-14t)\right]^{3/5}$ (6&11)

$\displaystyle = (16)^{-1/2} \left[\lim_{t\to16} t^2 - 14 \lim_{t\to16} t\right]^{3/5}$ (8,2,&3)

$\displaystyle = \frac{1}{4}\left[(16)^2 - 14(16)\right]^{3/5} = 2$ (9&8)

16. $\displaystyle\lim_{x\to3} \frac{x^2-x+12}{x+3} = \frac{\displaystyle\lim_{x\to3} x^2 - \lim_{x\to3} x + \lim_{x\to3} 12}{\displaystyle\lim_{x\to3} x + \lim_{x\to3} 3} = \frac{(3)^2 - 3 + 12}{3 + 3} = 3$

18. $\displaystyle\lim_{x\to-3} \frac{x^2-x-12}{x+3} = \lim_{x\to-3} \frac{(x-4)(x+3)}{x+3} = \lim_{x\to-3} (x-4) = -3 - 4 = -7$

20. $\displaystyle\lim_{x\to2} \frac{x^4-16}{x-2} = \lim_{x\to2} \frac{(x+2)(x-2)(x^2+4)}{x-2} = \lim_{x\to2} (x+2)(x^2+4)$

$\displaystyle = \lim_{x\to2} (x+2) \lim_{x\to2} (x^2+4) = (2+2)(2^2+4) = 32$

22. We factor t-1 as a difference of cubes:

$\displaystyle\lim_{t\to1} \frac{\sqrt[3]{t} - 1}{t - 1} = \lim_{t\to1} \frac{\sqrt[3]{t} - 1}{(\sqrt[3]{t} - 1)(t^{2/3} + t^{1/3} + 1)} = \lim_{t\to1} \frac{1}{(t^{2/3} + t^{1/3} + 1)}$

$\displaystyle = \frac{1}{\displaystyle\lim_{t\to1} t^{2/3} + \lim_{t\to1} t^{1/3} + \lim_{t\to1} 1} = \frac{1}{1 + 1 + 1} = \frac{1}{3}$

24. Write the denominator as (1+h) - 1 and factor it as a difference of fourth powers: $x^4-1 = (x^2-1)(x^2+1) = (x-1)(x+1)(x^2+1)$, with $x=\sqrt[4]{1+h}$.

$\displaystyle\lim_{h\to0} \frac{\sqrt[4]{1+h} - 1}{h} = \lim_{h\to0} \frac{\sqrt[4]{h+1} - 1}{(\sqrt[4]{1+h} - 1)(\sqrt[4]{1+h} + 1)(\sqrt{1+h} + 1)}$

31

$$= \lim_{h \to 0} \frac{1}{(\sqrt[4]{1+h} + 1)(\sqrt{1+h} + 1)} = \frac{1}{\lim\limits_{h \to 0} (\sqrt[4]{1+h} + 1) \; \lim\limits_{h \to 0} (\sqrt{1+h} + 1)}$$

$$= \frac{1}{(\sqrt[4]{1+0} + 1)(\sqrt{1+0} + 1)} = \frac{1}{4}$$

[Another method: Multiply numerator and denominator by $\sqrt[4]{1+h} + 1$.]

26. $\lim\limits_{x \to 1} \left[\dfrac{1}{x-1} - \dfrac{2}{x^2-1} \right] = \lim\limits_{x \to 1} \dfrac{(x+1) - 2}{(x-1)(x+1)} = \lim\limits_{x \to 1} \dfrac{x-1}{(x-1)(x+1)} = \lim\limits_{x \to 1} \dfrac{1}{x+1} = \dfrac{1}{2}$

28. $\lim\limits_{h \to 0} \dfrac{(3+h)^{-1} - 3^{-1}}{h} = \lim\limits_{h \to 0} \dfrac{\frac{1}{3+h} - \frac{1}{3}}{h} = \lim\limits_{h \to 0} \dfrac{3 - (3+h)}{h(3+h)3} = \lim\limits_{h \to 0} \dfrac{-h}{h(3+h)3}$

$= \lim\limits_{h \to 0} - \dfrac{1}{(3+h)3} = - \dfrac{1}{\lim\limits_{h \to 0} (3+h)3} = - \dfrac{1}{(3+0)3} = - \dfrac{1}{9}$

30. $\lim\limits_{x \to 2} \dfrac{\sqrt{2x}-x}{x-2} = \lim\limits_{x \to 2} \dfrac{\sqrt{2}\sqrt{x}-x}{x-2} = \lim\limits_{x \to 2} \dfrac{\sqrt{x}(\sqrt{2}-\sqrt{x})}{(\sqrt{x}-\sqrt{2})(\sqrt{x}+\sqrt{2})} = \lim\limits_{x \to 2} \dfrac{-\sqrt{x}}{\sqrt{x}+\sqrt{2}} = \dfrac{-\sqrt{2}}{\sqrt{2}+\sqrt{2}}$

$= - \dfrac{1}{2}$ \qquad\qquad [Another method: Rationalize the numerator.]

32. $1 \le f(x) \le x^2+2x+2$ for all x and $\lim\limits_{x \to -1} 1 = 1$ & $\lim\limits_{x \to -1} (x^2+2x+2)$

$= \lim\limits_{x \to -1} x^2 + 2 \lim\limits_{x \to -1} x + \lim\limits_{x \to -1} 2 = (-1)^2+2(-1)+2 = 1$. Therefore, by the

Squeeze Theorem, $\lim\limits_{x \to -1} f(x) = 1$.

34. $-1 \le \sin \dfrac{1}{x} \le 1 \;\Rightarrow\; -x^2 \le x^2 \sin \dfrac{1}{x} \le x^2$. Since $\lim\limits_{x \to 0} (-x^2) = 0$ and

$\lim\limits_{x \to 0} x^2 = 0$, we have $\lim\limits_{x \to 0} x^2 \sin \dfrac{1}{x} = 0$ by the Squeeze Theorem.

36. $\lim\limits_{x \to 0^+} (\sqrt[4]{x}-1) = \sqrt[4]{\lim\limits_{x \to 0^+} x} - \lim\limits_{x \to 0^+} 1 = 0 - 1 = -1$

38. $\lim\limits_{x \to 4^-} \sqrt{16-x^2} = \sqrt{\lim\limits_{x \to 4} 16 - \lim\limits_{x \to 4} x^2} = \sqrt{16 - 4^2} = 0$

40. If $x > -4$, then $|x+4| = x+4$, so $\lim\limits_{x \to -4^+} |x+4| = \lim\limits_{x \to -4^+} (x+4) = -4+4 = 0$.

If $x < -4$, then $|x+4| = -(x+4)$, so $\lim\limits_{x \to -4^-} |x+4| =$

$\lim\limits_{x \to -4^-} (-x-4) = 4-4 = 0$. Therefore $\lim\limits_{x \to -4} |x+4| = 0$.

42. $|x-2| = x-2$ if $x > 2$ so $\lim\limits_{x \to 2^+} \dfrac{|x-2|}{x-2} = \lim\limits_{x \to 2^+} \dfrac{x-2}{x-2} = \lim\limits_{x \to 2^+} 1 = 1$

$|x-2| = -(x-2)$ if $x < 2$ so $\lim\limits_{x \to 2^-} \dfrac{|x-2|}{x-2} = \lim\limits_{x \to 2^-} \dfrac{-(x-2)}{x-2} = \lim\limits_{x \to 2^-} (-1) = -1$

The right and left limits are different, so $\lim\limits_{x \to 2} \dfrac{|x-2|}{x-2}$ doesn't exist.

44. $[x] = 8$ for $8 \leq x < 9$, so $\lim\limits_{x \to 9^-} [x] = \lim\limits_{x \to 9^-} 8 = 8$.

46. $[x] = -2$ for $-2 \leq x < -1$, so $\lim\limits_{x \to -2^+} [x] = \lim\limits_{x \to -2^+} (-2) = -2$.

48. $[x] = -3$ for $-3 \leq x < -2$, so $\lim\limits_{x \to -2.4} [x] = \lim\limits_{x \to -2.4} (-3) = -3$.

50. $\lim\limits_{x \to 1^+} \sqrt{x^2 + x - 2} = \sqrt{\lim\limits_{x \to 1^+} x^2 + \lim\limits_{x \to 1^+} x - \lim\limits_{x \to 1^+} 2} = \sqrt{1^2 + 1 - 2} = 0$.

[Notice that the domain of $\sqrt{x^2 + x - 2}$ is $(-\infty, -2] \cup [1, \infty)$.]

52. $\lim\limits_{x \to 0^+} \dfrac{2 + x^{3/2}}{\sqrt{x+2}} = \dfrac{\lim\limits_{x \to 0^+} 2 + \lim\limits_{x \to 0^+} x^{3/2}}{\sqrt{\lim\limits_{x \to 0^+} x + \lim\limits_{x \to 0^+} 2}} = \dfrac{2 + 0}{\sqrt{0 + 2}} = \sqrt{2}$

54. Since $|x| = -x$ for $x < 0$, we have $\lim\limits_{x \to 0^-} \left[\dfrac{1}{x} - \dfrac{1}{|x|} \right] = \lim\limits_{x \to 0^-} \left[\dfrac{1}{x} - \dfrac{1}{-x} \right]$

$= \lim\limits_{x \to 0^-} \dfrac{2}{x}$ which does not exist since the denominator $\to 0$.

56. (a)

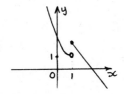

(b)(i) Since $\operatorname{sgn} x = 1$ for $x > 0$, $\lim\limits_{x \to 0^+} \operatorname{sgn} x = \lim\limits_{x \to 0^+} 1 = 1$.

(ii) Since $\operatorname{sgn} x = -1$ for $x < 0$. $\lim\limits_{x \to 0^-} \operatorname{sgn} x = \lim\limits_{x \to 0^-} (-1) = -1$.

(iii) Since $\lim\limits_{x \to 0^-} \operatorname{sgn} x \neq \lim\limits_{x \to 0^+} \operatorname{sgn} x$, $\lim\limits_{x \to 0} \operatorname{sgn} x$ does not exist.

(iv) Since $|\operatorname{sgn} x| = 1$ for $x \neq 0$, $\lim\limits_{x \to 0} |\operatorname{sgn} x| = \lim\limits_{x \to 0} 1 = 1$.

58. (a) $\lim\limits_{x \to 1^-} f(x) = \lim\limits_{x \to 1^-} (x^2 - 2x + 2) = \lim\limits_{x \to 1^-} x^2 - 2\lim\limits_{x \to 1^-} x + \lim\limits_{x \to 1^-} 2 = 1^2 - 2 + 2 = 1$

$\lim\limits_{x \to 1^+} f(x) = \lim\limits_{x \to 1^+} (3 - x) = \lim\limits_{x \to 1^+} 3 - \lim\limits_{x \to 1^+} x = 3 - 1 = 2$

(b) $\lim\limits_{x \to 1} f(x)$ does not exist because $\lim\limits_{x \to 1^-} f(x) \neq \lim\limits_{x \to 1^+} f(x)$.

(c)

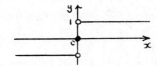

60. (a)(i) $\lim_{x \to 0^+} h(x) = \lim_{x \to 0^+} x^2 = 0^2 = 0$ (b)

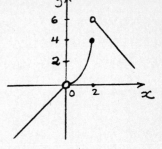

(ii) $\lim_{x \to 0^-} h(x) = \lim_{x \to 0^-} x = 0$.   So $\lim_{x \to 0} h(x) = 0$.

(iii) $\lim_{x \to 1} h(x) = \lim_{x \to 1} x^2 = 1^2 = 1$

(iv) $\lim_{x \to 2^-} h(x) = \lim_{x \to 2^-} x^2 = 2^2 = 4$

(v) $\lim_{x \to 2^+} h(x) = \lim_{x \to 2^+} (8-x) = 8 - 2 = 6$

(vi) Since $\lim_{x \to 2^-} h(x) \neq \lim_{x \to 2^+} h(x)$, $\lim_{x \to 2} h(x)$ does not exist.

62. (a)

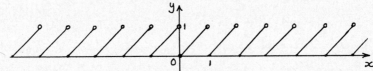

(b)(i) $\lim_{x \to n} f(x) = \lim_{x \to n} (x - [\![x]\!]) = \lim_{x \to n} [x - (n-1)] = n - (n-1) = 1$

(ii) $\lim_{x \to n^+} f(x) = \lim_{x \to n^+} (x - [\![x]\!]) = \lim_{x \to n^+} (x - n) = n - n = 0$

(c) $\lim_{x \to a} f(x)$ exists $\iff$ a is not an integer.

(d) FRAC(x) = f(x) if $x \geq 0$ or x is a negative integer, but for other negative x we have FRAC(x) = f(x) - 1.

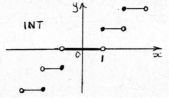
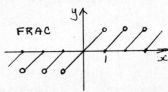

64. (a)

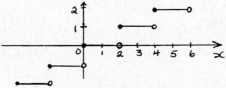

(b)(i) $\lim_{x \to 1^+} g(x) = 0$ (ii) $\lim_{x \to 1^-} g(x) = 0$ (iii) $\lim_{x \to 1} g(x) = 0$

since $[\![x/2]\!] = 0$ for $0 \leq x < 2$.

(iv) $\lim_{x \to 2^+} g(x) = 1$ since $[\![x/2]\!] = 1$ for $2 \leq x < 4$.

(v) $\lim\limits_{x \to 2^-} g(x) = 0$ since $[x/2] = 0$ for $0 \le x < 2$.

(vi) $\lim\limits_{x \to 2} g(x)$ does not exist because $\lim\limits_{x \to 2^+} g(x) \ne \lim\limits_{x \to 2^-} g(x)$.

(c) $\lim\limits_{x \to a} g(x)$ exists except when a is an even integer.

66. Let $f(x) = [x]$ and $g(x) = -[x]$. Then $\lim\limits_{x \to 3} f(x)$ and $\lim\limits_{x \to 3} g(x)$ do not

exist (Example 3) but $\lim\limits_{x \to 3} [f(x) + g(x)] = \lim\limits_{x \to 3} 0 = 0$.

68. Let $t = \sqrt[3]{1+cx}$. Then $t \to 1$ as $x \to 0$ and $t^3 = 1+cx \Rightarrow x = (t^3-1)/c$.
(If $c = 0$, the limit is obviously 0.) Therefore

$$\lim_{x \to 0} \frac{\sqrt[3]{1+cx} - 1}{x} = \lim_{t \to 1} \frac{t-1}{(t^3-1)/c} = \lim_{t \to 1} \frac{c}{t^2+t+1} = \frac{c}{1^2+1+1} = \frac{c}{3}$$

[Another method: multiply numerator and denominator by
$(1+cx)^{2/3} + (1+cx)^{1/3} + 1$.]

Section 2.5

Exercises 2.5

2. $\lim\limits_{x \to 2} f(x) = \lim\limits_{x \to 2} \left[x^2 + (x-1)^9 \right] = \lim\limits_{x \to 2} x^2 + \left[\lim\limits_{x \to 2} x - \lim\limits_{x \to 2} 1 \right]^9$

   $= 2^2 + (2-1)^9 = 5 = f(2)$. Thus f is continuous at 2.

4. $\lim\limits_{x \to 4} g(x) = \lim\limits_{x \to 4} \frac{x+1}{2x^2-1} = \frac{\lim\limits_{x \to 4} x + \lim\limits_{x \to 4} 1}{2 \lim\limits_{x \to 4} x^2 - \lim\limits_{x \to 4} 1} = \frac{4+1}{2(4)^2-1} = \frac{5}{31} = g(4)$

   Thus g is continuous at 4.

6. For $a > 1$ we have $\lim\limits_{x \to a} f(x) = \lim\limits_{x \to a} (x+\sqrt{x-1}) = \lim\limits_{x \to a} x + \sqrt{\lim\limits_{x \to a} x - \lim\limits_{x \to a} 1}$

   $= a + \sqrt{a-1} = f(a)$, so f is continuous on $(1, \infty)$. A similar
   calculation shows that $\lim\limits_{x \to 1^+} f(x) = 1 = f(1)$, so f is continuous from
   the right at 1. Thus f is continuous on $[1, \infty)$.

8. For $a < 3$, $\lim\limits_{x \to a} F(x) = \lim\limits_{x \to a} \frac{x+1}{x-3} = \frac{\lim\limits_{x \to a} x + \lim\limits_{x \to a} 1}{\lim\limits_{x \to a} x - \lim\limits_{x \to a} 3} = \frac{a+1}{a-3} = F(a)$, so F is

   continuous on $(-\infty, 3)$.

10. $f(x) = \dfrac{x^2-1}{x+1}$ is discontinuous at -1

    because $f(-1)$ is not defined.

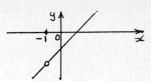

12. $f(x) = \dfrac{1}{x-1}$ is discontinuous at 1

    since $f(1)$ is not defined.

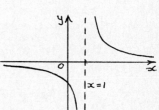

14. Since $f(x) = \dfrac{x^2-1}{x+1}$ for $x \neq -1$, we have

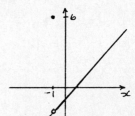

    $$\lim_{x \to -1} f(x) = \lim_{x \to -1} \frac{x^2-1}{x+1} = \lim_{x \to -1} (x-1) = -2$$

    But $f(-1) = 6$, so $\lim\limits_{x \to -1} f(x) \neq f(-1)$.

    Therefore f is discontinuous at -1.

16. Since $f(x) = \dfrac{x^2-2x-8}{x-4}$ if $x \neq 4$,

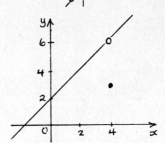

    $$\lim_{x \to 4} f(x) = \lim_{x \to 4} \frac{x^2-2x-8}{x-4} =$$

    $$\lim_{x \to 4} \frac{(x-4)(x+2)}{x-4} = \lim_{x \to 4} (x+2) = 4+2 = 6$$

    But $f(4) = 3$, so $\lim\limits_{x \to 4} f(x) \neq f(4)$.

    Therefore f is discontinuous at 4.

18. $\lim\limits_{x \to 0^+} \text{sgn } x = 1$ while $\lim\limits_{x \to 0^-} \text{sgn } x = -1$.

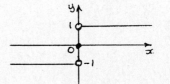

    Thus $\lim\limits_{x \to 0} \text{sgn } x$ does not exist.

    Therefore $f(x) = \text{sgn } x$ is

    discontinuous at 0.

20. $g(x) = (x^6-x^4+8x^2-7)^{10}$ is a polynomial, so by Theorem 2.23 it is

    continuous on R.

22. $G(x) = \dfrac{x^4+17}{6x^2+x-1}$ is a rational function, so by Theorem 2.23 it is

    continuous on its domain, which is $\{x \mid (3x-1)(2x+1) \neq 0\}$

    $= \{x \mid x \neq -\tfrac{1}{2}, \tfrac{1}{3}\}.$

24. $G(t) = 25-t^2$ is a polynomial, so it is continuous [Theorem 2.23]. $F(x) = \sqrt{x}$ is continuous by Theorem 2.25. So, by Theorem 2.27, $F(G(t)) = \sqrt{25-t^2}$ is continuous on its domain, which is $\{t \mid 25-t^2 \geq 0\} = \{t \mid |t| \leq 5\} = [-5,5]$. Also, $2t$ is continuous on R, so by Theorem 2.22(a), $f(t) = 2t + \sqrt{25-t^2}$ is continuous on its domain which is $[-5,5]$.

26. $G(t) = t^2-4$ is continuous since it is a polynomial [Theorem 2.23]. $F(x) = \sqrt{x}$ is continuous by Theorem 2.25. So by Theorem 2.27 $F(G(t)) = \sqrt{t^2-4}$ is continuous on its domain which is $D = \{t \mid t^2-4 \geq 0\}$ $= \{t \mid |t| \geq 2\}$. Also t is continuous so $t + \sqrt{t^2-4}$ is continuous on D by Theorem 2.22(a). Thus by Theorem 2.22(e) $g(t) = 1/(t + \sqrt{t^2-4})$ is continuous on its domain which is $\{t \in D \mid t + \sqrt{t^2-4} \neq 0\}$. But if $t + \sqrt{t^2-4} = 0$, then $\sqrt{t^2-4} = -t \Rightarrow t^2-4 = t^2 \Rightarrow -4 = 0$ which is false. So the domain of g is $\{t \mid |t| \geq 2\} = (-\infty,-2] \cup [2,\infty)$.

28. $G(x) = (x^2-1)^{-5/2} = 1/\sqrt{(x^2-1)^5}$. The domain is $\{x \mid x^2-1 > 0\}$ $= (-\infty,-1) \cup (1,\infty)$. By Theorem 2.23 the rational function $1/(x^2-1)^5$ is continuous. Since the square root function is continuous (Theorem 2.25), the composition $G(x) = \sqrt{1/(x^2-1)^5}$ is continuous by Theorem 2.27.

30. x^2-3x+2 is continuous on $(-\infty,\infty)$ since it is a polynomial [Theorem 2.23] and $\sqrt[4]{x}$ is continuous on $[0,\infty)$ by Theorem 2.25. By Theorem 2.27, $\sqrt[4]{x^2-3x+2}$ is continuous on its domain which is $\{x \mid x^2-3x+2 \geq 0\}$ $= \{x \mid (x-1)(x-2) \geq 0\} = (-\infty,1] \cup [2,\infty)$. Also $\sqrt{x}$ is continuous on $[0,\infty)$ by Theorem 2.25, so $f(x) = \sqrt{x} + \sqrt[4]{x^2-3x+2}$ is continuous, by Theorem 2.22(a), on its domain which is $[0,1] \cup [2,\infty)$.

32. g is continuous on $(-\infty,0)$, $(0,1)$, and $(1,\infty)$ since on each of these intervals it is a polynomial. Now $\lim_{x \to 0^-} g(x) = \lim_{x \to 0^-} x = 0 = \lim_{x \to 0^+} x^2 = \lim_{x \to 0^+} g(x)$, so $\lim_{x \to 0} g(x) = 0 = 0^2 = g(0)$. Also $\lim_{x \to 1^-} g(x) = \lim_{x \to 1^-} x^2 = 1 = \lim_{x \to 1^+} x^3 = \lim_{x \to 1^+} g(x)$, so $\lim_{x \to 1} g(x) = 1 = 1^2 = g(1)$. So g is also continuous at 0 and 1. Thus g is continuous on $(-\infty,\infty)$.

34. f is continuous on $(-\infty,-1)$, $(-1,1)$, and $(1,\infty)$. Now $\lim\limits_{x\to-1^-} f(x)$

$= \lim\limits_{x\to-1^-}(2x+1) = -1$ and $\lim\limits_{x\to-1^+}f(x) = \lim\limits_{x\to-1^+}3x = -3$, so f is

discontinuous at -1. Since $f(-1) = -1$, f is continuous from the

left at -1. Also $\lim\limits_{x\to1^-}f(x) = \lim\limits_{x\to1^-}3x$

$= 3$ and $\lim\limits_{x\to1^+}f(x) = \lim\limits_{x\to1^+}(2x-1)= 1$, so

f is discontinuous at 1. Since

$f(1) = 1$, f is continuous from the

right at 1.

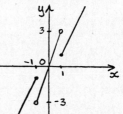

36. f is continuous on $(-\infty,0)$, $(0,1)$, and $(1,\infty)$. Since f is not

defined at $x = 0$, f is continuous neither from the left nor the

right at 0. Also $\lim\limits_{x\to1^-}f(x) = \lim\limits_{x\to1^-}1 = 1$ and $\lim\limits_{x\to1^+}f(x) = \lim\limits_{x\to1^+}\sqrt{x} = 1$,

so $\lim\limits_{x\to1} f(x) = 1 = f(1)$ and f is continuous at 1.

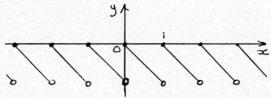

38. $\lim\limits_{x\to n} [\![x]\!]$ does not exist when n is an integer (Exercise 2.4.61), so

$f(x) = [\![x]\!] - x$ is discontinuous when $x = n$, an integer. Also

$\lim\limits_{x\to n^-}f(x) = (n-1) - n = -1$ and $\lim\limits_{x\to n^+}f(x) = n - n = 0 = f(n)$, so f is

continuous from the right at n.

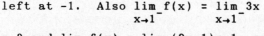

40. $f(x) = [\![1/x]\!]$ is continuous except when $x = 0$ (where f is not

defined) and when $x = 1/n$, n an integer. In fact, $\lim\limits_{x\to1/n^-}[\![1/x]\!]$

$= \lim\limits_{t\to n^+}[\![t]\!] = n = f(1/n)$ and $\lim\limits_{x\to1/n^+}[\![1/x]\!] = \lim\limits_{t\to n^-}[\![t]\!] = n-1$, so f is

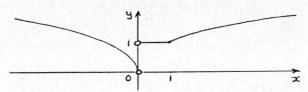

continuous only from the left at 1/n.

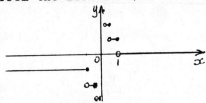

42. (a) $f(x) = \dfrac{x^2-2x-8}{x+2} = \dfrac{(x-4)(x+2)}{x+2}$ has a removable discontinuity at -2

because $g(x) = x-4$ is continuous on R and $f(x) = g(x)$ for $x \neq -2$.
[The discontinuity is removed by defining $f(-2) = -6$.]

(b) $f(x) = \dfrac{x-7}{|x-7|} \Rightarrow \lim\limits_{x \to 7^-} f(x) = -1$ and $\lim\limits_{x \to 7^+} f(x) = 1$. Thus $\lim\limits_{x \to 7} f(x)$

does not exist, so the discontinuity is not removable. (It is a
jump discontinuity.)

(c) $f(x) = \dfrac{x^3+64}{x+4} = \dfrac{(x+4)(x^2-4x+16)}{x+4}$ has a removable discontinuity at

-4 because $g(x) = x^2-4x+16$ is continuous on R and $f(x) = g(x)$ for
$x \neq -4$. [The discontinuity is removed by defining $f(-4) = 48$.]

(d) $f(x) = \dfrac{3-\sqrt{x}}{9-x} = \dfrac{3-\sqrt{x}}{(3-\sqrt{x})(3+\sqrt{x})}$ has a removable discontinuity at 9

because $g(x) = 1/(3+\sqrt{x})$ is continuous on R and $f(x) = g(x)$ for
$x \neq 9$. [The discontinuity is removed by defining $f(9) = 1/6$.]

44. $f(x) = x^2$ is continuous on the interval $[1,2]$ and $f(1) = 1$ and
$f(2) = 4$. Since $1 < 2 < 4$, there is a number c in $(1,2)$ such that
$f(c) = c^2 = 2$ by the Intermediate Value Theorem.

46. $g(x) = x^5-2x^3+x^2+2$ is continuous on $[-2,-1]$ and $g(-2) = -10$, $g(-1)$
$= 4$. Since $-10 < -1 < 4$, there is a number c in $(-2,-1)$ such that
$g(c) = -1$ by the Intermediate Value Theorem.

48. $f(x) = x^3-3x+1$ is continuous on $[1,2]$ and $f(1) = -1$, $f(2) = 3$.
Since $-1 < 0 < 3$, there is a number c in $(1,2)$ such that $f(c) = 0$
by the Intermediate Value Theorem. Thus there is a root of the
equation $x^3-3x+1 = 0$ in the interval $(1,2)$.

50. $f(x) = x^5-2x^4-x-3$ is continuous on $[2,3]$ and $f(2) = -5$, $f(3) = 75$.
Since $-5 < 0 < 75$, there is a number c in $(2,3)$ such that $f(c) = 0$
by the Intermediate Value Theorem. Thus there is a root of the
equation $x^5-2x^4-x-3 = 0$ in the interval $(2,3)$.

52. $f(x) = x^2 - \sqrt{x+1}$ is continuous on $[1,2]$ and $f(1) = 1 - \sqrt{2}$, $f(2) = 4 - \sqrt{3}$ Since $1 - \sqrt{2} < 0 < 4 - \sqrt{3}$, there is a number c in $(1,2)$ such that $f(c) = 0$ by the Intermediate Value Theorem. Thus there is a root of the equation $x^2 - \sqrt{x+1} = 0$, or $x^2 = \sqrt{x+1}$, in the interval $(1,2)$.

54. (a) $f(x) = x^5 - x^2 + 2x + 3$ is continuous on $[-1,0]$ and $f(-1) = -1$, $f(0) = 3$. Since $-1 < 0 < 3$, there is a number c in $(-1,0)$ such that $f(c) = 0$ by the Intermediate Value Theorem. Thus there is a root of the equation $x^5 - x^2 + 2x + 3 = 0$ in the interval $(-1,0)$.

(b) $f(-0.88) \approx -0.0062$ and $f(-0.87) \approx 0.0047$, so there is a root between -0.88 and -0.87.

56. $g(x) = \begin{cases} 0 & \text{if } x \text{ is rational} \\ x & \text{if } x \text{ is irrational} \end{cases}$ is continuous at 0. For,

$-|x| \le g(x) \le |x|$, so by the Squeeze Theorem $\lim_{x \to 0} g(x) = 0 = g(0)$.

But g is continuous nowhere else. For if $a \ne 0$ and $\delta > 0$, the interval $(a-\delta, a+\delta)$ contains both infinitely many rational and infinitely many irrational numbers. Since $g(a) = 0$ or a, there are infinitely many numbers x with $|x-a| < \delta$ and $|g(x)-g(a)| > a/2$ Thus $\lim_{x \to a} g(x) \ne g(a)$.

58. (a) Since f is continuous at a, $\lim_{x \to a} f(x) = f(a)$. Thus, using

Property 3 of limits, we have $\lim_{x \to a} (cf)(x) = \lim_{x \to a} cf(x) = c \lim_{x \to a} f(x)$

$= cf(a) = (cf)(a)$. Therefore cf is continuous at a.

(b) Since f and g are continuous at a, $\lim_{x \to a} f(x) = f(a)$ and

$\lim_{x \to a} g(x) = g(a)$. Since $g(a) \ne 0$, we can use Property 5 of limits:

$\lim_{x \to a} \left[\frac{f}{g}\right](x) = \lim_{x \to a} \frac{f(x)}{g(x)} = \frac{\lim_{x \to a} f(x)}{\lim_{x \to a} g(x)} = \frac{f(a)}{g(a)} = \left[\frac{f}{g}\right](a)$. Thus f/g is

continuous at a.

Review Exercises for Chapter 2

2. (a) $s = 1+2t+t^2/4$. The average velocity over the time interval

   $[1,1+h]$ is $\dfrac{s(1+h)-s(1)}{h} = \dfrac{1+2(1+h)+(1+h)^2/4 - 13/4}{h} = \dfrac{10h+h^2}{4h} = \dfrac{10+h}{4}$

   So for the following intervals the average velocities are:

   (i) $[1,3]$: $(10+2)/4 = 3$ m/s   (ii) $[1,2]$: $(10+1)/4 = 2.75$ m/s

   (iii) $[1,1.5]$: $(10+0.5)/4 = 2.625$ m/s

   (iv) $[1,1.1]$: $(10+0.1)/4 = 2.525$ m/s

   (b) When $t = 1$ the velocity is $\lim\limits_{h\to 0} \dfrac{s(1+h)-s(1)}{h} = \lim\limits_{h\to 0} \dfrac{10+h}{4} = 2.5$ m/s

4. $\lim\limits_{x\to 0^-} \sqrt{-x} = \sqrt{-0} = 0$ since $\sqrt{-x}$ is continuous on $(-\infty, 0]$.

6. $\lim\limits_{t\to 4} \dfrac{t-4}{t^2-3t-4} = \lim\limits_{t\to 4} \dfrac{t-4}{(t-4)(t+1)} = \lim\limits_{t\to 4} \dfrac{1}{t+1} = \dfrac{1}{4+1} = \dfrac{1}{5}$

8. $\lim\limits_{h\to 0} \dfrac{(1+h)^{-2} - 1}{h} = \lim\limits_{h\to 0} \dfrac{1-(1+h)^2}{h(1+h)^2} = \lim\limits_{h\to 0} \dfrac{-2h-h^2}{h(1+h)^2} = \lim\limits_{h\to 0} \dfrac{-2-h}{(1+h)^2} = \dfrac{-2-0}{(1+0)^2}$

   $= -2$

10. $\lim\limits_{x\to -1} \dfrac{x^2-x-2}{x^2+3x+2} = \lim\limits_{x\to -1} \dfrac{(x+1)(x-2)}{(x+1)(x+2)} = \lim\limits_{x\to -1} \dfrac{x-2}{x+2} = \dfrac{-1-2}{-1+2} = -3$

12. $\lim\limits_{v\to 2} \dfrac{v^2+2v-8}{v^4-16} = \lim\limits_{v\to 2} \dfrac{(v+4)(v-2)}{(v+2)(v-2)(v^2+4)} = \lim\limits_{v\to 2} \dfrac{v+4}{(v+2)(v^2+4)} = \dfrac{2+4}{(2+2)(2^2+4)}$

   $= 3/16$

14. $\lim\limits_{x\to 9^+}(\sqrt{x-9} + [x+1]) = \lim\limits_{x\to 9^+}\sqrt{x-9} + \lim\limits_{x\to 9^+}[x+1] = \sqrt{9-9} + 10 = 10$

16. Since $2x-1 \le f(x) \le x^2$ for $0 < x < 3$ and $\lim\limits_{x\to 1}(2x-1) = 1 = \lim\limits_{x\to 1} x^2$,

   we have $\lim\limits_{x\to 1} f(x) = 1$ by the Squeeze Theorem.

18. (a) $g(x) = 2x-x^2$ if $0 \le x \le 2$, $g(x) = 2-x$ if $2 < x \le 3$, $g(x) = x-4$

   if $3 < x < 4$, $g(x) = \pi$ if $x \ge 4$. Therefore

   $\lim\limits_{x\to 2^-} g(x) = \lim\limits_{x\to 2^-}(2x-x^2) = 0$ and $\lim\limits_{x\to 2^+} g(x) = \lim\limits_{x\to 2^+}(2-x) = 0$

   Thus $\lim\limits_{x\to 2} g(x) = 0 = g(2)$, so g is continuous at 2.

   $\lim\limits_{x\to 3^-} g(x) = \lim\limits_{x\to 3^-}(2-x) = -1$ and $\lim\limits_{x\to 3^+} g(x) = \lim\limits_{x\to 3^+}(x-4) = -1$

Thus $\lim\limits_{x \to 3} g(x) = -1 = g(3)$, so g is continuous at 3.

$\lim\limits_{x \to 4^-} g(x) = \lim\limits_{x \to 4^-}(x-4) = 0$ and $\lim\limits_{x \to 4^+} g(x) = \lim\limits_{x \to 4^+} \pi = \pi$

Thus $\lim\limits_{x \to 4} g(x)$ does not exist, so g is discontinuous at 4. But

$\lim\limits_{x \to 4^+} g(x) = \pi = g(4)$, so g is continuous from the right at 4.

(b)

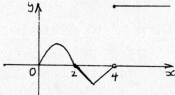

20. x^2-9 is continuous on R since it is a polynomial and $\sqrt{x}$ is

continuous on $[0,\infty)$, so the composition $\sqrt{x^2-9}$ is continuous on

$\{x \mid x^2-9 \geq 0\} = (-\infty,-3] \cup [3,\infty)$. Note that $x^2-2 \neq 0$ on this set and

so the quotient function $g(x) = \sqrt{x^2-9}/(x^2-2)$ is continuous on

$(-\infty,-3] \cup [3,\infty)$.

22. $f(x) = x^4+1-1/x$ is continuous on $[0.5,1]$ and $f(0.5) = -15/16 < 0$,

$f(1) = 1 > 0$. So by the Intermediate Value Theorem there is a

number c in $(0.5,1)$ such that $f(c) = 0$, i.e., the equation

$x^4+1 = 1/x$ has a root in $(0.5,1)$.

CHAPTER THREE

Exercises 3.1

2. slope = $f'(2) = \lim\limits_{h \to 0} \frac{f(2+h)-f(2)}{h} = \lim\limits_{h \to 0} \frac{\frac{1}{2+h} - \frac{1}{2}}{h} = \lim\limits_{h \to 0} \frac{2-(2+h)}{2h(2+h)}$

$= \lim\limits_{h \to 0} \frac{-h}{2h(2+h)} = \lim\limits_{h \to 0} \frac{-1}{2(2+h)} = -\frac{1}{4}$ So the equation of the tangent

line at $(2,\frac{1}{2})$ is $y-\frac{1}{2} = -\frac{1}{4}(x-2)$ or $x+4y = 4$.

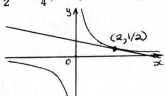

4. slope = $f'(0) = \lim\limits_{h \to 0} \frac{f(0+h)-f(0)}{h} = \lim\limits_{h \to 0} \frac{1-h^3-1}{h} = \lim\limits_{h \to 0} \frac{-h^3}{h} = \lim\limits_{h \to 0} (-h^2)$

$= 0$. So the equation of the tangent line at $(0,1)$ is $y-1 = 0(x-0)$

or $y = 1$.

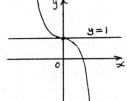

6. slope = $f'(2) = \lim\limits_{h \to 0} \frac{f(2+h)-f(2)}{h} = \lim\limits_{h \to 0} \frac{(2+h)-(2+h)^3-(-6)}{h}$

$= \lim\limits_{h \to 0} \frac{-11h-6h^2-h^3}{h} = \lim\limits_{h \to 0} (-11-6h-h^2) = -11$. So the equation of the

tangent line at $(2,-6)$ is $y+6 = -11(x-2)$ or $11x+y-16 = 0$.

8. slope = $h'(1) = \lim\limits_{h \to 0} \frac{h(1+h)-h(1)}{h} = \lim\limits_{h \to 0} \frac{\frac{1}{\sqrt{1+h}} - 1}{h} = \lim\limits_{h \to 0} \frac{1-\sqrt{1+h}}{h\sqrt{1+h}}$

$= \lim\limits_{h \to 0} \frac{(1-\sqrt{1+h})(1+\sqrt{1+h})}{h\sqrt{1+h}(1+\sqrt{1+h})} = \lim\limits_{h \to 0} \frac{-h}{h\sqrt{1+h}(1+\sqrt{1+h})} = \lim\limits_{h \to 0} \frac{-1}{\sqrt{1+h}(1+\sqrt{1+h})}$

$= -\frac{1}{2}$ So the equation of the tangent line at $(1,1)$ is

$y-1 = -\frac{1}{2}(x-1)$ or $x+2y = 3$.

10. Average velocity over $[2,2+h]$ is $\dfrac{f(2+h)-f(2)}{h} = \dfrac{2-(2+h)+3(2+h)^2-12}{h}$

$= \dfrac{11h+3h^2}{h} = 11+3h$. So the average velocity over $[2,2.5]$ is

$11+3(0.5) = 12.5$ m/s, over $[2,2.1]$ is $11+3(0.1) = 11.3$ m/s, over

$[2,2.01]$ is $11+3(0.01) = 11.03$ m/s. Instantaneous velocity when t

$= 2$ is $f'(2) = \lim\limits_{h\to0} \dfrac{f(2+h)-f(2)}{h} = \lim\limits_{h\to0} (11+3h) = 11$ m/s.

12. Average velocity over $[1,1+h]$ is $\dfrac{f(1+h)-f(1)}{h} = \dfrac{2(1+h)^3-(1+h)+1-2}{h}$

$= \dfrac{5h+6h^2+2h^3}{h} = 5+6h+2h^2$. So the average velocity over $[1,1.1]$ is

$5+6(.1)+2(.1)^2 = 5.62$ m/s, over $[1,1.01]$ is $5+6(.01)+2(.01)^2 =$

5.0602 m/s, over $[1,1.001]$ is $5+6(.001)+2(.001)^2 = 5.006002$ m/s.

Instantaneous velocity when t = 1 is $f'(1) = \lim\limits_{h\to0} \dfrac{f(1+h)-f(1)}{h}$

$= \lim\limits_{h\to0} (5+6h+2h^2) = 5$ m/s.

14. The velocity at time t is $v(t) = h'(t) = \lim\limits_{x\to t} \dfrac{h(x)-h(t)}{x-t} =$

$\lim\limits_{x\to t} \dfrac{80x-16x^2-(80t-16t^2)}{x-t} = \lim\limits_{x\to t} \dfrac{80(x-t)-16(x-t)(x+t)}{x-t}$

$= \lim\limits_{x\to t} [80-16(x+t)] = 80-32t$.

(a) $v(1) = 80-32(1) = 48$ ft/s $v(2) = 80-32(2) = 16$ ft/s

  $v(3) = 80-32(3) = -16$ ft/s $v(4) = 80-32(4) = -48$ ft/s

(b) $|v(1)| = 48$ ft/s, $|v(2)| = 16$ ft/s, $|v(3)| = 16$ ft/s,

  $|v(4)| = 48$ ft/s

(c) The maximum height is reached when $0 = v(t) = 80-32t \iff$

t = 2.5 s.   (d) The maximum height is $h(2.5) = 80(2.5)-16(2.5)^2$

$= 100$ ft.   (e) The ball hits the ground when $0 = h(t) = 80t-16t^2$

$= 16t(5-t)$, after 5 s.   (f) The velocity is then $v(5) = 80-32(5)$

$= -80$ ft/s.

16. (a) $v(a) = \lim\limits_{h\to0} \dfrac{f(a+h)-f(a)}{h}$

$= \lim\limits_{h\to0} \dfrac{4(a+h)^3-9(a+h)^2+6(a+h)+2-(4a^3-9a^2+6a+2)}{h}$

$= \lim_{h \to 0} \dfrac{12a^2h+12ah^2+4h^3-18ah-9h^2+6h}{h} = \lim_{h \to 0} (12a^2+12ah+4h^2-18a-9h+6)$

$= 12a^2-18a+6$ So $v(1) = 12(1)^2-18(1)+6 = 0$ ft/s   and

$v(2) = 12(2)^2-18(2)+6 = 18$ ft/s.

(b) It is at rest when $v(t) = 12t^2-18t+6 = 6(2t-1)(t-1) = 0 \Leftrightarrow$

　　$t = 1/2$ or 1.

(c) It moves in the positive direction when $v(t) = 6(2t-1)(t-1) > 0$

　　$\Leftrightarrow$ $0 \le t < 1/2$ or $t > 1$.

(d) Distance in positive direction $= |f(1/2)-f(0)|+|f(4)-f(1)|$

$= |3.25-2|+|138-3| = 136.25$ ft.   Distance in negative direction $=$

$|f(1)-f(1/2)| = |3-3.25| = 0.25$ ft.

Total distance traveled $= 136.25+0.25 = 136.5$ ft.

(e)

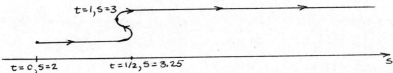

18.   (a) $v(a) = \lim_{h \to 0} \dfrac{f(a+h)-f(a)}{h} = \lim_{h \to 0} \dfrac{(a+h)^4-4(a+h)+1-(a^4-4a+1)}{h}$

$= \lim_{h \to 0} \dfrac{4a^3h+6a^2h^2+4ah^3+h^4-4h}{h} = \lim_{h \to 0} (4a^3+6a^2h+4ah^2+h^3-4) = 4a^3-4$

So $v(1) = 4(1)^3-4 = 0$ ft/s   and $v(2) = 4(2)^3-4 = 28$ ft/s.

(b) It is at rest when $v(t) = 4(t^3-1) = 4(t-1)(t^2+t+1) = 0 \Leftrightarrow t = 1$

(c) It moves in the positive direction when $4(t^3-1) > 0 \Leftrightarrow t > 1$.

(d) Distance in positive direction $= |f(4)-f(1)| = |241-(-2)|$

$= 243$.   Distance in negative direction $= |f(1)-f(0)| = |-2-1| = 3$

Total distance traveled $= 243+3 = 246$ ft.

(e)

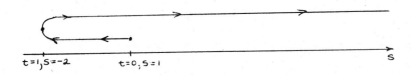

20. $f'(a) = \lim\limits_{h \to 0} \dfrac{f(a+h)-f(a)}{h} = \lim\limits_{h \to 0} \dfrac{\frac{a+h}{(a+h)^2-1} - \frac{a}{a^2-1}}{h}$

$= \lim\limits_{h \to 0} \dfrac{(a+h)(a^2-1)-a(a^2+2ah+h^2-1)}{h(a^2-1)(a^2+2ah+h^2-1)} = \lim\limits_{h \to 0} \dfrac{h(-a^2-1-ah)}{h(a^2-1)(a^2+2ah+h^2-1)}$

$= \lim\limits_{h \to 0} \dfrac{-a^2-1-ah}{(a^2-1)(a^2+2ah+h^2-1)} = \dfrac{-a^2-1}{(a^2-1)(a^2-1)} = -\dfrac{a^2+1}{(a^2-1)^2}$

22. $f'(a) = \lim\limits_{h \to 0} \dfrac{f(a+h)-f(a)}{h} = \lim\limits_{h \to 0} \dfrac{\sqrt{a+h-1}-\sqrt{a-1}}{h}$

$= \lim\limits_{h \to 0} \dfrac{(\sqrt{a+h-1}-\sqrt{a-1})}{h} \cdot \dfrac{(\sqrt{a+h-1}+\sqrt{a-1})}{(\sqrt{a+h-1}+\sqrt{a-1})} = \lim\limits_{h \to 0} \dfrac{(a+h-1)-(a-1)}{h(\sqrt{a+h-1}+\sqrt{a-1})}$

$= \lim\limits_{h \to 0} \dfrac{1}{\sqrt{a+h-1}+\sqrt{a-1}} = \dfrac{1}{\sqrt{a-1}+\sqrt{a-1}} = \dfrac{1}{2\sqrt{a-1}}$

24. $f'(0) = \lim\limits_{h \to 0} \dfrac{f(0+h)-f(0)}{h} = \lim\limits_{h \to 0} \dfrac{h^{2/3}-0}{h}$

$= \lim\limits_{h \to 0} \dfrac{1}{\sqrt[3]{h}}$ This limit does not exist.

Therefore $f'(0)$ does not exist.

26. $\lim\limits_{h \to 0} \dfrac{(2+h)^3-8}{h} = f'(2)$ where $f(x) = x^3$

28. $\lim\limits_{x \to 3\pi} \dfrac{\cos x + 1}{x - 3\pi} = f'(3\pi)$ where $f(x) = \cos x$

30. $\lim\limits_{t \to 0} \dfrac{3(5+t)^2+(5+t)-80}{t} = f'(5)$ where $f(x) = 3x^2+x-80$

32. $f'(x) = \lim\limits_{h \to 0} \dfrac{f(x+h)-f(x)}{h} = \lim\limits_{h \to 0} \dfrac{18-18}{h} = \lim\limits_{h \to 0} 0 = 0$

Domain of f = domain of f' = R

34. $f'(x) = \lim\limits_{h \to 0} \dfrac{f(x+h)-f(x)}{h} = \lim\limits_{h \to 0} \dfrac{(x+h)^4-x^4}{h} = \lim\limits_{h \to 0} \dfrac{4x^3h+6x^2h^2+4xh^3+h^4}{h}$

$= \lim\limits_{h \to 0} (4x^3+6x^2h+4xh^2+h^3) = 4x^3$ Domain of f = domain of f' = R

36. $f'(x) = \lim\limits_{h \to 0} \dfrac{f(x+h)-f(x)}{h} = \lim\limits_{h \to 0} \dfrac{\frac{x+h+1}{x+h-1} - \frac{x+1}{x-1}}{h}$

$= \lim\limits_{h \to 0} \dfrac{(x+h+1)(x-1)-(x+1)(x+h-1)}{h(x+h-1)(x-1)} = \lim\limits_{h \to 0} \dfrac{-2h}{h(x+h-1)(x-1)}$

$$= \lim_{h \to 0} \frac{-2}{(x+h-1)(x-1)} = \frac{-2}{(x-1)^2} \qquad \text{Domain of } f = \text{domain of } f' = \{x \mid x \neq 1\}$$

38. $g'(x) = \lim_{h \to 0} \dfrac{g(x+h)-g(x)}{h} = \lim_{h \to 0} \dfrac{\dfrac{1}{(x+h)^2} - \dfrac{1}{x^2}}{h} = \lim_{h \to 0} \dfrac{x^2-(x+h)^2}{h(x+h)^2 x^2}$

$$= \lim_{h \to 0} \frac{-2xh-h^2}{h(x+h)^2 x^2} = \lim_{h \to 0} \frac{-2x-h}{(x+h)^2 x^2} = \frac{-2x}{x^4} = -\frac{2}{x^3}$$

Domain of g = domain of g' = $\{x \mid x \neq 0\}$

40. $F'(x) = \lim_{h \to 0} \dfrac{F(x+h)-F(x)}{h} = \lim_{h \to 0} \dfrac{\dfrac{1}{\sqrt{x+h-1}} - \dfrac{1}{\sqrt{x-1}}}{h}$

$$= \lim_{h \to 0} \frac{\sqrt{x-1}-\sqrt{x+h-1}}{h\sqrt{x+h-1}\sqrt{x-1}}\left[\frac{\sqrt{x-1}+\sqrt{x+h-1}}{\sqrt{x-1}+\sqrt{x+h-1}}\right] = \lim_{h \to 0} \frac{-h}{h\sqrt{x+h-1}\sqrt{x-1}(\sqrt{x-1}+\sqrt{x+h-1})}$$

$$= \frac{-1}{\sqrt{x-1}\sqrt{x-1}(2\sqrt{x-1})} = -\frac{1}{2(x-1)^{3/2}} \qquad \text{Domain of } F = \text{domain of } F' = (1, \infty)$$

42. $f'(t) = \lim_{h \to 0} \dfrac{f(t+h)-f(t)}{h} = \lim_{h \to 0} \dfrac{\dfrac{6}{1+(t+h)^2} - \dfrac{6}{1+t^2}}{h}$

$$= \lim_{h \to 0} \frac{6[(1+t^2)-(1+t^2+2th+h^2)]}{h(1+t^2)[1+(t+h)^2]} = \lim_{h \to 0} \frac{6(-2th+h^2)}{h(1+t^2)[1+(t+h)^2]}$$

$$= \lim_{h \to 0} \frac{6(-2t+h)}{(1+t^2)[1+(t+h)^2]} = \frac{-12t}{(1+t^2)^2}$$

Domain of f = domain of f' = R

44. $f'(x) = \lim_{h \to 0} \dfrac{f(x+h)-f(x)}{h} = \lim_{h \to 0} \dfrac{\sqrt{c-x-h}-\sqrt{c-x}}{h}\left[\dfrac{\sqrt{c-x-h}+\sqrt{c-x}}{\sqrt{c-x-h}+\sqrt{c-x}}\right]$

$$= \lim_{h \to 0} \frac{-h}{h(\sqrt{c-x-h}+\sqrt{c-x})} = \lim_{h \to 0} \frac{-1}{\sqrt{c-x-h}+\sqrt{c-x}} = -\frac{1}{2\sqrt{c-x}}$$

$\text{Dom}(f) = (-\infty, c] \qquad \text{dom}(f') = (-\infty, c)$

46.   **48.**   **50.**

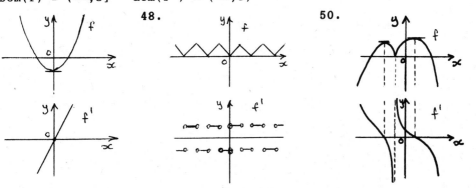

52. See Figure 3.10 in Section 3.3.

54. $f(x) = [x]$ is not continuous at any integer n (Example 2.5.4) so f is not differentiable at n by Theorem 3.8. If a is not an integer, then f is constant on an open interval containing a, so $f'(a) = 0$. Thus $f'(x) = 0$, x not an integer.

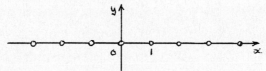

56. (a) $f(x) = \begin{cases} 0 & \text{if } x \leq 0 \\ 5-x & \text{if } 0 < x < 4 \\ 1/(5-x) & \text{if } x \geq 4 \end{cases}$

These expressions show that f is differentiable on the intervals $(-\infty,0)$, $(0,4)$, $(4,5)$, and $(5,\infty)$. Since $\lim\limits_{x \to 0^+} f(x) = \lim\limits_{x \to 0^+}(5-x)$

$= 5 \neq 0 = \lim\limits_{x \to 0^-} f(x)$, $\lim\limits_{x \to 0} f(x)$ does not exist, so f is discontinuous

(and therefore not differentiable) at 0. At 4 we have $\lim\limits_{x \to 4^-} f(x)$

$= \lim\limits_{x \to 4^-}(5-x) = 1$ and $\lim\limits_{x \to 4^+} f(x) = \lim\limits_{x \to 4^+}\frac{1}{5-x} = 1$, so $\lim\limits_{x \to 4} f(x) = 1 = f(4)$

and f is continuous at 4. But $\lim\limits_{h \to 0^-}\frac{f(4+h)-f(4)}{h} = \lim\limits_{h \to 0^-}\frac{5-(4+h)-1}{h}$

$= \lim\limits_{h \to 0^-}\frac{-h}{h} = \lim\limits_{h \to 0^-}(-1) = -1$ and $\lim\limits_{h \to 0^+}\frac{f(4+h)-f(4)}{h} = \lim\limits_{h \to 0^+}\frac{[1/(1-h)]-1}{h}$

$= \lim\limits_{h \to 0^+}\frac{1-(1-h)}{h(1-h)} = \lim\limits_{h \to 0}\frac{1}{1-h} = 1$, so $f'(4)$ does not exist, i.e., f is

not differentiable at 4. Since $f(5)$ is not defined, f is neither continuous nor differentiable at 5.

(a)

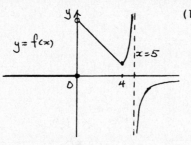

(b)

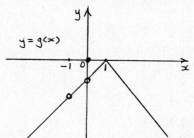

(b) $g(x) = \begin{cases} \dfrac{x^3-x}{x^2+x} & \text{if } x < 1,\ x \neq 0 \\ 0 & \text{if } x = 0 \\ 1-x & \text{if } x \geq 1 \end{cases}$

These expressions show that f is differentiable on the intervals $(-\infty,-1)$, $(-1,0)$, and $(0,\infty)$. Note that if x < 1 and x ≠ 0, -1, then $g(x) = \dfrac{x(x+1)(x-1)}{x(x+1)} = x-1$. g is discontinuous at x = -1 since it is not defined there. Also $\lim_{x\to 0} g(x) = \lim_{x\to 0}(x-1) = -1$, whereas g(0) = 0, so g is discontinuous at 0. g is not differentiable at -1 and 0 (since it is discontinuous there). Also g is not differentiable at 1 because $\lim_{h\to 0^+}\dfrac{g(1+h)-g(1)}{h} = \lim_{h\to 0^+}\dfrac{-h-0}{h} = \lim_{h\to 0^+}(-1) = -1$ but $\lim_{h\to 0^-}\dfrac{g(1+h)-g(1)}{h} = \lim_{h\to 0^-}\dfrac{h-0}{h} = \lim_{h\to 0^-}1 = 1$, so g'(0) does not exist.

58. Since $f(x) = x^2\sin(1/x)$ when x ≠ 0 and f(0) = 0, we have
$f'(0) = \lim_{h\to 0}\dfrac{f(0+h)-f(0)}{h} = \lim_{h\to 0}\dfrac{h^2\sin(1/h)-0}{h} = \lim_{h\to 0} h\sin\dfrac{1}{h} = 0$

(See Example 2.4.4.)

Section 3.2

Exercises 3.2

2. $g(x) = x^{100}+50x+1 \Rightarrow g'(x) = 100x^{99}+50$

4. $s(t) = t^8+6t^7-18t^2+2t \Rightarrow s'(t) = 8t^7+6(7t^6)-18(2t)+2$
   $= 8t^7+42t^6-36t+2$

6. $G(y) = (y^2+1)(2y-7) \Rightarrow G'(y) = (y^2+1)D(2y-7) + (2y-7)D(y^2+1)$
   $= (y^2+1)(2) + (2y-7)(2y) = 6y^2-14y+2$

8. $R(x) = \sqrt{10}/x^7 = \sqrt{10}x^{-7} \Rightarrow R'(x) = -7\sqrt{10}x^{-8} = -7\sqrt{10}/x^8$

10. $f(t) = \sqrt{t}-1/\sqrt{t} = t^{1/2}-t^{-1/2} \Rightarrow f'(t) = (1/2)t^{-1/2}-(-1/2)t^{-3/2}$
    $= 1/2\sqrt{t} + 1/2t\sqrt{t}$

12. $f(u) = \dfrac{1-u^2}{1+u^2} \Rightarrow f'(u) = \dfrac{(1+u^2)D(1-u^2)-(1-u^2)D(1+u^2)}{(1+u^2)^2}$
    $= \dfrac{(1+u^2)(-2u)-(1-u^2)(2u)}{(1+u^2)^2} = \dfrac{-4u}{(1+u^2)^2}$

14. $H(t) = \sqrt[3]{t}(t+2) = t^{4/3} + 2t^{1/3} \;\Rightarrow\; H'(t) = (4/3)t^{1/3}+(2/3)t^{-2/3}$

[Another method: Use the Product Rule.]

16. $y = \dfrac{\sqrt{x}-1}{\sqrt{x}+1} \;\Rightarrow\; y' = \dfrac{(\sqrt{x}+1)(1/2\sqrt{x})-(\sqrt{x}-1)(1/2\sqrt{x})}{(\sqrt{x}+1)^2} = \dfrac{1}{\sqrt{x}(\sqrt{x}+1)^2}$

18. $y = x^{4/3}-x^{2/3} \;\Rightarrow\; y' = (4/3)x^{1/3}-(2/3)x^{-1/3}$

20. $y = x^2+x+x^{-1}+x^{-2} \;\Rightarrow\; y' = 2x+1-x^{-2}-2x^{-3}$

22. $y = A+B/x+C/x^2 = A+Bx^{-1}+Cx^{-2} \;\Rightarrow\; y' = -Bx^{-2}-2Cx^{-3} = -B/x^2 - 2C/x^3$

24. $y = \dfrac{4t+5}{2-3t} \;\Rightarrow\; y' = \dfrac{(2-3t)(4)-(4t+5)(-3)}{(2-3t)^2} = \dfrac{23}{(2-3t)^2}$

26. $y = x^4-\sqrt[4]{x} = x^4-x^{1/4} \;\Rightarrow\; y' = 4x^3-(1/4)x^{-3/4} = 4x^3-1/4x^{3/4}$

28. $u = \sqrt[3]{t^2}+2\sqrt{t^3} = t^{2/3}+2t^{3/2} \;\Rightarrow\; u' = (2/3)t^{-1/3}+2(3/2)t^{1/2} = 2/3\sqrt[3]{t}+3\sqrt{t}$

30. $v = 6/\sqrt[3]{t^5} = 6t^{-5/3} \;\Rightarrow\; v' = 6(-5/3)t^{-8/3} = -10/\sqrt[3]{t^8}$

32. $f(x) = \dfrac{ax+b}{cx+d} \;\Rightarrow\; f'(x) = \dfrac{(cx+d)(a)-(ax+b)(c)}{(cx+d)^2} = \dfrac{ad-bc}{(cx+d)^2}$

34. $g(x) = \sqrt[5]{x}-6x^{-1.8}+0.1(x^{1.8}) \;\Rightarrow\; g'(x) = (1/5)x^{-4/5}-6(-1.8)x^{-2.8}$
$+0.1(1.8)x^{0.8} = 0.2x^{-0.8}+10.8x^{-2.8}+0.18x^{0.8}$

36. $s = \sqrt{t}(t^3-\sqrt{t}+1) = t^{7/2}-t+t^{1/2} \;\Rightarrow\; s' = (7/2)t^{5/2}-1+1/2\sqrt{t}$

[Another method: Use the Product Rule.]

38. $y = f(x) = \dfrac{x}{x-3} \;\Rightarrow\; f'(x) = \dfrac{(x-3)1-x(1)}{(x-3)^2} = \dfrac{-3}{(x-3)^2}$ So the slope of
the tangent line at $(6,2)$ is $f'(6) = -1/3$ and the equation is
$y-2 = (-1/3)(x-6)$ or $x+3y = 12$.

40. $y = f(x) = x^{5/2} \;\Rightarrow\; f'(x) = (5/2)x^{3/2}$ So the slope of the tangent
line at $(4,32)$ is $f'(4) = 20$ and the equation is $y-32 = 20(x-4)$ or
$y = 20x-48$.

42. If $y = x^2+x$, then $y' = 2x+1$. If the point at which a tangent meets
the parabola is (a,a^2+a), then the slope of the tangent is $2a+1$.
But since it passes through $(2,-3)$, the slope must also be $\dfrac{a^2+a+3}{a-2}$.
Therefore $2a+1 = \dfrac{a^2+a+3}{a-2}$. Solving this equation for a we get
$a^2+a+3 = 2a^2-3a-2 \;\Leftrightarrow\; a^2-4a-5 = (a-5)(a+1) = 0 \;\Leftrightarrow\; a = 5$ or -1.
If $a = -1$, the point is $(-1,0)$ and the slope is -1, so the equation
is $y-0 = (-1)(x+1)$ or $x+y+1 = 0$. If $a = 5$, the point is $(5,30)$ and
the slope is 11, so the equation is $y-30 = 11(x-5)$ or $11x-y = 25$.

44. $f(x) = 2x^3-3x^2-6x+87$ has a horizontal tangent when $f'(x) = 6x^2-6x-6$
$= 0 \iff x^2-x-1 = 0 \iff x = (1\pm\sqrt{5})/2$

46. $y = \frac{x-1}{x+1} \implies y' = \frac{(x+1)(1)-(x-1)(1)}{(x+1)^2} = \frac{2}{(x+1)^2}$ If the tangent

intersects the curve when $x = a$, then its slope is $2/(a+1)^2$.   But
if the tangent is parallel to $x-2y = 1$, its slope is $1/2$.   Thus
$\frac{2}{(a+1)^2} = \frac{1}{2} \implies (a+1)^2 = 4 \implies a+1 = \pm 2 \implies a = 1$ or -3.   When

$a = 1$, $y = 0$ and the tangent is $y = (1/2)(x-1)$ or $x-2y = 1$.   When
$a = -3$, $y = 2$ and the tangent is $y-2 = (1/2)(x+3)$ or $x-2y+7 = 0$.

48. The sides of the groove must be tangent to the parabola $y = 16x^2$.
$y' = 32x = 1.75$ when $x = \frac{1.75}{32} = \frac{7}{128}$ which $\implies y = 16\left[\frac{7}{128}\right]^2 = \frac{49}{1024}$

Therefore the points of contact are $(\pm 7/128, 49/1024)$.

50. $y = f(x) = \frac{1}{x-1} \implies f'(x) = \frac{(x-1)(0)-1(1)}{(x-1)^2} = -1/(x-1)^2$, so the

tangent line at $(2,1)$ has slope $f'(2) = -1$.   The normal line has
slope $-1/(-1) = 1$ and equation $y-1 = 1(x-2)$ or $y = x-1$.

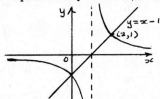

52. The slope of the tangent line to the curve $y = f(x)$ at $(a,f(a))$ is
$f'(a)$, so the slope of the normal line is $-1/f'(a)$ [if $f'(a) \ne 0$]
and its equation is $y-f(a) = -[1/f'(a)](x-a)$ or
$x+f'(a)y = a+f(a)f'(a)$.   [If $f'(a) = 0$, the normal is $x = a$.]

54. (a) $s = f(t) = 3-6t+t^3 \implies v(t) = f'(t) = -6+3t^2$
(b) It is at rest when $v(t) = -6+3t^2 = 0 \iff t^2 = 2 \iff t = \sqrt{2}$
(c) It moves in the positive direction when $v(t) = -6+3t^2 > 0 \iff$
$t^2 > 2 \iff t > \sqrt{2}$

56. $s = f(t) = \sqrt{t}(5-5t+2t^2) = 5t^{1/2}-5t^{3/2}+2t^{5/2}$
(a) $v = f'(t) = (5/2)t^{-1/2}-(15/2)t^{1/2}+5t^{3/2} = (5/2)t^{-1/2}(1-3t+2t^2)$
(b) It is at rest when $v = 0 \iff 1-3t+2t^2 = (2t-1)(t-1) = 0 \iff$
$t = 1/2$ or 1.
(c) It moves in the positive direction when $v > 0 \iff$
$(2t-1)(t-1) > 0 \iff 0 \le t < 1/2$ or $t > 1$.

58. (a) Note that $x^2-9 < 0$ for $x^2 < 9$ $\Leftrightarrow$ $|x| < 3$ $\Leftrightarrow$ $-3 < x < 3$. So

$$f(x) = \begin{cases} x^2-9 & \text{if } x \le -3 \\ -x^2+9 & \text{if } -3<x<3 \\ x^2-9 & \text{if } x \ge 3 \end{cases} \Rightarrow f'(x) = \begin{cases} 2x & \text{if } x<-3 \\ -2x & \text{if } -3<x<3 \\ 2x & \text{if } x>3 \end{cases}$$

To show that $f'(3)$ does not exist we investigate $\lim\limits_{h \to 0} \dfrac{f(3+h)-f(3)}{h}$.

$$\lim_{h \to 0^+} \frac{f(3+h)-f(3)}{h} = \lim_{h \to 0^+} \frac{[(3+h)^2-9]-0}{h} = \lim_{h \to 0^+} \frac{6h+h^2}{h} = \lim_{h \to 0^+} (6+h) = 6$$

$$\lim_{h \to 0^-} \frac{f(3+h)-f(3)}{h} = \lim_{h \to 0^-} \frac{[-(3+h)^2+9]-0}{h} = \lim_{h \to 0^-} (-6+h) = -6$$

Since the right and left limits are different, $\lim\limits_{h \to 0} \dfrac{f(3+h)-f(3)}{h}$ does

not exist, that is, $f'(3)$ does not exist. Similarly, $f'(-3)$ does not exist. Therefore f is not differentiable at 3 or -3.

(b)

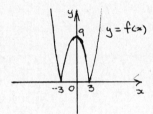

60. $g(x) = -1-2x$ if $x < -1$, $g(x) = x^2$ if $-1 \le x \le 1$, $g(x) = x$ if $x > 1$

$$\lim_{h \to 0^-} \frac{g(-1+h)-g(-1)}{h} = \lim_{h \to 0^-} \frac{[-1-2(-1+h)]-1}{h} = \lim_{h \to 0^-} \frac{-2h}{h} = \lim_{h \to 0^-} (-2) = -2$$

$$\lim_{h \to 0^+} \frac{g(-1+h)-g(-1)}{h} = \lim_{h \to 0^+} \frac{(-1+h)^2-1}{h} = \lim_{h \to 0^+} \frac{-2h+h^2}{h} = \lim_{h \to 0^+} (-2+h) = -2$$

So g is differentiable at -1 and $g'(-1) = -2$.

$$\lim_{h \to 0^-} \frac{g(1+h)-g(1)}{h} = \lim_{h \to 0^-} \frac{(1+h)^2-1}{h} = \lim_{h \to 0^-} \frac{2h+h^2}{h} = \lim_{h \to 0^-} (2+h) = 2$$

$$\lim_{h \to 0^+} \frac{g(1+h)-g(1)}{h} = \lim_{h \to 0^+} \frac{(1+h)-1}{h} = \lim_{h \to 0^+} \frac{h}{h} = \lim_{h \to 0^+} 1 = 1$$

So $g'(1)$ does not exist. Thus g is differentiable except when $x = 1$

and $g'(x) = \begin{cases} -2 & \text{if } x \le -1 \\ 2x & \text{if } -1 < x < 1 \\ 1 & \text{if } x > 1 \end{cases}$

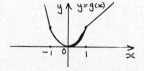

62. If $x \geq 1$, then $h(x) = |x-1| + |x+2| = x-1+x+2 = 2x+1$.

If $-2 < x < 1$, then $h(x) = -(x-1)+x+2 = 3$.

If $x \leq -2$, then $h(x) = -(x-1)-(x+2) = -2x-1$. Therefore

$$h(x) = \begin{cases} -2x-1 & \text{if } x \leq -2 \\ 3 & \text{if } -2 < x < 1 \\ 2x+1 & \text{if } x \geq 1 \end{cases} \Rightarrow h'(x) = \begin{cases} -2 & \text{if } x < -2 \\ 0 & \text{if } -2 < x < 1 \\ 2 & \text{if } x > 1 \end{cases}$$

To see that $h'(1) = \lim\limits_{x \to 1} \dfrac{h(x)-h(1)}{x-1}$ does not exist, observe that

$$\lim_{x \to 1^-} \frac{h(x)-h(1)}{x-1} = \lim_{x \to 1} \frac{3-3}{3-1} = 0 \text{ but } \lim_{x \to 1^+} \frac{h(x)-h(1)}{x-1} = \lim_{x \to 1^+} \frac{2x-2}{x-1} = 2$$

Similarly, $h'(-2)$ does not exist.

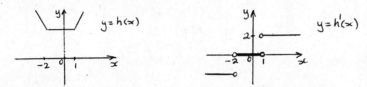

64. $y = (x+5)(x^2+7)(x-3)$ Using Exercise 63(a), we have

$y' = (x^2+7)(x-3)D(x+5) + (x+5)(x-3)D(x^2+7) + (x+5)(x^2+7)D(x-3)$

$= (x^2+7)(x-3) + (x+5)(x-3)(2x) + (x+5)(x^2+7) = 4x^3+6x^2-16x+14$

66. $y = (x^4+3x^3+17x+82)^3$ Using Exercise 63(b), we have $y' = $

$3(x^4+3x^3+17x+82)^2 D(x^4+3x^3+17x+82) = 3(x^4+3x^3+17x+82)^2(4x^3+9x^2+17)$

68. Let the coordinates of P be (a, a^3). Then the slope at P is $3a^2$ and the equation of the tangent at P is $y-a^3 = 3a^2(x-a)$ or $y = 3a^2x-2a^3$. To find Q we solve the equations $y = x^3$ and $y = 3a^2x-2a^3$. This gives $x^3-3a^2x+2a^3 = 0$. Note that $(x-a)^2$ must be a factor since $x = a$ is a double root. So we have $(x-a)^2(x+2a) = 0$. The other root is $x = -2a$, so Q is $(-2a, -8a^3)$. The slope at Q is $3(-2a)^2$ $= 12a^2 = 4(3a^2)$ which is four times the slope at P.

Section 3.3

Exercises 3.3

2. $\lim\limits_{x \to 0} \cos(\sin x) = \cos\left[\lim\limits_{x \to 0} \sin x\right] = \cos 0 = 1$

4. $\lim\limits_{x \to \pi} x^2\sec x = \left[\lim\limits_{x \to \pi} x^2\right]\left[\lim\limits_{x \to \pi} \sec x\right] = \pi^2\sec \pi = \pi^2(-1) = -\pi^2$

6. $\lim\limits_{x \to 0} \dfrac{\sin x}{3x} = \dfrac{1}{3} \lim\limits_{x \to 0} \dfrac{\sin x}{x} = \dfrac{1}{3} \cdot 1 = \dfrac{1}{3}$

8. $\lim\limits_{t \to \pi/6} \csc t \cot^2 t = \lim\limits_{t \to \pi/6} \csc t \left[\lim\limits_{t \to \pi/6} \cot t \right]^2 = 2(\sqrt{3})^2 = 6$

10. $\lim\limits_{t \to 0} \dfrac{\sin 8t}{\sin 9t} = \lim\limits_{t \to 0} \dfrac{8 \left[\dfrac{\sin 8t}{8t} \right]}{9 \left[\dfrac{\sin 9t}{9t} \right]} = \dfrac{8 \lim\limits_{t \to 0} \dfrac{\sin 8t}{8t}}{9 \lim\limits_{t \to 0} \dfrac{\sin 9t}{9t}} = \dfrac{8 \cdot 1}{9 \cdot 1} = \dfrac{8}{9}$

12. $\lim\limits_{\theta \to 0} \dfrac{\cos \theta - 1}{\sin \theta} = \lim\limits_{\theta \to 0} \dfrac{\dfrac{\cos \theta - 1}{\theta}}{\dfrac{\sin \theta}{\theta}} = \dfrac{\lim\limits_{\theta \to 0} \dfrac{\cos \theta - 1}{\theta}}{\lim\limits_{\theta \to 0} \dfrac{\sin \theta}{\theta}} = \dfrac{0}{1} = 0$

14. $\lim\limits_{x \to 0} \dfrac{\tan x}{4x} = \lim\limits_{x \to 0} \dfrac{1}{4} \dfrac{\sin x}{x} \cdot \dfrac{1}{\cos x} = \dfrac{1}{4} \lim\limits_{x \to 0} \dfrac{\sin x}{x} \lim\limits_{x \to 0} \dfrac{1}{\cos x} = \dfrac{1}{4} \cdot 1 \cdot 1 = \dfrac{1}{4}$

16. $\lim\limits_{x \to 0} \dfrac{\sec x}{1 - \sin x} = \dfrac{\sec 0}{1 - \sin 0} = \dfrac{1}{1-0} = 1$

18. $\lim\limits_{t \to 0} \dfrac{t^3}{\tan^3 2t} = \lim\limits_{t \to 0} \dfrac{t^3 \cos^3 2t}{\sin^3 2t} = \lim\limits_{t \to 0} \cos^3 2t \; \dfrac{1}{8 \dfrac{\sin^3 2t}{(2t)^3}}$

$= \lim\limits_{t \to 0} \cos^3 2t \cdot \dfrac{1}{8 \left[\lim\limits_{t \to 0} \dfrac{\sin 2t}{2t} \right]^3} = 1 \cdot \dfrac{1}{8 \cdot 1^3} = \dfrac{1}{8}$

20. $\dfrac{d}{dx}(\sec x) = \dfrac{d}{dx} \left[\dfrac{1}{\cos x} \right] = \dfrac{(\cos x)(0) - 1(-\sin x)}{\cos^2 x} = \dfrac{\sin x}{\cos^2 x}$

$= \dfrac{1}{\cos x} \cdot \dfrac{\sin x}{\cos x} = \sec x \tan x$

22. $y = \cos x - 2 \tan x \;\Rightarrow\; dy/dx = -\sin x - 2 \sec^2 x$

24. $y = x \csc x \;\Rightarrow\; dy/dx = \csc x - x \csc x \cot x = \csc x (1 - x \cot x)$

26. $y = \dfrac{\sin x}{1 + \cos x} \;\Rightarrow\; \dfrac{dy}{dx} = \dfrac{(1 + \cos x) \cos x - \sin x (-\sin x)}{(1 + \cos x)^2}$

$= \dfrac{\cos x + \cos^2 x + \sin^2 x}{(1 + \cos x)^2} = \dfrac{\cos x + 1}{(1 + \cos x)^2} = \dfrac{1}{1 + \cos x}$

28. $y = \dfrac{\tan x - 1}{\sec x} \;\Rightarrow\; \dfrac{dy}{dx} = \dfrac{\sec x \sec^2 x - (\tan x - 1) \sec x \tan x}{\sec^2 x}$

$= \dfrac{\sec x (\sec^2 x - \tan^2 x + \tan x)}{\sec^2 x} = \dfrac{1 + \tan x}{\sec x}$

[Another method: Write $y = \sin x - \cos x$. Then $y' = \cos x + \sin x$.]

30. $y = 2x(\sqrt{x} - \cot x) \;\Rightarrow\; dy/dx = 2(\sqrt{x} - \cot x) + 2x(1/2\sqrt{x} + \csc^2 x)$

$= 3\sqrt{x} - 2 \cot x + 2x \csc^2 x$

32. $y = x \sin x \cos x \;\Rightarrow\; dy/dx = \sin x \cos x + x \cos x \cos x$

$+ x \sin x (-\sin x) = \sin x \cos x + x \cos^2 x - x \sin^2 x$

34. $y = 2 \sin x \;\Rightarrow\; y' = 2 \cos x \;\Rightarrow\;$ The slope of the tangent line at

$(\pi/6, 1)$ is $2 \cos(\pi/6) = 2(\sqrt{3}/2) = \sqrt{3}$ and the equation is

$y - 1 = \sqrt{3}(x - \pi/6)$ or $y = \sqrt{3}x + 1 - \pi\sqrt{3}/6$.

36. $y = \sec x - 2 \cos x \;\Rightarrow\; y' = \sec x \tan x + 2 \sin x \;\Rightarrow\;$ The slope of

the tangent line at $(\pi/3, 1)$ is $\sec \dfrac{\pi}{3} \tan \dfrac{\pi}{3} + 2 \sin \dfrac{\pi}{3} = 2\sqrt{3} + 2\dfrac{\sqrt{3}}{2}$

$= 3\sqrt{3}$ and the equation is $y - 1 = 3\sqrt{3}(x - \pi/3)$ or $y = 3\sqrt{3}x + 1 - \pi\sqrt{3}$.

38. $f(x) = \cos x \;\Rightarrow\; f'(x) = \lim\limits_{h \to 0} \dfrac{f(x+h) - f(x)}{h} = \lim\limits_{h \to 0} \dfrac{\cos(x+h) - \cos x}{h}$

$= \lim\limits_{h \to 0} \dfrac{\cos x \cos h - \sin x \sin h - \cos x}{h}$

$= \lim\limits_{h \to 0} \left[\cos x \dfrac{\cos h - 1}{h} - \sin x \dfrac{\sin h}{h} \right]$

$= \cos x \lim\limits_{h \to 0} \dfrac{\cos h - 1}{h} - \sin x \lim\limits_{h \to 0} \dfrac{\sin h}{h}$

$= (\cos x)(0) - (\sin x)(1) = -\sin x$

40. Using the identity in the proof of (3.24), we have

$\lim\limits_{x \to 0} \dfrac{1 - \cos x}{2x^2} = \lim\limits_{x \to 0} \dfrac{2 \sin^2(x/2)}{2x^2} = \dfrac{1}{4} \left[\lim\limits_{x \to 0} \dfrac{\sin(x/2)}{x/2} \right]^2 = \dfrac{1}{4}(1)^2 = \dfrac{1}{4}$

[Another method: Multiply numerator and denominator by $1 + \cos x$.]

42. $\lim\limits_{x \to \pi/4} \dfrac{\sin x - \cos x}{\cos 2x} = \lim\limits_{x \to \pi/4} \dfrac{\sin x - \cos x}{\cos^2 x - \sin^2 x}$

$= \lim\limits_{x \to \pi/4} \dfrac{\sin x - \cos x}{(\cos x + \sin x)(\cos x - \sin x)} = \lim\limits_{x \to \pi/4} \dfrac{-1}{\cos x + \sin x}$

$= \dfrac{-1}{\cos(\pi/4) + \sin(\pi/4)} = -1/\sqrt{2}$

44. $\lim\limits_{x \to 0} \dfrac{x}{\sin(x/2)} = \lim\limits_{x \to 0} \dfrac{2}{\dfrac{\sin(x/2)}{x/2}} = \dfrac{2}{\lim\limits_{x \to 0} \dfrac{\sin(x/2)}{x/2}} = \dfrac{2}{1} = 2$

46. $\lim\limits_{x \to 1} \dfrac{\sin(x-1)}{x^2 + x - 2} = \lim\limits_{x \to 1} \dfrac{\sin(x-1)}{(x+2)(x-1)} = \lim\limits_{x \to 1} \dfrac{1}{x+2} \lim\limits_{x \to 1} \dfrac{\sin(x-1)}{x-1} = \dfrac{1}{3} \cdot 1 = \dfrac{1}{3}$

Section 3.4

Exercises 3.4

2. $y = u^2 - 2u + 3$, $u = 5 - 6x$ (a) $\dfrac{dy}{dx} = \dfrac{dy}{du} \dfrac{du}{dx} = (2u - 2)(-6) = 12(1 - u)$

When $x = 1$, $u = -1$, so $\dfrac{dy}{dx}\Big]_{x=1} = 12[1 - (-1)] = 24$

(b) $y = (5-6x)^2-2(5-6x)+3 = 36x^2-48x+18$, so $\frac{dy}{dx} = 72x-48$ and

$\frac{dy}{dx}\Big]_{x=1} = 72(1)-48 = 24$

4. $y = u-u^2, u = \sqrt{x}+\sqrt[3]{x}$ (a) $\frac{dy}{dx} = \frac{dy}{du}\frac{du}{dx} = (1-2u)\left[\frac{1}{2}x^{-1/2}+\frac{1}{3}x^{-2/3}\right]$

When $x = 1$, $u = 2$, so $\frac{dy}{dx}\Big]_{x=1} = (1-2\cdot2)\left[\frac{1}{2}1^{-1/2}+\frac{1}{3}1^{-2/3}\right] = -\frac{5}{2}$

(b) $y = u-u^2 = (\sqrt{x}+\sqrt[3]{x})-(\sqrt{x}+\sqrt[3]{x})^2 = x^{1/2}+x^{1/3}-x-2x^{5/6}-x^{2/3}$, so

$\frac{dy}{dx} = \frac{1}{2}x^{-1/2}+\frac{1}{3}x^{-2/3}-1-\frac{5}{3}x^{-1/6}-\frac{2}{3}x^{-1/3}$ and $\frac{dy}{dx}\Big]_{x=1} = \frac{1}{2}+\frac{1}{3}-1-\frac{5}{3}-\frac{2}{3} = -\frac{5}{2}$

6. $F(x) = (x^3-5x)^4 \Rightarrow F'(x) = 4(x^3-5x)^3\frac{d}{dx}(x^3-5x) = 4(x^3-5x)^3(3x^2-5)$

8. $g(t) = (6t^2+5)^3(t^3-7)^4$

$g'(t) = 3(6t^2+5)^2(12t)(t^3-7)^4 + (6t^2+5)^34(t^3-7)^3(3t^2)$

$= 36t(6t^2+5)^2(t^3-7)^4 + 12t^2(6t^2+5)^3(t^3-7)^3$

10. $f(t) = 1/(t^2-2t-5)^4 = (t^2-2t-5)^{-4}$

$f'(t) = -4(t^2-2t-5)^{-5}(2t-2) = \frac{8(1-t)}{(t^2-2t-5)^5}$

12. $k(x) = \sqrt[3]{1+\sqrt{x}} = (1+x^{1/2})^{1/3}$

$k'(x) = (1/3)(1+x^{1/2})^{-2/3}(1/2)x^{-1/2} = 1/6\sqrt{x}\sqrt[3]{(1+\sqrt{x})^2}$

14. $F(s) = \sqrt{s^3+1}(s^2+1)^4 = (s^3+1)^{1/2}(s^2+1)^4$

$F'(s) = (1/2)(s^3+1)^{-1/2}(3s^2)(s^2+1)^4 + (s^3+1)^{1/2}4(s^2+1)^3(2s)$

$= 3s^2(s^2+1)^4/2\sqrt{s^3+1} + 8s(s^2+1)^3\sqrt{s^3+1}$

16. $s(t) = \left[\frac{t^3+1}{t^3-1}\right]^{1/4}$

$s'(t) = \frac{1}{4}\left[\frac{t^3+1}{t^3-1}\right]^{-3/4}\frac{3t^2(t^3-1)-(t^3+1)3t^2}{(t^3-1)^2} = \frac{1}{4}\left[\frac{t^3+1}{t^3-1}\right]^{-3/4}\frac{-6t^2}{(t^3-1)^2}$

18. $f(x) = \frac{x}{\sqrt{7-3x}} \Rightarrow f'(x) = \frac{\sqrt{7-3x}-x(1/2)(7-3x)^{-1/2}(-3)}{7-3x}$

$= \frac{1}{\sqrt{7-3x}} + \frac{3x}{2(7-3x)^{3/2}}$ $\left[\text{OR:} \quad \frac{14-3x}{2(7-3x)^{3/2}} \quad\right]$

20. $y = (x^2+1)(x^2+2)^{1/3}$

$y' = 2x(x^2+2)^{1/3}+(x^2+1)\cdot\frac{1}{3}(x^2+2)^{-2/3}(2x) = 2x(x^2+2)^{1/3}\left[1 + \frac{x^2+1}{3(x^2+2)}\right]$

22. $y = 4 \sec 5x \Rightarrow y' = 4 \sec 5x \tan 5x (5) = 20 \sec 5x \tan 5x$

24. $y = \cos^3 x = (\cos x)^3 \Rightarrow y' = 3(\cos x)^2(-\sin x) = -3 \cos^2 x \sin x$

26. $y = \tan(x^2) + \tan^2 x \Rightarrow y' = \sec^2(x^2)(2x) + 2 \tan x \sec^2 x$

28. $y = \sin(\sin x) \Rightarrow y' = \cos (\sin x) \cos x$

30. $y = \sqrt{1 + 2\tan x} \Rightarrow y' = \frac{1}{2}(1 + 2\tan x)^{-1/2} \, 2\sec^2 x = \dfrac{\sec^2 x}{\sqrt{1 + 2\tan x}}$

32. $y = \cot\sqrt[3]{1+x^2}$

$y' = -\csc^2(\sqrt[3]{1+x^2})(1/3)(1+x^2)^{-2/3}(2x) = -2x\,\csc^2(\sqrt[3]{1+x^2})/3(1+x^2)^{2/3}$

34. $y = \sin^2(\cos 4x) \Rightarrow y' = 2\sin(\cos 4x)\cos(\cos 4x)(-\sin 4x)(4)$

$= -4\sin 4x \sin(2\cos 4x)$

36. $y = \dfrac{\sin^2 x}{\cos x} \Rightarrow y' = \dfrac{\cos x\,(2\sin x \cos x) - \sin^2 x\,(-\sin x)}{\cos^2 x}$

$= \dfrac{\sin x\,(2\cos^2 x + \sin^2 x)}{\cos^2 x} = \dfrac{\sin x\,(1 + \cos^2 x)}{\cos^2 x} = \sin x\,(1 + \sec^2 x)$

[Another method: $y = \tan x \sin x \Rightarrow y' = \sec^2 x \sin x + \tan x \cos x$

$= \sec^2 x \sin x + \sin x$.]

38. $y = x\sin\frac{1}{x} \Rightarrow y' = \sin\frac{1}{x} + x\cos\frac{1}{x}(-1/x^2) = \sin\frac{1}{x} - \frac{1}{x}\cos\frac{1}{x}$

40. $y = (\sin\sqrt{x^2+1})^{\sqrt{2}}$

$y' = \sqrt{2}(\sin\sqrt{x^2+1})^{\sqrt{2}-1}(\cos\sqrt{x^2+1})(1/2)(x^2+1)^{-1/2}(2x)$

$= \sqrt{2}x(\sin\sqrt{x^2+1})^{\sqrt{2}-1}(\cos\sqrt{x^2+1})/\sqrt{x^2+1}$

42. $y = \sqrt{1 + \tan(x+1/x)}$

$y' = \dfrac{1}{2\sqrt{1 + \tan(x+1/x)}}(\sec^2(x+1/x))(1-1/x^2) = \dfrac{(x^2-1)\,\sec^2(x+1/x)}{2x^2\sqrt{1 + \tan(x+1/x)}}$

44. $y = \sin(\sin(\sin x) \Rightarrow y' = \cos(\sin(\sin x))\frac{d}{dx}(\sin(\sin x))$

$= \cos(\sin(\sin x))\cos(\sin x)\cos x$

46. $y = \sqrt{x+\sqrt{x+\sqrt{x}}} \Rightarrow y' = \frac{1}{2}\left[x+\sqrt{x+\sqrt{x}}\right]^{-1/2}[1 + \frac{1}{2}(x+\sqrt{x})^{-1/2}(1+\frac{1}{2}x^{-1/2})]$

48. $g(t) = \sqrt[4]{(1-3t)^4+t^4} \quad g'(t) = (1/4)[(1-3t)^4+t^4]^{-3/4}[4(1-3t)^3(-3)+4t^3]$

$= [(1-3t)^4+t^4]^{-3/4}[t^3-3(1-3t^3)]$

50. $N(y) = \left[y+\sqrt[3]{y+\sqrt{2y-9}}\right]^8 = \left[y+[y+(2y-9)^{1/2}]^{1/3}\right]^8$

$N'(y) = 8\left[y+\sqrt[3]{y+\sqrt{2y-9}}\right]^7\left[1+\frac{1}{3}(y+\sqrt{2y-9})^{-2/3}[1+\frac{1}{2}(2y-9)^{-1/2}(2)]\right]$

$= 8\left[y+\sqrt[3]{y+\sqrt{2y-9}}\right]^7\left[1+\frac{1}{3}(y+\sqrt{2y-9})^{-2/3}(1+1/\sqrt{2y-9})\right]$

52. $y = \sqrt{\cos(\sin^2 x)}$

$y' = (1/2)[\cos(\sin^2 x)]^{-1/2}[-\sin(\sin^2 x)](2\sin x \cos x)$

$= -\sin(\sin^2 x)\sin x \cos x / \sqrt{\cos(\sin^2 x)}$

54. $y = f(x) = \sqrt{x+1/x} \Rightarrow f'(x) = (1/2)(x+1/x)^{-1/2}(1-1/x^2)$

    The slope of the tangent at $(1,\sqrt{2})$ is $f'(1) = 0$ and its equation is $y-\sqrt{2} = 0(x-1)$ or $y = \sqrt{2}$.

56. $y = f(x) = \dfrac{x}{(3-x^2)^5} \Rightarrow f'(x) = \dfrac{(3-x^2)^5(1)-x\cdot 5(3-x^2)^4(-2x)}{(3-x^2)^{10}}$

    $= \dfrac{3-x^2+10x^2}{(3-x^2)^6}$ The slope of the tangent at $(2,-2)$ is $f'(2) = 39$ and

    its equation is $y+2 = 39(x-2)$ or $y = 39x-80$.

58. $y = f(x) = \sin x + \cos 2x \Rightarrow f'(x) = \cos x - 2\sin 2x$

    The slope of the tangent at $(\pi/6,1)$ is $f'(\pi/6) = \sqrt{3}/2 - 2(\sqrt{3}/2) =$ $-\sqrt{3}/2$ and its equation is $y-1 = (-\sqrt{3}/2)(x-\pi/6)$ or $\sqrt{3}x+2y = 2+\pi\sqrt{3}/6$.

60. $w = u\circ v \Rightarrow w'(x) = u'(v(x))v'(x)$, so $w'(0) = u'(v(0))v'(0)$

    $= u'(2)v'(0) = 4\cdot 5 = 20$.

62. $f(x) = \sin\sqrt{2x+1} \Rightarrow f'(x) = \cos\sqrt{2x+1}(1/2\sqrt{2x+1})(2) = (\cos\sqrt{2x+1})/\sqrt{2x+1}$

    $\text{Dom}(f) = \{x\,|\,2x+1\geq 0\} = [-1/2,\infty)$ $\text{Dom}(f') = \{x\,|\,2x+1>0\} = (-1/2,\infty)$

64. $f(x) = \cos\sqrt{x} + \sqrt{\cos x}$

    $f'(x) = -\sin\sqrt{x}\,\dfrac{1}{2}x^{-1/2} + \dfrac{1}{2}(\cos x)^{-1/2}(-\sin x) = -\dfrac{\sin\sqrt{x}}{2\sqrt{x}} - \dfrac{\sin x}{2\sqrt{\cos x}}$

    Domain of $f = \{x\,|\,x\geq 0$ and $\cos x \geq 0\}$

    $= \{x\,|\,0\leq x\leq\pi/2$ or $(2n-1)\pi/2\leq x\leq(2n+1)\pi/2$ for some $n = 2,4,6\cdots\}$

    Domain of $f' = \{x\,|\,x>0$ and $\cos x>0\}$

    $= \{x\,|\,0<x<\pi/2$ or $(2n-1)\pi/2<x<(2n+1)\pi/2$ for some $n = 2,4,6\cdots\}$

66. (a) $s = A\cos(\omega t+\delta) \Rightarrow$ velocity $= s' = -\omega A\sin(\omega t+\delta)$

    (b) If $A \neq 0$ and $\omega \neq 0$, then $s' = 0 \Leftrightarrow \sin(\omega t+\delta) = 0 \Leftrightarrow$ $\omega t+\delta = n\pi \Leftrightarrow t = (n\pi-\delta)/\omega$, n an integer.

68. (a) $F(x) = f(x^\alpha) \Rightarrow F'(x) = f'(x^\alpha)(d/dx)(x^\alpha) = f'(x^\alpha)\alpha x^{\alpha-1}$

    (b) $G(x) = [f(x)]^\alpha \Rightarrow G'(x) = \alpha[f(x)]^{\alpha-1}f'(x)$

70. $g(t) = [f(\sin t)]^2 \Rightarrow g'(t) = 2f(\sin t)f'(\sin t)\cos t$

72. (a) $\dfrac{d}{dx}(\sin^n x\cos nx) = n\sin^{n-1}x\cos x\cos nx + \sin^n x\,(-n\sin nx)$

    $= n\sin^{n-1}x\,(\cos nx\cos x - \sin nx\sin x) = n\sin^{n-1}x\cos(n+1)x$

    (b) $\dfrac{d}{dx}(\cos^n x\cos nx) = n\cos^{n-1}x(-\sin x)\cos nx + \cos^n x(-n\sin nx)$

    $= -n\cos^{n-1}x\,(\cos nx\sin x + \sin nx\cos x) = -n\cos^{n-1}x\sin(n+1)x$

74. Using Exercise 73, we have $f(x) = \dfrac{|x|}{x} \Rightarrow f'(x) = \dfrac{x(x/|x|)-|x|(1)}{x^2}$

    $= \dfrac{x(|x|/x)-|x|}{x^2} = \dfrac{|x|-|x|}{x^2} = 0$ $\left[\text{Note that } \dfrac{x}{|x|} = \dfrac{|x|}{x}\right]$

Another method: Use the fact that $\dfrac{|x|}{x} = \begin{cases} 1 & \text{if } x > 0 \\ -1 & \text{if } x < 0 \end{cases}$

76. (a)

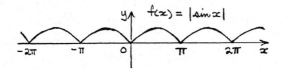

(b) f is not differentiable when $x = n\pi$, n an integer.

(c) $f(x) = |\sin x| = \sqrt{\sin^2 x} \;\Rightarrow\; f'(x) = \frac{1}{2}(\sin^2 x)^{-1/2} 2 \sin x \cos x$

$= \dfrac{\sin x}{|\sin x|} \cos x$ $\quad \left[\text{or} \quad f'(x) = \begin{cases} \cos x & \text{if } \sin x > 0 \\ -\cos x & \text{if } \sin x < 0 \end{cases} \right]$

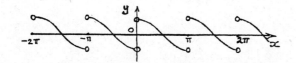

(d)

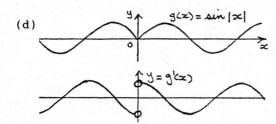

g is not differentiable at 0

$g(x) = \sin|x| = \sin \sqrt{x^2}$

$g'(x) = \cos|x| \cdot \dfrac{x}{|x|} = \dfrac{x}{|x|} \cos x$

or $\quad g'(x) = \begin{cases} \cos x & \text{if } x > 0 \\ -\cos x & \text{if } x < 0 \end{cases}$

Section 3.5

Exercises 3.5

2. (a) $\dfrac{x^2}{2} + \dfrac{y^2}{4} = 1 \;\Rightarrow\; x + \dfrac{y}{2}y' = 0 \;\Rightarrow\; y' = -\dfrac{2x}{y}$

(b) $\dfrac{y^2}{4} = 1 - \dfrac{x^2}{2} \;\Rightarrow\; y^2 = 4 - 2x^2 \;\Rightarrow\; y = \pm\sqrt{4-2x^2} \;\Rightarrow$

$y' = \pm \dfrac{1}{2\sqrt{4-2x^2}}(-4x) = \mp \dfrac{2x}{\sqrt{4-2x^2}}$

(c) $y' = \dfrac{-2x}{y} = \dfrac{-2x}{\pm\sqrt{4-2x^2}} = \mp \dfrac{2x}{\sqrt{4-2x^2}}$

4. (a) $x^2+xy-y^2 = 3 \Rightarrow 2x+y+xy'-2yy' = 0 \Rightarrow y' = \dfrac{2x+y}{2y-x}$

   (b) Use the quadratic formula: $y^2-xy+(3-x^2) = 0 \Rightarrow$

   $y = \dfrac{1}{2}\left[x \pm \sqrt{x^2-4(3-x^2)}\right] = \dfrac{1}{2}\left[x \pm \sqrt{5x^2-12}\right] \Rightarrow y' = \dfrac{1}{2}\left[1 \pm 5x/\sqrt{5x^2-12}\right]$

   (c) $y' = \dfrac{2x+y}{2y-x} = \dfrac{2x+(x\pm\sqrt{5x^2-12})/2}{x\pm\sqrt{5x^2-12} - x} = \dfrac{1}{2}\left[1 \pm \dfrac{5x}{\sqrt{5x^2-12}}\right]$

6. (a) $\sqrt{x}+\sqrt{y} = 4 \Rightarrow \dfrac{1}{2\sqrt{x}} + \dfrac{1}{2\sqrt{y}} y' = 0 \Rightarrow y' = -\dfrac{\sqrt{y}}{\sqrt{x}}$

   (b) $\sqrt{y} = 4-\sqrt{x} \Rightarrow y = (4-\sqrt{x})^2 = 16-8\sqrt{x}+x \Rightarrow y' = 1 - 4/\sqrt{x}$

   (c) $y' = -\dfrac{\sqrt{y}}{\sqrt{x}} = -\dfrac{4-\sqrt{x}}{\sqrt{x}} = -\dfrac{4}{\sqrt{x}} + 1$

8. $\sqrt{xy}-2x = \sqrt{y} \Rightarrow \dfrac{y+xy'}{2\sqrt{xy}} - 2 = \dfrac{y'}{2\sqrt{y}} \Rightarrow \dfrac{y-4\sqrt{xy}}{2\sqrt{xy}} = \dfrac{\sqrt{x}-x}{2\sqrt{xy}} y' \Rightarrow y' = \dfrac{y-4\sqrt{xy}}{\sqrt{x}-x}$

10. $y^5+3x^2y^2+5x^4 = 12 \Rightarrow 5y^4y'+6xy^2+6x^2yy'+20x^3 = 0 \Rightarrow y' = -\dfrac{20x^3+6xy^2}{5y^4+6x^2y}$

12. $\sqrt{x+y}+\sqrt{xy} = 6 \Rightarrow (1/2)(x+y)^{-1/2}(1+y') + (1/2)(xy)^{-1/2}(y+xy') = 0$

    $\Rightarrow y' = -\dfrac{(x+y)^{-1/2} + (xy)^{-1/2}y}{(x+y)^{-1/2} + (xy)^{-1/2}x} = -\dfrac{\sqrt{xy} + y\sqrt{x+y}}{\sqrt{xy} + x\sqrt{x+y}}$

14. $x^2 = \dfrac{y^2}{y^2-1} \Rightarrow 2x = \dfrac{(y^2-1)2yy' - y^2(2yy')}{(y^2-1)^2} = -\dfrac{2yy'}{(y^2-1)^2} \Rightarrow$

    $y' = -x(y^2-1)^2/y$

    [Another method: Write the equation as $x^2(y^2-1) = y^2$. This gives
    $y' = (x-xy^2)/(x^2y-y)$.]

16. $x\sqrt{1+y}+y\sqrt{1+2x} = 2x \Rightarrow \sqrt{1+y} + x\dfrac{1}{2\sqrt{1+y}} y' + y'\sqrt{1+2x} + y\dfrac{2}{2\sqrt{1+2x}} = 2$

    $\Rightarrow y' = \dfrac{2 - \sqrt{1+y} - y/\sqrt{1+2x}}{\sqrt{1+2x} + x/2\sqrt{1+y}}$

18. $x \sin y + \cos 2y = \cos y \Rightarrow$

    $\sin y + (x \cos y)y' - (2 \sin 2y)y' = (- \sin y)y' \Rightarrow$

    $y' = (\sin y)/(2 \sin 2y - x \cos y - \sin y)$

20. $x \cos y + y \cos x = 1 \Rightarrow$

    $\cos y + x(- \sin y)y' + y' \cos x - y \sin x = 0 \Rightarrow$

    $y' = \dfrac{y \sin x - \cos y}{\cos x - x \sin y}$

22. $(x^2+y^2)^2 = ax^2y \Rightarrow 2(x^2+y^2)(2x\dfrac{dx}{dy} + 2y) = 2ayx\dfrac{dx}{dy} + ax^2 \Rightarrow$

    $\dfrac{dx}{dy} = \dfrac{ax^2-4y(x^2+y^2)}{4x(x^2+y^2)-2axy}$

24. $[g(x)]^2 + 12x = x^2 g(x) \Rightarrow 2g(x)g'(x) + 12 = 2xg(x) + x^2 g'(x) \Rightarrow$

$g'(x) = \dfrac{2xg(x) - 12}{2g(x) - x^2} \Rightarrow g'(4) = \dfrac{2(4)(12) - 12}{2(12) - (4)^2} = \dfrac{21}{2}$

26. $\dfrac{x^2}{9} + \dfrac{y^2}{36} = 1 \Rightarrow \dfrac{2x}{9} + \dfrac{yy'}{18} = 0 \Rightarrow y' = -\dfrac{4x}{y}$ When $x = -1$ and

$y = 4\sqrt{2}$, we have $y' = -\dfrac{4(-1)}{4\sqrt{2}} = \dfrac{1}{\sqrt{2}}$ so the equation of the tangent

line is $y - 4\sqrt{2} = (1/\sqrt{2})(x+1)$ or $x - \sqrt{2}y + 9 = 0$.

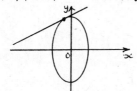

28. $x^{2/3} + y^{2/3} = 4 \Rightarrow (2/3)x^{-1/3} + (2/3)y^{-1/3}y' = 0 \Rightarrow y' = -\sqrt[3]{y}/\sqrt[3]{x}$

When $x = -3\sqrt{3}$ and $y = 1$, we have $y' = -1/(-3\sqrt{3})^{1/3} = 1/\sqrt{3}$, so the

equation of the tangent is $y - 1 = (1/\sqrt{3})(x + 3\sqrt{3})$ or $y = (1/\sqrt{3})x + 4$.

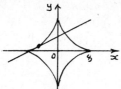

30. $x^2 y^2 = (y+1)^2 (4 - y^2) \Rightarrow 2xy^2 + 2x^2 yy' = 2(y+1)y'(4-y^2) + (y+1)^2(-2yy')$

$\Rightarrow y' = xy^2/[(y+1)(4-y^2) - y(y+1)^2 - x^2 y] = 0$ when $x = 0$. So the

equation of the tangent at $(0, -2)$ is $y + 2 = 0(x - 0)$ or $y = -2$.

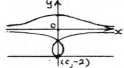

32. $\dfrac{x^2}{a^2} + \dfrac{y^2}{b^2} = 1 \Rightarrow \dfrac{2x}{a^2} + \dfrac{2yy'}{b^2} = 0 \Rightarrow y' = -\dfrac{b^2 x}{a^2 y} \Rightarrow$ the equation of

the tangent at (x_0, y_0) is $y - y_0 = (-b^2 x_0/a^2 y_0)(x - x_0)$ Multiplying

both sides by $\dfrac{y_0}{b^2}$ gives $\dfrac{y_0 y}{b^2} - \dfrac{y_0^2}{b^2} = -\dfrac{x_0 x}{a^2} + \dfrac{x_0^2}{a^2}$ Since (x_0, y_0) lies

on the ellipse, we have $\dfrac{x_0 x}{a^2} + \dfrac{y_0 y}{b^2} = \dfrac{x_0^2}{a^2} + \dfrac{y_0^2}{b^2} = 1$

34. $\sqrt{x}+\sqrt{y} = \sqrt{c}$ $\Rightarrow$ $\dfrac{1}{2\sqrt{x}} + \dfrac{y'}{2\sqrt{y}} = 0$ $\Rightarrow$ $y' = -\dfrac{\sqrt{y}}{\sqrt{x}}$ $\Rightarrow$ the equation of the tangent line at (x_0, y_0) is $y-y_0 = (-\sqrt{y_0}/\sqrt{x_0})(x-x_0)$. Setting $x = 0$ gives $y = y_0-(\sqrt{y_0}/\sqrt{x_0})(-x_0) = y_0+\sqrt{x_0}\sqrt{y_0}$ so the y-intercept is $y_0+\sqrt{x_0}\sqrt{y_0}$. Setting $y = 0$ gives $-y_0 = -(\sqrt{y_0}/\sqrt{x_0})(x-x_0)$ $\Rightarrow$ the x-intercept is $x_0+\sqrt{x_0}\sqrt{y_0}$. The sum of the intercepts is $(y_0+\sqrt{x_0}\sqrt{y_0}) + (x_0+\sqrt{x_0}\sqrt{y_0}) = x_0+2\sqrt{x_0}\sqrt{y_0}+y_0 = (\sqrt{x_0}+\sqrt{y_0})^2 = (\sqrt{c})^2 = c$.

36. $y^q = x^p$ $\Rightarrow$ $qy^{q-1}y' = px^{p-1}$ $\Rightarrow$
$y' = \dfrac{px^{p-1}}{qy^{q-1}} = \dfrac{px^{p-1}y}{qy^q} = \dfrac{px^{p-1}x^{p/q}}{qx^p} = \dfrac{p}{q}x^{(p/q)-1}$

38. $y = x$ and $y = x^2$ intersect at $(0,0)$ and $(1,1)$. $y = x$ $\Rightarrow$ $y' = 1$ and $y = x^2$ $\Rightarrow$ $y' = 2x$. At $(0,0)$ the slopes of the tangents are $m_1 = 1$, $m_2 = 0$, so Formula 3.40 gives $\tan\alpha = (0-1)/(1+1\cdot 0) = -1$ $\Rightarrow$ $\alpha = 135°$ (or $45°$). At $(1,1)$ the slopes are $m_1 = 1$, $m_2 = 2$, so $\tan\alpha = (2-1)/(1+1\cdot 2) = 1/3$ $\Rightarrow$ $\alpha \approx 18°$ (or $162°$).

40. $y = x^2$ and $y = 8-x^2$ intersect when $x^2 = 8-x^2$ $\Longleftrightarrow$ $x = \pm 2$. $y = x^2$ $\Rightarrow$ $y' = 2x$ and $y = 8-x^2$ $\Rightarrow$ $y' = -2x$. At $(2,4)$ the slopes of the tangents are $m_1 = 4$, $m_2 = -4$, so Formula 3.40 gives $\tan\alpha = (-4-4)/(1+4(-4)) = 8/15$ $\Rightarrow$ $\alpha \approx 28°$ (or $152°$). By symmetry, the angles at $(-2,4)$ are the same.

42. $y = x^3$ and $y = 2x-x^2$ intersect when $x^3 = 2x-x^2$ $\Longleftrightarrow$ $x^3+x^2-2x = 0$ $\Longleftrightarrow$ $x(x+2)(x-1) = 0$ $\Longleftrightarrow$ $x = -2, 0, 1$. $y = x^3$ $\Rightarrow$ $y' = 3x^2$ and $y = 2x-x^2$ $\Rightarrow$ $y' = 2-2x$. At $(-2,-8)$ the slopes of the tangents are $m_1 = 12$, $m_2 = 6$, so Formula 3.40 gives $\tan\alpha = (6-12)/(1+12\cdot 6) = -6/73$ $\Rightarrow$ $\alpha \approx 175°$ (or $5°$). At $(0,0)$ the slopes are $m_1 = 0$, $m_2 = 2$ so $\tan\alpha = (2-0)/(1+0\cdot 2) = 2$ $\Rightarrow$ $\alpha \approx 63°$ (or $117°$). At $(1,1)$ the slopes are $m_1 = 3$, $m_2 = 0$, so $\tan\alpha = (0-3)/(1+3\cdot 0) = -3$ $\Rightarrow$ $\alpha \approx 72°$ (or $108°$).

44. $x^2+y^2 = 16$ and $x^2 = 6y$ intersect when $6y+y^2 = 16$ $\Longleftrightarrow$ $y^2+6y-16 = 0$ $\Longleftrightarrow$ $(y+8)(y-2) = 0$ $\Longleftrightarrow$ $y = -8$ or 2, but -8 is an extraneous root. $x^2+y^2 = 16$ $\Rightarrow$ $2x+2yy' = 0$ $\Rightarrow$ $y' = -x/y$ and $x^2 = 6y$ $\Rightarrow$ $y' = x/3$. At $(2\sqrt{3},2)$ the slopes are $m_1 = -2\sqrt{3}/2 = -\sqrt{3}$ and $m_2 = 2\sqrt{3}/3$, so $\tan\alpha = \dfrac{2\sqrt{3}/3 - (-\sqrt{3})}{1+(-\sqrt{3})(2\sqrt{3}/3)} = -\dfrac{5\sqrt{3}}{3}$ $\Rightarrow$ $\alpha \approx 109°$ (or $71°$). By symmetry, the angle at $(-2\sqrt{3},2)$ is the same.

46. $x^2+y^2 = 1$ and $x^2+y^2-2y = 0$ intersect when $2y = 1$, so $y = 1/2$ and

62

$x = \pm\sqrt{3}/2$. $x^2+y^2 = 1 \Rightarrow 2x+2yy' = 0 \Rightarrow y' = -x/y$ and $x^2+y^2-2y = 0$ $\Rightarrow 2x+2yy'-2y' = 0 \Rightarrow y' = x/(1-y)$. At $(\sqrt{3}/2,1/2)$ the slopes are $m_1 = -\sqrt{3}$ and $m_2 = \sqrt{3}$, so $\tan \alpha = (\sqrt{3}-(-\sqrt{3}))/(1-\sqrt{3}\sqrt{3}) = -\sqrt{3} \Rightarrow \alpha = 60^{\circ}$ (or 120°). By symmetry, the angle at $(-\sqrt{3}/2,1/2)$ is the same.

48. $y = x^2+x$ and $y = x^3+1$ intersect when $x^2+x = x^3+1 \Leftrightarrow x^3-x^2-x+1 = 0$ $\Leftrightarrow (x-1)(x^2-1) = 0 \Leftrightarrow x = \pm1$. $y = x^2+x \Rightarrow y' = 2x+1$ and $y = x^3+1 \Rightarrow y' = 3x^2$. At $(-1,0)$ the slopes are $m_1 = -1$ and $m_2 = 3$ so $\tan \alpha = (3+1)/(1+3(-1)) = -2 \Rightarrow \alpha \approx 117^{\circ}$ (or 63°). At $(1,2)$ the slopes are $m_1 = 3$ and $m_2 = 3$, so $\alpha = 0^{\circ}$.

50. The curves intersect when $\sin x = \sin 2x = 2 \sin x \cos x \Leftrightarrow$ $\sin x = 0$ or $\cos x = 1/2 \Leftrightarrow x = n\pi$ or $2n\pi\pm\pi/3$, n an integer. Now $y = \sin x \Rightarrow y' = \cos x$ and $y = \sin 2x \Rightarrow y' = 2 \cos 2x$. At $(2n\pi,0)$ the slopes are $m_1 = 1$ and $m_2 = 2$, so $\tan \alpha = (2-1)/(1+1\cdot2)$ $= 1/3 \Rightarrow \alpha \approx 18^{\circ}$ (or 162°). At $((2n+1)\pi,0)$ the slopes are $m_1 = -1$ and $m_2 = 2$, so $\tan \alpha = (2-(-1))/(1-1\cdot2) = -3 \Rightarrow \alpha \approx 108^{\circ}$ (or 72°). At $(2n\pi+\pi/3,\sqrt{3}/2)$ the slopes are $m_1 = 1/2$ and $m_2 = -1$, so $\tan \alpha = (-1-1/2)/(1-1/2) = -3 \Rightarrow \alpha \approx 108^{\circ}$ (or 72°). By symmetry the angle at $(2n\pi-\pi/3,-\sqrt{3}/2)$ is also 108° (or 72°).

52. The curves intersect when $x-2x^2 = x^3+2x \Leftrightarrow x^3+2x^2+x = x(x+1)^2 = 0$ so $x = 0$ or -1. $y = x-2x^2 \Rightarrow y' = 1-4x$ and $y = x^3+2x \Rightarrow$ $y' = 3x^2+2$. At $(0,0)$ the slopes are $m_1 = 1$ and $m_2 = 2$, so the curves are not tangent there. At $(-1,-3)$ the slopes are $m_1 = 5$ $= m_2$ so the curves are tangent there.

54. $x^2-y^2 = 5$ and $4x^2+9y^2 = 72$ intersect when $4x^2+9(x^2-5) = 72 \Leftrightarrow$ $13x^2 = 117 \Leftrightarrow x = \pm3$, so there are 4 points of intersection: $(\pm3,\pm2)$. $x^2-y^2 = 5 \Rightarrow 2x-2yy' = 0 \Rightarrow y' = x/y$ and $4x^2+9y^2 = 72$ $\Rightarrow 8x+18yy' = 0 \Rightarrow y' = -4x/9y$. At $(3,2)$ the slopes are $m_1 = 3/2$ and $m_2 = -2/3$, so the curves are orthogonal there. By symmetry, they are also orthogonal at $(3,-2)$, $(-3,2)$, and $(-3,-2)$.

56. The circles $x^2+y^2 = ax$ and $x^2+y^2 = by$ intersect at the origin where the tangents are vertical and horizontal. If (x_0,y_0) is the other point of intersection, then

$$ax_0 = x_0^2+y_0^2 = by_0 \qquad (1)$$

Now $x^2+y^2 = ax \Rightarrow 2x+2yy' = a \Rightarrow y' = (a-2x)/2y$ and $x^2+y^2 = by$
$\Rightarrow 2x+2yy' = by' \Rightarrow y' = 2x/(b-2y)$. Thus the curves are
orthogonal at $(x_0,y_0) \Leftrightarrow \dfrac{a-2x_0}{2y_0} = -\dfrac{b-2y_0}{2x_0} \Leftrightarrow 2ax_0-4x_0^2 = 4y_0^2-2by_0$
$\Leftrightarrow 2ax_0+2by_0 = 4(x_0^2+y_0^2)$ which is true by Equation (1).

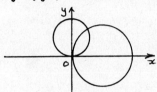

58. $y = ax^3 \Rightarrow y' = 3ax^2$ and $x^2+3y^2 = b \Rightarrow 2x+6yy' = 0 \Rightarrow$
$y' = -\dfrac{x}{3y} = -\dfrac{x}{3ax^3} = -\dfrac{1}{3ax^2}$ so the curves are orthogonal.

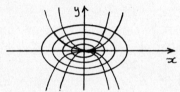

60. $y = x^3 \Rightarrow y' = 3x^2$, so $y = x^3$ has slope 3 at $(1,1)$. $y = x^2+ax+b$
$\Rightarrow y' = 2ax+b$, so if the curves are tangent at $(1,1)$ then $2a+1 = 3$
$\Rightarrow a = 1$. But for $y = x^2+x+b$ to pass through $(1,1)$, we must have
$1^2+1+b = 1 \Rightarrow b = -1$.

Section 3.6

Exercises 3.6

2. $f(t) = t^{10}-2t^7+t^4-6t+8 \Rightarrow f'(t) = 10t^9-14t^6+4t^3-6 \Rightarrow$
$f''(t) = 90t^8-84t^5+12t^2$

4. $G(r) = \sqrt{r}+\sqrt[3]{r} \Rightarrow G'(r) = \frac{1}{2}r^{-1/2}+\frac{1}{3}r^{-2/3} \Rightarrow G''(r) = -\frac{1}{4}r^{-3/2}-\frac{2}{9}r^{-5/3}$

6. $g(u) = 1/\sqrt{1-u} = (1-u)^{-1/2} \Rightarrow g'(u) = -\frac{1}{2}(1-u)^{-3/2}(-1) = \frac{1}{2}(1-u)^{-3/2}$
$\Rightarrow g''(u) = -\frac{3}{4}(1-u)^{-5/2}(-1) = \frac{3}{4}(1-u)^{-5/2}$

8. $y = x^\pi \Rightarrow y' = \pi x^{\pi-1} \Rightarrow y'' = \pi(\pi-1)x^{\pi-2}$

10. $y = \dfrac{x^2}{x+1}$ ⟹ $y' = \dfrac{(x+1)2x-x^2}{(x+1)^2} = \dfrac{x^2+2x}{(x+1)^2}$ ⟹

$y'' = \dfrac{(x+1)^2(2x+2)-(x^2+2x)2(x+1)}{(x+1)^4} = \dfrac{2(x+1)[(x+1)^2-(x^2+2x)]}{(x+1)^4} = \dfrac{2}{(x+1)^3}$

12. $f(x) = \csc^2(5x)$ ⟹

$f'(x) = 2\csc(5x)[-\csc(5x)\cot(5x)](5) = -10\csc^2(5x)\cot(5x)$

$f''(x) = -10[D_x\csc^2(5x)]\cot(5x) - 10\csc^2(5x)[-\csc^2(5x)](5)$

$= -10[-10\csc^2(5x)\cot(5x)]\cot(5x) + 50\csc^4(5x)$

$= 50\csc^2(5x)[2\cot^2(5x) + \csc^2(5x)]$

14. $g(s) = s^2\cos s$ ⟹ $g'(s) = 2s\cos s - s^2\sin s$ ⟹ $g''(s)$

$= 2\cos s - 2s\sin s - 2s\sin s - s^2\cos s = (2-s^2)\cos s - 4s\sin s$

16. $y = \dfrac{1-x}{1+x}$ ⟹ $y' = \dfrac{(1+x)(-1)-(1-x)}{(1+x)^2} = \dfrac{-2}{(1+x)^2} = -2(1+x)^{-2}$ ⟹

$y'' = 4(1+x)^{-3}$ ⟹ $y''' = -12(1+x)^{-4}$

18. $y = (1+x^2)^{-1}$ ⟹ $y' = -(1+x^2)^{-2}(2x)$ ⟹ $y'' = 2(1+x^2)^{-3}(2x)^2 - 2(1+x^2)^{-2}$

⟹ $y''' = 16x(1+x^2)^{-3} + 8x^2(-3)(1+x^2)^{-4}(2x) - 2(-2)(1+x^2)^{-3}(2x)$

$= 24x(1+x^2)^{-3} - 48x^3(1+x^2)^{-4} = 24x(1-x^2)(1+x^2)^{-4}$

20. $g(t) = (2-t^2)^6$ ⟹ $g(0) = 2^6 = 64$

$g'(t) = 6(2-t^2)^5(-2t) = -12t(2-t^2)^5$ ⟹ $g'(0) = 0$

$g''(t) = -12(2-t^2)^5 + 120t^2(2-t^2)^4$ ⟹ $g''(0) = -12(2)^5 = -384$

$g'''(t) = 360t(2-t^2)^4 - 960t^3(2-t^2)^3$ ⟹ $g'''(0) = 0$

22. $g(x) = \sec x$ ⟹ $g'(x) = \sec x\tan x$ ⟹ $g''(x) = (\sec x\tan x)\tan x$

$+ \sec x\sec^2 x = \sec x(\sec^2 x - 1 + \sec^2 x) = 2\sec^3 x - \sec x$ ⟹

$g'''(x) = 6\sec^2 x(\sec x\tan x) - \sec x\tan x$

$= (6\sec^2 x - 1)\sec x\tan x$ ⟹ $g^{(4)}(x) =$

$(12\sec x\sec x\tan x)(\sec x\tan x) + (6\sec^2 x - 1)(2\sec^3 x - \sec x)$

⟹ $g^{(4)}(\pi/4) = 12(\sqrt{2})^3(1)^2 + [6(\sqrt{2})^2-1][2(\sqrt{2})^3-\sqrt{2}] = 57\sqrt{2}$

24. $\sqrt{x}+\sqrt{y} = 1$ ⟹ $1/2\sqrt{x} + (1/2\sqrt{y})y' = 0$ ⟹ $y' = -\sqrt{y}/\sqrt{x}$ ⟹

$y'' = -\dfrac{\sqrt{x}(1/2\sqrt{y})y'-\sqrt{y}(1/2\sqrt{x})}{x} = -\dfrac{\sqrt{x}(1/\sqrt{y})(-\sqrt{y}/\sqrt{x})-\sqrt{y}(1/\sqrt{x})}{2x}$

$= \dfrac{1+\sqrt{y}/\sqrt{x}}{2x} = \dfrac{\sqrt{x}+\sqrt{y}}{2x\sqrt{x}} = \dfrac{1}{2x\sqrt{x}}$ since x, y must satisfy the original

equation $\sqrt{x}+\sqrt{y} = 1$.

26. $\dfrac{x^2}{a^2} - \dfrac{y^2}{b^2} = 1$ ⟹ $\dfrac{2x}{a^2} - \dfrac{2yy'}{b^2} = 0$ ⟹ $y' = \dfrac{b^2 x}{a^2 y}$ ⟹ $y'' = \dfrac{b^2}{a^2}\dfrac{y-xy'}{y^2}$

$= \dfrac{b^2}{a^2}\dfrac{y-x(b^2x/a^2y)}{y^2} = \dfrac{b^2}{a^2}\dfrac{a^2y^2-b^2x^2}{a^2y^3} = \dfrac{b^4}{a^2y^3}\left[\dfrac{y^2}{b^2} - \dfrac{x^2}{a^2}\right] = -\dfrac{b^4}{a^2y^3}$

since x, y must satisfy the original equation.

28. $f(x) = \sqrt{x} = x^{1/2} \Rightarrow f'(x) = (1/2)x^{-1/2} \Rightarrow f''(x) = (1/2)(-1/2)x^{-3/2}$
$\Rightarrow f'''(x) = \frac{1}{2}\left[-\frac{1}{2}\right]\left[-\frac{3}{2}\right]x^{-5/2} \Rightarrow$

$f^{(4)}(x) = \frac{1}{2}\left[-\frac{1}{2}\right]\left[-\frac{3}{2}\right]\left[-\frac{5}{2}\right]x^{-7/2} = -\frac{1\cdot3\cdot5}{2^4}x^{-7/2} \Rightarrow$

$f^{(5)}(x) = \frac{1}{2}\left[-\frac{1}{2}\right]\left[-\frac{3}{2}\right]\left[-\frac{5}{2}\right]\left[-\frac{7}{2}\right]x^{-9/2} = \frac{1\cdot3\cdot5\cdot7}{2^5}x^{-9/2} \Rightarrow \cdots \Rightarrow$

$f^{(n)}(x) = \frac{1}{2}\left[-\frac{1}{2}\right]\left[-\frac{3}{2}\right]\cdots\left[\frac{1}{2}-n+1\right]x^{-(2n-1)/2}$

$\qquad = (-1)^{n-1}\frac{1\cdot3\cdot5\cdots(2n-3)}{2^n}x^{-(2n-1)/2}$

30. $f(x) = (1-x)^{-2} \Rightarrow f'(x) = -2(1-x)^{-3}(-1) = 2(1-x)^{-3} \Rightarrow$
$f''(x) = 2(-3)(1-x)^{-4}(-1) = 2\cdot3(1-x)^{-4} \Rightarrow$
$f'''(x) = 2\cdot3(-4)(1-x)^{-5}(-1) = 2\cdot3\cdot4(1-x)^{-5} \Rightarrow \cdots \Rightarrow$
$f^{(n)}(x) = 2\cdot3\cdot4\cdots n(n+1)(1-x)^{-(n+2)} = \frac{(n+1)!}{(1-x)^{n+2}}$

32. $D\sin x = \cos x \Rightarrow D^2\sin x = -\sin x \Rightarrow D^3\sin x = -\cos x \Rightarrow$
$D^4\sin x = \sin x$. The derivatives of $\sin x$ occur in a cycle of 4.
Since $99 = 4(24)+3$, we have $D^{99}\sin x = D^3\sin x = -\cos x$.

34. Let $f(x) = x\sin x$ and $h(x) = \sin x$, so $f(x) = xh(x)$. Then
$f'(x) = h(x)+xh'(x)$, $f''(x) = h'(x)+h'(x)+xh''(x) = 2h'(x)+xh''(x)$,
$f'''(x) = 2h''(x)+h''(x)+xh'''(x) = 3h''(x)+xh'''(x)$, $\cdots$
$f^{(n)}(x) = nh^{(n-1)}(x) + xh^{(n)}(x)$. Since $34 = 4(8)+2$, we have
$h^{(34)}(x) = h^{(2)}(x) = D^2\sin x = -\sin x$ and $h^{(35)}(x) = -\cos x$. Thus
$D^{(35)}x\sin x = 35h^{(34)}(x) + xh^{(35)}(x) = -35\sin x - x\cos x$.

36. (a) $s = t^2-t+1 \Rightarrow v(t) = s'(t) = 2t-1 \Rightarrow a(t) = v'(t) = 2$
(b) $a(1) = 2$ m/s^2
(c) $v(t) = 2t-1 = 0$ when $t = 1/2$ and $a(1/2) = 2$ m/s^2

38. (a) $s = 2t^3-7t^2+4t+1 \Rightarrow v(t) = s'(t) = 6t^2-14t+4 \Rightarrow a(t) = 12t-14$
(b) $a(1) = 12-14 = -2$ m/s^2
(c) $v(t) = 2(3t^2-7t+2) = 2(3t-1)(t-2) = 0$ when $t = 1/3, 2$ and
$a(1/3) = 12(1/3)-14 = -10$ m/s^2, $a(2) = 12(2)-14 = 10$ m/s^2

40. (a) $s(t) = 2t^3-9t^2 \Rightarrow v(t) = s'(t) = 6t^2-18t \Rightarrow$
$a(t) = v'(t) = 12t-18 = 0$ when $t = 1.5$
(b) $s(1.5) = -13.5$ m, $v(1.5) = -13.5$ m/s

42. $f(x) = |x^2-x| = \begin{cases} x^2-x & \text{if } x\leq0 \text{ or } x\geq1 \\ x-x^2 & \text{if } 0<x<1 \end{cases}$ domain = R

$f'(x) = \begin{cases} 2x-1 & \text{if } x<0 \text{ or } x>1 \\ 1-2x & \text{if } 0<x<1 \end{cases}$ domain = $\{x|x\neq0,1\}$

[or use Exercise 3.4.73 and the Chain Rule: $f'(x) = \dfrac{x^2-x}{|x^2-x|}(2x-1)$]

$f''(x) = \begin{cases} 2 & \text{if } x<0 \text{ or } x>1 \\ -2 & \text{if } 0<x<1 \end{cases}$ domain = $\{x \mid x \neq 0, 1\}$

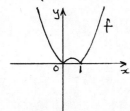 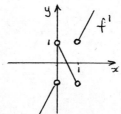 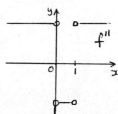

44. Let $Q(x) = ax^3+bx^2+cx+d$. Then $Q'(x) = 3ax^2+2bx+c$, $Q''(x) = 6ax+2b$, and $Q'''(x) = 6a$. Thus $Q(1) = a+b+c+d = 1$, $Q'(1) = 3a+2b+c = 3$, $Q''(1) = 6a+2b = 6$, $Q'''(1) = 6a = 12$. Solving these 4 equations in the 4 unknowns a,b,c,d, we get a = 2, b = -3, c = 3, d = -1, so $Q(x) = 2x^3-3x^2+3x-1$.

46. (a) Use the Product Rule repeatedly: $F = fg \Rightarrow F' = f'g+fg'$
    $\Rightarrow F'' = (f''g+f'g') + (f'g'+fg'') = f''g+2f'g'+fg''$

    (b) $F''' = f'''g+f''g'+2(f''g'+f'g'')+f'g''+fg''' = f'''g+3f''g'+3f'g''+fg'''$
    $\Rightarrow F^{(4)} = f^{(4)}g+f'''g'+3(f'''g'+f''g'')+3(f''g''+f'g''')+f'g'''+fg^{(4)}$
    $= f^{(4)}g+4f'''g'+6f''g''+4f'g'''+fg^{(4)}$

    (c) By analogy with the Binomial Theorem, we make the guess
    $F^{(n)} = f^{(n)}g+nf^{(n-1)}g'+\binom{n}{2}f^{(n-2)}g''+\cdots+\binom{n}{k}f^{(n-k)}g^{(k)}+\cdots+nf'g^{(n-1)}$
    $+fg^{(n)}$, where $\binom{n}{k} = \dfrac{n!}{k!(n-k)!} = \dfrac{n(n-1)(n-2)\cdots(n-k+1)}{k!}$

Section 3.7

Exercises 3.7

2. (a) $A(r) = \pi r^2 \Rightarrow$ the average rate of change is
   (i) $\dfrac{A(3)-A(2)}{3-2} = \dfrac{9\pi-4\pi}{1} = 5\pi$ (ii) $\dfrac{A(2.5)-A(2)}{2.5-2} = \dfrac{6.25\pi-4\pi}{0.5} = 4.5\pi$
   (iii) $\dfrac{A(2.1)-A(2)}{2.1-2} = \dfrac{4.41\pi-4\pi}{0.1} = 4.1\pi$

   (b) $A'(r) = 2\pi r$, so $A'(2) = 4\pi$.

   (c) The circumference is $C(r) = 2\pi r = A'(r)$.

4. (a) $V(r) = (4/3)\pi r^3 \Rightarrow$ the average rate of change is

(i) $\dfrac{V(8)-V(5)}{8-5} = \dfrac{(4/3)\pi(512) - (4/3)\pi(125)}{3} = 172\pi \ \mu m^3/\mu m$

(ii) $\dfrac{V(6)-V(5)}{6-5} = \dfrac{(4/3)\pi(216) - (4/3)\pi(125)}{1} = 121.\overline{3}\pi \ \mu m^3/\mu m$

(iii) $\dfrac{V(5.1)-V(5)}{5.1-5} = \dfrac{(4/3)\pi(5.1)^3 - (4/3)\pi(5)^3}{0.1} = 102.01\overline{3}\pi \ \mu m^3/\mu m$

(b) $V'(r) = 4\pi r^2$, so $V'(5) = 100\pi \ \mu m^3/\mu m$

6. $V(r) = (4/3)\pi r^3 \Rightarrow V'(r) = 4\pi r^2 = S(r)$

8. $V(t) = 5000(1-t/40)^2 \Rightarrow V'(t) = 5000(2)(1-t/40)(-1/40)$

$= -250(1-t/40)$ (a) $V'(5) = -250(1-5/40) = -218.75$ gal/min

(b) $V'(10) = -250(1-10/40) = -187.5$ gal/min

(c) $V'(20) = -250(1-20/40) = -125$ gal/min

10. $f = \dfrac{1}{2L}\sqrt{\dfrac{T}{\rho}}$ (a) $\dfrac{df}{dL} = -\dfrac{1}{2L^2}\sqrt{\dfrac{T}{\rho}}$ (b) $\dfrac{df}{dT} = \dfrac{1}{2L}\dfrac{1}{2\sqrt{T}}\dfrac{1}{\sqrt{\rho}} = \dfrac{1}{4L\sqrt{T\rho}}$

(c) $\dfrac{df}{d\rho} = \dfrac{1}{2L}\sqrt{T}\left[-\dfrac{1}{2}\rho^{-3/2}\right] = -\dfrac{\sqrt{T}}{4L\rho^{3/2}}$

12. (a) (i) $\dfrac{C(6)-C(2)}{6-2} = \dfrac{0.0295-0.0570}{4} = -0.006875$ moles/L/min

(ii) $\dfrac{C(4)-C(2)}{4-2} = \dfrac{0.0408-0.0570}{2} = -0.0081$ moles/L/min

(iii) $\dfrac{C(2)-C(0)}{2-0} = \dfrac{0.0570-0.0800}{2} = -0.0115$ moles/L/min

(b) Slope $\approx -\dfrac{0.075}{7.5} = -0.01$ moles/L/min

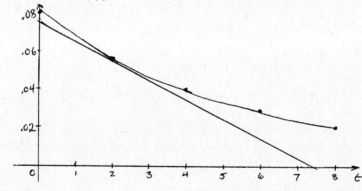

14. $n(t) = 100+24t+2t^2 \Rightarrow n'(t) = 24+4t \Rightarrow n'(2) = 32$ bacteria/h

16. $f(0) = 5000, \quad f(1/3) = 2f(0) = 5000\cdot 2, \quad f(2/3) = 2f(1/3) = 5000\cdot 2^2,$
$\ldots, \quad f(n/3) = 5000\cdot 2^n, \quad \ldots .$ In general, $f(t) = (5000)2^{3t}.$

18. $C(x) = 1200 + \frac{x}{10} + \frac{x^2}{10000} \Rightarrow C'(x) = \frac{1}{10} + \frac{x}{5000} \Rightarrow$

$C'(100) = \frac{1}{10} + \frac{100}{5000} = \$0.12/\text{item}$

$C(101)-C(100) = (1200+10.1+1.0201) - (1200+10+1) = \$0.1201$

20. $C(x) = 2500+2\sqrt{x} \Rightarrow C'(x) = 1/\sqrt{x} \Rightarrow C'(100) = 1/\sqrt{100} = \$0.10/\text{item}$

$C(101)-C(100) = (2500+2\sqrt{101}) - (2500+20) \approx \$0.0998$

Section 3.8

Exercises 3.8

2. $A = \pi r^2 \Rightarrow \frac{dA}{dt} = 2\pi r \frac{dr}{dt}$

4. $x^2+3xy+y^2 = 1 \Rightarrow 2x\frac{dx}{dt} + 3y\frac{dx}{dt} + 3x\frac{dy}{dt} + 2y\frac{dy}{dt} = 0 \Rightarrow \frac{dx}{dt} = -\frac{3x+2y}{2x+3y}\frac{dy}{dt}$

When $y = 1$, we have $x^2+3x = 0 \Rightarrow x = 0$ or -3. If $dy/dt = 2$ and

$x = 0$, $y = 1$, then $\frac{dx}{dt} = -\frac{3(0)+2(1)}{2(0)+3(1)}(2) = -\frac{4}{3}$ If $x = -3$, then

$\frac{dx}{dt} = -\frac{3(-3)+2(1)}{2(-3)+3(1)}(2) = -\frac{14}{3}$

6. If the radius is r and the diameter x, then $S = 4\pi r^2 = \pi x^2 \Rightarrow$

$-1 = \frac{dS}{dt} = 2\pi x\frac{dx}{dt} \Rightarrow \frac{dx}{dt} = -\frac{1}{2\pi x}$ When $x = 10$, $\frac{dx}{dt} = -\frac{1}{20\pi}$

So the rate of decrease is $1/20\pi$ cm/min.

8.

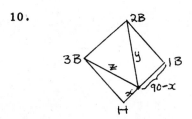

We are given that $dx/dt = 1.6$ m/s.

By similar triangles, $\frac{y}{12} = \frac{2}{x} \Rightarrow y = \frac{24}{x} \Rightarrow$

$\frac{dy}{dt} = -\frac{24}{x^2}\frac{dx}{dt} = -\frac{24}{x^2}(1.6)$ When $x = 8$,

$\frac{dy}{dt} = -\frac{24(1.6)}{64} = -0.6$ m/s, so the shadow is

decreasing at a rate of 0.6 m/s.

10.

We are given that $dx/dt = 24$ ft/s.

(a) $y^2 = (90-x)^2+90^2 \Rightarrow 2y\frac{dy}{dt} = 2(90-x)\left[-\frac{dx}{dt}\right]$

When $x = 45$, $y = 45\sqrt{5}$, so $\frac{dy}{dt} = \frac{45}{45\sqrt{5}}(-24) =$

$-24/\sqrt{5}$, so the distance from second base is

decreasing at rate of $24/\sqrt{5} \approx 10.7$ ft/s.

(b) $z^2 = x^2 + 90^2$ ⟹ $2z\frac{dz}{dt} = 2x\frac{dx}{dt}$ When $x = 45$, $z = 45\sqrt{5}$, so

$\frac{dz}{dt} = \frac{45}{45\sqrt{5}}(24) = \frac{24}{\sqrt{5}} \approx 10.7$ ft/s.

12.

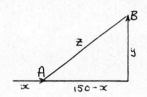

We are given that $\frac{dx}{dt} = 35$ km/h, $\frac{dy}{dt} = 25$ km/h.

$z^2 = (150-x)^2 + y^2$ ⟹ $2z\frac{dz}{dt} = 2(150-x)\left[-\frac{dx}{dt}\right] + 2y\frac{dy}{dt}$

At 4:00 P.M., $x = 140$, $y = 100$ ⟹ $z = \sqrt{10100}$

So $\frac{dz}{dt} = \frac{1}{z}\left[(x-150)\frac{dx}{dt} + y\frac{dy}{dt}\right] = \frac{10(35)+100(25)}{\sqrt{10100}}$

$= 215/\sqrt{101} \approx 21.4$ km/h

14.

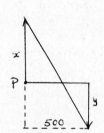

We are given that $\frac{dx}{dt} = 4$ ft/s, $\frac{dy}{dt} = 5$ ft/s.

$z^2 = (x+y)^2 + 500^2$ ⟹ $2z\frac{dz}{dt} = 2(x+y)\left[\frac{dx}{dt} + \frac{dy}{dt}\right]$

15 minutes after the woman starts, we have

$x = 4 \cdot 20 \cdot 60 = 4800$, $y = 5 \cdot 15 \cdot 60 = 4500$ ⟹

$z = \sqrt{9300^2 + 500^2}$, so $\frac{dz}{dt} = \frac{x+y}{z}\left[\frac{dx}{dt} + \frac{dy}{dt}\right]$

$= \frac{9300}{\sqrt{86740000}}(5+4) = \frac{837}{\sqrt{8674}} \approx 8.99$ ft/s

16.

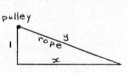

Given $dy/dt = -1$, find dx/dt when $x = 8$.

$y^2 = x^2 + 1$ ⟹ $2y\frac{dy}{dt} = 2x\frac{dx}{dt}$ ⟹ $\frac{dx}{dt} = \frac{y}{x}\frac{dy}{dt} = -\frac{y}{x}$

When $x = 8$, $y = \sqrt{65}$, so $dx/dt = -\sqrt{65}/8$. Thus the boat approaches the dock at $\sqrt{65}/8$ m/s.

18.

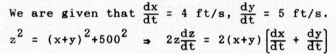

By similar triangles, $3/1 = b/h$, so $b = 3h$. The trough has volume $V = (1/2)bh(10)$

$= 5(3h)h = 15h^2$ ⟹ $12 = \frac{dV}{dt} = 30h\frac{dh}{dt}$ ⟹

$\frac{dh}{dt} = \frac{2}{5h}$ When $h = \frac{1}{2}$, $\frac{dh}{dt} = \frac{2}{5(1/2)} = \frac{4}{5}$ ft/min.

20.

$V = 20(1/2)((b+12)h = 10(b+12)h$ and, from similar triangles, $x = h$, $y/h = 16/6 = 8/3$, so $b = h+12+8h/3 = 12+11h/3$. Thus $V = 10(24+11h/3)h = 240h+110h^2/3$ and so

$.8 = \frac{dV}{dt} = (240+\frac{220}{3}h)\frac{dh}{dt}$ When $h = 5$, $\frac{dh}{dt} = \frac{.8}{240+5(220/3)} = \frac{3}{2275}$

≈ 0.00132 ft/min.

22. $PV^{1.4} = C$ ⟹ $V^{1.4}\frac{dP}{dt} + 1.4PV^{.4}\frac{dV}{dt} = 0$ ⟹ $\frac{dV}{dt} = -\frac{V}{1.4P}\frac{dP}{dt}$ When

$V = 400$, $P = 80$, and $\frac{dP}{dt} = -10$, we have $\frac{dV}{dt} = -\frac{400}{1.4(80)}(-10) = \frac{250}{7}$

so the volume is increasing at a rate of $250/7 \approx 36$ cm^3/min.

24.

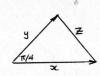

We are given that $\frac{dx}{dt} = 3$ mi/h, $\frac{dy}{dt} = 2$ mi/h.

By the Law of Cosines, $z^2 = x^2 + y^2 - 2xy \cos 45°$

$= x^2 + y^2 - \sqrt{2}xy$ $\Rightarrow$ $2z\frac{dz}{dt} = 2x\frac{dx}{dt} + 2y\frac{dy}{dt} - \sqrt{2}x\frac{dy}{dt}$

$- \sqrt{2}y\frac{dx}{dt}$ After 15 min, we have $x = \frac{3}{4}$, $y = \frac{1}{2}$

$\Rightarrow$ $z = \frac{\sqrt{13-6\sqrt{2}}}{4}$ and $\frac{dz}{dt} = \frac{2}{\sqrt{13-6\sqrt{2}}} \left[2\left[\frac{3}{4}\right](3) + 2\left[\frac{1}{2}\right](2) - \sqrt{2}\left[\frac{3}{4}\right](2) - \sqrt{2}\left[\frac{1}{2}\right] \right]$

$= \sqrt{13-6\sqrt{2}} \approx 2.125$ mi/h

26.

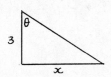

We are given that $d\theta/dt = 4(2\pi) = 8\pi$ rad/s.

$x = 3 \tan \theta$ $\Rightarrow$ $\frac{dx}{dt} = 3 \sec^2 \theta \frac{d\theta}{dt}$ When $x = 1$,

$\tan \theta = 3$, so $\sec^2 \theta = 1 + (1/3)^2 = 10/9$ and

$\frac{dx}{dt} = 3\left[\frac{10}{9}\right](8\pi) = \frac{80\pi}{3}$ km/min   (or 1600π km/h)

Section 3.9

Exercises 3.9

2. $y = \sqrt[4]{x} = x^{1/4}$ $\Rightarrow$ $dy = (1/4)x^{-3/4}dx$

4. $y = (x^2-2x-3)^{10}$ $\Rightarrow$ $dy = 10(x^2-2x-3)^9(2x-2)dx = 20(x-1)(x^2-2x-3)^9 dx$

6. $y = \sqrt{x+\sqrt{2x-1}}$ $\Rightarrow$ $dy = \frac{1}{2}(x+\sqrt{2x-1})^{-1/2}[1+\frac{1}{2}(2x-1)^{-1/2}2]$ dx

$= \frac{1+(2x-1)^{-1/2}}{2\sqrt{x+\sqrt{2x-1}}}$ dx

8. $y = x \tan x$ $\Rightarrow$ $dy = (\tan x + x \sec^2 x)dx$

10. (a) $y = x^4 - 3x^3 + x - 1$ $\Rightarrow$ $dy = (4x^3 - 9x^2 + 1)dx$

(b) When $x = 2$ and $dx = 0.1$, $dy = [4(2)^3 - 9(2)^2 + 1](0.1) = -0.3$

12. (a) $y = \sqrt{1-x}$ $\Rightarrow$ $dy = \frac{1}{2}(1-x)^{-1/2}(-1)dx = -\frac{1}{2\sqrt{1-x}}$ dx

(b) When $x = 0$ and $dx = 0.02$, $dy = -(1/2)(0.02) = -0.01$

14. (a) $y = \frac{x-1}{x^2+1}$ $\Rightarrow$ $dy = \frac{(x^2+1)-(x-1)(2x)}{(x^2+1)^2} dx = \frac{1+2x-x^2}{(x^2+1)^2} dx$

(b) When $x = 1$ and $dx = -0.3$, $dy = \frac{1+2(1)-1^2}{(1^2+1)^2}(-0.3) = -0.15$

16. (a) $y = \sin x \Rightarrow dy = \cos x\, dx$

(b) When $x = \pi/6$ and $dx = -0.1$, $dy = (\sqrt{3}/2)(-0.1) = -\sqrt{3}/20$

18. $y = \sqrt{x}$, $x = 1$, $\Delta x = 1 \Rightarrow$

$\Delta y = \sqrt{2} - \sqrt{1} = \sqrt{2} - 1 \approx 0.414$

$dy = (1/2\sqrt{x})dx = (1/2)(1) = 0.5$

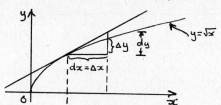

20. $y = \dfrac{16}{x}$, $x = 4$, $\Delta x = -1 \Rightarrow$

$\Delta y = \dfrac{16}{3} - \dfrac{16}{4} = \dfrac{4}{3}$

$dy = -(16/x^2)dx = -(16/4^2)(-1) = 1$

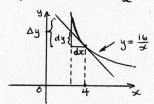

22. $y = f(x) = x^4 + x^2 + 1$, $x = 1 \Rightarrow dy = (4x^3 + 2x)dx = 6\, dx$

$\Delta x = 1 \Rightarrow \Delta y = f(2) - f(1) = 21 - 3 = 18$, $dy = 6(1) = 6$,

  $\Delta y - dy = 18 - 6 = 12$

$\Delta x = .5 \Rightarrow \Delta y = f(1.5) - f(1) = 8.3125 - 3 = 5.3125$, $dy = 6(.5) = 3$

  $\Delta y - dy = 5.3125 - 3 = 2.3125$

$\Delta x = .1 \Rightarrow \Delta y = f(1.1) - f(1) = 3.6741 - 3 = 0.6741$, $dy = 6(.1) = 0.6$

  $\Delta y - dy = 0.6741 - 0.6 = 0.0741$

$\Delta x = .01 \Rightarrow \Delta y = f(1.01) - f(1) = 3.06070401 - 3 = 0.06070401$

  $dy = 6(.01) = 0.06$, $\Delta y - dy = .06070401 - .06 = 0.00070401$

24. $y = f(x) = \sqrt{x} \Rightarrow dy = (1/2\sqrt{x})dx$. When $x = 100$ and $dx = -1$,

$dy = (1/2\sqrt{100})(-1) = -1/20 = -0.05$, so $\sqrt{99} = f(99) \approx f(100) + dy$

$= \sqrt{100} - 0.05 = 9.95$

26. $y = f(x) = \sqrt[3]{x} + \sqrt[4]{x} \Rightarrow dy = (\frac{1}{3}x^{-2/3} + \frac{1}{4}x^{-3/4})dx$. If $x = 1$ and

$dx = 0.02$, then $dy = (1/3 + 1/4)(0.02) = (7/12)(0.02)$. Thus

$\sqrt[3]{1.02} + \sqrt[4]{1.02} = f(1.02) \approx f(1) + dy = 2 + (7/12)(0.02) \approx 2.0117$

28. $y = f(x) = x^6 \Rightarrow dy = 6x^5 dx$. When $x = 2$ and $dx = -0.03$,

$dy = 6(2)^5(-0.03) = -5.76$, so $(1.97)^6 = f(1.97) \approx f(2) + dy$

$= 64 - 5.76 = 58.24$

30. $y = f(x) = \cos x \Rightarrow dy = -\sin x\, dx$. When $x = \pi/6$ and

$dx = 1.5\pi/180$, $dy = -\sin(\pi/6)(1.5\pi/180) = -(1/2)(\pi/120) = -\pi/240$,

so $\cos 31.5° = f(31.5\pi/180) \approx f(\pi/6) + dy = \sqrt{3}/2 - \pi/240 \approx 0.853$

32. $y = f(x) = \sec x \Rightarrow dy = \sec x \tan x\, dx$. When $x = \pi/3$ and

$dx = \pi/90$, $dy = \sec(\pi/3)\tan(\pi/3)(\pi/90) = 2\sqrt{3}(\pi/90) = \sqrt{3}\pi/45$, so

$$\sec 62° = f(62\pi/180) \approx f(\pi/3) + dy = 2 + \sqrt{3}\pi/45 \approx 2.12$$

34. (a) $A = \pi r^2 \Rightarrow dA = 2\pi r\, dr$. When $r = 24$ and $dr = 0.2$,
$dA = 2\pi(24)(.2) = 9.6\pi$, so the maximum error $\approx 9.6\pi \approx 30\ cm^2$
(b) Relative error $= \dfrac{\Delta A}{A} \approx \dfrac{dA}{A} = \dfrac{9.6\pi}{\pi(24)^2} = \dfrac{1}{60} \approx 0.0167$

36. (a) $V = (4/3)\pi r^3 = (4/3)\pi(C/2\pi)^3 = C^3/6\pi^2 \Rightarrow dV = (1/2\pi^2)C^2 dC$
When $C = 84$ and $dC = 0.5$, $dV = (1/2\pi^2)(84)^2(.5) = 1764/\pi^2$, so the
maximum error $\approx 1764/\pi^2 \approx 179\ cm^3$
(b) Relative error $\approx \dfrac{dV}{V} = \dfrac{1764/\pi^2}{(84)^3/6\pi^2} = \dfrac{1}{56} \approx 0.018$

38. $V = (2/3)\pi r^3 \Rightarrow dV = 2\pi r^2 dr$. When $r = 25$ and $dr = 0.0005$,
$dV = 2\pi(25)^2(0.0005) = 5\pi/8$, so the amount of paint $\approx 5\pi/8 \approx 2\ m^3$

Section 3.10

Exercises 3.10

2. $f(x) = x^3 + x^2 + 2 = 0 \Rightarrow f'(x) = 3x^2 + 2x$, so $x_{n+1} = x_n - \dfrac{x_n^3 + x_n^2 + 2}{3x_n^2 + 2x_n}$

$x_1 = -2 \Rightarrow x_2 = -2 - \dfrac{-2}{8} = -1.75 \Rightarrow x_3 = -1.75 - \dfrac{f(-1.75)}{f'(-1.75)} = -1.6978$

4. $f(x) = x^7 - 100 \Rightarrow f'(x) = 7x^6$, so $x_{n+1} = x_n - \dfrac{x_n^7 - 100}{7x_n^6}$ $x_1 = 2 \Rightarrow$

$x_2 = 1 - \dfrac{128 - 100}{7 \cdot 64} = 1.9375 \Rightarrow x_3 = 1 - \dfrac{(1.9375)^7 - 100}{7(1.9375)^6} \approx 1.9308$

6. Finding $\sqrt[10]{100}$ is equivalent to finding the positive root of
$x^{10} - 100 = 0$, so we take $f(x) = x^{10} - 100 \Rightarrow f'(x) = 10x^9$ and
$x_{n+1} = x_n - \dfrac{x_n^{10} - 100}{10x_n^9}$ Taking $x_1 = 1.5$, we get $x_2 \approx 1.610123$,

$x_3 \approx 1.586600$, $x_4 \approx 1.584901$, $x_5 \approx 1.584893$, $x_6 \approx 1.584893$
Thus $\sqrt[10]{100} \approx 1.584893$ to 6 decimal places.

8. $f(x) = x^3+x^2+x-2$ $\Rightarrow$ $f'(x) = 3x^2+2x+1$, so $x_{n+1} = x_n - \dfrac{x_n^3+x_n^2+x_n-2}{3x_n^2+2x_n+1}$

Taking $x_1 = 1$, we get $x_2 \approx 0.833333$, $x_3 \approx 0.810916$, $x_4 \approx 0.810536$

$x_5 \approx 0.810536$. So the root is 0.810536 to 6 decimal places.

10. $f(x) = x^4+x^3-22x^2-2x+41$ $\Rightarrow$ $f'(x) = 4x^3+3x^2-44x-2$, so

$x_{n+1} = x_n - \dfrac{x_n^4+x_n^3-22x_n^2-2x_n+41}{4x_n^3+3x_n^2-44x_n-2}$ Taking $x_1 = 1.5$, we get

$x_2 \approx 1.435864$, $x_3 \approx 1.435476$, $x_4 \approx 1.435476$. So the root in the

interval [1,2] is 1.435476 to 6 decimal places.

12.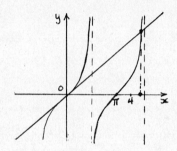

From the graph, it appears there is a root near 4.5. So we take $x_1 = 4.5$

Write the equation as
$$f(x) = \tan x - x = 0$$
Then $f'(x) = \sec^2 x - 1$, so
$$x_{n+1} = x_n - \frac{\tan x_n - x_n}{\sec^2 x_n - 1} \quad \Rightarrow$$

$x_1 = 4.5$, $x_2 \approx 4.493614$, $x_3 \approx 4.493410$, $x_4 \approx 4.493409$,

$x_5 \approx 4.493409$. To 6 decimal places, the root is 4.493409.

14. $f(x) = x^5-5x+2$ $\Rightarrow$ $f'(x) = 5x^4-5$, so $x_{n+1} = x_n - \dfrac{x_n^5-5x_n+2}{5x_n^4-5}$

Observe that $f(-2) = -20$, $f(-1) = 6$, $f(0) = 2$, $f(1) = -2$, $f(2) = 24$
so there are roots in [-2,-1], [0,1], and [1,2]. A sketch shows
that these are the only intervals with roots.

$x_1 = -1.5$	$x_1 = 0.5$	$x_1 = 1.5$
$x_2 \approx -1.593846$	$x_2 = 0.4$	$x_2 \approx 1.396923$
$x_3 \approx -1.582241$	$x_3 \approx 0.402102$	$x_3 \approx 1.373078$
$x_4 \approx -1.582036$	$x_4 \approx 0.402102$	$x_4 \approx 1.371885$
$x_5 \approx -1.582036$		$x_5 \approx 1.371882$
		$x_6 \approx 1.371882$

To 6 decimal places, the roots are -1.582036, 0.402102, 1.371882.

16. $f(x) = (x-2)^4 - x/2 \Rightarrow f'(x) = 4(x-2)^3 - 1/2$, so

$$x_{n+1} = x_n - \frac{(x_n-2)^4 - x_n/2}{4(x_n-2)^3 - 1/2}$$
Observe that $f(1) = 1/2$, $f(2) = -1$,

$f(3) = -1/2$, $f(4) = 14$, so there are roots in $[1,2]$ and $[3,4]$ and a
sketch shows that these are the only roots. Taking $x_1 = 1$, we get

$x_2 \approx 1.111111$, $x_3 \approx 1.131883$, $x_4 \approx 1.132529$, $x_5 \approx 1.132529$.

Taking $x_1 = 3$, we get $x_2 \approx 3.142857$, $x_3 \approx 3.118267$, $x_4 \approx 3.117350$

$x_5 \approx 3.117349$, $x_6 \approx 3.117349$. To 6 decimal places, the roots are

1.132529 and 3.117349.

18.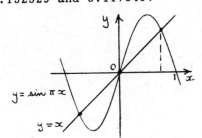

Obviously $x = 0$ is a root. From the
sketch, there appear to be roots
near -0.75 and 0.75. Write the
equation as $f(x) = \sin \pi x - x = 0$
Then $f'(x) = \pi \cos \pi x - 1$, so

$$x_{n+1} = x_n - \frac{\sin \pi x_n - x_n}{\pi \cos \pi x_n - 1}$$

Taking $x_1 = 0.75$, we get $x_2 \approx 0.736685$, $x_3 \approx 0.736484$

$x_4 \approx 0.736484$. To 6 decimal places, the roots are 0, 0.736484, and

-0.736484.

20. (a) $f(x) = 1/x - a \Rightarrow f'(x) = -1/x^2$, so

$$x_{n+1} = x_n - \frac{1/x_n - a}{-1/x_n^2} = x_n + x_n - ax_n^2 = 2x_n - ax_n^2$$

(b) Using (a) with $a = 1.6894$ and $x_1 = 0.6$, we get $x_2 = 0.588576$,

$x_3 \approx 0.588789$, $x_4 \approx 0.588789$. So $1/1.6984 \approx 0.588789$.

Review Exercises for Chapter 3

2. $f(x) = \frac{4-x}{3+x} \Rightarrow f'(x) = \lim\limits_{h\to 0} \frac{f(x+h)-f(x)}{h} = \lim\limits_{h\to 0} \frac{\frac{4-(x+h)}{3+(x+h)} - \frac{4-x}{3+x}}{h}$

$= \lim\limits_{h\to 0} \frac{(4-x-h)(3+x)-(4-x)(3+x+h)}{h(3+x+h)(3+x)} = \lim\limits_{h\to 0} \frac{-7h}{h(3+x+h)(3+x)}$

$= \lim\limits_{h\to 0} \frac{-7}{(3+x+h)(x+h)} = -\frac{7}{(3+x)^2}$

4. $f(x) = x \sin x \Rightarrow f'(x) = \lim\limits_{h\to 0} \frac{f(x+h)-f(x)}{h}$

$= \lim\limits_{h\to 0} \frac{(x+h) \sin(x+h) - x \sin x}{h}$

$= \lim\limits_{h\to 0} \frac{(x+h)(\sin x \cos h + \cos x \sin h) - x \sin x}{h}$

$= \lim\limits_{h\to 0} \frac{x \sin x (\cos h -1) + x \cos x \sin h + h(\sin x \cos h + \sin h \cos x)}{h}$

$= x \sin x \lim\limits_{h\to 0} \frac{\cos h - 1}{h} + x \cos x \lim\limits_{h\to 0} \frac{\sin h}{h} + \sin x \lim\limits_{h\to 0} \cos h$

$+ \cos x \lim\limits_{h\to 0} \sin h = x \sin x (0) + x \cos x (1) + \sin x (1)$

$+ \cos x (0) = x \cos x + \sin x$

6. $y = \sqrt[3]{x} + 1/\sqrt[3]{x} = x^{1/3} + x^{-1/3} \Rightarrow y' = (1/3)x^{-2/3} - (1/3)x^{-4/3}$

8. $y = (x+1/x^2)^{\sqrt{7}} \Rightarrow y' = \sqrt{7}(x+1/x^2)^{\sqrt{7}-1}(1-2/x^3)$

10. $y = (1-x^{-1})^{-1} \Rightarrow y' = -(1-x^{-1})^{-2}x^{-2} = -(x-1)^{-2}$

12. $y = -2/\sqrt[4]{x^3} = -2x^{-3/4} \Rightarrow y' = (-2)(-3/4)x^{-7/4} = (3/2)x^{-7/4}$

14. $y\sqrt{x-1}+x\sqrt{y-1} = xy \Rightarrow y'\sqrt{x-1}+y(1/2\sqrt{x-1})+\sqrt{y-1}+x(1/2\sqrt{y-1})y' = y+xy' \Rightarrow$

$y' = \dfrac{y-\sqrt{y-1}-y/2\sqrt{x-1}}{\sqrt{x-1}-x+x/2\sqrt{y-1}}$

16. $y = \sin(\cos x) \Rightarrow y' = \cos(\cos x)(-\sin x) = -\sin x \cos(\cos x)$

18. $y = (x+\sqrt{x})^{-1/3} \Rightarrow y' = -(1/3)(x+\sqrt{x})^{-4/3}(1+1/2\sqrt{x})$

20. $y = \sqrt{\sin\sqrt{x}} \Rightarrow y' = (1/2)(\sin\sqrt{x})^{-1/2}(\cos\sqrt{x})(1/2\sqrt{x}) = (\cos\sqrt{x})/4\sqrt{x\sin\sqrt{x}}$

22. $y = 1/\sin(x - \sin x) \Rightarrow y' = -\dfrac{\cos(x - \sin x)(1 - \cos x)}{\sin^2(x - \sin x)}$

24. $y = \dfrac{(x+\lambda)^4}{x^4+\lambda^4} \Rightarrow y' = \dfrac{(x^4+\lambda^4)4(x+\lambda)^3-(x+\lambda)^4(4x^3)}{(x^4+\lambda^4)^2} = \dfrac{4(x+\lambda)^3(\lambda^4-\lambda x^3)}{(x^4+\lambda^4)^2}$

26. $y = \dfrac{\cos^2 x}{1 + \tan x} + \dfrac{\sin^2 x}{1 + \cot x} \Rightarrow$

$y' = \dfrac{(1 + \tan x)(-2 \cos x \sin x) - \cos^2 x \sec^2 x}{(1 + \tan x)^2}$

$\quad + \dfrac{(1 + \cot x)(2 \sin x \cos x) - \sin^2 x (-\csc^2 x)}{(1 + \cot x)^2}$

$= \dfrac{-2 \sin x (\cos x + \sin x) - 1}{(1 + \tan x)^2} + \dfrac{2 \cos x (\sin x + \cos x) + 1}{(1 + \cot x)^2}$

28. $y = \left[4 + 7\sqrt[8]{x^5}\right]^{1/10} \Rightarrow y' = (1/10)\left[4 + 7\sqrt[8]{x^5}\right]^{-9/10} 7(5/8) x^{-3/8}$

$= (7/16)\left[4 + 7\sqrt[8]{x^5}\right]^{-9/10} x^{-3/8}$

30. $x \tan y = y - 1 \Rightarrow \tan y + (x \sec^2 y) y' = y' \Rightarrow y' = \dfrac{\tan y}{1 - x \sec^2 y}$

32. $y = \sqrt{x} \sec\sqrt{x} \Rightarrow y' = (1/2\sqrt{x}) \sec\sqrt{x} + \sqrt{x} \sec\sqrt{x} \tan\sqrt{x} (1/2\sqrt{x})$

$= (\sec\sqrt{x})/2\sqrt{x} + (1/2) \sec\sqrt{x} \tan\sqrt{x}$

34. $g(t) = \csc 2t \Rightarrow g'(t) = -2 \csc 2t \cot 2t \Rightarrow$

$g''(t) = -2(-2 \csc 2t \cot 2t) \cot 2t - 2 \csc 2t (-2 \csc^2 2t)$

$= 4 \csc 2t (\cot^2 2t + \csc^2 2t) = 8 \csc^3 2t - 4 \csc 2t$

$g'''(t) = 24 \csc^2 2t (-2 \csc 2t \cot 2t) - 4(-2 \csc 2t \cot 2t)$

$= -48 \csc^3 2t \cot 2t + 8 \csc 2t \cot 2t \Rightarrow$

$g'''(-\pi/8) = -48(-\sqrt{2})^3(-1) + 8(-\sqrt{2})(-1) = -88\sqrt{2}$

36. $f(x) = (2-x)^{-1} \Rightarrow f'(x) = (2-x)^{-2} \Rightarrow f''(x) = 2(2-x)^{-3} \Rightarrow$

$f'''(x) = 2 \cdot 3 (2-x)^{-4} \Rightarrow f^{(4)}(x) = 2 \cdot 3 \cdot 4 (2-x)^{-5}$. In general,

$f^{(n)}(x) = 2 \cdot 3 \cdot 4 \cdots n (2-x)^{-(n+1)} = n!/(2-x)^{(n+1)}$

38. $\sqrt{x} + \sqrt{y} = 3 \Rightarrow (1/2\sqrt{x}) + (1/2\sqrt{y})y' = 0 \Rightarrow y' = -\sqrt{y}/\sqrt{x}$ At $(4,1)$,

$y' = -1/2$, so the tangent is $y - 1 = (-1/2)(x-4)$ or $x + 2y = 6$.

40. $y = x\sqrt{1+x^2} \Rightarrow y' = \sqrt{1+x^2} + x^2/\sqrt{1+x^2}$ When $x = 1$, $y = \sqrt{2} + 1/\sqrt{2} = 3\sqrt{2}/2$

so the tangent at $(1, \sqrt{2})$ is $y - \sqrt{2} = (3\sqrt{2}/2)(x-1)$ or $3\sqrt{2}x - 2y = \sqrt{2}$.

42. $x^2 + 2y^2 = 1 \Rightarrow 2x + 4yy' = 0 \Rightarrow y' = -x/2y = 1 \iff x = -2y$. Since

the points lie on the ellipse, we have $(-2y)^2 + 2y^2 = 1 \Rightarrow 6y^2 = 1$

$\Rightarrow y = \pm 1/\sqrt{6}$. The points are $(-2/\sqrt{6}, 1/\sqrt{6})$ and $(2/\sqrt{6}, -1/\sqrt{6})$.

44. (a) $x = \sqrt{b^2 + c^2 t^2} \Rightarrow v(t) = x' = (1/2\sqrt{b^2 + c^2 t^2})2c^2 t = c^2 t/\sqrt{b^2 + c^2 t^2}$

$\Rightarrow a(t) = v'(t) = \dfrac{c^2 \sqrt{b^2 + c^2 t^2} - c^2 t(c^2 t/\sqrt{b^2 + c^2 t^2})}{b^2 + c^2 t^2} = \dfrac{b^2 c^2}{(b^2 + c^2 t^2)^{3/2}}$

(b) $v(t) > 0$ for $t > 0$, so the particle always moves in the positive direction.

46. $f(x) = g(x^2) \Rightarrow f'(x) = g'(x^2)(2x)$

48. $f(x) = x^a g(x^b) \Rightarrow f'(x) = ax^{a-1}g(x^b) + x^a g'(x^b)(bx^{b-1})$
$= ax^{a-1}g(x^b) + bx^{a+b-1}g'(x^b)$

50. (a) $V = (1/3)\pi r^2 h \Rightarrow dV/dh = (1/3)\pi r^2$ (b) $dV/dr = (2/3)\pi rh$

52. $C(x) = 950+12x+0.01x^2 \Rightarrow C'(x) = 12+0.02x$, so the marginal cost
when x = 200 is C'(200) = 12+0.02(200) = 12+4 = \$16/unit. The cost
to produce the 201st unit is C(201)-C(200) = 3766.01-3750 = \$16.01.

54.

Given $dV/dt = 2$, find dh/dt when $h = 5$.
$V = (1/3)\pi r^2 h$ and, from similar triangles,
$\dfrac{r}{h} = \dfrac{3}{10} \Rightarrow V = \dfrac{1}{3}\pi\left[\dfrac{3h}{10}\right]^2 h = \dfrac{3\pi}{100}h^3$, so
$2 = \dfrac{dV}{dt} = \dfrac{9\pi}{100}h^2\dfrac{dh}{dt} \Rightarrow \dfrac{dh}{dt} = \dfrac{200}{9\pi h^2} = \dfrac{200}{9\pi(5)^2}$
$= 8/9\pi$ cm/s when h = 5.

56.

Given $dx/dt = 4$, find $d\theta/dt$ when $x = 15$.
$x = 20\tan\theta \Rightarrow 4 = \dfrac{dx}{dt} = 20\sec^2\theta\dfrac{d\theta}{dt} \Rightarrow$
$d\theta/dt = (1/5)\cos^2\theta$. When x = 15, $\cos\theta = 4/5$
so $\dfrac{d\theta}{dt} = \dfrac{1}{5}\left[\dfrac{4}{5}\right]^2 = \dfrac{16}{125} = 0.128$ rad/s.

58. $y = x^3-2x^2+1 \Rightarrow dy = (3x^2-4x)dx$. When x = 2 and dx = 0.2,
$dy = [3(2)^2-4(2)](0.2) = 0.8$

60.

$A = x^2+(1/2)\pi(x/2)^2 = (1+\pi/8)x^2 \Rightarrow$
$dA = (2+\pi/4)x\ dx$. When x = 60 and dx = 0.1,
$dA = (2+\pi/4)60(0.1) = 12+3\pi/2$, so the maximum
error $\approx 12+3\pi/2 \approx 16.7$ cm^2

62. $f(x) = x - 6\cos x \Rightarrow f'(x) = 1 + 6\sin x \Rightarrow$
$x_{n+1} = x_n - \dfrac{x_n - 6\cos x_n}{1 + 6\sin x_n}$ From the graphs of $y = \cos x$ and
$y = x/6$, it appears there are roots near 1, -2, and -4.
If $x_1 = 1$, then $x_2 \approx 1.370620$, $x_3 \approx 1.344812$, $x_4 \approx 1.344751$,
$x_5 \approx 1.344751$. If $x_1 = -2$, then $x_2 \approx -1.888486$, $x_3 \approx -1.891518$,
$x_4 \approx -1.891520$, $x_5 \approx -1.891520$. If $x_1 = -4$, then $x_2 \approx -3.985898$,

$x_3 \approx -3.985826$, $x_4 \approx -3.985826$. So, to 6 decimal places, the roots are 1.344751, -1.891520, and -3.985826.

64. $f(x) = |x| + |x+1| + |x-1|$ For $x \geq 1$, $f(x) = x + (x+1) + (x-1) = 3x$. For $0 \leq x < 1$, $f(x) = x + (x+1) - (x-1) = x+2$. For $-1 \leq x < 0$, $f(x) = -x + (x+1) - (x-1) = -x+2$. For $x < -1$, $f(x) = -x - (x+1) - (x-1) = -3x$. f is differentiable everywhere except at -1, 0, and 1.

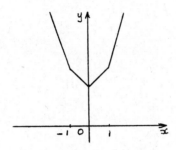

Exercises 4.1

2. Absolute maximum at e; absolute minimum at t; local maximum at c, e, s; local minimum at b , c, d, r.

4. $f(x) = 4x-1$, $x \leq 8$. Absolute maximum $f(8) = 31$; no local maximum. No local or absolute minimum.

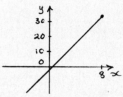

6. $f(x) = |4x-1|$, $0 \leq x \leq 2$. Absolute maximum $f(2) = 7$; no local maximum. Absolute and local minimum $f(1/4) = 0$ since $|4x-1| \geq 0$ for all x.

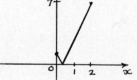

8. $f(x) = 1-x^2$, $0 < x \leq 1$. Absolute minimum $f(1) = 0$; no local minimum. No absolute or local maximum.

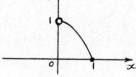

10. $f(x) = 1-x^2$, $0 \leq x \leq 1$. Absolute maximum $f(0) = 1$; no local maximum. Absolute minimum $f(1) = 0$; no local minimum.

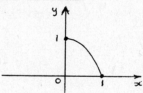

12. $f(x) = 1+(x+1)^2$, $-2 \leq x < 5$. No absolute or local maximum. Absolute and local minimum $f(-1) = 1$.

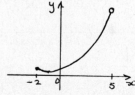

14. $f(t) = 1/t$, $0 < t \leq 1$. Absolute minimum $f(1) = 1$; no local minimum. No local or absolute maximum.

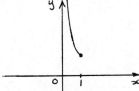

16. $f(\theta) = \tan\theta$, $-\pi/4 \leq \theta < \pi/2$. Absolute minimum $f(-\pi/4) = -1$; no local minimum. No absolute or local maximum.

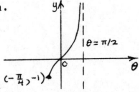

18. $f(\theta) = \sec\theta$, $-\pi/2 < \theta \leq \pi/3$. Local and absolute minimum $f(0) = 1$. No absolute or local maximum.

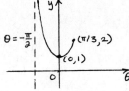

20. $f(x) = 2-x^4$. Local and absolute maximum $f(0) = 2$. No local or absolute minimum.

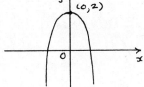

22. $f(x) = x^2$, if $-1 \leq x < 0$, $f(x) = 2-x^2$, if $0 \leq x \leq 1$. Absolute and local maximum $f(0) = 2$. No absolute or local minimum.

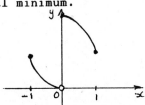

24. $f(x) = 5+8x \Rightarrow f'(x) = 8 \neq 0$. No critical number.

26. $f(x) = 4x^3-9x^2-12x+3 \Rightarrow f'(x) = 12x^2-18x-12 = 6(2x^2-3x-2)$
    $= 6(2x+1)(x-2)$. So the critical numbers are $x = -1/2, 2$.

28. $f(t) = t^3+6t^2+3t-1 \Rightarrow f'(t) = 3t^2+12t+3 = 3(t^2+4t+1)$. By the quadratic formula, solutions are $t = (-4\pm\sqrt{12})/2 = -2\pm\sqrt{3}$. Critical numbers are $t = -2\pm\sqrt{3}$.

30. $s(t) = t^4+4t^3+2t^2 \Rightarrow s'(t) = 4t^3+12t^2+4t = 4t(t^2+3t+1) = 0$ when $t = 0$ or $t^2+3t+1 = 0$. By the quadratic formula, the critical numbers are $t = 0$, $(-3\pm\sqrt{5})/2$.

32. $g(x) = |x+1| \Rightarrow g'(x) = 1$ if $x > -1$, $g'(x) = -1$ if $x < -1$, but $g'(-1)$ does not exist, so $x = -1$ is a critical number.

34. $g(t) = \sqrt{t}(1-t) = t^{1/2}-t^{3/2} \Rightarrow g'(t) = \dfrac{1}{2\sqrt{t}} - \dfrac{3}{2}\sqrt{t}$. $g'(0)$ does not

    exist, so $t = 0$ is a critical number. $0 = g'(t) = (1-3t)/2\sqrt{t} \Rightarrow$ $t = 1/3$, so $t = 1/3$ is also a critical number.

36. $f(z) = \dfrac{z+1}{z^2+z+1} \Rightarrow f'(z) = \dfrac{1(z^2+z+1)-(z+1)(2z+1)}{(z^2+z+1)^2} = \dfrac{-z^2-2z}{(z^2+z+1)^2} = 0 \Longleftrightarrow$

    $z(z+2) = 0 \Rightarrow z = 0, -2$ are the critical numbers. (Note that $z^2+z+1 \ne 0$ since the discriminant < 0.)

38. $G(x) = \sqrt[3]{x^2-x} \Rightarrow G'(x) = (1/3)(x^2-x)^{-2/3}(2x-1)$. $G'(x)$ does not exist when $x^2-x = 0$ or $x = 0,1$. $G'(x) = 0 \Longleftrightarrow 2x-1 = 0 \Longleftrightarrow$ $x = 1/2$. So the critical numbers are $x = 0, 1/2, 1$.

40. $T(x) = x^2(2x-1)^{2/3}$. $T'(x) = 2x(2x-1)^{2/3} + x^2(2/3)(2x-1)^{-1/3}(2)$. So $T'(1/2)$ does not exist. $T'(x) = 2x(2x-1)^{-1/3}(2x-1+(2/3)x)$ $= 2x(2x-1)^{-1/3}((8/3)x-1) = 0 \Longleftrightarrow x = 0$ or $x = 3/8$. So the critical numbers are $x = 0, 1/2, 3/8$.

42. $g(\theta) = \theta + \sin\theta \Rightarrow g'(\theta) = 1 + \cos\theta = 0 \Longleftrightarrow \cos\theta = -1$. The critical numbers are $\theta = (2n+1)\pi$, n an integer.

44. $f(x) = 1-2x-x^2$, $[-4,1]$. $f'(x) = -2-2x = 0 \Longleftrightarrow x = -1$. $f(-4) = -7$, $f(-1) = 2$, $f(1) = -2$. So $f(-4) = -7$ is the absolute minimum and $f(-1) = 2$ is the absolute maximum.

46. $f(x) = 4x^3-15x^2+12x+7$, $[0,3]$. $f'(x) = 12x^2-30x+12 = 6(2x-1)(x-2)$ $= 0 \Longleftrightarrow x = 1/2, 2$. $f(0) = 7$, $f(1/2) = 39/4$, $f(2) = 3$, $f(3) = 16$. So $f(3) = 16$ is the absolute maximum and $f(2) = 3$ the absolute minimum.

48. $f(x) = 18x+15x^2-4x^3$, $[-3,4]$. $f'(x) = 18+30x-12x^2 = 6(3-x)(1+2x)$ $= 0 \Longleftrightarrow x = 3,-1/2$. $f(-3) = 189$, $f(-1/2) = -19/4$, $f(3) = 81$, $f(4) = 56$. So $f(-3) = 189$ is the absolute maximum and $f(-1/2) = -19/4$ the absolute minimum.

50. $f(x) = 3x^5 - 5x^3 - 1$, $[-2,2]$. $f'(x) = 15x^4 - 15x^2 = 15x^2(x+1)(x-1) = 0$
    $\Leftrightarrow$ $x = -1, 0, 1$. $f(-2) = -57$, $f(-1) = -1$, $f(0) = -1$, $f(1) = -3$,
    $f(2) = 55$. So $f(-2) = -57$ is the absolute minimum and $f(2) = 55$ is
    the absolute maximum.

52. $f(x) = \sqrt{9-x^2}$, $[-1,2]$. $f'(x) = -x/\sqrt{9-x^2} = 0$ $\Leftrightarrow$ $x = 0$.
    $f(-1) = 2\sqrt{2}$, $f(0) = 3$, $f(2) = \sqrt{5}$. So $f(2) = \sqrt{5}$ is the absolute
    minimum and $f(0) = 3$ is the absolute maximum.

54. $f(x) = \frac{x}{x+1}$, $[1,2]$. $f'(x) = \frac{(x+1)-x}{(x+1)^2} = \frac{1}{(x+1)^2} \neq 0$ $\Rightarrow$ no critical
    numbers. $f(1) = 1/2$, $f(2) = 2/3$. So $f(1) = 1/2$ is the absolute
    minimum and $f(2) = 2/3$ the absolute maximum.

56. $f(x) = |x^2+x|$, $[-2,1]$. $f(x) = x^2+x$ if $x \leq -1$ or $x \geq 0$, $f(x) = -x^2-x$
    if $-1 < x < 0$ $\Rightarrow$ $f'(x) = 2x+1$ if $x < -1$ or $x > 0$, $f'(x) = -2x-1$ if
    $-1 < x < 0$. Since $f'(-1)$ and $f'(0)$ do not exist and $f'(x) = 0$ $\Leftrightarrow$
    $x = -1/2$, the critical numbers are $-1, -1/2, 0$. Now $f(-2) = 2$,
    $f(-1) = 0$, $f(-1/2) = 1/4$, $f(0) = 0$, $f(1) = 2$. So $f(-1) = f(0) = 0$
    is the absolute minimum and $f(-2) = f(1) = 2$ the absolute maximum.

58. $f(x) = x - 2\cos x$, $[-\pi,\pi]$. $f'(x) = 1 + 2\sin x = 0$ $\Leftrightarrow$
    $\sin x = -1/2$ $\Leftrightarrow$ $x = -5\pi/6, -\pi/6$. $f(-\pi) = 2-\pi \approx -1.14$, $f(-5\pi/6)$
    $= \sqrt{3} - 5\pi/6 \approx -.886$, $f(-\pi/6) = -\pi/6 - \sqrt{3} \approx -2.26$, $f(\pi) = \pi+2 \approx$
    5.14. So $f(-\pi/6) = -\pi/6 - \sqrt{3}$ is the absolute minimum and $f(\pi) =$
    $\pi+2$ the absolute maximum.

60. $g(x) = 2+(x-5)^3$ $\Rightarrow$ $g'(x) = 3(x-5)^2$ $\Rightarrow$ $f'(5) = 0$, so 5 is a
    critical number. But $g(5) = 2$ and g takes on values > 2 and values
    < 2 in any open interval containing 5, so g does not have a local
    extremum at 5.

62. (a) $f(x) = ax^3+bx^2+cx+d$, $a \neq 0$. So $f'(x) = 3ax^2+2bx+c$ is a
       quadratic and hence has either 2, 1, or 0 real roots, so $f(x)$
       has either 2, 1 or 0 critical numbers.
       <u>Case (i)</u>: 2 critical numbers: $f(x) = x^3-3x$ $\Rightarrow$ $f'(x) = 3x^2-3$,
       so $x = -1, 1$ are critical numbers.
       <u>Case (ii)</u>: 1 critical number: $f(x) = x^3$, $f'(x) = 3x^2$, $x = 0$
       is the only critical number.
       <u>Case (iii)</u>: 0 critical numbers: $f(x) = x^3+3x$, $f'(x) = 3x^2+3$,
       no real roots.

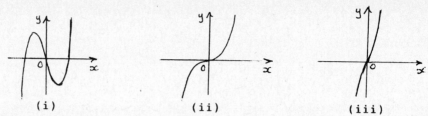

(i)   (ii)   (iii)

(b) Since there are at most two critical numbers, it can have at
most two local extreme values and by (i) this can occur. By
(iii) it can have no local extrema. However, if there is only
one critical number, then there is no local extremum.

64. Suppose that f has a minimum value at c, so $f(x) \geq f(c)$ for all x
near c. Then $g(x) = -f(x) \leq -f(c)$ for all x near c, so $g(x)$ has a
maximum value at c.

Section 4.2

Exercises 4.2

2. $f(x) = x^3 + x^2 - 2x + 1$, $[-2,0]$. f, being a polynomial, is continuous on
$[-2,0]$ and differentiable on $(-2,0)$. Also $f(-2) = 1 = f(0)$.
$f'(c) = 3c^2 + 2c - 2 = 0 \Rightarrow c = (-1 \pm \sqrt{7})/3$, but only $(-1-\sqrt{7})/3$ lies in
the interval $(-2,0)$.

4. $f(x) = \sin x + \cos x$, $[0,2\pi]$. Since sin x and cos x are continuous
on $[0,2\pi]$ and differentiable on $(0,2\pi)$ so is their sum $f(x)$.
$f(0) = 1 = f(2\pi)$. $f'(c) = \cos c - \sin c = 0 \iff \cos c = \sin c \iff$
$c = \pi/4$ or $5\pi/4$.

6. $f(x) = (x-1)^{-2}$. $f(0) = (0-1)^{-2} = 1 = (2-1)^{-2} = f(2)$.
$f'(x) = -2(x-1)^{-3} \Rightarrow f'(x)$ is never 0. This does not contradict
Rolle's Theorem since $f'(1)$ does not exist.

8. $f(x) = x^2 - 4x + 5$, $[1,5]$. f, being a polynomial, is continuous on
$[1,5]$ and differentiable on $(1,5)$. $\frac{f(5)-f(1)}{5-1} = \frac{10-2}{4} = 2$ and
$2 = f'(c) = 2c - 4 \Rightarrow c = 3$.

10. $f(x) = 2x^3 + x^2 - x - 1$, $[0,2]$. f, being a polynomial, is continuous on
$[0,2]$ and differentiable on $(0,2)$. $\frac{f(2)-f(0)}{2-0} = \frac{17-(-1)}{2} = 9$ and

$9 = f'(c) = 6c^2+2c-1 \Rightarrow 0 = 6c^2+2c-10 \Rightarrow c = (-2\pm\sqrt{244})/2$
$= (-1\pm\sqrt{61})/6$, but only $(-1+\sqrt{61})/6$ lies in $(0,2)$.

12. $f(x) = \sqrt{x}$, $[1,4]$. $f(x)$ is continuous on $[1,4]$ and differentiable on $(1,4)$. $\frac{f(4)-f(1)}{4-1} = \frac{2-1}{3} = 1/3$ and $1/3 = f'(c) = 1/2\sqrt{c} \Rightarrow$
$\sqrt{c} = 3/2 \Rightarrow c = (3/2)^2 = 9/4$.

14. $f(x) = \frac{x+1}{x-1}$. $f(2)-f(0) = 3-(-1) = 4$. $f'(x) = \frac{1(x-1)-1(x+1)}{(x+1)^2}$
$= \frac{-2}{(x+1)^2}$. Since $f'(x) < 0$ for all x (except $x = -1$), $f'(c)(2-0)$ is
always < 0 and hence cannot $= 4$. This does not contradict the Mean Value Theorem since f is not continuous at $x = 1$.

16. $f(x) = x^7+5x^3+x-6 = 0$. Since f is continuous and $f(0) = -6$ and $f(1) = 1$, the equation has at least one root in $(0,1)$ by the Intermediate Value Theorem. Suppose it has more than one root, say $a < b$ are both roots. Then $f(a) = 0 = f(b)$, so by Rolle's Theorem, $f'(x) = 7x^6+15x^2+1 = 0$ has a root in (a,b). But this is impossible since clearly $f'(x) \geq 1 > 0$ for all real x.

18. Suppose that $f(x) = x^4+4x+c = 0$ has three distinct real roots a,b,c where $a < b < c$. Then $f(a) = f(b) = f(c) = 0$. By Rolle's Theorem there are numbers c_1 and c_2 with $a < c_1 < b$ and $b < c_2 < c$ and
$0 = f'(c_1) = f'(c_2)$, so $f'(x) = 0$ must have at least two real
solutions. However $0 = f'(x) = 4x^3+4 = 4(x^3+1) = 4(x+1)(x^2-x+1)$
has as its only real solution $x = -1$. Thus $f(x)$ can have at most two real roots.

20. a) Suppose that $f(a) = f(b) = 0$ where $a < b$. By Rolle's Theorem applied to f on $[a,b]$ there is a number $a < c < b$ with $f'(c) = 0$.
(b) Suppose that $f(a) = f(b) = f(c) = 0$ where $a < b < c$. By Rolle's Theorem applied to $f(x)$ on $[a,b]$ and $[b,c]$ there are numbers $a < d < b$ and $b < e < c$ with $f'(d) = 0$ and $f'(e) = 0$. By Rolle's Theorem applied to $f'(x)$ on $[d,e]$ there is a number g with $d < g < e$ such that $f''(g) = 0$.
(c) Suppose that f is n times differentiable on R and has $n+1$ distinct real roots. Then $f^{(n)}$ has at least one real root.

22. By the Mean Value Theorem $\frac{f(5)-f(2)}{5-2} = f'(c)$ for some $c \in (2,5)$.

Since $1 \leq f'(x) \leq 4$, we have $1 \leq \dfrac{f(5)-f(2)}{5-2} \leq 4$ or $1 \leq \dfrac{f(5)-f(2)}{3} \leq 4$

or $3 \leq f(5)-f(2) \leq 12$.

24. Suppose that $f'(x) = c$. Let $g(x) = cx$, so $g'(x) = c$. Then, by Corollary 4.17, $f(x) = g(x)+d$, where d is a constant, so $f(x) = cx+d$.

26. Let $v(t)$ be the velocity of the car t hours after 2:00 P.M. Then $\dfrac{v(1/6)-v(0)}{1/6-0} = \dfrac{50-30}{1/6} = 120$. By the Mean Value Theorem there is a number $0 < c < 1/6$ with $v'(c) = 120$. Since $v'(t)$ is the acceleration at time t, at the instant c hours after 2:00 P.M., the acceleration is 120 mi/h^2.

Section 4.3

Exercises 4.3

2. $f(x) = x^3-x+1$. $f'(x) = 3x^2-1 = 0 \Rightarrow x = \pm 1/\sqrt{3}$ (the only critical numbers). (a) $f'(x) > 0 \Leftrightarrow 3x^2 > 1 \Leftrightarrow |x| > 1/3 \Leftrightarrow x < -1/\sqrt{3}$ or $x > 1/\sqrt{3}$ and $f'(x) < 0 \Leftrightarrow -1/\sqrt{3} < x < 1/\sqrt{3}$. So f is increasing on $(-\infty, -1/\sqrt{3}]$ and $[1/\sqrt{3}, \infty)$ and decreasing on $[-1/\sqrt{3}, 1/\sqrt{3}]$.   (c)

(b) By the First Derivative Test
$f(-1/\sqrt{3}) = 1+2/3\sqrt{3}$ is a
local maximum and $f(1/\sqrt{3})$
$= 1-2/3\sqrt{3}$ is a local minimum.

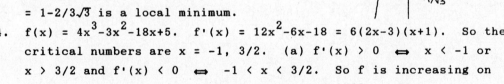

4. $f(x) = 4x^3-3x^2-18x+5$. $f'(x) = 12x^2-6x-18 = 6(2x-3)(x+1)$. So the critical numbers are $x = -1$, $3/2$. (a) $f'(x) > 0 \Leftrightarrow x < -1$ or $x > 3/2$ and $f'(x) < 0 \Leftrightarrow -1 < x < 3/2$. So f is increasing on $(-\infty, -1]$ and $[3/2, \infty)$ and decreasing on $[-1, 3/2]$.

(b) The local maximum is $f(-1)$ (c)
$= 16$. The local minimum is
$f(3/2) = -15.25$.

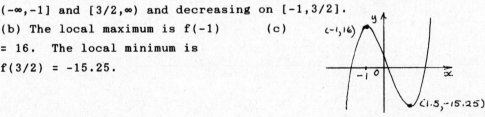

6. $f(x) = 2x^3-6x^2-18x+7$. $f'(x) = 6x^2-12x-18 = 6(x+1)(x-3)$, so the
    critical numbers are x = -1, 3. (a) $f'(x) > 0 \iff (x+1)(x-3) > 0$
    $\iff$ x < -1 or x > 3. $f'(x) < 0 \iff -1 < x < 3$. So f is
    increasing on $(-\infty,-1]$ and $[3,\infty)$ and decreasing on $[-1,3]$.
    (b) The local maximum is f(-1)   (c)
    = 17 and the local minimum
    is f(3) = -47.

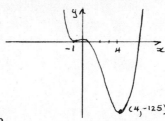

8. $f(x) = x^4-4x^3-8x^2+3$. $f'(x) = 4x^3-12x^2-16x = 4x(x-4)(x+1)$. So the
    critical numbers are x = -1, 0, 4.

    (a)

Interval	4x	x-4	x+1	f'(x)	f
x<-1	-	-	-	-	decreasing on $(-\infty,-1]$
-1<x<0	-	-	+	+	increasing on $[-1,0]$
0<x<4	+	-	+	-	decreasing on $[0,4]$
x<4	+	+	+	+	increasing on $[4,\infty)$

    (b) Local minimum f(-1) = 0,   (c)
    local maximum f(0) = 3,
    local minimum f(4) = -125.

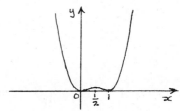

10. $f(x) = x^2(1-x)^2$. $0 = f'(x) = 2x(1-x)^2+x^2(2(1-x)(-1))$
     $= 2x(1-x)(1-2x)$. So the critical numbers are x = 0, 1/2, 1.

     (a)

Interval	2x	1-x	1-2x	f'(x)	f
x<0	-	+	+	-	decreasing on $(-\infty,0]$
0<x<1/2	+	+	+	+	increasing on $[0,1/2]$
1/2<x<1	+	+	-	-	decreasing on $[1/2,1]$
x>1	+	-	-	+	increasing on $[1,\infty)$

     (b) Local minimum f(0) = 0,
     local maximum f(1/2) = 1/16,
     local minimum f(1) = 0.

12. $f(x) = 3x^5-25x^3+60x$. $f'(x) = 15x^4-75x^2+60 = 15(x^4-5x^2+4)$
     $= 15(x^2-4)(x^2-1) = 15(x-2)(x+2)(x+1)(x-1)$. So the critical numbers
     are x = ±2,±1.

(a)

Interval	x+2	x-2	x+1	x-1	f'(x)	f
x<-2	-	-	-	-	+	increasing on $(-\infty,-2]$
-2<x<-1	+	-	-	-	-	decreasing on $[-2,-1]$
-1<x<1	+	-	+	-	+	increasing on $[-1,1]$
1<x<2	+	-	+	+	-	decreasing on $[1,2]$
x>2	+	+	+	+	+	increasing on $[2,\infty)$

(b) Local maximum $f(-2) = -16$ (c)

local minimum $f(-1) = -38$,

local maximum $f(1) = 38$,

local minimum $f(2) = 16$.

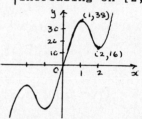

14. $f(x) = x\sqrt{1-x^2}$. $f'(x) = \sqrt{1-x^2} - x^2/\sqrt{1-x^2} = (1-2x^2)/\sqrt{1-x^2}$. Critical numbers are $\pm 1/\sqrt{2}$ and ± 1. (a) $f'(x) > 0 \iff 1-2x^2 > 0 \iff x^2 < 1/2 \iff |x| < 1/\sqrt{2} \iff -1/\sqrt{2} < x < 1/\sqrt{2}$. $f'(x) < 0 \iff -1 < x < -1/\sqrt{2}$ or $1/\sqrt{2} < x < 1$. So f is increasing on $[-1/\sqrt{2},1/\sqrt{2}]$ and decreasing on $[-1,-1/\sqrt{2}]$ and $[1/\sqrt{2},1]$.

(b) Local minimum $f(-1/\sqrt{2}) = -1/2$, (c)

local maximum $f(1/\sqrt{2}) = 1/2$.

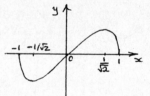

16. $f(x) = x^{2/3}(x-2)^2$. Domain is R. $f'(x)$

$= (2/3)x^{-1/3}(x-2)^2 + x^{2/3}[2(x-2)] = (2/3)x^{-1/3}(x-2)(4x-2)$.

Critical numbers are $x = 0, 1/2, 2$.

(a)

Interval	$x^{-1/3}$	x-2	2x-1	f'(x)	f
x<0	-	-	-	-	decreasing on $(-\infty,0]$
0<x<1/2	+	-	-	+	increasing on $[0,1/2]$
1/2<x<2	+	-	+	-	decreasing on $[1/2,2]$
x>2	+	+	+	+	increasing on $[2,\infty)$

(b) Local minimum $f(0) = 0$, (c)

local maximum $f(1/2) = 9/4^{4/3}$

≈ 1.42, local minimum $f(2) = 0$.

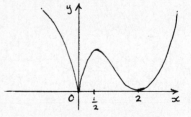

18. $f(x) = \sqrt[3]{x} - \sqrt[3]{x^2} = x^{1/3} - x^{2/3}$. $f'(x) = (1/3)x^{-2/3} - (2/3)x^{-1/3}$ $= \frac{1}{3}x^{-2/3}(1-2x^{1/3})$. So the critical numbers are $x = 0, 1/8$.

(a) $f'(x) > 0 \iff 1-2x^{1/3} > 0 \iff 1/2 > x^{1/3} \iff x < 1/8$
($x \neq 0$). $f'(x) < 0 \iff x > 1/8$. So f is increasing on $(-\infty, 1/8]$
and decreasing on $[1/8, \infty)$.   (c)
(b) Local maximum $f(1/8) = 1/4$.

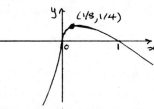

20. $f(x) = x^2 \sqrt[3]{6x-7}$. $f'(x) = 2x\sqrt[3]{6x-7} + x^2\left[6/3(6x-7)^{2/3}\right]$
$= 14x(x-1)/(6x-7)^{2/3}$.   Critical numbers are $x = 0, 1, 7/6$.
(a) $f'(x) > 0 \iff x(x-1) > 0$ ($x \neq 7/6$) $\iff x < 0$ or $x > 1$
($x \neq 7/6$). $f'(x) < 0 \iff 0 < x < 1$. So f is increasing on $(-\infty, 0]$
and $[1, \infty)$ and decreasing on $[0,1]$.
(b) Local maximum $f(0) = 0$,   (c)
local minimum $f(1) = -1$.

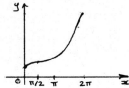

22. $f(x) = x + \cos x$, $0 \leq x \leq 2\pi$. $f'(x) = 1 - \sin x$.   Only critical
number is $x = \pi/2$. (a) $f'(x) > 0 \iff 1 > \sin x \iff x \neq \pi/2$. So
f is increasing on $[0, 2\pi]$.   (c)
(b) No local maximum or minimum.

24. $f(x) = x \sin x + \cos x$, $-\pi \leq x \leq \pi$. $f'(x) = \sin x + x \cos x - \sin x$
$= x \cos x$, $f'(x) = 0 \iff x = -\pi/2, 0, \pi/2$. (a) $f'(x) > 0 \iff$
$x \cos x > 0 \iff -\pi \leq x < -\pi/2$ or $0 < x < \pi/2$. So f is increasing
on $[-\pi, -\pi/2]$ and $[0, \pi/2]$ and is decreasing on $[-\pi/2, 0]$ and $[\pi/2, \pi]$.
(b) Local maximum $f(-\pi/2) = \pi/2$,   (c)
local minimum $f(0) = 1$,
local maximum $f(\pi/2) = \pi/2$.

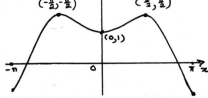

26. $f(x) = x^5+4x^3-6$. $f'(x) = 5x^4+12x^2 > 0$ for all $x \neq 0$. So f is increasing on R.

28. $f(x) = 2 \tan x - \tan^2 x$. $f'(x) = 2 \sec^2 x - 2 \tan x \sec^2 x$
$= 2 \sec^2 x(1 - \tan x)$. So $f'(x) > 0 \iff 1 - \tan x > 0 \iff$
$\tan x < 1 \iff x \in (n\pi-\pi/2, n\pi+\pi/4)$, n an integer. So f is increasing
on $(n\pi-\pi/2, n\pi+\pi/4]$, n an integer, and decreasing on
$[n\pi+\pi/4, n\pi+\pi/2)$, n an integer.

30. $f(x) = x+1/x$, $0.5 \leq x \leq 3$. $f'(x) = 1-1/x^2 = (x^2-1)/x^2$. So $x = 1$
is the only critical number in the interval. $f'(x) > 0$ for
$1 < x \leq 3$ and $f'(x) < 0$ for $0.5 \leq x < 1$. So the local minimum is
$f(1) = 2$. Also $f(0.5) = 2.5$ and $f(3) = 10/3$. So the absolute
minimum is $f(1) = 2$ and the absolute maximum is $f(3) = 10/3$.

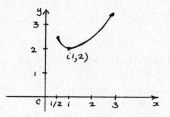

32. $f(x) = x^3+6x^2+9x+2$, $-4 \leq x \leq 0$. $f'(x) = 3x^2+12x+9 = 3(x+3)(x+1)$.
The critical numbers are $x = -3, -1$ and $f'(x) > 0$ if $x < -3$ or
$x > -1$ and $f'(x) < 0$ for $-3 < x < -1$. There is a local maximum at
$x = -3$ and $f(-3) = 2$ and a local minimum at $x = -1$ and $f(-1) = -2$.
Also $f(-4) = -2$ and $f(0) = 2$. So -2 is the absolute minimum and 2
is the absolute maximum.

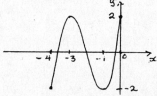

34. $g(x) = \sin x - \cos x$, $-\pi/2 \leq x \leq \pi/2$. Here $g'(x) = \cos x + \sin x$
$= 0$ when $x = -\pi/4$. $g'(x) > 0$ when $x > -\pi/4$ and $g'(x) < 0$ when
$x < -\pi/4$ $(-\pi/2 \leq x \leq \pi/2)$. So $g(-\pi/4) = -\sqrt{2}$ is a local minimum.
Now $g(-\pi/2) = -1$ and $g(\pi/2) = 1$. So $g(-\pi/4) = -\sqrt{2}$ is the absolute
minimum and $g(\pi/2) = 1$ is the absolute maximum.

90

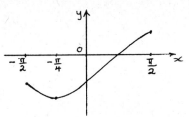

36. Let $f(x) = \dfrac{\tan x}{x}$. Then $f'(x) = \dfrac{x \sec^2 x - \tan x}{x^2}$. Now by (3.19)

$\sin x < x$ for $0 < x < \pi/2$. Hence $\tan x < x/\cos x$ so
$x \sec^2 x - \tan x > x \sec^2 x - x \sec x = x \sec x(\sec x - 1) > 0$ since
$\sec x > 1$ for $0 < x < \pi/2$. Hence $f'(x) > 0$ for $0 < x < \pi/2$ so f is
increasing on $(0,\pi/2)$. Thus for $0 < a < b < \pi/2$, we have
$\tan a/a < \tan b/b$ or $b/a < \tan b/\tan a$.

38. Let $f(x) = \cos x - 1 + x^2/2$. Then $f'(x) = - \sin x + x$. Now by
(3.19), for $0 < x \le \pi/2$, $\sin x < x$, so $x - \sin x > 0$. For $x > \pi/2$,
$x - \sin x \ge x-1 \ge \pi/2-1 > 0$. Thus f is increasing. So for $x > 0$,
$f(x) > f(0) = 0 \Rightarrow \cos x - 1 + x^2/2 > 0$ or $\cos x > 1-x^2/2$.

40. $f(x) = \tan x - x$. $f'(x) = \sec^2 x - 1 > 0$ for $0 < x < \pi/2$ since
$\sec^2 x > 1$ for $0 < x < \pi/2$. So f is increasing on $[0,\pi/2)$. Thus
$f(x) > f(0) = 0$ for $0 < x < \pi/2 \Rightarrow \tan x - x > 0 \Rightarrow \tan x > x$ for
$0 < x < \pi/2$.

42.

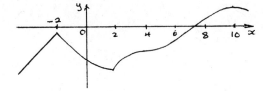

44. (a) (ii) Let $x\in(a,b)$. If $a < x < c$, then $f(x) > f(c)$ since $f' < 0$
implies f is decreasing on $[a,c]$. If $c < x < b$, then $f(x) > f(c)$
since $f' > 0$ implies that f is increasing on $[c,b]$. Therefore
$f(c) \le f(x)$ for all $x\in(a,b)$. Thus, by Definition 4.2, f has a
local minimum at c.

(b) (iii) If f' does not change sign at c, then either $f' > 0$ on
some open interval containing c (except at c) or $f' < 0$ on some
open interval containing c (except at c). Thus either f is
increasing on some interval containing c or f is decreasing on some
interval containing c. In either case, f does not have a local
extremum at c.

Exercises 4.4

2. (a) $f(x) = 2x^3 + 5x^2 - 4x$ ⟹ $f'(x) = 6x^2 + 10x - 4 = 2(3x-1)(x+2) = 0$ ⟺ $x = 1/3$ or -2. $f'(x) > 0$ ⟺ $x < -2$ or $x > 1/3$; $f'(x) < 0$ ⟺ $-2 < x < 1/3$. So f is increasing on $(-\infty, -2]$, $[1/3, \infty)$ and decreasing on $[-2, 1/3]$. (b) Local maximum $f(-2) = 12$, local minimum $f(1/3) = -19/27$. (c) $f''(x) = 12x + 10 > 0$ ⟺ $x > -5/6$, so f is CU on $(-5/6, \infty)$ and CD on $(-\infty, -5/6)$. (d) Inflection point at $x = -5/6$.

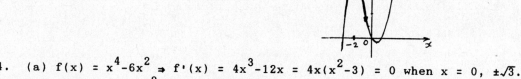

4. (a) $f(x) = x^4 - 6x^2$ ⟹ $f'(x) = 4x^3 - 12x = 4x(x^2 - 3) = 0$ when $x = 0$, $\pm\sqrt{3}$.

Interval	$4x$	x^2-3	$f'(x)$	f
$x < -\sqrt{3}$	$-$	$+$	$-$	decreasing on $(-\infty, -\sqrt{3}]$
$-\sqrt{3} < x < 0$	$-$	$-$	$+$	increasing on $[-\sqrt{3}, 0]$
$0 < x < \sqrt{3}$	$+$	$-$	$-$	decreasing on $[0, \sqrt{3}]$
$x > \sqrt{3}$	$+$	$+$	$+$	increasing on $[\sqrt{3}, \infty)$

(b) Local minima $f(\pm\sqrt{3}) = -9$, local maximum $f(0) = 0$.
(c) $f''(x) = 12x^2 - 12 = 12(x^2-1) > 0$ ⟺ $x^2 > 1$ ⟺ $|x| > 1$ ⟺ $x > 1$ or $x < -1$, so f is CU on $(-\infty, -1)$, $(1, \infty)$ and CD on $(-1, 1)$.
(d) Inflection points when $x = \pm 1$.

6. (a) $g(x) = 4 + 72x - 3x^2 - x^3$ ⟹ $g'(x) = 72 - 6x - 3x^2 = -3(x+6)(x-4) = 0$ when $x = -6$, 4. $g'(x) > 0$ ⟺ $-6 < x < 4$; $g'(x) < 0$ ⟺ $x < -6$ or $x > 4$. So g is increasing on $[-6, 4]$ and decreasing on $(-\infty, -6]$ and $[4, \infty)$. (b) Local maximum $g(4) = 180$, local minimum $g(-6) = -320$. (c) $g''(x) = -6(x+1) > 0$ ⟺ $x < -1$, so g is CU on $(-\infty, -1)$ and CD on $(-1, \infty)$. (d) Point of inflection at $x = -1$.

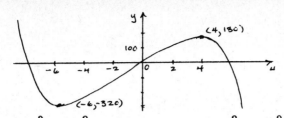

8. (a) $h(x) = (x+2)^3(x-1)^2 \Rightarrow h'(x) = 3(x+2)^2(x-1)^2 + 2(x+2)^3(x-1)$
    $= (x+2)^2(x-1)(5x+1) = 0$ when $x = -2$, 1, $-1/5$. $h'(x) > 0 \iff$
    $x < -1/5$ or $x > 1$; $h'(x) < 0 \iff -1/5 < x < 1$. So h is increasing
    on $(-\infty,-1/5]$, $[1,\infty)$ and decreasing on $[-1/5,1]$. (b) Local maximum
    $h(-1/5) = 26244/3125 \approx 8.4$, local minimum $h(1) = 0$.
    (c) $h''(x) = 2(x+2)(5x^2-4x-1) + (x+2)^2(10x-4) = 2(x+2)(10x^2+4x-5)$
    $= 0$ when $x = -2$ or $(-2\pm3\sqrt{6})/10 = \alpha,\beta$, say. $h''(x) > 0 \iff -2 < x < \alpha$
    or $x > \beta$, so h is CU on $(-2,\alpha)$, (β,∞) and CD on $(-\infty,-2)$, (α,β).
    (d) Points of inflection at $x = -2$, α, β.

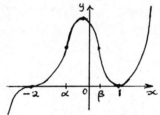

10. (a) $F(x) = x^3(x+6)^4 \Rightarrow F'(x) = 3x^2(x+6)^4+4x^3(x+6)^3 = x^2(x+6)^3(7x+18)$
    $= 0$ when $x = 0$, -6, $-18/7$. $F'(x) > 0 \iff x < -6$ or $x > -18/7$;
    $F'(x) < 0 \iff -6 < x < -18/7$. So F is increasing on $(-\infty,-6]$ and
    $[-18/7,\infty)$, and decreasing on $[-6,-18/7]$. (b) Local maximum
    $F(-6) = 0$, local minimum $F(-18/7) = -2^{15}3^{10}/7^7 \approx -2350$.
    (c) $F''(x) = 2x(x+6)^3(7x+18) + 3x^2(x+6)^2(7x+18) + 7x^2(x+6)^3$
    $= 6x(x+6)^2(7x^2+36x+36) = 0$ when $x = 0$, -6, $(-18\pm6\sqrt{2})/7 = \alpha,\beta$, say.
    $F''(x) > 0 \iff \alpha < x < \beta$ or $x > 0$, so f is CU on (α,β) and $(0,\infty)$
    and CD on $(-\infty,\alpha)$ and $(\beta,0)$. (d) Points of inflection at $x = \alpha,\beta,0$.

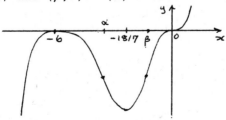

93

12. (a) $G(x) = x^{4/3} - 4x^{1/3}$ → $G'(x) = (4/3)x^{1/3} - (4/3)x^{-2/3}$

= $(4/3)x^{-2/3}(x-1) = 0$ when $x = 1$ and does not exist when $x = 0$.

$G'(x) > 0 \Leftrightarrow x > 1$; $G'(x) < 0 \Leftrightarrow x < 0$ or $0 < x < 1$. So G is

increasing on $[1,\infty)$ and decreasing on $(-\infty,1]$. (b) Local minimum

$G(1) = -3$. (c) $G''(x) = (4/9)x^{-2/3} + (8/9)x^{-5/3} = (4/9)x^{-5/3}(x+2) > 0$

$\Leftrightarrow x < -2$ or $x > 0$, so f is CU on $(-\infty,-2)$, $(0,\infty)$ and CD on $(-2,0)$.

(d) Inflection points at $x = -2, 0$.

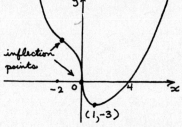

14. (a) $P(x) = x\sqrt{x+1}$, domain = $[-1,\infty)$. $P'(x) = \sqrt{x+1} + x \dfrac{1}{2\sqrt{x+1}} = \dfrac{3x+2}{2\sqrt{x+1}}$

> 0 when $x > -2/3$; $P'(x) < 0$ when $-1 < x < -2/3$, so P is increasing

on $[-2/3,\infty)$ and decreasing on $[-1,-2/3]$. (b) Local minimum

$P(-2/3) = -2/3\sqrt{3}$. (c) $P''(x) = \dfrac{3(2\sqrt{x+1}) - (3x+2)(1/\sqrt{x+1})}{4(x+1)}$

= $(3x+4)/4(x+1)^{3/2} > 0$ when $x > -1$, so P is CU on $(-1,\infty)$. (d) No

inflection point.

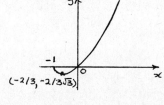

16. (a) $Q(x) = x^{1/3} - x^{1/5}$ → $Q'(x) = (1/3)x^{-2/3} - (1/5)x^{-4/5}$

= $(5x^{2/15} - 3)/15x^{4/5} = 0 \Leftrightarrow x^{2/15} = 3/5 \Leftrightarrow x = \pm.6^{7.5}$, so the

critical numbers are $\pm.6^{7.5}$ and 0. $Q'(x) > 0$ when $5x^{2/15} - 3 > 0 \Leftrightarrow$

$x > .6^{7.5}$ or $x < -.6^{7.5}$; $Q'(x) < 0$ when $-.6^{7.5} < x < .6^{7.5}$. So Q

is increasing on $(-\infty,-.6^{7.5}]$ and $[.6^{7.5},\infty)$, and decreasing on

$[-.6^{7.5}, .6^{7.5}]$. (b) Local minimum $Q(.6^{7.5}) = .6^{2.5} - .6^{1.5} \approx -.19$,

local maximum $Q(-.6^{7.5}) \approx .19$. (c) $Q''(x) = -(2/9)x^{-5/3} + (4/25)x^{-9/5}$

= $(-50x^{2/15} + 36)/225x^{9/5} = 0$ when $x = \pm(18/25)^{7.5}$. $Q''(x) > 0 \Leftrightarrow$

$x < -.72^{7.5}$ or $0 < x < .72^{7.5}$, so Q is CU on $(-\infty, -.72^{7.5})$ and $(0, .72^{7.5})$, and CD on $(-.72^{7.5}, 0)$ and $(.72^{7.5}, \infty)$. (d) Points of inflection at $x = 0, \pm.72^{7.5}$.

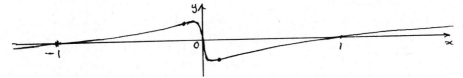

18. (a) $f(\theta) = \cos^2\theta \Rightarrow f'(\theta) = -2\cos\theta\sin\theta = -\sin 2\theta = 0$ when $\theta = n\pi/2$, n an integer. $f'(\theta) > 0 \Leftrightarrow n\pi+\pi/2 < \theta < (n+1)\pi$, so f is increasing on $[n\pi+\pi/2, (n+1)\pi]$ and decreasing on $[n\pi, n\pi+\pi/2]$.
(b) Local maxima $f(n\pi) = 1$, local minima $f(n\pi+\pi/2) = 0$.
(c) $f''(\theta) = -2\cos 2\theta > 0 \Leftrightarrow n\pi+\pi/4 < \theta < n\pi+3\pi/4$, so f is CU on $(n\pi+\pi/4, n\pi+3\pi/4)$ and CD on $(n\pi-\pi/4, n\pi+\pi/4)$. (d) Points of inflection at $x = n\pi\pm\pi/4$.

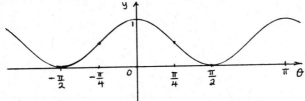

20. (a) $f(t) = t + \cos t \Rightarrow f'(t) = 1 - \sin t \geq 0$ for all t and $= 0$ when $\sin t = 1 \Leftrightarrow t = 2n\pi+\pi/2$, so f is increasing on $(-\infty, \infty)$.
(b) No extrema. (c) $f''(t) = -\cos t > 0 \Leftrightarrow 2n\pi+\pi/2 < t < 2n\pi+3\pi/2$, so f is CU on $(2n\pi+\pi/2, 2n\pi+3\pi/2)$ and CD on $(2n\pi-\pi/2, 2n\pi+\pi/2)$.
(d) Points of inflection at $t = 2n\pi\pm\pi/2$, i.e., $t = n\pi+\pi/2$.

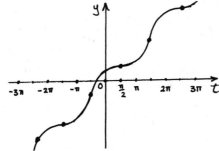

95

22.

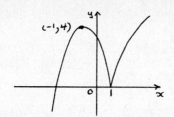

24.

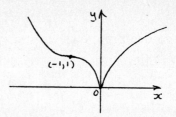

26. Since f is concave upward on I, the graph of f lies above all of its tangents on I. Thus the graph of -f lies below all of its tangents on I, so -f is concave downward on I.

28. $f(x) = x^4 \Rightarrow f'(x) = 4x^3 \Rightarrow f''(x) = 12x^2 \Rightarrow f''(0) = 0.$ For x<0, $f''(x) > 0$, so f is CU on $(-\infty,0)$; for x>0, $f''(x) > 0$, so f is also CU on $(0,\infty)$. Since f does not change concavity at 0, (0,0) is not an inflection point.

30. Since f is positive and CU on I, f > 0 and f" > 0 on I. So $g(x) = [f(x)]^2 \Rightarrow g' = 2ff' \Rightarrow g" = 2f'f'+2ff" = 2(f')^2+2ff" > 0 \Rightarrow$ g is CU on I.

32. Since f and g are CU on $(-\infty,\infty)$, f" > 0 and g" > 0 on $(-\infty,\infty)$. $h(x) = f(g(x)) \Rightarrow h'(x) = f'(g(x))g'(x) \Rightarrow h"(x) = f"(g(x))g'(x)g'(x) + f'(g(x))g"(x) = f"(g(x))[g'(x)]^2 + f'(g(x))g"(x) > 0$ if f' > 0. So h will be CU if f is increasing.

Section 4.5

Exercises 4.5

2. $\lim\limits_{x\to-\infty} 5x^{-2/3} \underset{(3)}{=} 5 \lim\limits_{x\to-\infty} \dfrac{1}{x^{2/3}} = 5\cdot 0 = 0$ by Theorem 4.32.

4. $\lim\limits_{x\to\infty} \dfrac{x+4}{x^2-2x+5} = \lim\limits_{x\to\infty} \dfrac{\dfrac{1}{x} + \dfrac{4}{x^2}}{1 - \dfrac{2}{x} + \dfrac{5}{x^2}} \underset{(5)}{=} \dfrac{\lim\limits_{x\to\infty}\left[\dfrac{1}{x} + \dfrac{4}{x^2}\right]}{\lim\limits_{x\to\infty}\left[1 - \dfrac{2}{x} + \dfrac{5}{x^2}\right]} \underset{(1,2,3)}{=}$

$\dfrac{\lim\limits_{x\to\infty}\dfrac{1}{x} + 4\lim\limits_{x\to\infty}\dfrac{1}{x^2}}{\lim\limits_{x\to\infty}1 - 2\lim\limits_{x\to\infty}\dfrac{1}{x} + 5\lim\limits_{x\to\infty}\dfrac{1}{x^2}} = \dfrac{0+4(0)}{1-2(0)+5(0)} = 0$ by 7 and Theorem 4.32.

96

6. $\lim\limits_{t\to\infty} \dfrac{7t^3+4t}{2t^3-t^2+3} = \lim\limits_{t\to\infty} \dfrac{7+\dfrac{4}{t^2}}{2-\dfrac{1}{t}+\dfrac{3}{t^3}}$ $(5,1,2,3)$ $= \dfrac{\lim\limits_{t\to\infty} 7 + 4 \lim\limits_{t\to\infty} \dfrac{1}{t^2}}{\lim\limits_{t\to\infty} 2 - \lim\limits_{t\to\infty} \dfrac{1}{t} + 3 \lim\limits_{t\to\infty} \dfrac{1}{t^3}}$

$= \dfrac{7+4(0)}{2-0+3(0)} = \dfrac{7}{2}$ by (7) and Theorem 4.32.

8. $\lim\limits_{x\to\infty} \left[\dfrac{2x^2-1}{x+8x^2}\right]^{1/2} \underset{(11)}{=} \left[\lim\limits_{x\to\infty} \dfrac{2-\dfrac{1}{x^2}}{\dfrac{1}{x}+8}\right]^{1/2} \underset{(5,1,2)}{=} \left[\dfrac{\lim\limits_{x\to\infty} 2 - \lim\limits_{x\to\infty} \dfrac{1}{x^2}}{\lim\limits_{x\to\infty} \dfrac{1}{x} + \lim\limits_{x\to\infty} 8}\right]^{1/2}$

$= \left[\dfrac{2-0}{0+8}\right]^{1/2} = \dfrac{1}{2}$ by (7) and Theorem 4.32.

10. Since $0 \leq \sin^2 x \leq 1$, we have $0 \leq \dfrac{\sin^2 x}{x^2} \leq \dfrac{1}{x^2}$ for all $x \neq 0$.

By (7) and Theorem 4.32 we have $\lim\limits_{x\to\infty} 0 = 0$ and $\lim\limits_{x\to\infty} \dfrac{1}{x^2} = 0$. So, by

the Squeeze Theorem, $\lim\limits_{x\to\infty} \dfrac{\sin^2 x}{x^2} = 0$.

12. $\lim\limits_{t\to-\infty} \dfrac{6t^2+5t}{(1-t)(2t-3)} = \lim\limits_{t\to-\infty} \dfrac{6t^2+5t}{-2t^2+5t-3} = \lim\limits_{t\to-\infty} \dfrac{6+5/t}{-2+5/t-3/t^2}$

$= \dfrac{\lim\limits_{t\to-\infty} 6 + 5 \lim\limits_{t\to-\infty} (1/t)}{\lim\limits_{t\to-\infty} (-2) + 5 \lim\limits_{t\to-\infty} (1/t) - 3 \lim\limits_{t\to-\infty} (1/t^2)} = \dfrac{6+5(0)}{-2+5(0)-3(0)} = -3$

14. $\lim\limits_{x\to-\infty} \dfrac{\sqrt{x^2+4x}}{4x+1} = \lim\limits_{x\to-\infty} \dfrac{-\sqrt{1+4/x}}{4+1/x} = \dfrac{-\sqrt{1+0}}{4+0} = -\dfrac{1}{4}$ Note: In dividing numerator

and denominator by x, we used the fact that, for $x<0$, $x = -\sqrt{x^2}$.

16. $\lim\limits_{x\to\infty} \dfrac{\sqrt[3]{x^3+8}}{x+2} = \lim\limits_{x\to\infty} \dfrac{\sqrt[3]{1+8/x^3}}{1+2/x} = \dfrac{\sqrt[3]{1+0}}{1+0} = 1$

18. $\lim\limits_{x\to\infty} (\sqrt{x^2+3x+1} - x) = \lim\limits_{x\to\infty} (\sqrt{x^2+3x+1} - x) \dfrac{\sqrt{x^2+3x+1} + x}{\sqrt{x^2+3x+1} + x}$

$= \lim\limits_{x\to\infty} \dfrac{x^2+3x+1 - x^2}{\sqrt{x^2+3x+1} + x} = \lim\limits_{x\to\infty} \dfrac{3x+1}{\sqrt{x^2+3x+1} + x} = \lim\limits_{x\to\infty} \dfrac{3 + 1/x}{\sqrt{1+(3/x)+(1/x^2)} + 1}$

$= \dfrac{3+0}{\sqrt{1+3\cdot 0+0} + 1} = \dfrac{3}{2}$

20. $\lim\limits_{x\to-\infty} (x+\sqrt{x^2+2x}) = \lim\limits_{x\to-\infty} (x+\sqrt{x^2+2x}) \dfrac{x-\sqrt{x^2+2x}}{x-\sqrt{x^2+2x}} = \lim\limits_{x\to-\infty} \dfrac{x^2-(x^2+2x)}{x-\sqrt{x^2+2x}}$

$= \lim\limits_{x\to-\infty} \dfrac{-2x}{x-\sqrt{x^2+2x}} = \lim\limits_{x\to-\infty} \dfrac{-2}{1+\sqrt{1+2/x}} = \dfrac{-2}{1+\sqrt{1+2\cdot 0}} = -1$

Note: In dividing numerator and denominator by x, we used the fact
that, for x<0, $x = -\sqrt{x^2}$.

22. Using $a^3-b^3 = (a-b)(a^2+ab+b^2)$ with $a = \sqrt[3]{1+x}$ and $b = \sqrt[3]{x}$, we have
$\lim\limits_{x\to\infty} (\sqrt[3]{1+x}-\sqrt[3]{x}) = \lim\limits_{x\to\infty} \dfrac{(1+x) - x}{(1+x)^{2/3}+(1+x)^{1/3}x^{1/3}+x^{2/3}}$

$= \lim\limits_{x\to\infty} \dfrac{1}{(1+x)^{2/3}+(1+x)^{1/3}x^{1/3}+x^{2/3}} = 0$

24. If $t = \dfrac{1}{x}$ then $\lim\limits_{x\to\infty} \cos \dfrac{1}{x} = \lim\limits_{t\to 0^+} \cos t = \cos 0 = 1$.

26. If $t = \dfrac{1}{x}$ then $\lim\limits_{x\to\infty} (x - x \cos \dfrac{1}{x}) = \lim\limits_{t\to 0^+}(\dfrac{1}{t} - \dfrac{1}{t} \cos t) = \lim\limits_{t\to 0^+}\dfrac{1 - \cos t}{t}$

$= 0$ by Corollary 3.24.

28. $\lim\limits_{x\to\pm\infty} \dfrac{3x^4+6x^2-x}{2x^4-5x^3+9} = \lim\limits_{x\to\pm\infty} \dfrac{3+(6/x^2)-(1/x^3)}{2-(5/x)+(9/x^4)} = \dfrac{3+0-0}{2-0+0} = \dfrac{3}{2}$ So $y = \dfrac{3}{2}$ is the
horizontal asymptote.

30. $\lim\limits_{x\to\infty} \dfrac{x-9}{\sqrt{4x^2+3x+2}} = \lim\limits_{x\to\infty} \dfrac{1-9/x}{\sqrt{4+(3/x)+(2/x^2)}} = \dfrac{1-0}{\sqrt{4+0+0}} = \dfrac{1}{2}$

$\lim\limits_{x\to-\infty} \dfrac{x-9}{\sqrt{4x^2+3x+2}} = \lim\limits_{x\to-\infty} \dfrac{1-9/x}{-\sqrt{4+(3/x)+(2/x^2)}} = \dfrac{1-0}{-\sqrt{4+0+0}} = -\dfrac{1}{2}$

The horizontal asymptotes are $y = \dfrac{1}{2}$ and $y = -\dfrac{1}{2}$.

32. $\lim\limits_{x\to\pm\infty} \dfrac{2x^2-x+2}{x^2+1} = \lim\limits_{x\to\pm\infty} \dfrac{2-(1/x)+(2/x^2)}{1+1/x^2} = \dfrac{2-0+0}{1+0} = 2$, so $y = 2$ is a

horizontal asymptote. $y' = \dfrac{(x^2+1)(4x-1)-(2x^2-x+2)(2x)}{(x^2+1)^2} = \dfrac{x^2-1}{(x^2+1)^2}$

$y' > 0 \Leftrightarrow x^2 > 1 \Leftrightarrow x > 1$ or $x < -1$ and $y' < 0 \Leftrightarrow -1 < x < 1$, so y
is increasing on $(-\infty,-1]$ and $[1,\infty)$ and decreasing on $[-1,1]$.

$y'' = \dfrac{(x^2+1)^2(2x)-(x^2-1)2(x^2+1)(2x)}{(x^2+1)^4} = \dfrac{2x(3-x^2)}{(x^2+1)^3} > 0 \Leftrightarrow x < -\sqrt{3}$ or

$0 < x < \sqrt{3}$, so y is CU on $(-\infty,-\sqrt{3})$ and $(0,\sqrt{3})$, and CD on $(-\sqrt{3},0)$
and $(\sqrt{3},\infty)$.

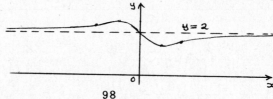

98

34. $\lim\limits_{x\to\pm\infty}\dfrac{1}{x^2+x+1}=\lim\limits_{x\to\pm\infty}\dfrac{1/x^2}{1+(1/x)+(1/x^2)}=\dfrac{0}{1+0+0}=0$, so $y=0$ is a

horizontal asymptote. $y' = -(2x+1)/(x^2+x+1)^2 > 0 \iff 2x+1 < 0 \iff$

$x < -1/2$, and $y' < 0 \iff x > -1/2$, so y is increasing on $(-\infty,-1/2]$

and decreasing on $[-1/2,\infty)$. $y'' = -\dfrac{2(x^2+x+1)^2-(2x+1)2(x^2+x+1)(2x+1)}{(x^2+x+1)^4}$

$= 6x(x+1)/(x^2+x+1)^3 > 0 \iff x < -1$ or $x > 0$, so y is CU on $(-\infty,-1)$

and $(0,\infty)$ and CD on $(-1,0)$.

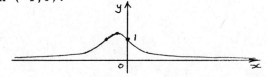

36. (a) Since $-1 \leq \sin x \leq 1$, we have $-\dfrac{1}{x} \leq \dfrac{\sin x}{x} \leq \dfrac{1}{x}$ for $x > 0$. We know

that $\lim\limits_{x\to\infty} -\dfrac{1}{x} = 0 = \lim\limits_{x\to\infty}\dfrac{1}{x}$ so $\lim\limits_{x\to\infty}\dfrac{\sin x}{x} = 0$ by the Squeeze Theorem.

(b)

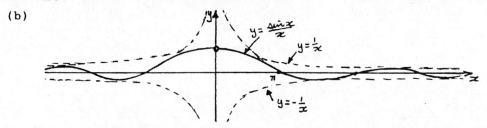

38.

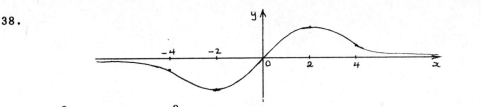

40. $1/x^2 < 0.0001 \iff x^2 > 1/0.0001 = 10000 \iff x > 100 \quad (x > 0)$

42. $1/\sqrt{x} < 0.0001 \iff \sqrt{x} > 1/0.0001 = 10^4 \iff x > 10^8$

44. For $x < 0$, $|1/x - 0| = -1/x$. If $\epsilon > 0$ is given, then $-1/x < \epsilon \iff$

$x < -1/\epsilon$. Take $N = -1/\epsilon$. Then $x < N \implies x < -1/\epsilon \implies |1/x - 0| =$

$-1/x < \epsilon$, so $\lim\limits_{x\to-\infty}\dfrac{1}{x} = 0$.

Exercises 4.6

2. $\lim\limits_{x\to 0} \dfrac{2}{x^4} = \infty$ since $x^4 \to 0$ as $x \to 0$ and $\dfrac{2}{x^4} > 0$

4. $\lim\limits_{x\to 3} \dfrac{1}{(x-3)^8} = \infty$ since $(x-3)^8 \to 0$ as $x \to 3$ and $\dfrac{1}{(x-3)^8} > 0$

6. $\lim\limits_{x\to 5^-} \dfrac{6}{x-5} = -\infty$ since $x-5 \to 0$ as $x \to 5^-$ and $\dfrac{6}{x-5} < 0$ for $x < 5$

8. $\lim\limits_{x\to -6^+} \dfrac{x}{x+6} = -\infty$ since $x+6 \to 0$ as $x \to -6^+$ and $\dfrac{x}{x+6} < 0$ for $-6 < x < 0$

10. $\lim\limits_{x\to 0^+} \dfrac{3}{x^2+2x} = \infty$ since $x^2+2x \to 0$ as $x \to 0^+$ and $\dfrac{3}{x^2+2x} > 0$ for $x > 0$

12. $\lim\limits_{x\to 0} \dfrac{x-1}{x^2(x+2)} = -\infty$ since $x^2(x+2) \to 0$ as $x \to 0$ and $\dfrac{x-1}{x^2(x+2)} < 0$ for

$0 < x < 1$ or $-2 < x < 0$

14. $\lim\limits_{x\to 0^+} \left[\dfrac{1}{x} - \dfrac{1}{x^2}\right] = \lim\limits_{x\to 0^+} \dfrac{x-1}{x^2} = -\infty$ since $x^2 \to 0$ as $x\to 0^+$ and $\dfrac{x-1}{x^2} < 0$ if $x<1$

16. $\lim\limits_{x\to 5^-} \dfrac{2}{\sqrt{5-x}} = \infty$ since $\sqrt{5-x} \to 0$ as $x \to 5^-$ and $\dfrac{2}{\sqrt{5-x}} > 0$

18. $\lim\limits_{x\to 0^+} \cot x = \lim\limits_{x\to 0^+} \dfrac{\cos x}{\sin x} = \infty$ since $\sin x \to 0$ as $x \to 0$ and $\cot x > 0$ for $0 < x < \pi/2$

20. $\lim\limits_{t\to \pi/4^+} \sec 2t = \lim\limits_{t\to \pi/4^+} \dfrac{1}{\cos 2t} = -\infty$ since $\cos 2t \to 0^-$ as $t \to \pi/4^+$

22. $\lim\limits_{x\to \pi} \csc x = \lim\limits_{x\to \pi} \dfrac{1}{\sin x}$ does not exist since $\lim\limits_{x\to \pi^+} \csc x = -\infty$ but

$\lim\limits_{x\to \pi^-} \csc x = \infty$ ($\sin x < 0$ for $\pi < x < 2\pi$; $\sin x > 0$ for $0 < x < \pi$)

24. $\sqrt{x}$ is large when x is large, so $\lim\limits_{x\to\infty} \sqrt{x} = \infty$

26. $\lim\limits_{x\to\infty} (x-\sqrt{x}) = \lim\limits_{x\to\infty} \sqrt{x}(\sqrt{x}-1) = \infty$ since $\sqrt{x} \to \infty$ and $\sqrt{x}-1 \to \infty$ as $x \to \infty$

28. $\lim\limits_{x\to -\infty} (x^3-5x^2) = -\infty$ since $x^3 \to -\infty$ and $-5x^2 \to -\infty$ as $x \to -\infty$

[OR: $\lim\limits_{x\to -\infty} (x^3-5x^2) = \lim\limits_{x\to -\infty} x^2(x-5) = -\infty$ since $x^2 \to \infty$ and $x-5 \to -\infty$]

30. $\lim\limits_{x\to\infty} \dfrac{x^7-1}{x^6-1} = \lim\limits_{x\to\infty} \dfrac{1-1/x^7}{(1/x)-(1/x^7)} = \infty$ since $1-\dfrac{1}{x^7} \to 1$ while $\dfrac{1}{x}-\dfrac{1}{x^7} \to 0^+$ as

$x \to \infty$ [OR: divide numerator and denominator by x^6 instead of x^7]

32. $\lim\limits_{x\to\infty} \dfrac{\sqrt{x}+3}{x+3} = \lim\limits_{x\to\infty} \dfrac{(1/\sqrt{x})+(3/x)}{1+3/x} = \dfrac{0+0}{1+0} = 0$

34. $\lim\limits_{x\to\infty} \dfrac{\sqrt{x}}{\sqrt[3]{x}} = \lim\limits_{x\to\infty} \dfrac{x^{1/2}}{x^{1/3}} = \lim\limits_{x\to\infty} x^{1/6} = \infty$

36. $\lim\limits_{x\to\pm\infty} \dfrac{x}{x+4} = \lim\limits_{x\to\pm\infty} \dfrac{1}{1+4/x} = \dfrac{1}{1+0} = 1$, so $y = 1$ is a horizontal asymptote

$\lim\limits_{x\to-4^-} \dfrac{x}{x+4} = \infty$ and $\lim\limits_{x\to-4^+} \dfrac{x}{x+4} = -\infty$, so $x = -4$ is a vertical asymptote

38. $\lim\limits_{x\to\pm\infty} \dfrac{x^3}{x^2+3x-10} = \lim\limits_{x\to\pm\infty} \dfrac{x}{1+(3/x)-(10/x^2)} = \pm\infty$, so there is no

horizontal asymptote. $\lim\limits_{x\to2^+} \dfrac{x^3}{x^2+3x-10} = \lim\limits_{x\to2^+} \dfrac{x^3}{(x+5)(x-2)} = \infty$, since

$\dfrac{x^3}{(x+5)(x-2)} > 0$ for $x > 2$. Similarly, $\lim\limits_{x\to2^-} \dfrac{x^3}{x^2+3x-10} = -\infty$ and

$\lim\limits_{x\to-5^-} \dfrac{x^3}{x^2+3x-10} = -\infty$, $\lim\limits_{x\to-5^+} \dfrac{x^3}{x^2+3x-10} = \infty$, so $x = 2$ and $x = -5$ are

vertical asymptotes.

40. $\lim\limits_{x\to\pm\infty} \dfrac{x-2}{x+2} = \lim\limits_{x\to\pm\infty} \dfrac{1-2/x}{1+2/x} = \dfrac{1-0}{1+0} = 1$, so $y = 1$ is a horizontal asymptote

$\lim\limits_{x\to-2^+} \dfrac{x-2}{x+2} = -\infty$ and $\lim\limits_{x\to-2^-} \dfrac{x-2}{x+2} = \infty$, so $x = -2$ is a vertical asymptote

$y' = \dfrac{(x+2)\cdot 1 - (x-2)\cdot 1}{(x+2)^2} = \dfrac{4}{(x+2)^2} > 0$ for $x \neq -2$, so y is increasing on

$(-\infty,-2)$ and $(-2,\infty)$. $y'' = -8/(x+2)^3 > 0$ for $x < -2$, so y is CU on

$(-\infty,-2)$ and CD on $(-2,\infty)$.

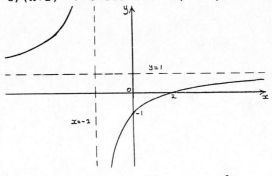

42. $y = f(x) = x/(x+1)^2$ $\lim\limits_{x\to\pm\infty} \dfrac{x}{(x+1)^2} = \lim\limits_{x\to\pm\infty} \dfrac{1/x}{(1+1/x)^2} = \dfrac{0}{(1+0)^2} = 0$

so $y = 0$ is a horizontal asymptote. $\lim\limits_{x\to-1} \dfrac{x}{(x+1)^2} = -\infty$ since

$(x+1)^2 \to 0$ and $y < 0$ for $x < 0$, so $x = -1$ is a vertical asymptote.

$f'(x) = \dfrac{(x+1)^2 - x\cdot 2(x+1)}{(x+1)^4} = \dfrac{1-x}{(x+1)^3}$ so $f'(x) > 0$ if $-1 < x < 1$ and $f'(x) < 0$

if $x > 1$ or $x < -1$. Thus f is increasing on $(-1,1]$ and decreasing on

$(-\infty,-1)$ and $[1,\infty)$. $f(1) = 1/4$ is a local maximum.

$$f''(x) = \frac{(x+1)^3(-1)-(1-x)3(x+1)^2}{(x+1)^6} = \frac{2(x-2)}{(x+1)^4} \Rightarrow f''(x)>0 \text{ for } x>2 \text{ and}$$

$f''(x)<0$ for $x<2$ $(x\neq-1)$, so f is CU on $(2,\infty)$ and CD on $(-\infty,-1)$ and $(-1,2)$. The inflection point is $(2,2/9)$.

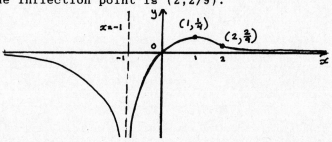

44. (i) $n = 0$ (ii) $n > 0$ (iii) $n > 0$ (iv) $n < 0$ (v) $n < 0$
            n odd   n even   n odd   n even

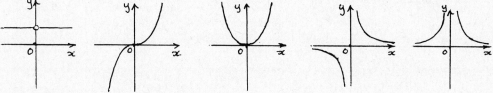

From these sketches we see that

(a) $\lim\limits_{x\to0^+} x^n = \begin{cases} 1 & \text{if } n = 0 \\ 0 & \text{if } n > 0 \\ \infty & \text{if } n < 0 \end{cases}$ (b) $\lim\limits_{x\to0^-} x^n = \begin{cases} 1 & \text{if } n = 0 \\ 0 & \text{if } n > 0 \\ -\infty & \text{if } n < 0, \text{ n odd} \\ \infty & \text{if } n < 0, \text{ n even} \end{cases}$

(c) $\lim\limits_{x\to\infty} x^n = \begin{cases} 1 & \text{if } n = 0 \\ \infty & \text{if } n > 0 \\ 0 & \text{if } n < 0 \end{cases}$ (d) $\lim\limits_{x\to-\infty} x^n = \begin{cases} 1 & \text{if } n = 0 \\ -\infty & \text{if } n > 0, \text{ n odd} \\ \infty & \text{if } n > 0, \text{ n even} \\ 0 & \text{if } n < 0 \end{cases}$

46. (a) $y = \sqrt[3]{x} = x^{1/3}$ is continuous at 0 and $\lim\limits_{x\to0} |y'| = \lim\limits_{x\to0} \frac{1}{3x^{2/3}} = \infty$,

so $y = \sqrt[3]{x}$ has a vertical tangent line at $(0,0)$.

(b) $y = x^{2/3}$ is continuous at 0 and $\lim\limits_{x\to0} |y'| = \lim\limits_{x\to0} \left|\frac{2}{3x^{1/3}}\right| = \infty$, so

$y = x^{2/3}$ has a vertical tangent line at $(0,0)$.

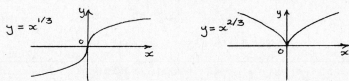

48. Given $M > 0$, we need $\delta > 0$ such that $|x+3| < \delta \Rightarrow 1/(x+3)^4 > M$.

Now $\frac{1}{(x+3)^4} > M \Leftrightarrow (x+3)^4 < \frac{1}{M} \Leftrightarrow |x+3| < \frac{1}{\sqrt[4]{M}}$. So take $\delta = \frac{1}{\sqrt[4]{M}}$.

Then $0 < |x+3| < \delta = \dfrac{1}{\sqrt[4]{M}} \Rightarrow \dfrac{1}{(x+3)^4} > M$, so $\lim\limits_{x \to -3} \dfrac{1}{(x+3)^4} = \infty$.

50. Given $M > 0$, we need $N > 0$ such that $x > N \Rightarrow x^3 > M$. Now $x^3 > M \Longleftrightarrow x > \sqrt[3]{M}$, so take $N = \sqrt[3]{M}$. Then $x > N = \sqrt[3]{M} \Rightarrow x^3 > M$, so $\lim\limits_{x \to \infty} x^3 = \infty$.

52. (a) Let $M > 0$ be given. Since $\lim\limits_{x \to a} g(x) = c > 0$, there exists $\delta_1 > 0$ such that $0 < |x-a| < \delta_1 \Rightarrow |g(x)-c| < \dfrac{c}{2} \Rightarrow g(x) > \dfrac{c}{2}$. Since $\lim\limits_{x \to a} f(x) = \infty$, there exists $\delta_2 > 0$ such that $0 < |x-a| < \delta_2 \Rightarrow f(x) > \dfrac{2M}{c}$. Let $\delta = \min\{\delta_1, \delta_2\}$. Then $0 < |x-a| < \delta \Rightarrow f(x)g(x) > \dfrac{2M}{c}\dfrac{c}{2} = M$, so $\lim\limits_{x \to a} f(x)g(x) = \infty$.

(b) Let $N < 0$ be given. Since $\lim\limits_{x \to a} g(x) = c < 0$, there exists $\delta_1 > 0$ such that $0 < |x-a| < \delta_1 \Rightarrow |g(x)-c| < -\dfrac{c}{2} \Rightarrow g(x) < \dfrac{c}{2}$. Since $\lim\limits_{x \to a} f(x) = \infty$, there exists $\delta_2 > 0$ such that $0 < |x-a| < \delta_2 \Rightarrow f(x) > \dfrac{2N}{c}$. (Note that $c < 0$ and $N < 0 \Rightarrow \dfrac{2N}{c} > 0$.) Let $\delta = \min\{\delta_1, \delta_2\}$. Then $0 < |x-a| < \delta \Rightarrow f(x) > \dfrac{2N}{c} \Rightarrow f(x)g(x) < \dfrac{2N}{c}\dfrac{c}{2} = N$, so $\lim\limits_{x \to a} f(x)g(x) = -\infty$.

Section 4.7

Exercises 4.7

Abbreviations: D : the domain of f,   VA : vertical asymptote(s),
                HA : horizontal asymptote,   IP : inflection point(s)

2. $y = f(x) = x/(x-1)$ A. $D = \{x \mid x \neq 1\} = (-\infty, 1) \cup (1, \infty)$

B. x-intercept = 0, y-intercept = $f(0) = 0$ C. No symmetry

D. $\lim\limits_{x \to \pm\infty} \dfrac{x}{x-1} = 1$, so $y = 1$ is a HA. $\lim\limits_{x \to 1^-} \dfrac{x}{x-1} = -\infty$, $\lim\limits_{x \to 1^+} \dfrac{x}{x-1} = \infty$, so

$x = 1$ is a VA. E. $f'(x) = \dfrac{(x-1)-x}{(x-1)^2} = \dfrac{-1}{(x-1)^2} < 0$ for $x \ne 1$, so f is

decreasing on $(-\infty,1)$ and $(1,\infty)$.   H.

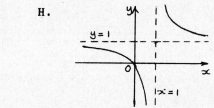

F. No extrema

G. $f''(x) = \dfrac{2}{(x-1)^3} > 0 \Longleftrightarrow x > 1$,

so f is CU on $(1,\infty)$ and CD on

$(-\infty,1)$. No IP.

4. $y = f(x) = x/(x^2-9)$ A. $D = \{x \mid x \ne \pm 3\} = (-\infty,-3) \cup (-3,3) \cup (3,\infty)$

B. x-intercept = 0, y-intercept = $f(0) = 0$ C. $f(-x) = -f(x)$, so f

is odd; the curve is symmetric about the origin.

D. $\displaystyle\lim_{x\to\pm\infty} \frac{x}{x^2-9} = 0$ so $y = 0$ is a HA. $\displaystyle\lim_{x\to 3^+} \frac{x}{x^2-9} = \infty$, $\displaystyle\lim_{x\to 3^-} \frac{x}{x^2-9} = -\infty$,

$\displaystyle\lim_{x\to -3^+} \frac{x}{x^2-9} = \infty$, $\displaystyle\lim_{x\to -3^-} \frac{x}{x^2-9} = -\infty$, so $x = 3$ and $x = -3$ are VA.

E. $f'(x) = \dfrac{(x^2-9)-x(2x)}{(x^2-9)^2} = -\dfrac{x^2+9}{(x^2-9)^2} < 0$ $(x \ne \pm 3)$ so f is decreasing

on $(-\infty,-3)$, $(-3,3)$, and $(3,\infty)$.   F. No extrema

G. $f''(x) = -\dfrac{2x(x^2-9)^2-(x^2+9)\cdot 2(x^2-9)(2x)}{(x^2-9)^4} = \dfrac{2x(x^2+27)}{(x^2-9)^3} > 0$ when

$-3 < x < 0$ or $x > 3$, so f is CU on $(-3,0)$ and $(3,\infty)$; CD on $(-\infty,-3)$

and $(0,3)$. IP is $(0,0)$.

H.

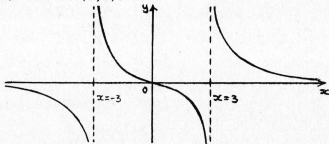

6. $y = f(x) = 4/(x-5)^2$ A. $D = \{x \mid x \ne 5\} = (-\infty,5) \cup (5,\infty)$

B. y-intercept = $f(0) = 4/25$, no x-intercept   C. No symmetry

D. $\displaystyle\lim_{x\to\pm\infty} \frac{4}{(x-5)^2} = 0$, so $y = 0$ is a HA. $\displaystyle\lim_{x\to 5} \frac{4}{(x-5)^2} = \infty$, so $x = 5$ is a VA. E. $f'(x) = -8/(x-5)^3 > 0$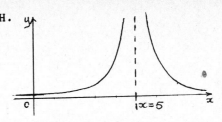

$\Leftrightarrow$ x < 5 and f'(x) < 0 $\Leftrightarrow$ x > 5.

So f is increasing on $(-\infty,5)$ and

decreasing on $(5,\infty)$. F. No extrema

G. $f''(x) = 24/(x-5)^4 > 0$ for $x \neq 5$,

so f is CU on $(-\infty,5)$ and $(5,\infty)$.

8. $y = f(x) = x-1/x$ A. D = {x| x $\neq$ 0} = $(-\infty,0) \cup (0,\infty)$

B. x-intercepts ± 1, no y-intercept C. $f(-x) = -f(x)$, so the curve

is symmetric about the origin. D. $\lim\limits_{x\to\pm\infty} (x-\frac{1}{x}) = \pm\infty$, so no HA. But

$(x-1/x)-x = -1/x \to 0$ as $x \to \pm\infty$, so y = x is a slant asymptote.

Also $\lim\limits_{x\to 0^+}(x-\frac{1}{x}) = -\infty$ and $\lim\limits_{x\to 0^-}(x-\frac{1}{x}) = \infty$, so x = 0 is a VA.

E. $f'(x) = 1+1/x^2 > 0$, so f is   H.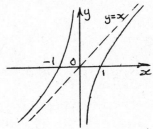

increasing on $(-\infty,0)$ and $(0,\infty)$.

F. No extrema G. $f''(x) = -2/x^3$

$\Rightarrow$ $f''(x) > 0 \Leftrightarrow x < 0$, so f is

CU on $(-\infty,0)$ and CD on $(0,\infty)$.

No IP.

10. $y = f(x) = \dfrac{x^2+x+1}{x} = x+1+\dfrac{1}{x}$ A. D = {x| x $\neq$ 0} = $(-\infty,0) \cup (0,\infty)$

B. No intercepts (x-intercepts occur when $x^2+x+1 = 0$ but this

equation has no real roots since $b^2-4ac = -3 < 0$) C. No symmetry

D. $\lim\limits_{x\to\pm\infty} (x+1+\frac{1}{x}) = \pm\infty$, so no HA. But $(x+1+\frac{1}{x})-(x+1) = \frac{1}{x} \to 0$ as x$\to\pm\infty$,

so y = x+1 is a slant asymptote. Also $\lim\limits_{x\to 0^+}(x+1+\frac{1}{x}) = \infty$, $\lim\limits_{x\to 0^-}(x+1+\frac{1}{x})$

= $-\infty$, so x = 0 is a VA. E. $f'(x) = 1-1/x^2 > 0$ when $x^2>1 \Leftrightarrow$ x>1 or

x<-1; f'(x) < 0 $\Leftrightarrow$ -1<x<1. So f is increasing on $(-\infty,-1]$, $[1,\infty)$ and

decreasing on $[-1,0)$, $(0,1]$.   H.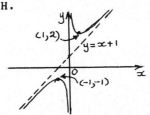

F. f(1) = 3 is a local minimum,

f(-1) = -1 is a local maximum.

G. $f''(x) = 2/x^3 > 0 \Leftrightarrow$ x > 0,

so f is CU on $(0,\infty)$ and CD on

$(-\infty,0)$. No IP.

12. $y = f(x) = x^2/(2x+5)$ A. D = {x| x $\neq$ -5/2} = $(-\infty,-5/2) \cup (-5/2,\infty)$

B. Intercepts are 0 C. No symmetry D. $\lim\limits_{x\to\pm\infty} \dfrac{x^2}{2x+5} = \pm\infty$, so no HA.

$\lim\limits_{x\to-5/2^+}\dfrac{x^2}{2x+5}=\infty$, $\lim\limits_{x\to-5/2^-}\dfrac{x^2}{2x+5}=-\infty$, so $x=-\dfrac{5}{2}$ is a VA. By long

division, $\dfrac{x^2}{2x+5}=\dfrac{1}{2}x-\dfrac{5}{4}+\dfrac{25/4}{2x+5}$, so $\dfrac{x^2}{2x+5}-\left(\dfrac{1}{2}x-\dfrac{5}{4}\right)=\dfrac{25/4}{2x+5}\to 0$ as $x\to\pm\infty$,

so $y=\dfrac{1}{2}x-\dfrac{5}{4}$ is a slant asymptote. E. $f'(x)=\dfrac{2x(x+5)-2x^2}{(2x+5)^2}=\dfrac{2x(x+5)}{(2x+5)^2}$

$\Rightarrow$ $f'(x)>0 \Leftrightarrow x<-5$ or $x>0$; $f'(x)<0 \Leftrightarrow -5<x<0$. So f is

increasing on $(-\infty,-5]$ and $[0,\infty)$, decreasing on $[-5,-5/2)$, $(-5/2,0]$.

F. $f(0)=0$ is a local minimum, $f(-5)=-5$ is a local maximum.

G. $f''(x)=\dfrac{(4x+10)(2x+5)^2-(2x^2+10x)\cdot2(2x+5)(2)}{(2x+5)^4}=\dfrac{50}{(2x+5)^3}>0 \Leftrightarrow$

$x>-5/2$, so f is CU on $(-5/2,\infty)$ H.

and CD on $(-\infty,-5/2)$.   No IP.

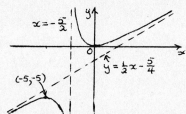

14. $y=f(x)=1/x^2(x+3)$ A. $D=\{x\mid x\neq 0,-3\}=(-\infty,-3)\cup(-3,0)\cup(0,\infty)$

B. No intercepts C. No symmetry D. $\lim\limits_{x\to\pm\infty}\dfrac{1}{x^2(x+3)}=0$, so $y=0$ is

a HA. $\lim\limits_{x\to0}\dfrac{1}{x^2(x+3)}=\infty$ and $\lim\limits_{x\to-3^+}\dfrac{1}{x^2(x+3)}=\infty$, $\lim\limits_{x\to-3^-}\dfrac{1}{x^2(x+3)}=-\infty$,

so $x=0$ and $x=-3$ are VA. E. $f'(x)=-3(x+2)/x^3(x+3)^2>0 \Leftrightarrow$

$-2<x<0$; $f'(x)<0 \Leftrightarrow x<-2$ or $x>0$. So f is increasing on $[-2,0)$ and

decreasing on $(-\infty,-3)$, $(-3,-2]$, and $(0,\infty)$. F. $f(-2)=1/4$ is a

local minimum. G. $f''(x)=-3\dfrac{x^3(x+3)^2-(x+2)[3x^2(x+3)^2+x^32(x+3)]}{x^6(x+3)^4}$

$=\dfrac{6(2x^2+8x+9)}{x^4(x+3)^3}$ Since $2x^2+8x+9>0$ H.

for all x, $f''(x)>0 \Leftrightarrow x>-3$

$(x\neq 0)$, so f is CU on $(-3,0)$

and $(0,\infty)$, and CD on $(-\infty,-3)$.

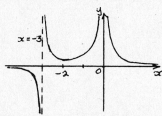

16. $y=f(x)=1/x(4x^2-9)$ A. $D=\{x\mid x\neq0,\pm3/2\}$ B. No intercepts

C. $f(-x)=-f(x)$, so the curve is symmetric about the origin.

D. $\lim\limits_{x\to\pm\infty}\dfrac{1}{x(4x^2-9)}=0$ so $y=0$ is a HA. $\lim\limits_{x\to0^+}\dfrac{1}{x(4x^2-9)}=-\infty$,

$\lim\limits_{x \to 0^-} \dfrac{1}{x(4x^2-9)} = \infty$, $\lim\limits_{x \to 3/2^+} \dfrac{1}{x(4x^2-9)} = \infty$, $\lim\limits_{x \to 3/2^-} \dfrac{1}{x(4x^2-9)} = -\infty$,

$\lim\limits_{x \to -3/2^+} \dfrac{1}{x(4x^2-9)} = \infty$, $\lim\limits_{x \to -3/2^-} \dfrac{1}{x(4x^2-9)} = -\infty$, so $x = 0$, $x = \pm\frac{3}{2}$ are

VA. E. $f'(x) = -\dfrac{12x^2-9}{(4x^3-9x)^2} > 0 \Leftrightarrow x^2 < \frac{3}{4} \Leftrightarrow |x| < \frac{\sqrt{3}}{2} \Leftrightarrow -\frac{\sqrt{3}}{2} < x < \frac{\sqrt{3}}{2}$ and

$f'(x) < 0 \Leftrightarrow x > \sqrt{3}/2$ or $x < -\sqrt{3}/2$, so f is increasing on $[-\sqrt{3}/2,0)$ and

$(0,\sqrt{3}/2]$, and decreasing on $(-\infty,-3/2)$, $(-3/2,-\sqrt{3}/2]$, $[\sqrt{3}/2,3/2)$,

$(3/2,\infty)$. F. $f(-\sqrt{3}/2) = 1/3\sqrt{3}$ is a local minimum, $f(\sqrt{3}/2) = -1/3\sqrt{3}$

is a local maximum. G. $f''(x) = \dfrac{-24x(4x^3-9x)^2+(12x^2-9)^2 2(4x^3-9x)}{(4x^3-9x)^4}$

$= \dfrac{6(32x^4-36x^2+27)}{x^3(4x^2-9)^3}$

H.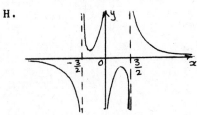

Since $32x^4-36x^2+27 > 0$ for all x,

$f''(x) > 0 \Leftrightarrow -3/2 < x < 0$ or $x > 3/2$,

so f is CU on $(-3/2,0)$, $(3/2,\infty)$

and CD on $(-\infty,-3/2)$, $(0,3/2)$.

18. $y = f(x) = \dfrac{x^3-1}{x} = x^2-\dfrac{1}{x}$ A. $D = \{x \mid x \neq 0\}$ B. x-intercept 1, no

y-intercept C. No symmetry D. $\lim\limits_{x \to \pm\infty} \dfrac{x^3-1}{x} = \infty$, so no HA.

$\lim\limits_{x \to 0^+} \dfrac{x^3-1}{x} = -\infty$ and $\lim\limits_{x \to 0^-} \dfrac{x^3-1}{x} = \infty$, so $x = 0$ is a VA.

E. $f'(x) = 2x+\dfrac{1}{x^2} = \dfrac{2x^3+1}{x^2} > 0 \Leftrightarrow 2x^3+1 > 0 \Leftrightarrow x > -1/\sqrt[3]{2}$ $(x \neq 0)$, so f is

increasing on $[-1/\sqrt[3]{2},0)$ and $(0,\infty)$, and decreasing on $(-\infty,-1/\sqrt[3]{2}]$.

F. $f(-1/\sqrt[3]{2}) = (3/2)\sqrt[3]{2}$ is a local   H.

minimum. G. $f''(x) = 2-\dfrac{2}{x^3} = \dfrac{2(x^3-1)}{x^3}$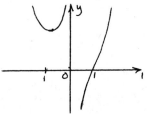

$\Rightarrow$ $f''(x) > 0 \Leftrightarrow x > 1$ or $x < 0$, so

f is CU on $(-\infty,0)$ and $(1,\infty)$ and

CD on $(0,1)$. IP is $(1,0)$.

20. $y = f(x) = 1/(x-1)^2(x+5)$ A. $D = \{x \mid x \neq 1,-5\}$ B. No x-intercept,

y-intercept $= f(0) = 1/5$. C. No symmetry D. $\lim\limits_{x \to \pm\infty} \dfrac{1}{(x-1)^2(x+5)} = 0$

so $y = 0$ is a HA. $\lim\limits_{x \to 1} \dfrac{1}{(x-1)^2(x+5)} = \infty$, $\lim\limits_{x \to -5^+} \dfrac{1}{(x-1)^2(x+5)} = \infty$ and

$\lim\limits_{x\to-5^-} \dfrac{1}{(x-1)^2(x+5)} = -\infty$, so x = 1 and x = -5 are VA. E. f'(x) =

$-\dfrac{2(x-1)(x+5)+(x-1)^2}{(x-1)^4(x+5)^2} = \dfrac{-3(x+3)}{(x-1)^3(x+5)^2} > 0 \iff -3 < x < 1$ and f'(x)<0 $\iff$

x<-3 or x>1 (x≠-5), so f is increasing on [-3,1) and decreasing on

$(-\infty,-5)$, $(-5,-3]$, and $(1,\infty)$. F. f(-3) = 1/32 is a local minimum

G. f"(x) = $(-3)\dfrac{(x-1)^3(x+5)^2-(x+3)[3(x-1)^2(x+5)^2+(x-1)^3 2(x+5)]}{(x-1)^6(x+5)^4}$

$= \dfrac{12(x^2+6x+11)}{(x-1)^4(x+5)^3}$ Since $x^2+6x+11>0$ for all x, f"(x)>0 $\iff$ x>-5 (x≠1),

so f is CU on (-5,1) and (1,∞) and CD on (-∞,-5). No IP.

H.

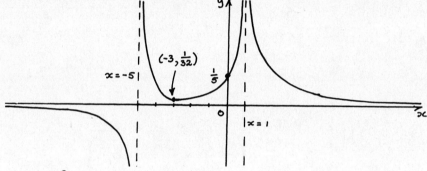

22. y = f(x) = $\dfrac{1-x^2}{x^3} = \dfrac{1}{x^3} - \dfrac{1}{x}$ A. D = {x| x ≠ 0} B. x-intercepts ±1,

no y-intercepts C. f(-x) = -f(x), so the curve is symmetric about

(0,0). D. $\lim\limits_{x\to\pm\infty} \dfrac{1-x^2}{x^3} = 0$ so y = 0 is a HA. $\lim\limits_{x\to0^+} \dfrac{1-x^2}{x^3} = \infty$, $\lim\limits_{x\to0^-} \dfrac{1-x^2}{x^3}$

= -∞, so x = 0 is a VA. E. f'(x) = $-\dfrac{3}{x^4} + \dfrac{1}{x^2} = \dfrac{x^2-3}{x^4} > 0 \iff |x| > \sqrt{3}$,

so f is increasing on $(-\infty,-\sqrt{3}]$, $[\sqrt{3},\infty)$ and decreasing on $[-\sqrt{3},0)$

and $(0,\sqrt{3}]$. F. f($\sqrt{3}$) = $-2/3\sqrt{3}$ is a local minimum, f($-\sqrt{3}$) = $2/3\sqrt{3}$

is a local maximum. H.

G. f"(x) = $\dfrac{12}{x^5} - \dfrac{2}{x^3} = \dfrac{2(6-x^2)}{x^5}$

$\Rightarrow$ f"(x)>0 $\iff$ x<$-\sqrt{6}$ or 0<x<$\sqrt{6}$,

so f is CU on $(-\infty,-\sqrt{6})$, $(0,\sqrt{6})$

and CD on$(-\sqrt{6},0)$ and $(\sqrt{6},\infty)$

IP ($\sqrt{6}$,$-5/6\sqrt{6}$) and ($-\sqrt{6}$,$5/6\sqrt{6}$).

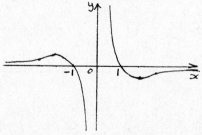

24. $y = f(x) = x\sqrt{x+3}$ A. $D = \{x \mid x \geq -3\} = [-3,\infty)$ B. x-intercepts $0,-3$

y-intercept $= f(0) = 0$ C. No symmetry D. $\lim\limits_{x\to\infty} x\sqrt{x+3} = \infty$, no

asymptote E. $f'(x) = \sqrt{x+3} + \dfrac{x}{2\sqrt{x+3}} = \dfrac{3(x+2)}{2\sqrt{x+3}} > 0 \iff x > -2$ and $f'(x) < 0$

$\iff -3 < x < -2$. So f is increasing on $[-2,\infty)$, decreasing on $[-3,-2]$.

F. $f(-2) = -2$ is a local minimum. H.

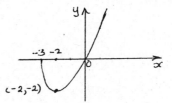

G. $f''(x) = \dfrac{6\sqrt{x+3} - 3(x+2)(1/\sqrt{x+3})}{4(x+3)}$

$= \dfrac{3(x+4)}{4(x+3)^{3/2}} > 0$ for all $x > -3$, so

f is CU on $(-3,\infty)$.

26. $y = f(x) = \sqrt{x} - \sqrt{x-1}$ A. $D = \{x \mid x \geq 0 \text{ and } x \geq 1\} = \{x \mid x \geq 1\} = [1,\infty)$

B. No intercepts C. No symmetry D. $\lim\limits_{x\to\infty} (\sqrt{x} - \sqrt{x-1}) =$

$\lim\limits_{x\to\infty} (\sqrt{x} - \sqrt{x-1}) \dfrac{\sqrt{x} + \sqrt{x-1}}{\sqrt{x} + \sqrt{x-1}} = \lim\limits_{x\to\infty} \dfrac{1}{\sqrt{x} + \sqrt{x-1}} = 0$, so $y = 0$ is a HA

E. $f'(x) = \dfrac{1}{2\sqrt{x}} - \dfrac{1}{2\sqrt{x-1}} < 0$ for all $x > 1$, since $x - 1 < x \Rightarrow \sqrt{x-1} < \sqrt{x}$, so

f is decreasing on $[1,\infty)$. F. No local extrema.

G. $f''(x) = -\dfrac{1}{4}\left[\dfrac{1}{x^{3/2}} - \dfrac{1}{(x-1)^{3/2}}\right]$ H.

$\Rightarrow f''(x) > 0$ for $x > 1$, so f is

CU on $(1,\infty)$.

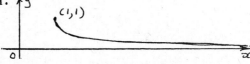

28. $y = f(x) = \sqrt{x/(x-5)}$ A. $D = \{x \mid x/(x-5) \geq 0\} = (-\infty,0] \cup (5,\infty)$

B. Intercepts are 0 C. No symmetry D. $\lim\limits_{x\to\pm\infty} \sqrt{\dfrac{x}{x-5}} = \lim\limits_{x\to\pm\infty} \sqrt{\dfrac{1}{1-5/x}} = 1$

so $y = 1$ is a HA. $\lim\limits_{x\to 5^+} \sqrt{\dfrac{x}{x-5}} = \infty$, so $x = 5$ is a VA.

E. $f'(x) = \dfrac{1}{2}\left[\dfrac{x}{x-5}\right]^{-1/2} \dfrac{-5}{(x-5)^2} = -\dfrac{5}{2}[x(x-5)^3]^{-1/2} < 0$, so f is

decreasing on $(-\infty,0]$ and $(5,\infty)$. F. No local extrema.

G. $f''(x) = (5/4)[x(x-5)^3]^{-3/2}(x-5)^2(4x-5) > 0$ for $x > 5$, and $f''(x) < 0$

for $x < 0$, so f is CU on $(5,\infty)$ and CD on $(-\infty,0)$. No IP.

H.

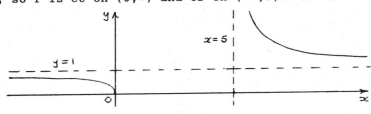

30. $y = f(x) = \sqrt{x}-1/\sqrt{x}$ A. D = {x | x>0} = (0,∞)   B. x-intercept is 1

C. No symmetry   D. $\lim\limits_{x\to\infty} (\sqrt{x} - \dfrac{1}{\sqrt{x}}) = \infty$, no HA. $\lim\limits_{x\to 0^+}(\sqrt{x} - \dfrac{1}{\sqrt{x}}) = -\infty$,

so x = 0 is a VA.   E. $f'(x) = (1/2)x^{-1/2}+(1/2)x^{-3/2} > 0$, so f is

increasing on (0,∞).

F. No extrema

G. $f''(x) = -(1/4)x^{-3/2}-(3/4)x^{-5/2}$

➡ $f''(x)<0$, so f is CD on (-∞,0)

H.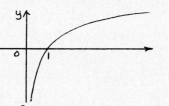

32. $y = f(x) = \sqrt{x-\sqrt{x}}$ A. D = {x | x≥$\sqrt{x}$} = {x | x^2≥x} = {x | x≥1} = [1,∞)

B. x-intercept is 1   C. No symmetry   D. $\lim\limits_{x\to\infty} \sqrt{x-\sqrt{x}} = \infty$, no asymptote

E. $f'(x) = (1/2)(x-\sqrt{x})^{-1/2}[1-(1/2)x^{-1/2}] > 0$ for all x>1, so f is

increasing on [1,∞).   F. No local extrema   G. $f''(x) =$

$-(1/4)(x-\sqrt{x})^{-3/2}[1-(1/2)x^{-1/2}]^2+(1/2)(x-\sqrt{x})^{-1/2}(1/4)x^{-3/2}$

$= (-4x+6\sqrt{x}-3)/16x(x-\sqrt{x})^{3/2} < 0$

since $-4x+6\sqrt{x}-3<0$ (negative

discriminant as a quadratic in $\sqrt{x}$)

So f is CD on (1,∞).

H.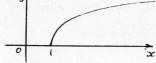

34. $y = f(x) = x^2/\sqrt{1-x^2}$ A. Domain = {x | x^2<1} = (-1,1)

B. x-intercept = 0 = y-intercept   C. f(-x) = f(x), so f is even.

D. $\lim\limits_{x\to 1^-} \dfrac{x^2}{\sqrt{1-x^2}} = \infty = \lim\limits_{x\to -1^+} \dfrac{x^2}{\sqrt{1-x^2}}$ so x = ±1 are vertical asymptotes.

E. $f'(x) = \dfrac{2x\sqrt{1-x^2}-x^2(-x/\sqrt{1-x^2})}{1-x^2} = \dfrac{x(2-x^2)}{(1-x^2)^{3/2}}$ Since $2-x^2$>0 and

$(1-x^2)^{3/2}$>0, f'(x)>0 if 0<x<1 and f'(x)<0 if -1<x<0, so f is

increasing on [0,1), decreasing on (-1,0].   F. Local min: f(0) = 0

G. $f''(x) = \dfrac{(1-x^2)^{3/2}(2-3x^2)-(2x-x^3)(3/2)(1-x^2)^{1/2}(-2x)}{(1-x^2)^3} = \dfrac{x^2+2}{(1-x^2)^{5/2}}$

f''(x)>0 for all x, so f is CU on (-1,1)

H.

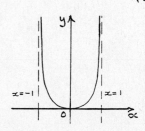

36. $y = f(x) = (2x+1)/\sqrt{3x^2+4}$ A. $D = (-\infty,\infty)$ B. x-intercept $= -1/2$,
    y-intercept $= f(0) = \frac{1}{2}$ C. No symmetry D. $\lim\limits_{x\to\pm\infty} \dfrac{2x+1}{\sqrt{3x^2+4}} = \pm\dfrac{2}{\sqrt{3}}$, so

    $y = 2/\sqrt{3}$ and $y = -2/\sqrt{3}$ are HA. E. $f'(x) =$

    $\dfrac{2\sqrt{3x^2+4} - (2x+1)(3x/\sqrt{3x^2+4})}{3x^2+4} = \dfrac{8-3x}{(3x^2+4)^{3/2}} > 0 \Longleftrightarrow x < \dfrac{8}{3}$ and $f'(x) < 0$

    $\Longleftrightarrow x>8/3$. So f is increasing on $(-\infty,8/3]$ and decreasing on $[8/3,\infty)$.
    F. $f(8/3) = (1/2)\sqrt{19/3} \approx 1.26$ is a local maximum

    G. $f''(x) = \dfrac{-3(3x^2+4)^{3/2}-(8-3x)(3/2)(3x^2+4)^{1/2}\cdot 6x}{(3x^2+4)^3} = \dfrac{6(3x^2-12x-2)}{(3x^2+4)^{5/2}}$

    The roots of $3x^2-12x-2 = 0$ are   H.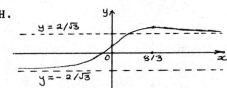
    $2\pm\sqrt{42}/3 = \alpha, \beta$. $f''(x)>0 \Longleftrightarrow x>\alpha$
    or $x<\beta$, so f is CU on $(-\infty,\beta)$ and
    (α,∞), and CD on (β,α).
    IP when $x = \alpha$ and β.

38. $y = f(x) = x^{5/3}-5x^{2/3} = x^{2/3}(x-5)$ A. $D = R$. B. x-intercepts 0, 5,
    y-intercept 0 C. No symmetry D. $\lim\limits_{x\to\pm\infty} x^{2/3}(x-5) = \pm\infty$, so no

    asymptote. E. $f'(x) = \dfrac{5}{3}x^{2/3}-\dfrac{10}{3}x^{-1/3} = \dfrac{5}{3}x^{-1/3}(x-2) > 0 \Longleftrightarrow x<0$ or

    $x>2$, so f is increasing on $(-\infty,0]$, $[2,\infty)$ and decreasing on $[0,2]$.
    F. $f(0) = 0$ is a local maximum.   H.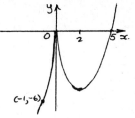
    $f(2) = -3\sqrt[3]{4}$ is a local minimum.
    G. $f''(x) = (10/9)x^{-1/3}+(10/9)x^{-4/3}$
    $= (10/9)x^{-4/3}(x+1) > 0 \Longleftrightarrow x>-1$,
    so f is CU on $(-1,0)$ and $(0,\infty)$,
    CD on $(-\infty,-1)$. IP $(-1,-6)$.

40. $y = f(x) = (x^2-1)^{2/3}$ A. $D = R$ B. x-intercepts ±1, y-intercept 1
    C. $f(-x) = f(x)$, so the curve is symmetric about the y-axis.
    D. $\lim\limits_{x\to\pm\infty} (x^2-1)^{2/3} = \infty$, no asymptote. E. $f'(x) = \dfrac{4}{3}x(x^2-1)^{-1/3} \Rightarrow$

    $f'(x)>0 \Longleftrightarrow x>1$ or $-1<x<0$, $f'(x)<0 \Longleftrightarrow x<-1$ or $0<x<1$. So f is
    increasing on $[-1,0]$, $[1,\infty)$ and decreasing on $(-\infty,-1]$, $[0,1]$.
    F. $f(-1) = f(1) = 0$ are local minima, $f(0) = 1$ is a local maximum.

G. $f''(x) = (4/3)(x^2-1)^{-1/3}$
$+ (4/3)x(-1/3)(x^2-1)^{-4/3}(2x)$
$= (4/9)(x^2-3)(x^2-1)^{-4/3} > 0 \iff$
$|x|>3$ so f is CU on $(-\infty,-\sqrt{3})$, $(\sqrt{3},\infty)$
and CD on $(-\sqrt{3},-1)$, $(-1,1)$, $(1,\sqrt{3})$.
IP $(\pm\sqrt{3},\sqrt[3]{4})$.

H.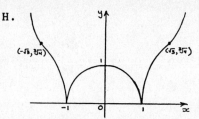

42. $y = f(x) = \sin x + \cos x$ A. $D = R$ B. y-intercept $= f(0) = 1$,
x-intercepts occur when $\sin x = -\cos x \iff \tan x = -1 \iff$
$x = n\pi+3\pi/4$ (n an integer).   C. $f(x+2\pi) = f(x)$, so f is periodic
with period 2π.   So in what follows we consider only $0 \leq x \leq 2\pi$ and
extend the graph by periodicity in H.   D. No asymptote
E. $f'(x) = \cos x - \sin x > 0$ when $\cos x > \sin x \iff 0 \leq x < \pi/4$ or
$5\pi/4 < x \leq 2\pi$, $f'(x)<0 \iff \pi/4 < x < 5\pi/4$, so f is increasing on $[0,\pi/4]$,
$[5\pi/4,2\pi]$ and decreasing on $[\pi/4,5\pi/4]$.   F. $f(\pi/4) = \sqrt{2}$ is a local
maximum, $f(5\pi/4) = -\sqrt{2}$ is a local minimum.
G. $f''(x) = -\sin x - \cos x > 0 \iff 3\pi/4 < x < 7\pi/4$, so f is CU on
$(3\pi/4,7\pi/4)$ and CD on $(0,3\pi/4)$ and $(7\pi/4,2\pi)$. IP $(3\pi/4,0)$, $(7\pi/4,0)$

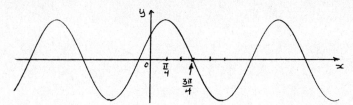

44. $y = f(x) = \sin x + \sqrt{3} \cos x$ A. $D = R$ Note: f is periodic with
period 2π, so we determine B-G on $[0,2\pi]$.   B. y-intercept $= \sqrt{3}$,
x-intercepts occur when $\sin x = -\sqrt{3} \cos x \iff \tan x = -\sqrt{3} \iff$
$x = 2\pi/3$, $5\pi/3$.   C. No symmetry other than periodicity.   D. No
asymptote   E. $f'(x) = \cos x - \sqrt{3} \sin x = 0$ when $\cos x = \sqrt{3} \sin x \iff$
$\tan x = 1/\sqrt{3} \iff x = \pi/6$ or $7\pi/6$. $f'(x)>0 \iff 0 \leq x < \pi/6$ or $7\pi/6 < x \leq 2\pi$,
$f'(x)<0 \iff \pi/6 < x < 7\pi/6$.   So f is increasing on $[0,\pi/6]$, $[7\pi/6,2\pi]$,
and decreasing on $[\pi/6,7\pi/6]$.   F. $f(\pi/6) = 2$ is a local maximum,
$f(7\pi/6) = -2$ is a local minimum.   G. $f''(x) = -\sin x - \sqrt{3} \cos x = 0$
when $\tan x = -\sqrt{3} \iff x = 2\pi/3$, $5\pi/3$. $f''(x)>0 \iff 2\pi/3 < x < 5\pi/3$, so f
is CU on $(2\pi/3,5\pi/3)$ and CD on $(0,2\pi/3)$ and $(5\pi/3,2\pi)$. IP $(2\pi/3,0)$,
$(5\pi/3,0)$.

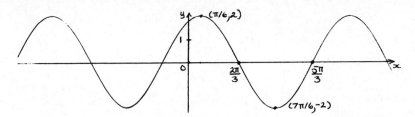

46. $y = f(x) = 2x + \cot x$, $0 < x < \pi$ A. D = $(0, \pi)$ B. No y-intercept
C. No symmetry D. $\lim_{x \to 0^+}(2x + \cot x) = \infty$, $\lim_{x \to \pi^-}(2x + \cot x) = -\infty$, so
$x = 0$ and $x = \pi$ are VA. E. $f'(x) = 2 - \csc^2 x > 0$ when $\csc^2 x < 2 \Leftrightarrow$
$\sin x > 1/\sqrt{2} \Leftrightarrow \pi/4 < x < 3\pi/4$, so f is increasing on $[\pi/4, 3\pi/4]$ and
decreasing on $(0, \pi/4]$ and $[3\pi/4, \pi)$. F. $f(\pi/4) = 1 + \pi/2$ is a local
minimum, $f(3\pi/4) = (3\pi/2) - 1$ is a   H.
local maximum.

G. $f''(x) = -2 \csc x(-\csc x \cot x)$
$= 2 \csc^2 x \cot x > 0 \Leftrightarrow \cot x > 0$
$\Leftrightarrow 0 < x < \pi/2$, so f is CU on $(0, \pi/2)$,
CD on $(\pi/2, \pi)$. IP $(\pi/2, \pi)$

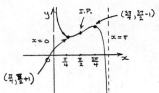

48. $y = f(x) = 2 \sin x + \sin^2 x$ A. D = R Note: f is periodic with
period 2π, so we determine B-G on $[0, 2\pi]$. B. y-intercept =
0, x-intercepts occur when $2 \sin x (2 + \sin x) = 0 \Leftrightarrow \sin x = 0 \Leftrightarrow x$
$= 0$, π, 2π. C. No symmetry other than periodicity. D. No asymptote
E. $f'(x) = 2 \cos x + 2 \sin x \cos x = 2 \cos x (1 + \sin x) > 0 \Leftrightarrow$
$\cos x > 0 \Leftrightarrow 0 < x < \pi/2$ or $3\pi/2 < x < 2\pi$, so f is increasing on $[0, \pi/2]$,
$[3\pi/2, 2\pi]$ and decreasing on $[\pi/2, 3\pi/2]$. F. $f(\pi/2) = 3$ is a local
maximum, $f(3\pi/2) = -1$ is a local minimum.

G. $f''(x) = -2 \sin x + 2 \cos^2 x - 2 \sin^2 x = 2(-\sin x + 1 - 2 \sin^2 x)$
$= 2(1 + \sin x)(1 - 2 \sin x) > 0 \Leftrightarrow 1 - 2 \sin x > 0 \Leftrightarrow \sin x < 1/2$
$\Leftrightarrow 0 \le x < \pi/6$ or $5\pi/6 < x \le 2\pi$. So f is CU on $(0, \pi/6)$, $(5\pi/6, 2\pi)$, and CD
on $(\pi/6, 5\pi/6)$. IP $(\pi/6, 5/4)$ and $(5\pi/6, 5/4)$.

H.

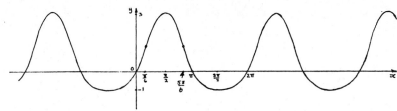

50. $f(x) = \sin x - x$ A. Domain = R   B. x-intercept = 0 = y-intercept
C. $f(-x) = \sin(-x) - (-x) = -(\sin x - x) = -f(-x)$, so f is odd.
D. No asymptotes.   E. $f'(x) = \cos x - 1 \leq 0$ for all x, so f is
decreasing on $(-\infty,\infty)$.   F. No local extrema.   G. $f''(x) = -\sin x$
$\Rightarrow f''(x) > 0 \iff \sin x < 0 \iff$ H.
$(2n-1)\pi < x < 2n\pi$, so f is CU on
$((2n-1)\pi, 2n\pi)$, n an integer,
and CD on $(2n\pi, (2n+1)\pi)$.
Points of inflection occur
when $x = n\pi$.

52. $y = f(x) = \cos x / (2 + \sin x)$ A. D = R   Note: f is periodic with
period 2π, so we determine B-G on $[0, 2\pi]$. B. x-intercepts: $\pi/2, 3\pi/2$
y-intercept = $f(0) = 1/2$ C. No symmetry other than periodicity.
D. No asymptote   E. $f'(x) = \dfrac{(2 + \sin x)(-\sin x) - \cos x (\cos x)}{(2 + \sin x)^2}$
$= -\dfrac{2 \sin x + 1}{(2 + \sin x)^2} \Rightarrow f'(x) > 0 \iff 2 \sin x + 1 < 0 \iff \sin x < -1/2 \iff$
$7\pi/6 < x < 11\pi/6$, so f is increasing on $[7\pi/6, 11\pi/6]$ and decreasing on
$[0, 7\pi/6]$, $[11\pi/6, 2\pi]$. F. $f(7\pi/6) = -1/\sqrt{3}$ is a local min,
$f(11\pi/6) = 1/\sqrt{3}$ is a local max.
G. $f''(x) = -\dfrac{(2 + \sin x)^2 (2 \cos x) - (2 \sin x + 1)2(2 + \sin x)\cos x}{(2 + \sin x)^4}$
$= -\dfrac{2 \cos x (1 - \sin x)}{(2 + \sin x)^3} > 0 \iff \cos x < 0 \iff \pi/2 < x < 3\pi/2$, so f is CU
on $(\pi/2, 3\pi/2)$ and CD on $(0, \pi/2)$ and $(3\pi/2, 2\pi)$. IP $(\pi/2, 0)$, $(3\pi/2, 0)$
H.

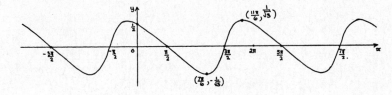

Exercises 4.8

2. The two numbers are x+100 and x. Minimize $f(x) = (x+100)x$
$= x^2+100x$. $f'(x) = 2x+100 = 0 \Rightarrow x = -50$. Since $f''(x) = 2 > 0$,
there is an absolute minimum at $x = -50$. The two numbers are 50
and -50.

4. The two numbers are x and 100-x. Minimize $f(x) = x^2+(100-x)^2$ where
$0 \leq x \leq 100$. $f'(x) = 2x+2(100-x)(-1) = 4x-200 = 0 \Rightarrow x = 50$.
$f(0) = f(100) = 100^2 > 2(50)^2 = f(50)$. So the absolute minimum is
at $x = 50$ and the two numbers are 50 and 50.

6. Let the rectangle have sides x and y and area A, so A = xy or y
= A/x. The problem is to minimize the perimeter = 2x+2y = 2x+2A/x
= P(x). Now $P'(x) = 2-2A/x^2 = 2(x^2-A)/x^2$. So the critical number
is $x = \sqrt{A}$. Since $P'(x) < 0$ for $0 < x < \sqrt{A}$ and $P'(x) > 0$ for $x >$
$\sqrt{A}$, there is an absolute minimum at $x = \sqrt{A}$. The sides of the
rectangle are $\sqrt{A}$ and $A/\sqrt{A} = \sqrt{A}$, so the rectangle is a square.

8.

$xy = 1.5 \times 10^6$, so $y = 1.5 \times 10^6/x$
Minimize the amount of fencing which
is $3x+2y = 3x+2(1.5 \times 10^6/x)$
$= 3x+3 \times 10^6/x = F(x)$. $F'(x)$
$= 3-3 \times 10^6/x^2 = 3(x^2-10^6)/x^2$. The

critical number is $x = 10^3$ and $F'(x) < 0$ for $0 < x < 10^3$ and $F'(x)$
> 0 if $x > 10^3$, so the absolute minimum occurs when $x = 10^3$ and
$y = 1.5 \times 10^3$. The field should be 1000 feet by 1500 feet with the
middle fence parallel to the short side of the field.

10. Let b be the base of the box and h be its height, so $32,000 = hb^2$
or $h = 32,000/b^2$. The surface area of the open box is b^2+4hb
$= b^2+4(32,000/b^2)b = b^2+4(32,000)/b$. So $V'(b) = 2b-4(32,000)/b^2$
$= 2(b^3-64,000)/b^2 = 0 \iff b = \sqrt[3]{64,000} = 40$. This gives an
absolute minimum since $V'(b) < 0$ if $b < 40$ and $V'(b) > 0$ if $b > 40$.
The box should be 40 × 40 × 20.

12.

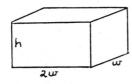

$10 = (2w)(w)h = 2w^2h$ so $h = 5/w^2$.
The cost is $10(2w^2)+6[2(2wh)+2hw] =$
$20w^2+36wh$, so $C(w) = 20w^2+36w(5/w^2)$
$= 20w^2+180/w$. $C'(w) = 40w-180/w^2$
$= 40(w^3-9/2)/w^2 \Rightarrow w = \sqrt[3]{9/2}$ is the

critical number. There is an absolute minimum for $w = \sqrt[3]{9/2}$ since
$C'(w) < 0$ for $0 < w < \sqrt[3]{9/2}$ and $C'(w) > 0$ for $w > \sqrt[3]{9/2}$. $C(\sqrt[3]{9/2})$
$= 20(\sqrt[3]{9/2})^2 + 180/\sqrt[3]{9/2} \approx \$163.54$.

14.

$V(x) = x(3-2x)^2 = x(4x^2-12x+9)$
$= 4x^3-12x^2+9x$. $V'(x) = 12x^2-24x+9$
$= 3(4x^2-8x+3) = 3(2x-1)(2x-3)$, so
the critical numbers are $x = 1/2$,
$x = 3/2$. Now $0 \leq x \leq 3/2$ and

$V(0) = V(3/2) = 0$, so the maximum is $V(1/2) = (1/2)(2)^2 = 2$ ft^3.

16. Here $y = -(2/3)x-5/3$. Let (x,y) be on the line, so the square of
its distance from $(-1,-2)$ is $D(x) = (x+1)^2+[-(2/3)x-(5/3)+2]^2$
$= (13x^2+14x+10)/9$. $D'(x) = (26x+14)/9 = 0 \Rightarrow x = -7/13$. Since
there is a point closest to $(-1,-2)$, we must have $x = -7/13 \Rightarrow$
$y = -17/13$, so the point is $(-7/13,-17/13)$.

18. The square of the distance from a point (x,y) on the parabola
$x = -y^2$ is $x^2+(y+3)^2 = y^4+y^2+6y+9 = D(y)$. Now $D'(y) = 4y^3+2y+6$
$= 2(y+1)(2y^2-2y+3)$. Since $2y^2-2y+3 = 0$ has no real roots, $y = -1$
is the only critical number. Then $x = -(-1)^2 = -1$, so the point is
$(-1,-1)$.

20.

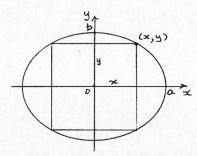

Area is $4xy$. Now the equation of
the ellipse gives $y = (b/a)\sqrt{a^2-x^2}$,
so we maximize $A(x) = 4(b/a)x\sqrt{a^2-x^2}$.
$A'(x) = \dfrac{4b}{a}\sqrt{a^2-x^2} + \dfrac{4bx}{a}\left[-\dfrac{2x}{2\sqrt{a^2-x^2}}\right] =$
$\dfrac{4b}{a\sqrt{a^2-x^2}}\left[a^2-2x^2\right]$.

So the critical number is $x = a/\sqrt{2}$, and this clearly gives a
maximum. Then $y = b/\sqrt{2}$, so the maximum area is $4(a/\sqrt{2})(b/\sqrt{2}) = 2ab$.

22.

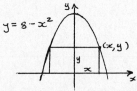

The rectangle has area $A(x) = 2xy$
$= 2x(8-x^2) = 16x-2x^3$, where $0 \leq x \leq 2\sqrt{2}$.
Now $A'(x) = 16-6x^2 = 0 \Rightarrow x = 2\sqrt{2}/3$.
Since $A(0) = A(2\sqrt{2}) = 0$, there is a
maximum when $x = 2\sqrt{2}/3$.

Then $y = 16/3$, so the rectangle has dimensions $4\sqrt{2}/3$ and $16/3$.

24.

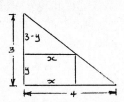

The rectangle has area xy. By similar triangles $\frac{3-y}{x} = \frac{3}{4}$ ⟹ $-4y+12 = 3x$ or $y = -(3/4)x+3$. So the area is $A(x) = x[-(3/4)x+3] = -(3/4)x^2+3x$ where $0 \le x \le 4$. Now $0 = A'(x) = -(3/2)x+3$ ⟹ $x = 2$. Since $A(0) = A(4) = 0$, the maximum area is $A(2) = 2(3/2) = 3$ cm^2.

26.

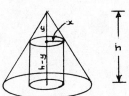

By similar triangles $y/x = h/r$, so $y = hx/r$. The volume of the cylinder is $\pi x^2(h-y) = \pi hx^2-(\pi h/r)x^3 = V(x)$. Now $V'(x) = 2\pi hx-(3\pi h/r)x^2 = \pi hx(2-3x/r)$. So $0 = V'(x)$ ⟹ $x = 0$ or $x = 2r/3$. The maximum clearly occurs when $x = 2r/3$ and then the volume is $\pi(2r/3)^2h(1-2/3) = 4\pi r^2h/27$.

28.

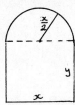

Given that $2y+x+\pi\frac{x}{2} = 30$, so $y = \frac{1}{2}\left[30-x-\frac{\pi x}{2}\right]$. The area is $xy+\frac{1}{2}\pi\left(\frac{x}{2}\right)^2$, so $A(x) = x\left[15-\frac{x}{2}-\frac{\pi x}{4}\right]+\frac{1}{8}\pi x^2$ $= 15x - \frac{1}{2}x^2 - \frac{\pi}{8}x^2$.

$A'(x) = 15-(1+\pi/4)x = 0$ ⟹ $x = 15/(1+\pi/4) = 60/(4+\pi)$. Clearly this gives a maximum, so the dimensions are $x = 60/(4+\pi)$ ft and $y = 15 - \frac{30}{4+\pi} - \frac{15\pi}{4+\pi} = \frac{30}{4+\pi}$ ft.

30.

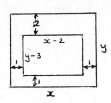

$xy = 180$, so $y = 180/x$. The printed area is $(x-2)(y-3) = (x-2)(\frac{180}{x}-3)$ $= 186-3x-360/x = A(x)$. $A'(x) = -3+360/x^2 = 0$ when $x^2 = 120$ ⟹ $x = 2\sqrt{30}$. This gives an absolute maximum since $A'(x)>0$ for $0<x<2\sqrt{30}$ and $A'(x)<0$ for $x>2\sqrt{30}$. When $x = 2\sqrt{30}$, $y = 180/2\sqrt{30}$, so the dimensions are $2\sqrt{30}$ in. and $90/\sqrt{30}$ in.

32.

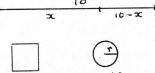

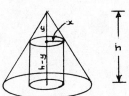

$r = \frac{10-x}{2\pi}$

Total area is $A(x) = \left(\frac{x}{4}\right)^2 + \pi\left[\frac{10-x}{2\pi}\right]^2$ $= \frac{x^2}{16} + \frac{(10-x)^2}{4\pi}$, $0 \le x \le 10$.

$A'(x) = \frac{x}{8} - \frac{10-x}{2\pi} = \left[\frac{1}{2\pi} + \frac{1}{8}\right]x - \frac{5}{\pi} = 0$ ⟹ $x = 40/(4+\pi)$. $A(0) = 25/\pi \approx 7.96$

117

$A(10) = 6.25$, $A(40/(4+\pi)) \approx 3.5$, so the maximum occurs when $x = 0$ and the minimum when $x = 40/(4+\pi)$ m.

34.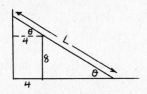

$L = 8 \csc \theta + 4 \sec \theta$, $0 < \theta < \pi/2$

$\dfrac{dL}{d\theta} = - 8 \csc \theta \cot \theta + 4 \sec \theta \tan \theta$

$= 0$ when $\sec \theta \tan \theta = 2 \csc \theta \cot \theta$

$\Leftrightarrow \tan^3 \theta = 2 \Leftrightarrow \tan \theta = \sqrt[3]{2} \Leftrightarrow$

$\theta = \tan^{-1}(\sqrt[3]{2})$. $dL/d\theta < 0$ when

$0 < \theta < \tan^{-1}(\sqrt[3]{2})$, $dL/d\theta > 0$ when $\tan^{-1}(\sqrt[3]{2}) < \theta < \pi/2$, so L has an absolute minimum when $\theta = \tan^{-1}(\sqrt[3]{2})$ and the shortest ladder has length

$L = 8(\sqrt{1+2^{2/3}}/2^{1/3}) + 4\sqrt{1+2^{2/3}} \approx 16.65$ ft.

[Another method:

Minimize $L^2 = x^2 + (4+y)^2$,

where $\dfrac{x}{4+y} = \dfrac{8}{y}$.]

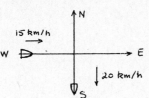

36. $v = K\sqrt{(L/C)+(C/L)} \Rightarrow dv/dL = \dfrac{K}{2\sqrt{(L/C)+(C/L)}} \left[\dfrac{1}{C} - \dfrac{C}{L^2}\right] = 0 \Leftrightarrow \dfrac{1}{C} = \dfrac{C}{L^2}$

$\Leftrightarrow L^2 = C^2 \Leftrightarrow L = C$. This gives the minimum velocity since $v' < 0$ for $0 < L < C$ and $v' > 0$ for $L > C$.

38.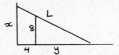

Let t be the time, in hours, after 2:00 PM. The position of the boat heading south at time t is $(0, -20t)$. The position of the boat heading east at time t is $(-15+15t, 0)$.

If $D(t)$ is the distance between the boats at time t, we minimize $f(t) = [D(t)]^2 = 20^2 t^2 + 15^2(t-1)^2$. $f'(t) = 800t + 450(t-1)$ $= 1250t - 450 = 0$ when $t = 450/1250 = .36$. Since $f''(t) > 0$, this gives a minimum. The boats are closest together at 2:21:36 PM.

40. Here $T(x) = \dfrac{\sqrt{x^2+25}}{6} + \dfrac{5-x}{8}$, $0 \le x \le 5$, $\Rightarrow T'(x) = \dfrac{x}{6\sqrt{x^2+25}} - \dfrac{1}{8} = 0 \Leftrightarrow$

$8x = 6\sqrt{x^2+25} \Leftrightarrow 16x^2 = 9(x^2+25) \Leftrightarrow x = 15/\sqrt{7}$. But $15/\sqrt{7} > 5$, so T has no critical number. Since $T(0) \approx 1.46$ and $T(5) \approx 1.18$, he should row directly to B.

42.

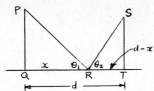

If $d = |QT|$, we minimize $f(x) = |PR| + |RS| = x \sec\theta_1 + (d-x)\sec\theta_2$

$f'(x) = \sec\theta_1 - \sec\theta_2 = 0 \iff \theta_1 = \theta_2$

since $0 < \theta_1 < \theta_2 < \pi/2$. So the shortest rope occurs when $\theta_1 = \theta_2$.

44.

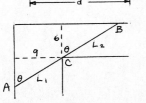

Paradoxically, we solve this maximum problem by solving a minimum problem. Let L be the length of the line ACB going from wall to wall touching the inner corner C. As $\theta \to 0$ or $\theta \to \pi/2$, we have $L \to \infty$ and there will be an angle that makes L a minimum. A pipe of this length will just fit around the corner. From the diagram, $L = L_1 + L_2 = 9 \csc\theta + 6 \sec\theta \Rightarrow dL/d\theta = -9 \csc\theta \cot\theta + 6 \sec\theta \tan\theta = 0$ when $6 \sec\theta \tan\theta = 9 \csc\theta \cot\theta \iff \tan^3\theta = 9/6 = 1.5 \iff \tan\theta = \sqrt[3]{1.5}$. Then $\csc^2\theta = 1 + (3/2)^{-2/3}$ and $\sec^2\theta = 1 + (3/2)^{2/3}$, so the longest pipe has length $L = 9(1 + (3/2)^{-2/3})^{1/2} + 6(1 + (3/2)^{2/3})^{1/2} \approx 21.07$ ft. [Or, use $\theta = \tan^{-1}(\sqrt[3]{1.5}) \approx .852 \Rightarrow L = 9 \csc\theta + 6 \sec\theta \approx 21.07.$]

46.

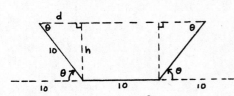

We maximize the cross-sectional area

$A(\theta) = 10h + 2[(1/2)dh] = 10h + dh$

$= 10(10 \sin\theta) + (10 \cos\theta)(10 \sin\theta)$

$= 100(\sin\theta + \sin\theta \cos\theta)$, $0 \le \theta \le \pi/2$.

$A'(\theta) = 100(\cos\theta + \cos^2\theta - \sin^2\theta)$

$= 100(\cos\theta + 2\cos^2\theta - 1) = 100(2\cos\theta - 1)(\cos\theta + 1) = 0$ when $\cos\theta = 1/2 \iff \theta = \pi/3$. [$\cos\theta \ne -1$ since $0 \le \theta \le \pi/2$.] Now $A(0) = 0$, $A(\pi/2) = 100$ and $A(\pi/3) = 100 \cdot 3\sqrt{3}/4 > 100$, so the maximum occurs when $\theta = \pi/3$.

48. (a) $|BC|/b = \cot\theta$, so $|BC| = b \cot\theta \Rightarrow |AB| = a - b \cot\theta$.

$|BD|/b = \csc\theta \Rightarrow |BD| = b \csc\theta$. The total resistance is

$R(\theta) = C \dfrac{|AB|}{r_1^4} + C \dfrac{|BD|}{r_2^4} = C\left[\dfrac{a - b\cot\theta}{r_1^4} + \dfrac{b\csc\theta}{r_2^4}\right]$

(b) $R'(\theta) = C\left[\dfrac{b \csc^2\theta}{r_1^4} - \dfrac{b \csc\theta \cot\theta}{r_2^4}\right] = bC \csc\theta \left[\dfrac{\csc\theta}{r_1^4} - \dfrac{\cot\theta}{r_2^4}\right]$

$R'(\theta) = 0 \iff \dfrac{\csc\theta}{r_1^4} = \dfrac{\cot\theta}{r_2^4} \iff \dfrac{r_2^4}{r_1^4} = \dfrac{\cot\theta}{\csc\theta} = \cos\theta \qquad R'(\theta) > 0 \iff$

$\dfrac{\csc\theta}{r_1^4} > \dfrac{\cot\theta}{r_2^4} \iff \cos\theta < \dfrac{r_2^4}{r_1^4}$ and $R'(\theta)<0$ when $\cos\theta < \dfrac{r_2^4}{r_1^4}$ so there is

an absolute minimum when $\cos\theta = r_2^4/r_1^4$

(c) When $r_2 = (2/3)r_1$, we have $\cos\theta = (2/3)^4$, so $\theta = \cos^{-1}(2/3)^4 \approx 79°$.

Section 4.9

Exercises 4.9

2. (a) $C(x) = 1600+8x+0.01x^2$, $C(1000) = \$19600$. $c(x) = \dfrac{1600}{x} + 8 + 0.01x$, $c(1000) = \$19.60$. $C'(x) = 8+0.02x$, $C'(1000) = \$28$.
(b) We must have $C'(x) = c(x)$ or $8+0.02x = \dfrac{1600}{x} + 8 + 0.01x$ or $0.01x = \dfrac{1600}{x}$ or $x^2 = \dfrac{1600}{.01} = 160000$ or $x = 400$. This is a minimum since $c''(x) = 3200/x^3 > 0$ for $x > 0$. (c) The minimum average cost is $c(400) = \$16$.

4. (a) $C(x) = 2000+10x+.001x^3$. $C(1000) = \$1012000$. $c(x) = \dfrac{2000}{x} + 10 + .001x^2$, $c(1000) = \$1012$. $C'(x) = 10+.003x^2$, $C'(1000) = \$3010$.
(b) We must have $C'(x) = c(x)$ or $10+.003x^2 = \dfrac{2000}{x} + 10 + .001x^2$ or $2000/x = .002x^2$ or $x^3 = 2000/.002 = 1000000$ or $x = 100$. This is a minimum since $c''(x) = 4000/x^3+.002 > 0$ for $x > 0$.
(c) The minimum average cost is $c(100) = \$40$.

6. (a) $C(x) = 1000+96x+2x^{3/2}$, $C(1000) = \$160245.55$. $c(x) = \dfrac{1000}{x} + 96 + 2\sqrt{x}$, $c(1000) = \$160.25$. $C'(x) = 96+3\sqrt{x}$, $C'(1000) = \$190.87$. (b) We must have $C'(x) = c(x)$ or $96+3\sqrt{x} = 1000/x+96+2\sqrt{x}$ or $\sqrt{x} = 1000/x$ or $x^{3/2} = 1000$ or $x = (1000)^{2/3} = 100$. Since $c'(x) = (x^{3/2}-1000)/x^2 < 0$ for $0 < x < 100$ and $c'(x) > 0$ for $x > 100$, there is an absolute minimum at $x = 100$.
(c) The minimum average cost is $c(100) = \$126$.

8. $C(x) = 680+4x+0.01x^2$, $p(x) = 12-x/500$. Then $R(x) = xp(x) = 12x-x^2/500$. If the profit is maximum, then $R'(x) = C'(x)$ or $12-x/250 = 4+.02x$ or $8 = 0.024x$ or $x = 8/0.024 = 1000/3$. Now $R''(x) = -1/250 < .02 = C''(x)$, so $x = 1000/3$ gives a maximum.

10. $C(x) = 900+110x-0.1x^2+0.02x^3$, $p(x) = 260-0.1x$. Then $R(x) = xp(x)$ $= 260x-0.1x^2$. If the profit is maximum, then $C'(x) = R'(x)$ or $110-0.2x+.06x^2 = 260-0.2x$ or $0.06x^2 = 150$ or $x^2 = 150/.06 = 2500$ so $x = 50$. Now $R''(x) = -.2 < -.2+.12x = C''(x)$ for all $x > 0$, so $x = 50$ gives a maximum.

12. $C(x) = 10000+28x-0.01x^2+0.002x^3$, $p(x) = 90-0.02x$. Then $R(x)$ $= xp(x) = 90x-0.02x^2$. If the profit is maximum, then $R'(x) = C'(x)$ $\iff 90-.04x = 28-.02x+.006x^2 \iff .006x^2+0.02x-62 = 0 \iff$ $3x^2+10x-31000 = 0 \iff (x-100)(3x+310) = 0 \iff x = 100$ (since $x>0$). Now $R''(x) = -.04 < -.02+.012x = C''(x)$ for $x > 0$, so there is a maximum at $x = 100$.

14. $C(x) = .0002x^3-0.25x^2+4x+1500$. The marginal cost is $C'(x) =$ $.0006x^2-0.50x+4$. $C'(x)$ is increasing when $C''(x) > 0$ or $.0012x-.5>0$ or $x > .5/.0012 \approx 417$. So $C'(x)$ starts to increase when $x = 417$.

16. (a) Let $p(x)$ be the demand function. Then $p(x)$ is linear and y $= p(x)$ passes through $(20,10)$ and $(18,11)$, so the slope is $-1/2$ and the equation of the line is $y-10 = -(1/2)(x-10)$ or $y = -(1/2)x+20$. Thus the demand is $p(x) = -(1/2)x+20$ and the revenue is $R(x) = xp(x) = -(1/2)x^2+20x$. The cost is $C(x) = 6x$, so the profit is $P(x) = R(x)-C(x) = -(1/2)x^2+14x$. Then $0 = P'(x) = -x+14 \Rightarrow$ $x = 14$. Since $P''(x) = -1<0$, the selling price for maximum profit is $p(14) = 20-(1/2)14 = \$13$.

Section 4.10

Exercises 4.10

2. $f(x) = x^3-4x^2+17 \Rightarrow F(x) = (x^4/4)-4(x^3/3)+17x+C$

4. $f(x) = x^{99}-2x^{49}-1 \Rightarrow F(x) = (x^{100}/100)-2(x^{50}/50)-x+C$ $= (1/100)x^{100}-(1/25)x^{50}-x+C$

6. $f(x) = \sqrt[3]{x^2}-\sqrt{x^3} = x^{2/3}-x^{3/2} \Rightarrow F(x) = x^{5/3}/(5/3)-x^{5/2}/(5/2)+C$ $= (3/5)x^{5/3}-(2/5)x^{5/2}+C$

121

8. $f(x) = 3x^{-2}-5x^{-4}$ has domain $(-\infty,0) \cup (0,\infty)$, so
    $F(x) = 3x^{-1}/(-1)-5x^{-3}/(-3)+C_1 = -(3/x)+(5/3x^3)+C_1$ if $x>0$ and
    $F(x) = -(3/x)+(5/3x^3)+C_2$ if $x<0$.

10. $f(x) = x^{2/3}+2x^{-1/3}$ has domain $(-\infty,0) \cup (0,\infty)$, so
    $F(x) = x^{5/3}/(5/3)+2x^{2/3}/(2/3)+C_1 = (3/5)x^{5/3}+3x^{2/3}+C_1$ if $x>0$ and
    $F(x) = (3/5)x^{5/3}+3x^{2/3}+C_2$ if $x<0$.

12. $g(t) = t^{4/5}+t^{-6}$ has domain $(-\infty,0) \cup (0,\infty)$, so
    $G(t) = t^{9/5}/(9/5)+t^{-5}/(-5)+C_1 = (5/9)t^{9/5}-(1/5t^5)+C_1$ if $t>0$ and
    $G(t) = (5/9)t^{9/5}-(1/5t^5)+C_2$ if $t<0$.

14. $f(t) = \sin t - 2\sqrt{t} \Rightarrow F(t) = -\cos t - 2t^{3/2}/(3/2) + C$
    $= -\cos t - (4/3)t^{3/2} + C$

16. $f(\theta) = \theta + \sec \theta \tan \theta \Rightarrow F(\theta) = \theta^2/2 + \sec \theta + C_n$ on the interval
    $((2n-1)\pi/2,(2n+1)\pi/2)$.

18. $f'(x) = \sin x - x^{2/5} \Rightarrow f(x) = -\cos x - (5/7)x^{7/5} + C$

20. $f''(x) = 60x^4-45x^2 \Rightarrow f'(x) = 60(x^5/5)-45(x^3/3)+C = 12x^5-15x^3+C \Rightarrow$
    $f(x) = 12(x^6/6)-15(x^4/4)+Cx+D = 2x^6-(15/4)x^4+Cx+D$

22. $f''(x) = \sin x \Rightarrow f'(x) = -\cos x + C \Rightarrow f(x) = -\sin x + Cx + D$

24. $f'''(x) = x^{1/2} \Rightarrow f''(x) = (2/3)x^{3/2}+C \Rightarrow f'(x) = (2/3)(2/5)x^{5/2}+Cx+D$
    $= (4/15)x^{5/2}+Cx+D \Rightarrow f(x) = (4/15)(2/7)x^{7/2}+C(x^2/2)+Dx+E$
    $= (8/105)x^{7/2}+(C/2)x^2+Dx+E$

26. $f'(x) = 12x^2-24x+1 \Rightarrow f(x) = 4x^3-12x^2+x+C \Rightarrow f(1) = 4-12+1+C = -2$
    $\Rightarrow C = 5$, so $f(x) = 4x^3-12x^2+x+5$

28. $f'(x) = 1+x^{-2}$, $x>0$, $\Rightarrow f(x) = x-1/x+C \Rightarrow f(1) = 1-1+C = 1 \Rightarrow$
    $C = 1$, so $f(x) = 1+x-1/x$

30. $f'(x) = \sin x - 2x^{1/2} \Rightarrow f(x) = -\cos x - (4/3)x^{3/2} + C \Rightarrow$
    $f(0) = -1-0+C = 0 \Rightarrow C = 1$, so $f(x) = -\cos x - (4/3)x^{3/2} + 1$

32. $f'(x) = 3x^{-2} \Rightarrow f(x) = -3/x + C_1$ if $x>0$, $f(x) = -3/x + C_2$ if $x<0$.
    $f(1) = -3+C_1 = 0 \Rightarrow C_1 = 3$, $f(-1) = 3+C_2 = 0 \Rightarrow C_2 = -3$. So
    $f(x) = -3/x + 3$ if $x>0$, $f(x) = -3/x - 3$ if $x<0$.

34. $f''(x) = x \Rightarrow f'(x) = (1/2)x^2+C \Rightarrow 2 = f'(0) = C \Rightarrow f'(x) = (1/2)x^2+2$
    $\Rightarrow f(x) = (1/6)x^3+2x+D \Rightarrow -3 = f(0) = D \Rightarrow f(x) = (1/6)x^3+2x-3$

36. $f''(x) = 12x^2-6x+8 \Rightarrow f'(x) = 4x^3-3x^2+8x+C \Rightarrow -21 = f'(-1) = -4-3-8+C$
    $\Rightarrow C = -6 \Rightarrow f'(x) = 4x^3-3x^2+8x-6 \Rightarrow f(x) = x^4-x^3+4x^2-6x+D \Rightarrow$
    $5 = f(-1) = 1+1+4+6+D \Rightarrow D = -7$, so $f(x) = x^4-x^3+4x^2-6x-7$.

38. $f''(x) = x+x^{1/2} \Rightarrow f'(x) = \frac{1}{2}x^2+\frac{2}{3}x^{3/2}+C \Rightarrow 2 = f'(1) = \frac{1}{2}+\frac{2}{3}+C \Rightarrow C = \frac{5}{6} \Rightarrow$

122

$f'(x) = \frac{1}{2}x^2 + \frac{2}{3}x^{3/2} + \frac{5}{6} \Rightarrow f(x) = \frac{1}{6}x^3 + \frac{4}{15}x^{5/2} + \frac{5}{6}x + D \Rightarrow 1 = f(1) = \frac{1}{6} + \frac{4}{15} + \frac{5}{6} + D$

$\Rightarrow D = -\frac{4}{15} \Rightarrow f(x) = \frac{1}{6}x^3 + \frac{4}{15}x^{5/2} + \frac{5}{6}x - \frac{4}{15}$

40. $f''(x) = 12x^2 - 6x + 2 \Rightarrow f'(x) = 4x^3 - 3x^2 + 2x + C \Rightarrow f(x) = x^4 - x^3 + x^2 + Cx + D$

$1 = f(0) = D$ and $11 = f(2) = 16 - 8 + 4 + 2C + D = 13 + 2C \Rightarrow C = -1$, so

$f(x) = x^4 - x^3 + x^2 - x + 1$.

42. $f'''(x) = \sin x \Rightarrow f''(x) = -\cos x + C \Rightarrow 1 = f''(0) = -1 + C = 1 \Rightarrow$

$C = 2$, so $f''(x) = -\cos x + 2 \Rightarrow f'(x) = -\sin x + 2x + D \Rightarrow$

$1 = f'(0) = D \Rightarrow f'(x) = -\sin x + 2x + 1 \Rightarrow$

$f(x) = \cos x + x^2 + x + E \Rightarrow 1 = f(0) = 1 + E \Rightarrow E = 0$, so

$f(x) = \cos x + x^2 + x$

44. $v(t) = s'(t) = 3\sqrt{t} \Rightarrow s(t) = 2t^{3/2} + C \Rightarrow 5 = s(1) = 2 + C \Rightarrow C = 3$,

so $s(t) = 2t^{3/2} + 3$.

46. $a(t) = v'(t) = \cos t + \sin t \Rightarrow v(t) = \sin t - \cos t + C \Rightarrow$

$5 = v(0) = -1 + C \Rightarrow C = 6$, so $v(t) = \sin t - \cos t + 6 \Rightarrow$

$s(t) = -\cos t - \sin t + 6t + D \Rightarrow 0 = s(0) = -1 + D \Rightarrow D = 1$, so

$s(t) = -\cos t - \sin t + 6t + 1$.

48. $a(t) = v'(t) = 10 + 3t - 3t^2 \Rightarrow v(t) = 10t + (3/2)t^2 - t^3 + C \Rightarrow$

$s(t) = 5t^2 + (1/2)t^3 - (1/4)t^4 + Ct + D \Rightarrow 0 = s(0) = D$ and $10 = s(2)$

$= 20 + 4 - 4 + 2C \Rightarrow C = -5$, so $s(t) = -5t + 5t^2 + (1/2)t^3 - (1/4)t^4$.

50. (a) $v'(t) = a(t) = -9.8 \Rightarrow v(t) = -9.8t + C$ and $-5 = v(0) = C \Rightarrow$

$v(t) = -9.8t - 5 \Rightarrow s(t) = -4.9t^2 - 5t + D \Rightarrow 450 = s(0) = D$, so

$s(t) = -4.9t^2 - 5t + 450$.   (b) $s(t) = 0 \Rightarrow 4.9t^2 + 5t - 450 = 0 \Rightarrow$

$t = (-5 + \sqrt{25 + 4(4.9)(450)})/9.8 \approx 9.1$ s.   (c) $v(9.1) \approx -94.05$ m/s.

52. $v'(t) = a(t) = a \Rightarrow v(t) = at + C$ and $v_0 = v(0) = C \Rightarrow v(t) = at + v_0$

$\Rightarrow s(t) = at^2/2 + v_0 t + D \Rightarrow s_0 = s(0) = D \Rightarrow s(t) = \frac{1}{2}at^2 + v_0 t + s_0$

54. $v'(t) = a(t) = -40$. The initial velocity is 50 mi/h $= \dfrac{50 \cdot 5280}{3600} =$

220/3 ft/s, so $v(t) = -40t + 220/3$. The car stops when $v(t) = 0 \Longleftrightarrow$

$t = 220/(3 \cdot 40) = 11/6$. Since $s(t) = -20t^2 + (220/3)t$, the distance

covered is $s(11/6) = -20(11/6)^2 + (220/3)(11/6) \approx 67.2$ ft.

56. $a(t) = -40 \Rightarrow v(t) = -40t + v_0$ where v_0 is the speed of the car (in

ft/s) when the brakes were applied. The car stops when $-40t + v_0 = 0$

$\Longleftrightarrow t = v_0/40$. Since $s(t) = -20t^2 + v_0 t$, we have $160 = s(v_0/40) =$

$-20(v_0/40)^2 + v_0(v_0/40) = v_0^2/80 \Rightarrow v_0^2 = 12800 \Rightarrow v_0 = 80\sqrt{2} \approx 113$ ft/s.

Review Exercises for Chapter 4

2. $f(x) = 3x^5 - 25x^3 + 60x$, $-1 \leq x \leq 3$. $f'(x) = 15x^4 - 75x^2 + 60 = 15(x^2-4)(x^2-1)$
$= 0$ when $x = \pm 1, \pm 2$ (but -2 is not in the interval).
$f''(x) = 60x^3 - 150x \Rightarrow f''(1) = -90 < 0$, $f''(2) = 180 > 0$, so $f(1) = 38$ is
a local maximum, $f(2) = 16$ is a local minimum. Also $f(-1) = -38$
and $f(3) = 234$, so $f(-1) = -38$ is an absolute minimum and
$f(3) = 234$ is an absolute maximum.

4. $f(x) = \sqrt{x^2+4x+8}$, $-3 \leq x \leq 0$. $f'(x) = (x+2)/\sqrt{x^2+4x+8} = 0$ when $x = -2$,
and $f'(x) < 0$ for $x < -2$, $f'(x) > 0$ for $x > -2$. So $f(-2) = 2$ is a local
and absolute minimum. Also $f(-3) = \sqrt{5}$, $f(0) = 2\sqrt{2}$, so $f(0) = 2\sqrt{2}$
is an absolute maximum.

6. $f(x) = 2x + 2\cos x - 4\sin x - \cos 2x$, $0 \leq x \leq \pi$. $f'(x) = 2 - 2\sin x$
$- 4\cos x + 2\sin 2x = 2(1 - \sin x - 2\cos x + 2\sin x \cos x)$
$= 2(\sin x - 1)(2\cos x - 1) = 0$ when $\sin x = 1$ or $\cos x = 1/2$, so
$x = \pi/2$ or $\pi/3$. $f'(x) < 0$ for $0 < x < \pi/3$, $f'(x) \geq 0$ for $\pi/3 < x < \pi$, so
$f(\pi/3) = 2\pi/3 + 1.5 - 2\sqrt{3}$ is a local minimum. Also $f(\pi/3) \approx 0.13$,
$f(0) = 1$, $f(\pi) = 2\pi - 3 \approx 3.28$, so $f(\pi/3) = 2\pi/3 + 1.5 - 2\sqrt{3}$ is an
absolute minimum and $f(\pi) = 2\pi - 3$ is a absolute maximum.

8. $\lim\limits_{x \to 9^-} \left[\dfrac{-2}{x+9}\right] = \dfrac{-2}{9+9} = -\dfrac{1}{9}$

10. $\lim\limits_{x \to \infty} \dfrac{1+2x-x^2}{1-x+2x^2} = \lim\limits_{x \to \infty} \dfrac{(1/x^2)+(2/x)-1}{(1/x^2)-(1/x)+2} = \dfrac{0+0-1}{0-0+2} = -\dfrac{1}{2}$

12. If $t = \dfrac{1}{x}$ then $\lim\limits_{x \to \infty} x \tan\dfrac{1}{x} = \lim\limits_{t \to 0^+} \dfrac{\tan t}{t} = \lim\limits_{t \to 0^+} \dfrac{\sin t}{t}\dfrac{1}{\cos t} = 1 \cdot 1 = 1$

14. $\lim\limits_{x \to 3^+} \dfrac{\sqrt{x^2-9}}{2x-6} = \lim\limits_{x \to 3^+} \dfrac{\sqrt{x+3}\sqrt{x-3}}{2(x-3)} = \lim\limits_{x \to 3^+} \dfrac{\sqrt{x+3}}{2\sqrt{x-3}} = \infty$ since $\sqrt{x-3} \to 0^+$ as $x \to 3^+$

16. $0 \leq \cos^2 x \leq 1 \Rightarrow 0 \leq \dfrac{\cos^2 x}{x^2} \leq \dfrac{1}{x^2}$ and $\lim\limits_{x \to -\infty} 0 = 0$, $\lim\limits_{x \to -\infty} \dfrac{1}{x^2} = 0$, so by
the Squeeze Theorem, $\lim\limits_{x \to -\infty} \dfrac{\cos^2 x}{x^2} = 0$.

18. $\lim\limits_{x \to 2\pi^-} \dfrac{\cot x}{1+x^2} = \lim\limits_{x \to 2\pi^-} \dfrac{\cos x}{(1+x^2)\sin x} = -\infty$ since $\sin x \to 0^-$ as $x \to 2\pi^-$

20. $\lim\limits_{x \to \infty} (\sqrt{x^2+x+1} - \sqrt{x^2-x}) = \lim\limits_{x \to \infty} (\sqrt{x^2+x+1} - \sqrt{x^2-x}) \dfrac{\sqrt{x^2+x+1}+\sqrt{x^2-x}}{\sqrt{x^2+x+1}+\sqrt{x^2-x}}$

$$= \lim_{x\to\infty} \frac{(x^2+x+1)-(x^2-x)}{\sqrt{x^2+x+1}+\sqrt{x^2-x}} = \lim_{x\to\infty} \frac{2x+1}{\sqrt{x^2+x+1}+\sqrt{x^2-x}}$$

$$= \lim_{x\to\infty} \frac{2+1/x}{\sqrt{1+(1/x)+(1/x^2)}+\sqrt{1-1/x}} = \frac{2+0}{\sqrt{1+0+0}+\sqrt{1-0}} = 1$$

22. $y = f(x) = 3x^4-4x^3-12x^2+2$ A. $D = R$ B. y-intercept $= f(0) = 2$

C. No symmetry   D. $\lim_{x\to\pm\infty}(3x^4-4x^3-12x^2+2) = \infty$, no asymptote.

E. $f'(x) = 12x^3-12x^2-24x = 12x(x-2)(x+1) = 0$ when $x = -1, 0, 2$.

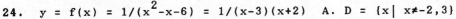

Interval	$12x$	$x-2$	$x+1$	$f'(x)$	f
$x<-1$	$-$	$-$	$-$	$-$	decreasing on $(-\infty,-1]$
$-1<x<0$	$-$	$-$	$+$	$+$	increasing on $[-1,0]$
$0<x<2$	$+$	$-$	$+$	$-$	decreasing on $[0,2]$
$x>2$	$+$	$+$	$+$	$+$	increasing on $[2,\infty)$

F. $f(-1) = -3$ is a local minimum, $f(0) = 2$ is a local maximum,

$f(2) = -30$ is a local minimum.   H.

G. $f''(x) = 12(3x^2-2x-2) = 0 \Rightarrow$

$x = (1\pm\sqrt{7})/3$. $f''(x)>0 \Leftrightarrow x>(1+\sqrt{7})/3$

or $x<(1-\sqrt{7})/3$, so f is CU on

$(-\infty,(1-\sqrt{7})/3)$ and $((1+\sqrt{7})/3,\infty)$ and

CD on $((1-\sqrt{7})/3,(1+\sqrt{7})/3)$. IP at

$x = (1\pm\sqrt{7})/3$.

24. $y = f(x) = 1/(x^2-x-6) = 1/(x-3)(x+2)$ A. $D = \{x \mid x \neq -2, 3\}$

B. No x-intercept, y-intercept $= f(0) = -1/6$ C. No symmetry

D. $\lim_{x\to\pm\infty} \frac{1}{x^2-x-6} = 0$, so $y = 0$ is a HA. $\lim_{x\to 3^+} \frac{1}{(x-3)(x+2)} = \infty$,

$\lim_{x\to 3^-} \frac{1}{(x-3)(x+2)} = -\infty$, $\lim_{x\to -2^+} \frac{1}{(x-3)(x+2)} = -\infty$, $\lim_{x\to -2^-} \frac{1}{(x-3)(x+2)} = \infty$,

so $x = 3$, $x = -2$ are VA.   E. $f'(x) = (1-2x)/(x^2-x-6)^2 > 0 \Leftrightarrow x<1/2$,

so f is increasing on $(-\infty,-2)$ and $(-2,1/2]$, and decreasing on

$[1/2,3)$ and $(3,\infty)$.   F. $f(1/2) = -4/25$ is a local maximum.

G. $f''(x) = \frac{(x^2-x-6)^2(-2)-(1-2x)2(x^2-x-6)(2x-1)}{(x^2-x-6)^4} = \frac{2(3x^2-3x+7)}{(x^2-x-6)^3}$

Since $3x^2-3x+7>0$ for all x,   H.

$f''(x)>0 \Leftrightarrow (x-3)(x+2)>0 \Leftrightarrow x<-2$

or $x>3$.   So f is CU on $(-\infty,-2)$,

$(3,\infty)$ and CD on $(-2,3)$. No IP.

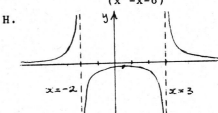

26. $y = \sqrt{1-x} + \sqrt{x-2}$ A. $D = \{x \mid x \le 1 \text{ and } x \ge 2\}$ which is the empty set. So the graph of f is empty.

28. $y = f(x) = 1/x + 1/(x+1) = (2x+1)/x(x+1)$ A. $D = \{x \mid x \ne 0, -1\}$ B. No y-intercept, x-intercept $= -1/2$. C. No symmetry. D. $\lim\limits_{x \to \pm\infty} f(x) = 0$, so $y = 0$ is a HA. $\lim\limits_{x \to 0^+} \dfrac{2x+1}{x(x+1)} = \infty$, $\lim\limits_{x \to 0^-} \dfrac{2x+1}{x(x+1)} = -\infty$, $\lim\limits_{x \to -1^+} \dfrac{2x+1}{x(x+1)}$

$= \infty$, $\lim\limits_{x \to -1^-} \dfrac{2x+1}{x(x+1)} = -\infty$, so $x = 0$, $x = -1$ are VA.

E. $f'(x) = -\dfrac{1}{x^2} - \dfrac{1}{(x+1)^2} < 0$, so f is decreasing on $(-\infty, -1)$, $(-1, 0)$

and $(0, \infty)$. F. No extrema. G. $f''(x) = \dfrac{2}{x^3} + \dfrac{2}{(x+1)^3} = \dfrac{2(2x+1)(x^2+x+1)}{x^3(x+1)^3}$

$\Rightarrow$ $f''(x) > 0 \iff x > 0$ or $-1 < x < -1/2$,   H.
so f is CU on $(0, \infty)$ and $(-1, -1/2)$
and CD on $(-\infty, -1)$ and $(-1/2, 0)$.
IP $(-1/2, 0)$.

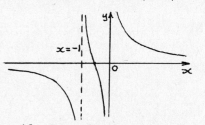

30. $y = f(x) = x + \sqrt{1-x}$ A. $D = \{x \mid x \le 1\} = (-\infty, 1]$ B. y-intercept $= 1$, x-intercepts occur when $x + \sqrt{1-x} = 0 \Rightarrow \sqrt{1-x} = -x \Rightarrow 1-x = x^2 \Rightarrow$ $x^2 + x - 1 = 0 \Rightarrow x = (-1 \pm \sqrt{5})/2$, but the larger root is extraneous, so the only x-intercept is $(-1 - \sqrt{5})/2$. C. No symmetry D. No asymptote E. $f'(x) = 1 - 1/2\sqrt{1-x} = 0 \iff 2\sqrt{1-x} = 1 \iff 1-x = 1/4 \iff x = 3/4$ and $f'(x) > 0 \iff x < 3/4$, so f is increasing on $(-\infty, 3/4]$, decreasing on $[3/4, 1]$. F. $f(3/4) = 5/4$ is a   H.
local maximum. G. $f''(x) =$
$-1/4(1-x)^{3/2} < 0 \iff x < 1$, so f
is CD on $(-\infty, 1)$. No IP.

32. $y = f(x) = \sqrt{x} - \sqrt[3]{x}$ A. $D = [0, \infty)$ B. y-intercept 0, x-intercepts 0, 1. C. No symmetry D. $\lim\limits_{x \to \infty}(x^{1/2} - x^{1/3}) = \lim\limits_{x \to \infty} x^{1/3}(x^{1/6} - 1) = \infty$, no asymptote. E. $f'(x) = (1/2)x^{-1/2} - (1/3)x^{-2/3} = (3x^{1/6} - 2)/6x^{2/3} > 0$ $\iff 3x^{1/6} > 2 \iff x > (2/3)^6$, so f is increasing on $[(2/3)^6, \infty)$ and decreasing on $[0, (2/3)^6]$. F. $f((2/3)^6) = -4/27$ is a local minimum.

G. $f''(x) = -(1/4)x^{-3/2}+(2/9)x^{-5/3}$ H.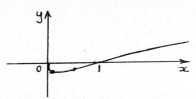

$= (8-9x^{1/6})/36x^{5/3} > 0 \Leftrightarrow$

$x^{1/6}<8/9 \Leftrightarrow x<(8/9)^6$, so f is

CU on $(0,(8/9)^6)$ and CD on

$((8/9)^6,\infty)$.   IP $(8/9,-64/729)$

34. $y = f(x) = |\cos x - \sin x|$ A. D = R   B. y-intercept = f(0) = 1,

x-intercepts occur when $\cos x = \sin x \Leftrightarrow x = n\pi+\pi/4$ C. f is

periodic with period π.   D. No asymptote   E. Using the rule

$(d/dx)|x| = x/|x|$ from Exercise 3.4.73, we have f'(x) =

$\dfrac{\cos x - \sin x}{|\cos x - \sin x|}(-\sin x - \cos x) = \dfrac{-\cos 2x}{|\cos x - \sin x|} > 0 \Leftrightarrow$

$\cos 2x < 0 \Leftrightarrow n\pi+\pi/4<x<n\pi+3\pi/4$, so f is increasing on

$[n\pi+\pi/4,n\pi+3\pi/4]$ and decreasing on $[n\pi-\pi/4,n\pi+\pi/4]$.   F. $f(n\pi+\pi/4)$

= 0 is a local minimum, $f(n\pi-\pi/4) = \sqrt{2}$ is a local maximum. G. f''(x)

$= \dfrac{|\cos x - \sin x|(2 \sin 2x) + \cos 2x(-\cos 2x)/|\cos x - \sin x|}{(\cos x - \sin x)^2}$

$= \dfrac{2(\cos x - \sin x)^2\sin 2x - \cos^2 2x}{|\cos x - \sin x|^3} = -\dfrac{(\cos x - \sin x)^4}{|\cos x - \sin x|^3} < 0$ when

$\cos x \neq \sin x$, so f is CD on $(n\pi+\pi/4,n\pi+5\pi/4)$.

H.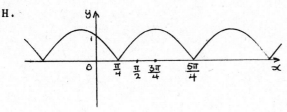

[Another method: First
graph $g(x) = \cos x - \sin x$
and then reflect the part
of the graph of g that lies
below the x-axis.]

36.   By the Mean Value Theorem, $f(4)-1 = f(4)-f(0) = f'(c)(4-0) = 4f'(c)$
for some c with $0<c<4$.   Since $2\leq f'(c)\leq5$, we have $4(2)\leq f(4)-1\leq4(5)$
or $8\leq f(4)-1\leq20$ or $9\leq f(4)\leq21$.

38.   For $0<x<1$, f'(x) = 2x, so $f(x) = x^2+C$.   Since f(0) = 0, $f(x) = x^2$
on [0,1].   For $1<x<3$, f'(x) = -1, so f(x) = -x+D.   1 = f(1) = -1+D
$\Rightarrow$ D = 2, so f(x) = 2-x.   For x>3, f'(x) = 1, so f(x) = x+E.
-1 = f(3) = 3+E $\Rightarrow$ E = -4, so f(x) = x-4.   Since f is even, its
graph is symmetric about the y-axis.

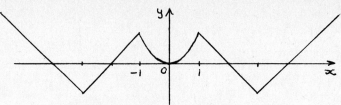

40. If d(x) is the distance from the point (x,8/x) on the hyperbola to (3,0), then $[d(x)]^2 = (x-3)^2+64/x^2 = f(x)$. $f'(x) = 2(x-3)-128/x^3$ $= 0 \Rightarrow x^4-3x^3-64 = 0 \Rightarrow (x-4)(x^3+x^2+4x+16) = 0 \Rightarrow x = 4$ since the solution must have x>0. Then y = 8/4 = 2, so the point is (4,2).

42.

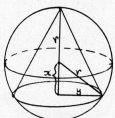

The volume is $V = (1/3)\pi y^2(r+x)$
$= (1/3)\pi(r^2-x^2)(r+x)$
$= (1/3)\pi(r^3+r^2x-rx^2-x^3)$, $-r \leq x \leq r$.
$V'(x) = (\pi/3)(r^2-2rx-3x^2)$
$= -(\pi/3)(3x-r)(x+r) = 0$ when x = -r
or x = r/3. Now V(r) = 0 = V(-r),

so the maximum occurs at x = r/3 and the volume is
$V(r/3) = (\pi/3)(r^2-r^2/9)(4r/3) = 32\pi r^3/81$.

44.

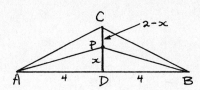

We minimize L(x) = |PA|+|PB|+|PC|
$= 2\sqrt{x^2+16} + (2-x)$, $0 \leq x \leq 2$.
$L'(x) = 2x/\sqrt{x^2+16} - 1 = 0 \Leftrightarrow 2x =$
$\sqrt{x^2+16} \Leftrightarrow 4x^2 = x^2+16 \Leftrightarrow x = 4/\sqrt{3}$
≈ 2.3 which isn't in the interval

[0,2]. Now L(0) = 10 and L(2) = $2\sqrt{20} = 4\sqrt{5} \approx 8.9$. The minimum occurs when P = C.

46.

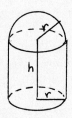

We minimize the surface area
$S = \pi r^2+2\pi rh+2\pi r^2 = 3\pi r^2+2\pi rh$.
Solving $V = \pi r^2 h+(2/3)\pi r^3$ for h, we
get $h = V/\pi r^2 - (2/3)r$, so
$S(r) = 3\pi r^2+2\pi r[V/\pi r^2 - (2/3)r]$
$= (5/3)\pi r^2+2V/r$.

$S'(r) = -2V/r^2 + (10/3)\pi r = [(10/3)\pi r^3-2V]/r^2 = 0 \Leftrightarrow (10/3)\pi r^3 = 2V$ $\Leftrightarrow r^3 = 3V/5\pi \Leftrightarrow r = \sqrt[3]{3V/5\pi}$. This gives an absolute minimum since $S'(r)<0$ for $0<r<\sqrt[3]{3V/5\pi}$ and $S'(r)>0$ for $r>\sqrt[3]{3V/5\pi}$. Thus $r = \sqrt[3]{3V/5\pi} = h$.

48. $f'(x) = 2x^{-5/2}$ ⇒ $f(x) = 2x^{-3/2}/(-3/2) + C = -(4/3)x^{-3/2} + C$

50. $f'(x) = 1 + 2 \sin x - \cos x$ ⇒ $f(x) = x - 2 \cos x - \sin x + C$ ⇒

$3 = f(0) = -2+C$ ⇒ $C = 5$, so $f(x) = x - 2 \cos x - \sin x + 5$.

52. $f''(x) = x^4-4x^2+3x-2$ ⇒ $f'(x) = (1/5)x^5-(4/3)x^3+(3/2)x^2-2x+C$ ⇒

$f(x) = (1/30)x^6-(1/3)x^4+(1/2)x^3-x^2+Cx+D.$ $0 = f(0) = D$ ⇒

$f(x) = (1/30)x^6-(1/3)x^4+(1/2)x^3-x^2+Cx.$ $1 = f(1) = \frac{1}{30}-\frac{1}{3}+\frac{1}{2}-1+C$ ⇒

$C = 9/5$, so $f(x) = (1/30)x^6-(1/3)x^4+(1/2)x^3-x^2+(9/5)x.$

54. Let $s_A(t)$ and $s_B(t)$ be the position functions for cars A and B and

let $f(t) = s_A(t)-s_B(t)$. Since A passed B twice, there must be 3

values of t such that $f(t) = 0$. Then by 3 applications of Rolle's

Theorem (see Exercise 4.2.20(b)) there is a number c such that

$f''(c) = 0$. So $s_A''(c) = s_B''(c)$, i.e., A and B had equal accelerations

at t = c.

CHAPTER 5

Exercises 5.1

2. $\displaystyle\sum_{i=1}^{6} \frac{1}{i+1} = \frac{1}{2} + \frac{1}{3} + \frac{1}{4} + \frac{1}{5} + \frac{1}{6} + \frac{1}{7}$

4. $\displaystyle\sum_{i=4}^{6} i^3 = 4^3 + 5^3 + 6^3$

6. $\displaystyle\sum_{k=5}^{8} x^k = x^5 + x^6 + x^7 + x^8$

8. $\displaystyle\sum_{j=n}^{n+3} j^2 = n^2 + (n+1)^2 + (n+2)^2 + (n+3)^2$

10. $\displaystyle\sum_{i=1}^{n} f(x_i)\Delta x_i = f(x_1)\Delta x_1 + f(x_2)\Delta x_2 + f(x_3)\Delta x_3 + \cdots + f(x_n)\Delta x_n$

12. $\sqrt{3} + \sqrt{4} + \sqrt{5} + \sqrt{6} + \sqrt{7} = \displaystyle\sum_{i=3}^{7} \sqrt{i}$

14. $\dfrac{3}{7} + \dfrac{4}{8} + \dfrac{5}{9} + \dfrac{6}{10} + \cdots + \dfrac{23}{27} = \displaystyle\sum_{i=3}^{23} \dfrac{i}{i+4}$

16. $1 + 3 + 5 + 7 + \cdots + (2n-1) = \displaystyle\sum_{i=1}^{n} (2i-1)$

18. $\dfrac{1}{1} + \dfrac{1}{4} + \dfrac{1}{9} + \dfrac{1}{16} + \dfrac{1}{25} + \dfrac{1}{36} = \displaystyle\sum_{i=1}^{6} \dfrac{1}{i^2}$

20. $1 - x + x^2 - x^3 + \cdots + (-1)^n x^n = \displaystyle\sum_{i=0}^{n} (-1)^i x^i$

22. $\displaystyle\sum_{i=3}^{6} i(i+2) = 3\cdot5 + 4\cdot6 + 5\cdot7 + 6\cdot8 = 15 + 24 + 35 + 48 = 122$

24. $\displaystyle\sum_{k=0}^{8} \cos k\pi = \cos 0 + \cos \pi + \cos 2\pi + \cos 3\pi + \cos 4\pi + \cos 5\pi$

$+ \cos 6\pi + \cos 7\pi + \cos 8\pi = 1 - 1 + 1 - 1 + 1 - 1 + 1 - 1 + 1 = 1$

26. $\displaystyle\sum_{i=1}^{100} 4 = 4 + 4 + 4 \cdots + 4 = 100\cdot4 = 400$
    (100 summands)

28. $\displaystyle\sum_{i=-2}^{4} 2^{3-i} = 2^5 + 2^4 + 2^3 + 2^2 + 2^1 + 2^0 + 2^{-1} = 63.5$

30. $\displaystyle\sum_{k=1}^{n} (\sqrt{k} - \sqrt{k-1}) = (\sqrt{1} - \sqrt{0}) + (\sqrt{2} - \sqrt{1}) + (\sqrt{3} - \sqrt{2}) + (\sqrt{4} - \sqrt{3}) +$

$\cdots + (\sqrt{n} - \sqrt{n-1}) = -\sqrt{0} + \sqrt{n} = \sqrt{n}$

32. $\displaystyle\sum_{i=1}^{n} (2-5i) = \sum_{i=1}^{n} 2 - \sum_{i=1}^{n} 5i = 2n - 5\sum_{i=1}^{n} i = 2n - 5n(n+1)/2$

$= \dfrac{4n}{2} - \dfrac{5n^2+5n}{2} = -\dfrac{5n^2+n}{2} = -\dfrac{n(5n+1)}{2}$

34. $\displaystyle\sum_{i=1}^{n} (3+2i)^2 = \sum_{i=1}^{n} (9+12i+4i^2) = \sum_{i=1}^{n} 9 + 12\sum_{i=1}^{n} i + 4\sum_{i=1}^{n} i^2$

$= 9n + 6n(n+1) + 2n(n+1)(2n+1)/3 = (1/3)[27n+18n^2+18n+4n^3+6n^2+2n]$

$= (4n^3+24n^2+47n)/3 = n(4n^2+24n+47)/3$

36. $\displaystyle\sum_{i=1}^{n} i(i+1)(i+2) = \sum_{i=1}^{n} (i^3+3i^2+2i) = \sum_{i=1}^{n} i^3 + 3\sum_{i=1}^{n} i^2 + 2\sum_{i=1}^{n} i$

$= \left[\dfrac{n(n+1)}{2}\right]^2 + 3\,\dfrac{n(n+1)(2n+1)}{6} + 2\,\dfrac{n(n+1)}{2}$

$= n(n+1)\left[\dfrac{n(n+1)}{4} + \dfrac{2n+1}{2} + 1\right] = \dfrac{n(n+1)}{4}\,[n^2+n+4n+2+4]$

$= \dfrac{n(n+1)}{4}\,(n^2+5n+6) = \dfrac{n(n+1)(n+2)(n+3)}{4}$

38. $\displaystyle\sum_{k=1}^{n} k^2(k^2-k+1) = \sum_{k=1}^{n} k^4 - \sum_{k=1}^{n} k^3 + \sum_{k=1}^{n} k^2 = \dfrac{n(n+1)(2n+1)(3n^2+3n-1)}{30}$

$- \dfrac{n^2(n+1)^2}{4} + \dfrac{n(n+1)(2n+1)}{6} = \dfrac{n(n+1)}{60}\,[2(2n+1)(3n^2+3n-1)-15n(n+1)$

$+ 10(2n+1)] = n(n+1)(12n^3+3n^2+7n+8)/60$

40. Let S_n be the given statement, namely $\displaystyle\sum_{i=1}^{n} i^2 = \dfrac{n(n+1)(2n+1)}{6}$

1. S_1 is true because $1^2 = \dfrac{1\cdot2\cdot3}{6}$

2. Assume that S_k is true; that is, $1^2+2^2+\cdots+k^2 = \dfrac{k(k+1)(2k+1)}{6}$

Then $1^2 + 2^2 + \cdots + (k+1)^2 = \dfrac{k(k+1)(2k+1)}{6} + (k+1)^2$

$= \dfrac{k+1}{6}\,[k(2k+1) + 6(k+1)] = \dfrac{k+1}{6}\,[2k^2+7k+6] = (k+1)(k+2)(2k+3)/6$

$= (k+1)[(k+1)+1][2(k+1)+1]/6$, so S_{k+1} is true.

Therefore S_n is true for all n by mathematical induction.

42. (a) Let S_n be the statement $\displaystyle\sum_{i=1}^{n} i^4 = n(n+1)(2n+1)(3n^2+3n-1)/30$.

1. S_1 is true since $1^4 = 1\cdot2\cdot3\cdot5/30$.

2. Assume S_k is true; that is, $\displaystyle\sum_{i=1}^{k} i^4 = k(k+1)(2k+1)(3k^2+3k-1)/30$.

Then $\displaystyle\sum_{i=1}^{k+1} i^4 = (k+1)^4 + k(k+1)(2k+1)(3k^2+3k-1)/30$

$= \dfrac{k+1}{30}[30(k+1)^3 + k(2k+1)(3k^2+3k-1)] = \dfrac{k+1}{30}[30(k^3+3k^2+3k+1)$

$+ 6k^4+9k^3+k^2-k] = \dfrac{k+1}{30}[6k^4+39k^3+91k^2+89k+30]$

$= \dfrac{k+1}{30}(k+2)(6k^3+27k^2+37k+15) = (k+1)(k+2)(2k+3)(3k^2+9k+5)/30 =$

$(k+1)[(k+1)+1][2(k+1)+1][3(k+1)^2+3(k+1)-1]/30$, so S_{k+1} is true.

   Therefore S_n is true for all n by mathematical induction.

(b) Let $S = \displaystyle\sum_{i=1}^{n} i^4$. We calculate $\displaystyle\sum_{i=1}^{n}[(i+1)^5 - i^5] = (2^5-1^5)$

$+ (3^5-2^5) + \cdots + [(n+1)^5 - n^5] = (n+1)^5 - 1^5 = n^5 + 5n^4 + 10n^3 +$

$10n^2 + 5n$. On the other hand, $\displaystyle\sum_{i=1}^{n}[(i+1)^5 - i^5]$

$= \displaystyle\sum_{i=1}^{n}(5i^4+10i^3+10i^2+5i+1) = 5S + 10\sum_{i=1}^{n} i^3 + 10\sum_{i=1}^{n} i^2 + 5\sum_{i=1}^{n} i + \sum_{i=1}^{n} 1$

$= 5S + \dfrac{5n^2(n+1)^2}{2} + \dfrac{5n(n+1)(2n+1)}{3} + \dfrac{5n(n+1)}{2} + n$

$= 5S + \dfrac{5}{6}n(n+1)[3n(n+1)+2(2n+1)+3] + n = 5S + \dfrac{5}{6}n(n+1)(3n^2+7n+5) + n$

$= 5S + \dfrac{5}{6}(3n^4+10n^3+12n^2+5n) + n$. It follows that $5S = n^5+5n^4+10n^3+$

$10n^2 + 5n - \dfrac{5}{6}(3n^4+10n^3+12n^2+5n) - n$, hence $30S = 6n^5+30n^4+60n^3+60n^2$

$+30n-15n^4-50n^3-60n^2-25n-6n = 6n^5+15n^4+10n^3-n = n(n+1)(6n^3+9n^2+n-1)$

$= n(n+1)(2n+1)(3n^2+3n-1)$ and $S = n(n+1)(2n+1)(3n^2+3n-1)/30$

44. Summing the inequalities $-|a_i| \leq a_i \leq |a_i|$ for $i = 1,2,\cdots,n$, we get

$-\displaystyle\sum_{i=1}^{n}|a_i| \leq \sum_{i=1}^{n} a_i \leq \sum_{i=1}^{n}|a_i|$ Since $|x| \leq c \iff -c \leq x \leq c$, we have

$\left|\displaystyle\sum_{i=1}^{n} a_i\right| \leq \sum_{i=1}^{n}|a_i|$ [Another method: Use mathematical induction.]

46. $\displaystyle\lim_{n\to\infty}\sum_{i=1}^{n}\dfrac{1}{n}\left[\left(\dfrac{i}{n}\right)^3 + 1\right] = \lim_{n\to\infty}\sum_{i=1}^{n}\left[\dfrac{i^3}{n^4} + \dfrac{1}{n}\right] = \lim_{n\to\infty}\left[\dfrac{1}{n^4}\sum_{i=1}^{n} i^3 + \dfrac{1}{n}\sum_{i=1}^{n} 1\right]$

$= \displaystyle\lim_{n\to\infty}\left[\dfrac{1}{n^4}\left[\dfrac{n(n+1)}{2}\right]^2 + \dfrac{1}{n}(n)\right] = \lim_{n\to\infty}\dfrac{1}{4}\left[1 + \dfrac{1}{n}\right]^2 + 1 = \dfrac{1}{4} + 1 = \dfrac{5}{4}$

48. $\displaystyle\lim_{n\to\infty}\sum_{i=1}^{n}\dfrac{3}{n}\left[\left(1 + \dfrac{3i}{n}\right)^3 - 2\left(1 + \dfrac{3i}{n}\right)\right]$

$= \displaystyle\lim_{n\to\infty}\sum_{i=1}^{n}\dfrac{3}{n}\left[1 + \dfrac{9i}{n} + \dfrac{27i^2}{n^2} + \dfrac{27i^3}{n^3} - 2 - \dfrac{6i}{n}\right]$

$$= \lim_{n \to \infty} \sum_{i=1}^{n} \left[\frac{81}{n^4} i^3 + \frac{81}{n^3} i^2 + \frac{9}{n^2} i - \frac{3}{n} \right]$$

$$= \lim_{n \to \infty} \left[\frac{81}{n^4} \frac{n^2(n+1)^2}{4} + \frac{81}{n^3} \frac{n(n+1)(2n+1)}{6} + \frac{9}{n^2} \frac{n(n+1)}{2} - \frac{3}{n} n \right]$$

$$= \lim_{n \to \infty} \left[\frac{81}{4} \left[1 + \frac{1}{n} \right]^2 + \frac{27}{2} \left[1 + \frac{1}{n} \right] \left[2 + \frac{1}{n} \right] + \frac{9}{2} \left[1 + \frac{1}{n} \right] - 3 \right]$$

$$= \frac{81}{4} + \frac{54}{2} + \frac{9}{2} - 3 = \frac{195}{4}$$

50. (a) By Formula 18a in Appendix B (with different names for the variables), 2 sin u cos v = sin(u+v) + sin(u-v).

   Taking $u = \frac{1}{2}x$ and $v = ix$, we get $2 \sin \frac{1}{2}x \cos ix$

   $= \sin(\frac{1}{2}x + ix) + \sin(\frac{1}{2}x - ix) = \sin(i + \frac{1}{2})x + \sin(\frac{1}{2} - i)x$

   $= \sin(i + \frac{1}{2})x - \sin(i - \frac{1}{2})x.$

   (b) $2 \sin \frac{1}{2}x \sum_{i=1}^{n} \cos ix = \sum_{i=1}^{n} 2 \sin \frac{1}{2}x \cos ix$

   $= \sum_{i=1}^{n} [\sin(i+\frac{1}{2})x - \sin(i-\frac{1}{2})x] = \sin(n+\frac{1}{2})x - \sin \frac{1}{2}x$ [by #43]

   Hence $\sum_{i=1}^{n} \cos ix = \dfrac{\sin(n+\frac{1}{2})x - \sin \frac{1}{2}x}{2 \sin \frac{1}{2}x}$. [$\sin \frac{1}{2}x \neq 0$ since x is not

   an integer multiple of 2π.] Now $\sin(n+\frac{1}{2})x = \sin[\frac{1}{2}(n+1)x + \frac{1}{2}nx]$

   $= \sin \frac{1}{2}(n+1)x \cos \frac{1}{2}nx + \cos \frac{1}{2}(n+1)x \sin \frac{1}{2}nx$ and $\sin \frac{1}{2}x$

   $= \sin[\frac{1}{2}(n+1)x - \frac{1}{2}nx] = \sin \frac{1}{2}(n+1)x \cos \frac{1}{2}nx - \cos \frac{1}{2}(n+1)x \sin \frac{1}{2}nx.$

   Subtracting, we get $\sin(n+\frac{1}{2})x - \sin \frac{1}{2}x = 2 \cos \frac{1}{2}(n+1)x \sin \frac{1}{2}nx.$

   Thus $\sum_{i=1}^{n} \cos ix = \dfrac{\cos \frac{1}{2}(n+1)x \sin \frac{1}{2}nx}{\sin \frac{1}{2}x}$

Exercises 5.2

2. (a) $\|P\| = \max\{1,1,1,1\} = 1$

    (b) $\sum_{i=1}^{n} f(x_i^*)\Delta x_i = \sum_{i=1}^{4} f(i)\cdot 1$

    $= 15 + 12 + 7 + 0 = 34$

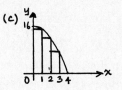

4. (a) $\|P\| = \max\{1,1,1,1,1,1,1,1\} = 1$

    (b) $\sum_{i=1}^{n} f(x_i^*)\Delta x_i = \sum_{i=-3}^{4} f(i - \tfrac{1}{2})\cdot 1$

    $= f(-3.5) + f(-2.5) + f(-1.5)$

    $+ f(-.5) + f(.5) + f(1.5) + f(2.5)$

    $+ f(3.5) = 2[f(.5) + f(1.5) + f(2.5)$

    $+ f(3.5)] = 2\cdot 43 = 86$

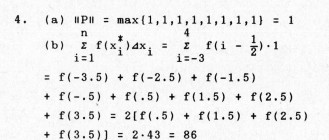

6. (a) $\|P\| = \max\{.5,.5,1,2\} = 2$

    (b) $\sum_{i=1}^{n} f(x_i^*)\Delta x_i = f(0)(0.5) +$

    $f(.5)(.5) + f(1)(1) + f(2)(2)$

    $= .5 + 1 + 3 + 10 = 14.5$

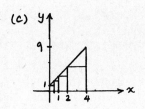

8. (a) $\|P\| = \max\{.5,.5,.5,.5\} = .5$

    (b) $\sum_{i=1}^{n} f(x_i^*)\Delta x_i = f(.25)(.5) +$

    $f(1)(.5) + f(1.25)(.5) + f(2)(.5)$

    $= \frac{1}{2}[f(.25) + f(1) + f(1.25) + f(2)]$

    $= \frac{1}{2}\left[\frac{4}{5} + \frac{1}{2} + \frac{4}{9} + \frac{1}{3}\right] = \frac{187}{180} = 1.03\overline{8}$

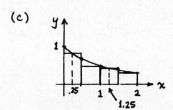

10. (a) $\|P\| = \max\left\{\frac{\pi}{6}, \frac{\pi}{12}, \frac{\pi}{12}, \frac{\pi}{6}\right\} = \frac{\pi}{6}$

    (b) $\sum_{i=1}^{n} f(x_i^*)\Delta x_i = f(0)\frac{\pi}{6} + f(\frac{\pi}{6})\frac{\pi}{12}$

    $+ f(\frac{\pi}{4})\frac{\pi}{12} + f(\frac{\pi}{3})\frac{\pi}{6} = 4\cdot\frac{\pi}{6} + 2\sqrt{3}\cdot\frac{\pi}{12}$

    $+ 2\sqrt{2}\,\frac{\pi}{12} + 2\cdot\frac{\pi}{6} = \pi(6 + \sqrt{3} + \sqrt{2})/6$

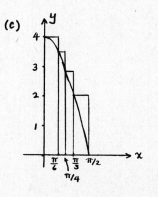

134

12. $f(x) = 3 - \dfrac{x}{2}$ on $[-2,2]$ with partition points $x_i = -2 + \dfrac{4i}{n}$

$(i = 0,1,\cdots,n)$, so $\varDelta x_i = 4/n$ for all i and $\|P\| = \max\{\varDelta x_i\} = 4/n$.

$\|P\| \to 0$ is equivalent to $n \to \infty$.

(a) $x_i^* = x_{i-1} = -2 + \dfrac{4(i-1)}{n}$ for $i = 1,2,\cdots,n$.

$$A = \lim_{n\to\infty} \sum_{i=1}^{n} f(x_i^*)\varDelta x_i = \lim_{n\to\infty} \sum_{i=1}^{n} \left[3 - \frac{x_i^*}{2}\right]\frac{4}{n} = \lim_{n\to\infty} \sum_{i=1}^{n} \left[4 - \frac{2(i-1)}{n}\right]\frac{4}{n}$$

$$= \lim_{n\to\infty} \sum_{i=1}^{n} \left[\left(4 + \frac{2}{n}\right) - \frac{2i}{n}\right]\frac{4}{n} = \lim_{n\to\infty} \left[\left(4 + \frac{2}{n}\right)\frac{4}{n} \sum_{i=1}^{n} 1 - \frac{8}{n^2} \sum_{i=1}^{n} i\right]$$

$$= \lim_{n\to\infty} \left[\left(4 + \frac{2}{n}\right)\left(\frac{4}{n}\right)n - \frac{8}{n^2}\frac{n(n+1)}{2}\right] = \lim_{n\to\infty} \left[\left(4 + \frac{2}{n}\right)\cdot 4 - 4\left(1 + \frac{1}{n}\right)\right]$$

$$= 4\cdot 4 - 4\cdot 1 = 12$$

(b) $x_i^* = x_i = -2 + \dfrac{4i}{n}$ for $i = 1,2,\ldots,n$

$$A = \lim_{n\to\infty} \sum_{i=1}^{n} \left[3 - \left(-2 + \frac{4i}{n}\right)/2\right]\frac{4}{n} = \lim_{n\to\infty} \sum_{i=1}^{n} \left[4 - \frac{2i}{n}\right]\frac{4}{n}$$

$$= \lim_{n\to\infty} \left[\frac{16}{n} \sum_{i=1}^{n} 1 - \frac{8}{n^2} \sum_{i=1}^{n} i\right] = \lim_{n\to\infty} \left[\frac{16}{n}\cdot n - \frac{8}{n^2}\frac{n(n+1)}{2}\right]$$

$$= \lim_{n\to\infty} \left[16 - 4\left(1 + \frac{1}{n}\right)\right] = 16 - 4 = 12$$

(c) $x_i^* = -2 + \dfrac{4i-2}{n}$ for $i = 1,2,\ldots,n$

$$A = \lim_{n\to\infty} \sum_{i=1}^{n} \left[3 - \left(-2 + \frac{4i-2}{n}\right)/2\right]\frac{4}{n} = \lim_{n\to\infty} \sum_{i=1}^{n} \left[4 - \frac{2i-1}{n}\right]\frac{4}{n}$$

$$= \lim_{n\to\infty} \left[\left(\frac{16}{n} + \frac{4}{n^2}\right) \sum_{i=1}^{n} 1 - \frac{8}{n^2} \sum_{i=1}^{n} i\right] = \lim_{n\to\infty} \left[\left(\frac{16}{n} + \frac{4}{n^2}\right)\cdot n - \frac{8}{n^2}\frac{n(n+1)}{2}\right]$$

$$= \lim_{n\to\infty} \left[16 + \frac{4}{n} - 4\left(1 + \frac{1}{n}\right)\right] = 16 + 0 - 4\cdot 1 = 12$$

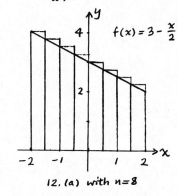

12.(a) with n=8

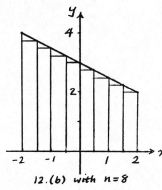

12.(b) with n=8

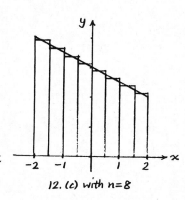

12.(c) with n=8

14. $f(x) = x^3$ on $[0,1]$ with partition points $x_i = \frac{i}{n}$ $(i = 0,1,\ldots,n)$,

$\Delta x_i = \frac{1}{n}$ for all i, and $\|P\| = \frac{1}{n}$.   (a) $x_i^* = \frac{i-1}{n}$ $(i = 1,\ldots,n)$

$A = \lim_{n\to\infty} \sum_{i=1}^{n} \left[\frac{i-1}{n}\right]^3 \frac{1}{n} = \lim_{n\to\infty} \sum_{i=2}^{n} \left[\frac{i-1}{n}\right]^3 \frac{1}{n}$ (The term for $i = 1$ is zero.)

$= \lim_{n\to\infty} \sum_{i=1}^{n-1} \left[\frac{i}{n}\right]^3 \frac{1}{n} = \lim_{n\to\infty} \frac{1}{n^4} \sum_{i=1}^{n-1} i^3 = \lim_{n\to\infty} \frac{1}{n^4} \frac{(n-1)^2 n^2}{4}$

$= \lim_{n\to\infty} \frac{1}{4}\left[1 - \frac{1}{n}\right]^2 \cdot 1^2 = \frac{1}{4}\cdot 1 \cdot 1 = \frac{1}{4}$

(b) $x_i^* = \frac{i}{n}$ $(i = 1,\ldots,n)$ $A = \lim_{n\to\infty} \sum_{i=1}^{n} \left[\frac{i}{n}\right]^3 \frac{1}{n} = \lim_{n\to\infty} \frac{1}{n^4} \sum_{i=1}^{n} i^3$

$= \lim_{n\to\infty} \frac{1}{n^4} \frac{n^2(n+1)^2}{4} = \lim_{n\to\infty} \left[1 + \frac{1}{n}\right]^2 \frac{1}{4} = 1 \cdot \frac{1}{4} = \frac{1}{4}$

(c) $x_i^* = \frac{i}{n} - \frac{1}{2n}$ $(i = 1,\ldots,n)$

$A = \lim_{n\to\infty} \sum_{i=1}^{n} \left[\frac{i}{n} - \frac{1}{2n}\right]^3 \frac{1}{n} = \lim_{n\to\infty} \sum_{i=1}^{n} \left[\frac{i^3}{n^3} - \frac{3i^2}{2n^3} + \frac{3i}{4n^3} + \frac{1}{8n^3}\right] \frac{1}{n}$

$= \lim_{n\to\infty} \left[\frac{1}{n^4} \sum_{i=1}^{n} i^3 - \frac{3}{2n^4} \sum_{i=1}^{n} i^2 + \frac{3}{4n^4} \sum_{i=1}^{n} i + \frac{1}{8n^4}\right]$

$= \lim_{n\to\infty} \left[\frac{1}{n^4} \frac{n^2(n+1)^2}{4} - \frac{3}{2n^4} \frac{n(n+1)(2n+1)}{6} + \frac{3}{4n^4} \frac{n(n+1)}{2} + \frac{1}{8n^4}\right]$

$= \lim_{n\to\infty} \left[\frac{1}{4}\left[1+\frac{1}{n}\right]^2 - \frac{1}{4} \frac{1}{n}\left[1+\frac{1}{n}\right]\left[2+\frac{1}{n}\right] + \frac{3}{8} \frac{1}{n^2}\left[1+\frac{1}{n}\right] + \frac{1}{8n^4}\right]$

$= \frac{1}{4}\cdot 1 - \frac{1}{4}\cdot 0 \cdot 1 \cdot 2 + \frac{3}{8}\cdot 0 \cdot 1 + 0 = \frac{1}{4}$

14. (a) with n=4   14. (b) with n=4   14. (c) with n=4

16. $f(x) = 2x + 1$ on $[0,5]$. $x_i^* = x_i = \frac{5i}{n}$ for $i = 1,\ldots,n$ and $\Delta x_i = \frac{5}{n}$

$A = \lim_{n\to\infty} \sum_{i=1}^{n} \left[2\left[\frac{5i}{n}\right] + 1\right] \frac{5}{n} = \lim_{n\to\infty} \left[\frac{50}{n^2} \sum_{i=1}^{n} i + \frac{5}{n} \sum_{i=1}^{n} 1\right]$

$= \lim_{n\to\infty} \left[\frac{50}{n^2} \frac{n(n+1)}{2} + \frac{5}{n}n\right]$

$= \lim_{n\to\infty} \left[25 \cdot 1 \cdot \left[1+\frac{1}{n}\right] + 5\right] = 25 + 5 = 30.$

$y = 2x+1$

18. $f(x) = 2x^2 - 4x + 5$ on $[-3,2]$. $x_i^* = x_i = -3 + \frac{5i}{n}$ $(i = 1, 2, \ldots, n)$

$A = \lim\limits_{n\to\infty} \sum\limits_{i=1}^{n} \left[2\left[-3 + \frac{5i}{n}\right]^2 - 4\left[-3 + \frac{5i}{n}\right] + 5 \right] \frac{5}{n}$

$= \lim\limits_{n\to\infty} \sum\limits_{i=1}^{n} \left[\frac{50i^2}{n^2} - \frac{80i}{n} + 35 \right] \frac{5}{n}$

$= \lim\limits_{n\to\infty} \left[\frac{250}{n^3} \Sigma\, i^2 - \frac{400}{n^2} \Sigma\, i + \frac{175}{n} \Sigma\, 1 \right]$

$= \lim\limits_{n\to\infty} \left[\frac{250}{n^3} \frac{n(n+1)(2n+1)}{6} - \frac{400}{n^2} \frac{n(n+1)}{2} + \frac{175}{n}\, n \right]$

$= \lim\limits_{n\to\infty} \left[\frac{125}{3} \cdot 1 \cdot \left[1+\frac{1}{n}\right]\left[2+\frac{1}{n}\right] - 200\cdot 1 \cdot \left[1+\frac{1}{n}\right] + 175 \right]$

$= \frac{125}{3} \cdot 1 \cdot 1 \cdot 2 - 200 \cdot 1 \cdot 1 + 175 = \frac{175}{3}$

$y = 2x^2 - 4x + 5$

20. $f(x) = x^3 + 2x^2 + x$ on $[0,1]$. $x_i^* = x_i = \frac{i}{n}$, $\varDelta x_i = \frac{1}{n}$. $A =$

$\lim\limits_{n\to\infty} \sum\limits_{i=1}^{n} \left[\frac{i^3}{n^3} + 2\frac{i^2}{n^2} + \frac{i}{n} \right] \frac{1}{n} = \lim\limits_{n\to\infty} \left[\frac{1}{n^4} \Sigma i^3 + \frac{2}{n^3} \Sigma i^2 + \frac{1}{n^2} \Sigma i \right]$

$= \lim\limits_{n\to\infty} \left[\frac{1}{n^4} \frac{n^2(n+1)^2}{4} + \frac{2}{n^3} \frac{n(n+1)(2n+1)}{6} + \frac{1}{n^2} \cdot \frac{n(n+1)}{2} \right]$

$= \lim\limits_{n\to\infty} \left[\frac{1}{4}\left[1+\frac{1}{n}\right]^2 + \frac{1}{3}\left[1+\frac{1}{n}\right]\left[2+\frac{1}{n}\right] + \frac{1}{2}\left[1+\frac{1}{n}\right] \right]$

$= \frac{1}{4} \cdot 1 + \frac{1}{3} \cdot 1 \cdot 2 + \frac{1}{2} \cdot 1 = \frac{17}{12}$

22. $f(x) = x^4 + 3x + 2$ on $[0,3]$, $x_i^* = x_i = \frac{3i}{n}$, $\varDelta x_i = \frac{3}{n}$

$A = \lim\limits_{n\to\infty} \sum\limits_{i=1}^{n} \left[\left[\frac{3i}{n}\right]^4 + 3\left[\frac{3i}{n}\right] + 2 \right] \frac{3}{n} = \lim\limits_{n\to\infty} \left[\frac{243}{n^5} \Sigma\, i^4 + \frac{27}{n^2} \Sigma\, i + \frac{6}{n} \Sigma\, 1 \right]$

$= \lim\limits_{n\to\infty} \left[\frac{243}{n^5} \frac{n(n+1)(2n+1)(3n^2+3n-1)}{30} + \frac{27}{n^2} \frac{n(n+1)}{2} + \frac{6}{n}\cdot n \right]$

$= \lim\limits_{n\to\infty} \left[\frac{81}{10} \cdot 1 \cdot \left[1+\frac{1}{n}\right]\left[2+\frac{1}{n}\right]\left[3 + \frac{1}{n} - \frac{1}{n^2}\right] + \frac{27}{2} \cdot 1 \cdot \left[1+\frac{1}{n}\right] + 6 \right]$

$= \frac{81}{10} \cdot 1^2 \cdot 2 \cdot 3 + \frac{27}{2} \cdot 1^2 + 6 = \frac{243}{5} + \frac{27}{2} + 6 = 68.1$

(3,92)

Exercises 5.3

2. $f(x) = 3x - 1$ (a) $\|P\| = \max\{.8, .6, .6, .8, .8, .4\} = .8$

(b) $\sum\limits_{i=1}^{6} f(x_i^*)\Delta x_i = f(-1.6)(.8) + f(-.9)(.6) + f(-.3)(.6) + f(.4)(.8)$

$+ f(1.2)(.8) + f(1.8)(.4) = (-5.8)(.8) + (-3.7)(.6) + (-1.9)(.6) +$

$(.2)(.8) + (2.6)(.8) + (4.4)(.4) = -4$

4. $f(x) = x + x^2$ (a) $\|P\| = \max\{.5, .5, .3, .3, .4\} = .5$

(b) $\sum\limits_{i=1}^{5} f(x_i^*)\Delta x_i = f(-2)(.5) + f(-1.5)(.5) + f(-1)(.3) + f(-.7)(.3)$

$+ f(-.4)(.4) = 2(.5) + (.75)(.5) + (0)(.3) + (-.21)(.3) +$

$(-.24)(.4) = 1.216$

6. $f(x) = \sin x$ (a) $\|P\| = \max\{(\pi/2)-1, 1, 1, 1, \pi-2\} = \pi-2 \approx 1.14$

(b) $\sum\limits_{i=1}^{5} f(x_i^*)\Delta x_i = \sin(-1.5)(\pi/2 - 1) + \sin(-.5)\cdot 1 + \sin(.5)\cdot 1$

$+ \sin(1.5)\cdot 1 + \sin 3 \cdot (\pi-2) \approx .589$

8. $\int_{-2}^{7}(6-2x)dx = \lim\limits_{n\to\infty} \dfrac{9}{n} \sum\limits_{i=1}^{n} \left[6 - 2\left[-2 + \dfrac{9i}{n}\right]\right]$

$= \lim\limits_{n\to\infty} \dfrac{9}{n} \sum\limits_{i=1}^{n} \left[10 - \dfrac{18i}{n}\right] = \lim\limits_{n\to\infty}\left[\dfrac{90}{n}\sum 1 - \dfrac{162}{n^2}\sum i\right]$

$= \lim\limits_{n\to\infty}\left[\dfrac{90}{n}\cdot n - \dfrac{162}{n^2}\dfrac{n(n+1)}{2}\right] = \lim\limits_{n\to\infty}\left[90 - 81\cdot 1 \cdot\left[1+\dfrac{1}{n}\right]\right] = 90 - 81 = 9$

10. $\int_{0}^{1}(ax+b)dx = \lim\limits_{n\to\infty} \dfrac{1}{n} \sum\limits_{i=1}^{n}\left[a\left[\dfrac{i}{n}\right] + b\right] = \lim\limits_{n\to\infty}\left[\dfrac{a}{n^2}\sum i + \dfrac{b}{n}\sum 1\right]$

$= \lim\limits_{n\to\infty}\left[\dfrac{a}{n^2}\dfrac{n(n+1)}{2} + \dfrac{b}{n}n\right] = \lim\limits_{n\to\infty}\left[\dfrac{a}{2}\cdot 1\cdot\left[1+\dfrac{1}{n}\right] + b\right] = \dfrac{a}{2} + b$

12. $\int_{1}^{5}(2+3x-x^2)dx = \lim\limits_{n\to\infty} \dfrac{4}{n} \sum\limits_{i=1}^{n}\left[2 + 3\left[1 + \dfrac{4i}{n}\right] - \left[1 + \dfrac{4i}{n}\right]^2\right]$

$= \lim\limits_{n\to\infty} \dfrac{4}{n} \sum\limits_{i=1}^{n}\left[-\dfrac{16i^2}{n^2} + \dfrac{4i}{n} + 4\right] = \lim\limits_{n\to\infty}\left[\dfrac{-64}{n^3}\sum i^2 + \dfrac{16}{n^2}\sum i + \dfrac{16}{n}\sum 1\right]$

$= \lim\limits_{n\to\infty}\left[\dfrac{-64}{n^3}\cdot\dfrac{n(n+1)(2n+1)}{6} + \dfrac{16}{n^2}\cdot\dfrac{n(n+1)}{2} + \dfrac{16}{n}\cdot n\right]$

$= \lim\limits_{n\to\infty}\left[-\dfrac{32}{3}\cdot 1\cdot\left[1+\dfrac{1}{n}\right]\left[2+\dfrac{1}{n}\right] + 8\cdot 1\cdot\left[1+\dfrac{1}{n}\right] + 16\right] = -\dfrac{64}{3} + 8 + 16 = \dfrac{8}{3}$

14. $\int_{a}^{b}(Px^2+Qx+R)dx = \lim\limits_{n\to\infty} \dfrac{b-a}{n} \sum\limits_{i=1}^{n}\left[P\left[a + \dfrac{b-a}{n}i\right]^2 + Q\left[a + \dfrac{b-a}{n}i\right] + R\right]$

$= \lim\limits_{n\to\infty} \dfrac{b-a}{n} \sum\limits_{i=1}^{n}\left[P\dfrac{(b-a)^2}{n^2}i^2 + (2Pa+Q)\dfrac{b-a}{n}i + (Pa^2+Qa+R)\right]$

$$= \lim_{n \to \infty} \left[P \frac{(b-a)^3}{n^3} \Sigma\, i^2 + (2Pa+Q) \frac{(b-a)^2}{n^2} \Sigma\, i + (Pa^2+Qa+R) \frac{b-a}{n} \Sigma\, 1 \right]$$

$$= \lim_{n \to \infty} \left[P \frac{(b-a)^3}{n^3} \frac{n(n+1)(2n+1)}{6} + (2Pa+Q) \frac{(b-a)^2}{n^2} \frac{n(n+1)}{2} \right.$$
$$\left. + (Pa^2+Qa+R) \frac{b-a}{n} \cdot n \right]$$

$$= \lim_{n \to \infty} \left[\frac{P(b-a)^3}{6} \cdot 1 \cdot \left[1+\frac{1}{n} \right] \left[2+\frac{1}{n} \right] + \left(Pa + \frac{Q}{2} \right)(b-a)^2 \cdot 1 \cdot \left[1+\frac{1}{n} \right] \right.$$
$$\left. + (Pa^2+Qa+R)(b-a) \right]$$

$$= P \frac{(b-a)^3}{3} + \left(Pa + \frac{Q}{2} \right)(b-a)^2 + (Pa^2+Qa+R)(b-a)$$

$$= P \left(\frac{b^3}{3} - b^2 a + ba^2 - \frac{a^3}{3} + ab^2 - 2a^2 b + a^3 + a^2 b - a^3 \right)$$
$$+ Q \left(\frac{b^2}{2} - ab + \frac{a^2}{2} + ab - a^2 \right) + R(b-a)$$

$$= P \left(\frac{b^3}{3} - \frac{a^3}{3} \right) + Q \left(\frac{b^2}{2} - \frac{a^2}{2} \right) + R(b-a)$$

16. $\displaystyle \int_2^5 (t^3 - 2t + 3)\,dt = \lim_{n \to \infty} \frac{3}{n} \sum_{i=1}^{n} \left[\left[2 + \frac{3i}{n} \right]^3 - 2 \left[2 + \frac{3i}{n} \right] + 3 \right]$

$$= \lim_{n \to \infty} \frac{3}{n} \sum_{i=1}^{n} \left[\frac{27i^3}{n^3} + \frac{54i^2}{n^2} + \frac{36i}{n} + 8 - 4 - \frac{6i}{n} + 3 \right]$$

$$= \lim_{n \to \infty} \frac{3}{n} \sum_{i=1}^{n} \left[\frac{27i^3}{n^3} + \frac{54i^2}{n^2} + \frac{30i}{n} + 7 \right]$$

$$= \lim_{n \to \infty} \left[\frac{81}{n^4} \Sigma\, i^3 + \frac{162}{n^3} \Sigma\, i^2 + \frac{90}{n^2} \Sigma\, i + \frac{21}{n} \Sigma\, 1 \right]$$

$$= \lim_{n \to \infty} \left[\frac{81}{n^4} \frac{n^2(n+1)^2}{4} + \frac{162}{n^3} \frac{n(n+1)(2n+1)}{6} + \frac{90}{n^2} \frac{n(n+1)}{2} + \frac{21}{n} \cdot n \right]$$

$$= \lim_{n \to \infty} \left[\frac{81}{4} \cdot 1^2 \left[1+\frac{1}{n} \right]^2 + 27 \cdot 1 \cdot \left[1+\frac{1}{n} \right] \left[2+\frac{1}{n} \right] + 45 \cdot 1 \cdot \left[1+\frac{1}{n} \right] + 21 \right]$$

$$= \frac{81}{4} + 54 + 45 + 21 = 140.25$$

18. $\displaystyle \int_0^1 (x^3 - 5x^4)\,dx = \lim_{n \to \infty} \frac{1}{n} \sum_{i=1}^{n} \left[\left[\frac{i}{n} \right]^3 - 5 \left[\frac{i}{n} \right]^4 \right] = \lim_{n \to \infty} \left[\frac{1}{n^4} \Sigma i^3 - \frac{5}{n^5} \Sigma i^4 \right]$

$$= \lim_{n \to \infty} \left[\frac{n^2(n+1)^2}{4n^4} - \frac{5n(n+1)(2n+1)(3n^2+3n-1)}{30n^5} \right]$$

$$= \lim_{n \to \infty} \left[\frac{1}{4} \cdot 1^2 \cdot \left[1+\frac{1}{n} \right]^2 - \frac{1}{6} \cdot 1 \cdot \left[1+\frac{1}{n} \right] \left[2+\frac{1}{n} \right] \left[3 + \frac{3}{n} - \frac{1}{n^2} \right] \right] = \frac{1}{4} - 1 = -\frac{3}{4}$$

20. Take $P = 1$ and $Q = R = 0$ in # 14.

22. $\displaystyle \lim_{\|P\| \to 0} \sum_{i=1}^{n} \sqrt{x_i^*}\ \Delta x_i = \int_1^4 \sqrt{x}\ dx$

24. $\displaystyle\lim_{\|P\|\to 0} \sum_{i=1}^{n} \frac{\tan x_i}{x_i} \, \varDelta x_i = \int_{2}^{4} \frac{\tan x}{x} \, dx$

26. $\displaystyle\lim_{n\to\infty} \frac{1}{n} \sum_{i=1}^{n} \frac{1}{1 + (i/n)^2} = \int_{0}^{1} \frac{dx}{1 + x^2}$

28. $\int_{1}^{1} x^2 \cos x \, dx = 0$ by the definition in Note 6.

30. (a) f is not continuous on [0,1] because $\displaystyle\lim_{x\to 0^+} f(x) = \lim_{x\to 0^+} \frac{1}{x}$ does

not exist.

(b) f is unbounded on [0,1] since if we pick any proposed positive number M to serve as a bound, then for 0 < x < 1/M, we see that f(x) = 1/x > M.

(c) $\int_{0}^{1} f(x)dx$ does not exist since an approximating sum $\sum\limits_{i=1}^{n} f(x_i^*)\varDelta x_i$

can be made arbitrarily large, no matter how small the norm $\|P\|$ is. The first subinterval of the partition P of [0,1] will be of the form $[0, x_1]$. By choosing x_i^* to be positive but sufficiently small, we can make $f(x_i^*)$ as large as we like. This means that we can make $\sum\limits_{i=1}^{n} f(x_i^*)\varDelta x_i$ as large as we like by an appropriate choice of x_i^*.

Thus $\sum\limits_{i=1}^{n} f(x_i^*)\varDelta x_i$ cannot approach a limiting value as $\|P\| \to 0$.

32. First notice that if $x_i^* = x_i = 2^{i/n}$ for i = 1,2,...,n, then $\varDelta x_i = x_i - x_{i-1} = 2^{i/n} - 2^{(i-1)/n}$ and $\|P\| = 2 - 2^{(n-1)/n}$, so $\|P\| \to 2-2$

$= 0$ as $n \to \infty$. Thus $\int_{1}^{2} x^3 dx = \displaystyle\lim_{n\to\infty} \sum_{i=1}^{n} x_i^3 \, \varDelta x_i$

$= \displaystyle\lim_{n\to\infty} \sum_{i=1}^{n} 2^{3i/n}(2^{i/n} - 2^{(i-1)/n})$

$= \displaystyle\lim_{n\to\infty} \sum_{i=1}^{n} 2^{4i/n}(1 - 2^{-1/n}) = \lim_{n\to\infty} (1 - 2^{-1/n}) \sum_{i=1}^{n} (2^{4/n})^i$

$= \displaystyle\lim_{n\to\infty} (1 - 2^{-1/n}) \cdot 2^{4/n} \frac{(2^{4/n})^n - 1}{2^{4/n} - 1}$ [by Exer. 5.1.49, which says in

particular that $\sum\limits_{i=1}^{n} r^i = \sum\limits_{i=1}^{n} r \cdot r^{i-1} = \dfrac{r(r^n - 1)}{r - 1}$. Here $r = 2^{4/n}$.]

$= \displaystyle\lim_{n\to\infty} (2^4 - 1) \cdot \frac{2^{4/n} - 2^{3/n}}{2^{4/n} - 1} = 15 \lim_{n\to\infty} \frac{(2^{1/n})^4 - (2^{1/n})^3}{(2^{1/n})^4 - 1}$

$$= 15 \lim_{n \to \infty} \frac{(2^{1/n})^3 (2^{1/n} - 1)}{(2^{1/n} - 1)(2^{1/n} + 1)[(2^{1/n})^2 + 1]}$$

$$= 15 \lim_{n \to \infty} \frac{(2^{1/n})^3}{(2^{1/n} + 1)(2^{2/n} + 1)} = 15 \cdot \frac{1}{2 \cdot 2} = \frac{15}{4}$$

Section 5.4

Exercises 5.4

2. $\int_{-1}^{4} \pi \, dx = \pi[4-(-1)] = 5\pi$ [by Property 1]

4. $\int_{-1}^{-\sqrt{2}} (\sqrt{2}-1)dx = (\sqrt{2}-1)(-\sqrt{2}+1) = -(\sqrt{2}-1)^2 = 2\sqrt{2} - 3$

6. $\int_{3}^{6} (4-7x)dx = \int_{3}^{6} 4 \, dx - \int_{3}^{6} 7x \, dx$ [Property 4]

    $= 4(6-3) - 7 \int_{3}^{6} x \, dx$ [Properties 1 and 3]

    $= 12 - 7 \cdot \frac{1}{2}(6^2 - 3^2) = 12 - \frac{7}{2}(27) = -\frac{165}{2}$

8. $\int_{-2}^{0} (3x^2 + 2x - 4)dx = 3 \int_{-2}^{0} x^2 \, dx + 2 \int_{-2}^{0} x \, dx - \int_{-2}^{0} 4 \, dx$

    $= 3 \cdot \frac{1}{3}[0^3 - (-2)^3] + 2 \cdot \frac{1}{2}[0^2 - (-2)^2] - 4[0 - (-2)] = -4$

10. $\int_{1}^{3} (x-2)(x+3)dx = \int_{1}^{3} (x^2 + x - 6)dx = \int_{1}^{3} x^2 \, dx + \int_{1}^{3} x \, dx + \int_{1}^{3} (-6)dx$

    $= \frac{1}{3}(3^3 - 1^3) + \frac{1}{2}(3^2 - 1^2) + (-6)(3-1) = \frac{2}{3}$

12. $\int_{0}^{1} (5 \cos x + 4x)dx = 5 \int_{0}^{1} \cos x \, dx + 4 \int_{0}^{1} x \, dx$

    $= 5 \sin 1 + 4 \cdot \frac{1}{2}(1^2 - 0^2) = 5 \sin 1 + 2$

14. $\int_{0}^{2} |2x-3|dx = \int_{0}^{3/2} |2x-3|dx + \int_{3/2}^{2} |2x-3|dx$ [Property 5]

    $= \int_{0}^{3/2} (3-2x)dx + \int_{3/2}^{2} (2x-3)dx$

    $= \int_{0}^{3/2} 3 \, dx - 2 \int_{0}^{3/2} x \, dx + 2 \int_{3/2}^{2} x \, dx - \int_{3/2}^{2} 3 \, dx$

    $= 3 \cdot \left[\frac{3}{2} - 0\right] - 2 \cdot \frac{1}{2}\left[\left[\frac{3}{2}\right]^2 - 0^2\right] + 2 \cdot \frac{1}{2}\left[2^2 - \left[\frac{3}{2}\right]^2\right] - 3 \cdot \left[2 - \frac{3}{2}\right] = \frac{5}{2}$

16. $\int_{0}^{2} [2x]dx = \int_{0}^{1/2} [2x]dx + \int_{1/2}^{1} [2x]dx + \int_{1}^{3/2} [2x]dx + \int_{3/2}^{2} [2x]dx$

    $= \int_{0}^{1/2} 0 \, dx + \int_{1/2}^{1} 1 \, dx + \int_{1}^{3/2} 2 \, dx + \int_{3/2}^{2} 3 \, dx$

    $= 0 \cdot (\frac{1}{2} - 0) + 1 \cdot (1 - \frac{1}{2}) + 2 \cdot (\frac{3}{2} - 1) + 3 \cdot (2 - \frac{3}{2}) = 3$

18. $\int_0^3 g(x)dx = \int_0^1 g(x)dx + \int_1^3 g(x)dx = \int_0^1 (1-x)dx + \int_1^3 (x-1)dx$

$= \int_0^1 1\ dx - \int_0^1 x\ dx + \int_1^3 x\ dx - \int_1^3 1\ dx$

$= 1\cdot(1-0) - \frac{1}{2}[1^2-0^2] + \frac{1}{2}[3^2-1^2] - 1\cdot(3-1) = \frac{5}{2}$

20. $\int_{-\pi/2}^{\pi/2} G(x)dx = \int_{-\pi/2}^0 G(x)dx + \int_0^{\pi/4} G(x)dx + \int_{\pi/4}^{\pi/2} G(x)dx$

$= \int_{-\pi/2}^0 (1+x)dx + \int_0^{\pi/4} \cos x\ dx + \int_{\pi/4}^{\pi/2} 1\ dx$

$= \int_{-\pi/2}^0 1\ dx + \int_{-\pi/2}^0 x\ dx + \int_0^{\pi/4} \cos x\ dx + \int_{\pi/4}^{\pi/2} 1\ dx$

$= 1\cdot\left[0-\left[-\frac{\pi}{2}\right]\right] + \frac{1}{2}\left[0^2-\left[-\frac{\pi}{2}\right]^2\right] + \sin\frac{\pi}{4} + 1\cdot\left[\frac{\pi}{2} - \frac{\pi}{4}\right] = \frac{3\pi}{4} - \frac{\pi^2}{8} + \frac{\sqrt{2}}{2}$

22. $\int_3^4 f(x)dx + \int_1^3 f(x)dx + \int_4^1 f(x)dx$

$= \int_1^3 f(x)dx + \int_3^4 f(x)dx - \int_1^4 f(x)dx = \int_1^4 f(x)dx - \int_1^4 f(x)dx = 0$

24. $\int_5^8 f(x)dx + \int_0^5 f(x)dx = \int_0^5 f(x)dx + \int_5^8 f(x)dx = \int_0^8 f(x)dx$

26. $\int_{-3}^5 f(x)dx - \int_{-3}^0 f(x)dx + \int_5^6 f(x)dx$

$= \int_{-3}^0 f(x)dx + \int_0^5 f(x)dx - \int_{-3}^0 f(x)dx + \int_5^6 f(x)dx = \int_0^6 f(x)dx$

28. $x \leq x^2$ on $[1,2]$, so $\int_1^2 x\ dx \leq \int_1^2 x^2\ dx$ [Property 7]

30. $x^2-3x+4 \geq 0$ on $[-2,8]$ (in fact, $x^2-3x+4 = \left[x - \frac{3}{2}\right]^2 + \frac{7}{4} \geq \frac{7}{4}$ for all

x), so $\int_{-2}^8 (x^2-3x+4)dx \geq 0$ [Property 6]

32. $4x^4-3 = (3x^4-4) + (x^4+1) \geq 3x^4-4$ on $[0,5]$,

so $\int_0^5 (4x^4-3)dx \geq \int_0^5 (3x^4-4)dx$ [Property 7]

34. $x \geq 4 \geq 8-x$ on $[4,6]$, so $\frac{1}{x} \leq \frac{1}{8-x}$ on $[4,6]$, and $\int_4^6 \frac{1}{x}\ dx \leq \int_4^6 \frac{1}{8-x}\ dx$

36. $\frac{1}{2} \leq \sin x \leq 1$ for $\frac{\pi}{6} \leq x \leq \frac{\pi}{2}$, so $\frac{1}{2}\left[\frac{\pi}{2} - \frac{\pi}{6}\right] \leq \int_{\pi/6}^{\pi/2} \sin x\ dx \leq 1\left[\frac{\pi}{2} - \frac{\pi}{6}\right]$

[Property 8]; that is, $\frac{\pi}{6} \leq \int_{\pi/6}^{\pi/2} \sin x\ dx \leq \frac{\pi}{3}$

38. $x^2-4x+5 = (x-2)^2 + 1 \geq 1$, so $1 \leq x^2 - 4x + 5 \leq 5$ for $1 \leq x \leq 4$. By

Property 8, $1\cdot(4-1) \leq \int_1^4 (x^2-4x+5)dx \leq 5\cdot(4-1)$; that is,

$3 \leq \int_1^4 (x^2-4x+5)dx \leq 15$

40. If $0 \leq x \leq 2$, then $0 \leq x^3 \leq 8$, so $1 \leq x^3+1 \leq 9$ and $1 \leq \sqrt{x^3+1} \leq 3$.

Thus $1\cdot(2-0) \leq \int_0^2 \sqrt{x^3+1}\ dx \leq 3\cdot(2-0)$; that is, $2 \leq \int_0^2 \sqrt{x^3+1}\ dx \leq 6$

42. If $\frac{\pi}{4} \leq x \leq \frac{\pi}{3}$, then $\frac{1}{2} \leq \cos x \leq \frac{\sqrt{2}}{2}$, so $\frac{1}{2}\cdot(\frac{\pi}{3} - \frac{\pi}{4}) \leq \int_{\pi/4}^{\pi/3} \cos x\ dx$

$\leq \frac{\sqrt{2}}{2}\cdot(\frac{\pi}{3} - \frac{\pi}{4})$ or $\frac{\pi}{24} \leq \int_{\pi/4}^{\pi/3} \cos x\ dx \leq \frac{\sqrt{2}\pi}{24}$

44. If $f(x) = x^2 - 3x$, $-1 \le x \le 3$, then $f'(x) = 2x - 3 = 0$ when $x = 3/2$, and $f(3/2) = -9/4$. At the endpoints, $f(-1) = 4$, $f(3) = 0$. Thus the absolute minimum is $m = -9/4$ and the absolute maximum $M = 4$. Thus $-\frac{9}{4}[3-(-1)] \le \int_{-1}^{3} (x^2-3x)\,dx \le 4[3-(-1)]$ or $-9 \le \int_{-1}^{3} (x^2-3x)\,dx \le 16$

46. If $\frac{\pi}{4} \le x \le \frac{3\pi}{4}$, then $\frac{\sqrt{2}}{2} \le \sin x \le 1$ and $\frac{1}{2} \le \sin^2 x \le 1$, so $\frac{1}{2}\cdot\left[\frac{3\pi}{4} - \frac{\pi}{4}\right] \le \int_{\pi/4}^{3\pi/4} \sin^2 x\, dx \le 1\cdot\left[\frac{3\pi}{4} - \frac{\pi}{4}\right]$; that is, $\frac{\pi}{4} \le \int_{\pi/4}^{3\pi/4} \sin^2 x\, dx \le \frac{\pi}{2}$

48. $x^2 - 1 < x^2 \Rightarrow \sqrt{x^2-1} < \sqrt{x^2} = |x| = x$ for $x \ge 0$, so $\int_{2}^{5} \sqrt{x^2-1} \le \int_{2}^{5} x\, dx = \frac{1}{2}(5^2-2^2) = 10.5$

50. By Properties 9 and 7 we have $\left|\int_{0}^{\pi} x^2 \cos x\, dx\right| \le \int_{0}^{\pi} |x^2 \cos x|\,dx \le \int_{0}^{\pi} x^2\, dx = \frac{1}{3}(\pi^3 - 0^3) = \pi^3/3$

52. Let S_n be the statement that $\int_{a}^{b} \left[\sum_{i=1}^{n} f_i(x)\right] dx = \sum_{i=1}^{n} \int_{a}^{b} f_i(x)\,dx$

(i) S_1 is obviously true. (ii) Assume that S_k is true; that is, $\int_{a}^{b} \left[\sum_{i=1}^{k} f_i(x)\right] dx = \sum_{i=1}^{k} \int_{a}^{b} f_i(x)\,dx.$

Then $\int_{a}^{b} \left[\sum_{i=1}^{k+1} f_i(x)\right] dx = \int_{a}^{b} \left[\sum_{i=1}^{k} f_i(x) + f_{k+1}(x)\right] dx$

$= \int_{a}^{b} \left[\sum_{i=1}^{k} f_i(x)\right] dx + \int_{a}^{b} f_{k+1}(x)\,dx$ [Property 2]

$= \sum_{i=1}^{k} \int_{a}^{b} f_i(x)\,dx + \int_{a}^{b} f_{k+1}(x)\,dx$ [since S_k is true]

$= \sum_{i=1}^{k+1} \int_{a}^{b} f_i(x)\,dx$, which shows that S_{k+1} is true.

Therefore S_n is true for all n, by mathematical induction.

54. Using a regular partition and right endpoints as in the proof of Property 2, we calculate $\int_{a}^{b} cf(x)\,dx = \lim_{n\to\infty} \sum_{i=1}^{n} cf(x_i)\Delta x_i = \lim_{n\to\infty} c\sum_{i=1}^{n} f(x_i)\Delta x_i$

$= c\lim_{n\to\infty} \sum_{i=1}^{n} f(x_i)\Delta x_i = c\int_{a}^{b} f(x)\,dx$

56. Since f is continuous on [a,b], f attains an absolute minimum value m at some point of [a,b] by the Extreme Value Theorem (Theorem 4.3). Since $f(x) > 0$ for all x in [a,b], it follows that $m > 0$. Now $f(x) \geq m$ for $a \leq x \leq b$, so $\int_a^b f(x)dx \geq m(b-a)$ by Property 8. Assuming that $a < b$, we see that $m > 0$ and $b-a > 0$, so $m(b-a) > 0$. This proves that $\int_a^b f(x)dx > 0$.

Section 5.5

Exercises 5.5

2. $g(x) = \int_{-1}^x \sqrt{t^3+1}\ dt \ \Rightarrow\ g'(x) = \sqrt{x^3+1}$

4. $g(t) = \int_0^t \sin(x^2)dx;\ g'(t) = \sin(t^2)$

6. $F(x) = \int_x^4 (2+\sqrt{u})^8 du = -\int_4^x (2+\sqrt{u})^8 du \ \Rightarrow\ F'(x) = -(2+\sqrt{x})^8$

8. Let $u = \sqrt{x}$. Then $\dfrac{d}{dx}\int_1^{\sqrt{x}} \dfrac{s^2}{s^2+1}\ ds = \dfrac{d}{du}\int_1^u \dfrac{s^2}{s^2+1}\ ds \cdot \dfrac{du}{dx}$

   $= \dfrac{u^2}{u^2+1}\dfrac{du}{dx} = \dfrac{x}{x+1}\dfrac{1}{2\sqrt{x}} = \dfrac{\sqrt{x}}{2(x+1)}$

10. Let $u = x^2$. Then $\dfrac{d}{dx}\int_{x^2}^\pi \dfrac{\sin t}{t}\ dt = -\dfrac{d}{dx}\int_\pi^{x^2} \dfrac{\sin t}{t}\ dt$

    $= -\dfrac{d}{du}\int_\pi^u \dfrac{\sin t}{t}\ dt \cdot \dfrac{du}{dx} = -\dfrac{\sin u}{u}\cdot\dfrac{du}{dx} = -\dfrac{\sin(x^2)}{x^2}\cdot 2x = -\dfrac{2\sin(x^2)}{x}$

12. Let $u = \sin x$. Then $\dfrac{dy}{dx} = \dfrac{dy}{du}\dfrac{du}{dx} = \dfrac{d}{du}\int_{-5}^u t\cos(t^3)dt \cdot \dfrac{du}{dx}$

    $= u\cos(u^3)\dfrac{du}{dx} = \sin x\cos(\sin^3 x)\cdot\cos x = \sin x\cos x\cos(\sin^3 x)$

14. $g(x) = \int_{\tan x}^{x^2} \dfrac{1}{\sqrt{2+t^4}}\ dt = \int_{\tan x}^1 \dfrac{dt}{\sqrt{2+t^4}} + \int_1^{x^2} \dfrac{dt}{\sqrt{2+t^4}}$

    $= -\int_1^{\tan x} \dfrac{dt}{\sqrt{2+t^4}} + \int_1^{x^2} \dfrac{dt}{\sqrt{2+t^4}} \ \Rightarrow\ g'(x) = -\dfrac{1}{\sqrt{2+\tan^4 x}}\cdot\sec^2 x + \dfrac{1}{\sqrt{2+x^8}}\cdot 2x$

16. $y = \int_{\cos x}^{5x} \cos(u^2)du = \int_0^{5x} \cos(u^2)du - \int_0^{\cos x} \cos(u^2)du;$

    $y' = \cos(25x^2)\cdot 5 - \cos(\cos^2 x)\cdot(-\sin x)$

    $= 5\cos(25x^2) + \sin x\cos(\cos^2 x)$

18. $\int_{-2}^{4} (3x-5)dx = 3\frac{x^2}{2} - 5x\Big]_{-2}^{4} = (3\cdot 8 - 5\cdot 4) - [3\cdot 2 - (-10)] = -12$

20. $\int_{1}^{2} (5x^2-4x+3)dx = 5\frac{x^3}{3} - 4\frac{x^2}{2} + 3x\Big]_{1}^{2} = 5\cdot\frac{8}{3} - 4\cdot 2 + 6 - (\frac{5}{3} - 2 + 3)$

$= 26/3$

22. $\int_{0}^{1} (y^9-2y^5+3y)dy = \frac{y^{10}}{10} - 2\frac{y^6}{6} + 3\frac{y^2}{2}\Big]_{0}^{1} = \left[\frac{1}{10} - \frac{1}{3} + \frac{3}{2}\right] - 0 = \frac{19}{15}$

24. $\int_{1}^{2} \frac{t^6 - t^2}{t^4} dt = \int_{1}^{2} (t^2-t^{-2})dt = \frac{t^3}{3} - \frac{t^{-1}}{-1}\Big]_{1}^{2} = \frac{t^3}{3} + \frac{1}{t}\Big]_{1}^{2}$

$= \left[\frac{8}{3} + \frac{1}{2}\right] - \left[\frac{1}{3} + 1\right] = \frac{11}{6}$

26. $\int_{0}^{2} (x^3-1)^2 dx = \int_{0}^{2} (x^6-2x^3+1)dx = \frac{x^7}{7} - 2\frac{x^4}{4} + x\Big]_{0}^{2}$

$= (\frac{128}{7} - 2\cdot 4 + 2) - 0 = \frac{86}{7}$

28. $\int_{-1}^{1} \frac{3}{t^4} dt$ does not exist since $f(t) = 3/t^4$ has an infinite

discontinuity at 0.

30. $\int_{1}^{2} \left[x+\frac{1}{x}\right]^2 dx = \int_{1}^{2} (x^2+2+x^{-2})dx = \frac{x^3}{3} + 2x + \frac{x^{-1}}{-1}\Big]_{1}^{2} = \frac{x^3}{3} + 2x - \frac{1}{x}\Big]_{1}^{2}$

$= \left[\frac{8}{3} + 4 - \frac{1}{2}\right] - \left[\frac{1}{3} + 2 - 1\right] = \frac{29}{6}$

32. $\int_{-1}^{2} |x-x^2|dx = \int_{-1}^{0} (x^2-x)dx + \int_{0}^{1} (x-x^2)dx + \int_{1}^{2} (x^2-x)dx$

$= \left[\frac{x^3}{3} - \frac{x^2}{2}\right]\Big]_{-1}^{0} + \left[\frac{x^2}{2} - \frac{x^3}{3}\right]\Big]_{0}^{1} + \left[\frac{x^3}{3} - \frac{x^2}{2}\right]\Big]_{1}^{2}$

$= 0 - (-\frac{1}{3} - \frac{1}{2}) + (\frac{1}{2} - \frac{1}{3}) - 0 + (\frac{8}{3} - 2) - (\frac{1}{3} - \frac{1}{2}) = \frac{11}{6}$

34. $\int_{1}^{-1} (x-1)(3x+2)dx = -\int_{-1}^{1} (3x^2-x-2)dx = -\left[3\frac{x^3}{3} - \frac{x^2}{2} - 2x\right]\Big]_{-1}^{1}$

$= -x^3 + \frac{x^2}{2} + 2x\Big]_{-1}^{1} = \left[-1 + \frac{1}{2} + 2\right] - \left[1 + \frac{1}{2} - 2\right] = 2$

36. $\int_{1}^{8} \left[\sqrt[3]{r} + \frac{1}{\sqrt[3]{r}}\right]dr = \int_{1}^{8} (r^{1/3}+r^{-1/3})dr = \frac{r^{4/3}}{4/3} + \frac{r^{2/3}}{2/3}\Big]_{1}^{8}$

$= \frac{3}{4} r^{4/3} + \frac{3}{2} r^{2/3}\Big]_{1}^{8} = \left[\frac{3}{4}\cdot 16 + \frac{3}{2}\cdot 4\right] - \left[\frac{3}{4} + \frac{3}{2}\right] = \frac{63}{4}$

38. $\int_{-5}^{-2} \frac{x^4-1}{x^2+1} dx = \int_{-5}^{-2} (x^2-1)dx = \frac{x^3}{3} - x\Big]_{-5}^{-2} = \left[\frac{-8}{3} + 2\right] - \left[\frac{-125}{3} + 5\right] = 36$

40. $\int_{0}^{\pi/2} (\cos\theta + 2\sin\theta)d\theta = \sin\theta - 2\cos\theta\Big]_{0}^{\pi/2}$

$= (1 - 2\cdot 0) - (0 - 2\cdot 1) = 3$

42. $\int_{\pi/3}^{\pi/2} \csc x \cot x\, dx = -\csc x\Big]_{\pi/3}^{\pi/2} = -\csc\frac{\pi}{2} + \csc\frac{\pi}{3} = -1 + \frac{2}{3}\sqrt{3}$

44. $\int_{\pi/4}^{\pi} \sec^2\theta \; d\theta$ does not exist since $\sec^2\theta$ has an infinite

discontinuity at $\pi/2$.

46. $\int_1^8 \dfrac{x-1}{\sqrt[3]{x^2}} \; dx = \int_1^8 (x^{1/3} - x^{-2/3}) dx = \dfrac{x^{4/3}}{4/3} - \dfrac{x^{1/3}}{1/3} \Big]_1^8$

$= \dfrac{3}{4} x^{4/3} - 3x^{1/3} \Big]_1^8 = \left[\dfrac{3}{4}\cdot 16 - 3\cdot 2\right] - \left[\dfrac{3}{4} - 3\right] = \dfrac{33}{4}$

48. $\int_0^2 (x^2 - |x-1|) dx = \int_0^1 (x^2 + x - 1) dx + \int_1^2 (x^2 - x + 1) dx$

$= \dfrac{x^3}{3} + \dfrac{x^2}{2} - x \Big]_0^1 + \left[\dfrac{x^3}{3} - \dfrac{x^2}{2} + x\right]\Big]_1^2$

$= (\dfrac{1}{3} + \dfrac{1}{2} - 1) - 0 + (\dfrac{8}{3} - 2 + 2) - (\dfrac{1}{3} - \dfrac{1}{2} + 1) = \dfrac{5}{3}$

50. $\int_{-\pi}^{\pi} f(x) dx = \int_{-\pi}^0 x \; dx + \int_0^{\pi} \sin x \; dx = \dfrac{x^2}{2}\Big]_{-\pi}^0 - \cos x\Big]_0^{\pi}$

$= (0 - \pi^2/2) - (\cos \pi - \cos 0) = -(\pi^2/2) - (-1-1) = 2 - \pi^2/2$

52. area $= \int_0^4 (1+x^3) dx = x + \dfrac{x^4}{4}\Big]_0^4 = 4 + 64 - 0 = 68$

54. area $= \int_1^6 x^{-4} \; dx = \dfrac{x^{-3}}{-3}\Big]_1^6 = \dfrac{-1}{3x^3}\Big]_1^6 = -\dfrac{1}{3\cdot 216} + \dfrac{1}{3} = \dfrac{215}{648}$

56. area $= \int_0^{\pi/3} \sec^2 x \; dx = \tan x\Big]_0^{\pi/3} = \sqrt{3} - 0 = \sqrt{3}$

58. area $= \int_1^2 x^{-2} \; dx = -\dfrac{1}{x}\Big]_1^2 = -\dfrac{1}{2} - (-1) = \dfrac{1}{2}$

60. $\dfrac{d}{dx}\left[-\dfrac{\sqrt{x^2+a^2}}{a^2 x} + C\right] = \dfrac{-1}{a^2}\dfrac{d}{dx}\left[\dfrac{\sqrt{x^2+a^2}}{x}\right] = -\dfrac{x(x/\sqrt{x^2+a^2}) - \sqrt{x^2+a^2}\cdot 1}{a^2 x^2}$

$= -\dfrac{x^2 - (x^2+a^2)}{a^2 x^2 \sqrt{x^2+a^2}} = \dfrac{1}{x^2\sqrt{x^2+a^2}}$

62. $\dfrac{d}{dx}(-x^2 \cos x + 2\int x \cos x \; dx)$

$= -x^2(-\sin x) - 2x \cos x + 2\cdot x \cos x = x^2 \sin x$

64. $\int \sqrt{x}\,(x^2 - \dfrac{1}{x}) dx = \int (x^{5/2} - x^{-1/2}) dx = \dfrac{2}{7} x^{7/2} - 2x^{1/2} + C$

66. $\int (\cos x - 2 \sin x) dx = \sin x + 2 \cos x + C$

68. $\int \left[x^2 + 1 + \dfrac{1}{x^2}\right] dx = \dfrac{x^3}{3} + x - \dfrac{1}{x} + C$

70. $\dfrac{d}{dx}\int_{g(x)}^{h(x)} f(t) dt = \dfrac{d}{dx}\left[\int_{g(x)}^a f(t) dt + \int_a^{h(x)} f(t) dt\right]$

[where a is some number in the domain of f]

$= \dfrac{d}{dx}\left[-\int_a^{g(x)} f(t) dt\right] + \dfrac{d}{dx}\left[\int_a^{h(x)} f(t) dt\right]$

$= -f(g(x))g'(x) + f(h(x))h'(x) = f(h(x))h'(x) - f(g(x))g'(x)$

72. $\int_{\ln 3}^{\ln 6} 8e^x \, dx = 8e^x \,]_{\ln 3}^{\ln 6} = 8(e^{\ln 6} - e^{\ln 3}) = 8(6-3) = 24$

74. $\int_{-e^2}^{-e} \frac{3}{x} \, dx = 3 \ln|x| \,]_{-e^2}^{-e} = 3 \ln e - 3 \ln(e^2) = 3 \cdot 1 - 3 \cdot 2 = -3$

76. $\int_0^{0.5} \frac{dx}{\sqrt{1-x^2}} = \sin^{-1} x \,]_0^{0.5} = \sin^{-1}\left[\frac{1}{2}\right] - \sin^{-1} 0 = \frac{\pi}{6}$

78. $\int_4^9 \left[\sqrt{x} + \frac{1}{\sqrt{x}}\right]^2 dx = \int_4^9 \left[x + 2 + \frac{1}{x}\right] dx = \frac{x^2}{2} + 2x + \ln x \,]_4^9$

$= \frac{81}{2} + 18 + \ln 9 - (8 + 8 + \ln 4) = \frac{85}{2} + \ln \frac{9}{4}$

80. area $= \int_1^2 \frac{1}{x} \, dx = \ln x \,]_1^2 = \ln 2 - \ln 1 = \ln 2$

Section 5.6

Exercises 5.6

2. Let $u = 2+x^3$. Then $du = 3x^2 \, dx$, so $\int \frac{x^2 \, dx}{\sqrt{2+x^3}} = \int \frac{(1/3) \, du}{\sqrt{u}}$

$= \frac{1}{3} \int u^{-1/2} \, du = \frac{1}{3} \frac{u^{1/2}}{1/2} + C = \frac{2}{3} \sqrt{2 + x^3} + C$

4. Let $u = 2x+1$. Then $du = 2 \, dx$, so $\int \frac{dx}{(2x+1)^2} = \int \frac{(1/2) \, du}{u^2}$

$= (1/2) \int u^{-2} \, du = -(1/2)u^{-1} + C = -1/2(2x+1) + C$

6. Let $u = a\theta$. Then $du = a \, d\theta$, so $\int \sec a\theta \tan a\theta \, d\theta$

$= \int \sec u \tan u \frac{1}{a} \, du = \frac{1}{a} \sec u + C = \frac{1}{a} \sec a\theta + C$

8. Let $u = 1-x^4$. Then $du = -4x^3 \, dx$, so $\int x^3(1-x^4)^5 \, dx$

$= \int u^5 \cdot (-1/4) du = -(1/4)(u^6/6) + C = -(1-x^4)^6/24 + C$

10. Let $u = 1-x$. Then $du = -dx$, so $\int \sqrt[3]{x-1} \, dx$

$= -\int u^{1/3} \, du = -(3/4)u^{4/3} + C = -(3/4)(1-x)^{4/3} + C$

12. Let $u = x^2+1$. Then $du = 2x \, dx$, so $\int x(x^2+1)^{3/2} \, dx$

$= \int u^{3/2} \frac{1}{2} \, du = \frac{1}{2} \cdot \frac{u^{5/2}}{5/2} + C = \frac{1}{5} u^{5/2} + C = \frac{1}{5}(x^2+1)^{5/2} + C$

14. Let $u = x^2+1$. Then $du = 2x \, dx$, so $\int \frac{x \, dx}{\sqrt{x^2+1}} = \int \frac{(1/2) \, du}{\sqrt{u}}$

$= \frac{1}{2} \int u^{-1/2} \, du = \frac{1}{2} \cdot 2u^{1/2} + C = \sqrt{u} + C = \sqrt{x^2+1} + C$

16. Let $u = 1-3t$. Then $du = -3\,dt$, so $\displaystyle\int \frac{1}{(1-3t)^4}\,dt = \int u^{-4} \cdot (-1/3)du$

$= (-1/3)\dfrac{u^{-3}}{-3} + C = 1/9u^3 + C = 1/9(1-3t)^3 + C$

18. Let $u = 3-5y$. Then $du = -5\,dy$, so $\displaystyle\int \sqrt[5]{3-5y}\,dy$
$= \displaystyle\int u^{1/5}(-1/5)du = \dfrac{-1}{5}\dfrac{5}{6}u^{6/5} + C = -\dfrac{1}{6}(3-5y)^{6/5} + C$

20. Let $u = 3\theta$. Then $du = 3\,d\theta$, so $\displaystyle\int \sec^2 3\theta\,d\theta = \int \sec^2 u\,(1/3)du$
$= \dfrac{1}{3}\tan u + C = \dfrac{1}{3}\tan 3\theta + C$

22. Let $u = 1-x$. Then $x = 1-u$ and $dx = -du$, so $\displaystyle\int \frac{x^2}{\sqrt{1-x}}\,dx$

$= \displaystyle\int \frac{(1-u)^2}{\sqrt{u}}\,(-du) = -\int \frac{1-2u+u^2}{\sqrt{u}}\,du = -\int (u^{-1/2}-2u^{1/2}+u^{3/2})du$

$= -[2u^{1/2}-2(2/3)u^{3/2}+(2/5)u^{5/2}] + C$

$= -2\sqrt{1-x} + (4/3)(1-x)^{3/2} - (2/5)(1-x)^{5/2} + C$

24. Let $u = 1+\sqrt{x}$. Then $du = \dfrac{dx}{2\sqrt{x}}$ so $\displaystyle\int \frac{(1+\sqrt{x})^9}{\sqrt{x}}\,dx = \int u^9 \cdot 2\,du$

$= 2\cdot\dfrac{u^{10}}{10} + C = \dfrac{(1+\sqrt{x})^{10}}{5} + C$

26. Let $u = 1-t^3$. Then $du = -3t^2\,dt$, so $\displaystyle\int t^2 \cos(1-t^3)dt$
$= \displaystyle\int \cos u\,(-1/3)du = -(1/3)\sin u + C = -(1/3)\sin(1-t^3) + C$

28. Let $u = \sqrt{x}$. Then $du = \dfrac{dx}{2\sqrt{x}}$ so $\displaystyle\int \frac{\cos\sqrt{x}}{\sqrt{x}}\,dx = \int \cos u \cdot 2\,du$

$= 2\sin u + C = 2\sin\sqrt{x} + C$

30. Let $u = \cos x$. Then $du = -\sin x\,dx$, so $\displaystyle\int \cos^4 x \sin x\,dx$
$= \displaystyle\int u^4(-du) = -u^5/5 + C = -(1/5)\cos^5 x + C$

32. Let $u = \tan\theta$. Then $du = \sec^2\theta\,d\theta$, so $\displaystyle\int \tan^2\theta \sec^2\theta\,d\theta$
$= \displaystyle\int u^2\,du = u^3/3 + C = (1/3)\tan^3\theta + C$

34. Let $u = 7-3x$. Then $du = -3\,dx$, so $\displaystyle\int \cos(7-3x)dx$
$= \displaystyle\int \cos u\,(-1/3)du = -(1/3)\sin u + C = -(1/3)\sin(7-3x) + C$

36. Let $u = x^3+1$. Then $x^3 = u-1$ and $du = 3x^2\,dx$, so
$\displaystyle\int \sqrt[3]{x^3+1}\,x^5\,dx = \int u^{1/3}(u-1)\cdot(1/3)du = \dfrac{1}{3}\int (u^{4/3}-u^{1/3})du$
$= \dfrac{1}{3}\left[\dfrac{3}{7}u^{7/3} - \dfrac{3}{4}u^{4/3}\right] + C = \dfrac{1}{7}(x^3+1)^{7/3} - \dfrac{1}{4}(x^3+1)^{4/3} + C$

38. Let $u = \sin x$. Then $du = \cos x\,dx$, so $\displaystyle\int \cos x \cos(\sin x)dx$
$= \displaystyle\int \cos u\,du = \sin u + C = \sin(\sin x) + C$

40. Let $u = 1-2x$. Then $du = -2\,dx$, so $\int_0^{-4} \sqrt{1-2x}\,dx$

$= \int_1^9 u^{1/2}\left[-\frac{1}{2}\right]du = -\frac{1}{2}\cdot\frac{2}{3}\cdot u^{3/2}\Big]_1^9 = -\frac{1}{3}(27-1) = -\frac{26}{3}$

42. Let $u = x^3-x$. Then $du = (3x^2-1)dx$, so $\int_2^3 \frac{3x^2-1}{(x^3-x)^2}\,dx = \int_6^{24} \frac{du}{u^2}$

$= -\frac{1}{u}\Big]_6^{24} = -\frac{1}{24} + \frac{1}{6} = \frac{1}{8}$

44. Let $u = 1+2x$. Then $du = 2\,dx$, so $\int_0^4 \frac{x\,dx}{\sqrt{1+2x}} = \int_1^9 \frac{(1/2)(u-1)}{\sqrt{u}}\,\frac{du}{2}$

$= \frac{1}{4}\int_1^9 (u^{1/2}-u^{-1/2})du = \frac{1}{4}\left[\frac{2}{3}u^{3/2}-2u^{1/2}\right]\Big]_1^9 = \frac{1}{2}\left[\frac{1}{3}u^{3/2}-u^{1/2}\right]_1^9$

$= \frac{1}{2}\left[(9-3) - \left[\frac{1}{3}-1\right]\right] = \frac{10}{3}$

46. Let $u = 4t$. Then $du = 4\,dt$, so $\int_0^{\pi/4} \sin 4t\,dt = \int_0^{\pi} \sin u \left(\frac{1}{4}\,du\right)$

$= -(1/4)\cos u\big]_0^\pi = \frac{1}{4} - \left[-\frac{1}{4}\right] = \frac{1}{2}$

48. $\int_0^2 \frac{dx}{(2x-3)^2}$ does not exist since $1/(2x-3)^2$ has an infinite

discontinuity at $3/2$

50. $\int_{-\pi/2}^{\pi/2} \frac{x^2 \sin x}{1 + x^6}\,dx = 0$ since $f(x) = \frac{x^2 \sin x}{1 + x^6}$ is an odd function.

52. $\int_{-\pi/3}^{\pi/3} \sin^5\theta\,d\theta = 0$ since $f(\theta) = \sin^5\theta$ is an odd function.

54. Let $u = x^2+a^2$. Then $du = 2x\,dx$, so $\int_0^a x\sqrt{x^2+a^2}\,dx = \int_{a^2}^{2a^2} u^{1/2}\,\frac{1}{2}\,du$

$= \frac{1}{2}\cdot\frac{2}{3}u^{3/2}\Big]_{a^2}^{2a^2} = \frac{1}{3}u^{3/2}\Big]_{a^2}^{2a^2} = \frac{1}{3}(2\sqrt{2}-1)a^3$

56. $\int_0^4 \frac{dx}{(x-2)^3}$ does not exist since $1/(x-2)^3$ has an infinite

discontinuity at 2.

58. area $= \int_0^1 \sqrt{2px}\,dx = \sqrt{2p}\int_0^1 x^{1/2}\,dx = \sqrt{2p}\,\frac{2}{3}x^{3/2}\Big]_0^1 = \frac{2\sqrt{2p}}{3}$

60. Let $u = x/3$. Then $du = dx/3$, so area $= \int_{-\pi}^{\pi} 3\cos(x/3)dx$

$= 2\int_0^\pi 3\cos(x/3)dx = 6\int_0^\pi \cos(x/3)dx = 6\int_0^{\pi/3} \cos u \cdot 3\,du$

$= 18\sin u\big]_0^{\pi/3} = 18(\sqrt{3}/2) - 0 = 9\sqrt{3}$

62. Let $u = x^2+1$. Then $du = 2x\,dx$, so area $= \int_1^2 x(x^2+1)^4\,dx$

$= \int_2^5 u^4\,\frac{1}{2}\,du = \frac{1}{2}\frac{u^5}{5}\Big]_2^5 = \frac{5^4}{2} - \frac{2^4}{5} = \frac{625}{2} - \frac{16}{5} = 309.3$

64. Let $u = x+c$. Then $du = dx$. When $x = a$, $u = a+c$; when $x = b$,

$u = b+c$. So $\int_a^b f(x+c)dx = \int_{a+c}^{b+c} f(u)du = \int_{a+c}^{b+c} f(x)dx$

66. Let $u = x^2+1$. Then $du = 2x\ dx$, so $\int \dfrac{x\ dx}{x^2 + 1} = \int \dfrac{(1/2)du}{u}$

$= (1/2)\ln|u| + C = (1/2)\ln(x^2+1) + C$ or $\ln\sqrt{x^2 + 1} + C$

68. Let $u = x^2$. Then $du = 2x\ dx$, so $\int xe^{x^2}\ dx = \int e^u\ (1/2)du$

$= e^u/2 + C = (1/2)e^{x^2} + C$

70. Let $u = \tan^{-1}x$. Then $du = \dfrac{dx}{1 + x^2}$, so $\int \dfrac{\tan^{-1}x}{1 + x^2}\ dx = \int u\ du$

$= u^2/2 + C = (\tan^{-1}x)^2/2 + C$

72. Let $u = e^x$. Then $du = e^x\ dx$, so $\int e^x \sin(e^x)dx = \int \sin u\ du$

$= -\cos u + C = -\cos(e^x) + C$

74. Let $u = e^x + 1$. Then $du = e^x\ dx$, so $\int \dfrac{e^x}{e^x + 1}\ dx = \int \dfrac{du}{u}$

$= \ln|u| + C = \ln(e^x+1) + C$

76. Let $u = \cos x$. Then $du = -\sin x\ dx$, so $\int \dfrac{\sin x}{1 + \cos^2 x}\ dx$

$= \int \dfrac{-du}{1 + u^2} = -\tan^{-1}u + C = -\tan^{-1}(\cos x) + C$

78. Let $u = 3x$. Then $du = 3\ dx$, so $\int \dfrac{dx}{1 + 9x^2} = \int \dfrac{(1/3)du}{1 + u^2}$

$= (1/3)\tan^{-1}u + C = (1/3)\tan^{-1}(3x) + C$

80. Let $u = x^3+3x+1$. Then $du = 3(x^2+1)dx$, so $\int \dfrac{x^2 + 1}{x^3 + 3x + 1}\ dx$

$= \dfrac{1}{3}\int \dfrac{du}{u} = \dfrac{1}{3}\ln|u| + C = \dfrac{1}{3}\ln|x^3+3x+1| + C$

82. Let $u = x+1$. Then $du = dx$ and $x = u-1$, so $\int \dfrac{x}{x+1}\ dx = \int \dfrac{u-1}{u}\ du$

$= \int \left[1 - \dfrac{1}{u}\right]du = u - \ln|u| + C = x + 1 - \ln|x+1| + C$

(or $x - \ln|x+1| + K$)

84. Let $u = -t^3$. Then $du = -3t^2\ dt$, so $\int_0^1 t^2\ 2^{-t^3}\ dt = \int_0^{-1} 2^u \left[-\dfrac{1}{3}\right]du$

$= \dfrac{1}{3}\int_{-1}^0 2^u\ du = \dfrac{1}{3}\left.\dfrac{2^u}{\ln 2}\right]_{-1}^0 = \dfrac{1}{3\ln 2}\left[1 - \dfrac{1}{2}\right] = \dfrac{1}{6\ln 2}$

86. Let $u = \sin^{-1}x$. Then $du = \dfrac{dx}{\sqrt{1-x^2}}$ so $\int_0^{1/2} \dfrac{\sin^{-1}x}{\sqrt{1-x^2}}\ dx$

$= \int_0^{\pi/6} u\ du = \left.u^2/2\right]_0^{\pi/6} = \pi^2/72$

88. Let $u = x-2$. Then $du = dx$, so area $= \int_3^5 \dfrac{2\ dx}{x - 2} = \int_1^3 \dfrac{2\ du}{u}$

$= 2\ln u\Big]_1^3 = 2\ln 3 - 2\ln 1 = 2\ln 3$

Exercises 5.7

2. area = $\int_{-2}^{0} [x^4 - (-x-1)]dx$

    $= \int_{-2}^{0} (x^4+x+1)dx = \frac{x^5}{5} + \frac{x^2}{2} + x \Big]_{-2}^{0}$

    $= 0 - (-32/5 + 2 - 2) = 32/5$

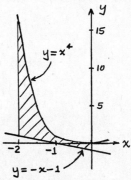

4. area = $\int_{0}^{3} [(y^2+1)-(-y^2)]dy = \int_{0}^{3} (2y^2+1)dy = \frac{2y^3}{3} + y \Big]_{0}^{3} = 18+3 = 21$

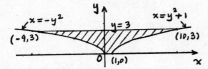

6. area = $\int_{-2}^{1} [-x^2-2x - (-x-2)]dx = \int_{-2}^{1} (-x^2-x+2)dx$

    $= -\frac{x^3}{3} - \frac{x^2}{2} + 2x \Big]_{-2}^{1}$

    $= \left[\frac{-1}{3} - \frac{1}{2} = 2\right] - \left[\frac{8}{3} - 2 - 4\right] = 4.5$

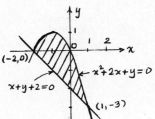

8. area = $\int_{-1}^{0} (x^3-x)dx + \int_{0}^{1} (x-x^3)dx$

    $= 2\int_{0}^{1} (x-x^3)dx = 2\left[\frac{x^2}{2} - \frac{x^4}{4}\right]\Big]_{0}^{1}$

    $= 2\left[\frac{1}{2} - \frac{1}{4}\right] = \frac{1}{2}$

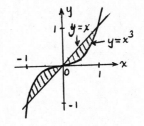

10. area = $\int_{-1}^{1} (x^2-x^4)dx = 2\int_{0}^{1} (x^2-x^4)dx$

    $= 2\left[\frac{x^3}{3} - \frac{x^5}{5}\right]_{0}^{1} = 2\left[\frac{1}{3} - \frac{1}{5}\right] = \frac{4}{15}$

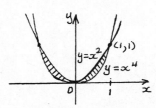

12. area $= \int_{-1}^{1} [(1-x^2) - (x^4-x^2)]dx = 2\int_{0}^{1} (1-x^4)dx = 2\left[x - \frac{x^5}{5}\right]\Big]_{0}^{1}$

$= 2\left[1 - \frac{1}{5}\right] = \frac{8}{5}$

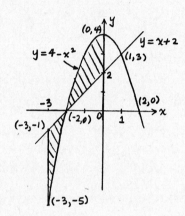

14. area $= \int_{-3}^{0} |(4-x^2) - (x+2)|dx$

$= \int_{-3}^{-2} [(x+2) - (4-x^2)]dx$

$+ \int_{-2}^{0} [(4-x^2) - (x+2)]dx$

$= \int_{-3}^{-2} (x^2+x-2)dx + \int_{-2}^{0} (-x^2-x+2)dx$

$= \left[\frac{x^3}{3} + \frac{x^2}{2} - 2x\right]_{-3}^{-2} + \left[\frac{-x^3}{3} - \frac{x^2}{2} + 2x\right]_{-2}^{0}$

$= \left[\frac{-8}{3} + 2 + 4\right] - \left[-9 + \frac{9}{2} + 6\right]$

$+ 0 - \left[\frac{8}{3} - 2 - 4\right] = \frac{31}{6}$

16. area $= \int_{-3}^{-2} [(x^2+2x+2) - (x+4)]dx + \int_{-2}^{1} [(x+4) - (x^2+2x+2)]dx$

$+ \int_{1}^{2} [(x^2+2x+2) - (x+4)]dx$

$= \int_{-3}^{-2} (x^2+x-2)dx + \int_{-2}^{1} (-x^2-x+2)dx + \int_{1}^{2} (x^2+x-2)dx$

$= \frac{x^3}{3} + \frac{x^2}{2} - 2x\Big]_{-3}^{-2} + \left[- \frac{x^3}{3} - \frac{x^2}{2} + 2x\right]\Big]_{-2}^{1} + \left[\frac{x^3}{3} + \frac{x^2}{2} - 2x\right]\Big]_{1}^{2}$

$= \left[\left[\frac{-8}{3} + 2 + 4\right] - \left[-9 + \frac{9}{2} + 6\right]\right] + \left[\left[-\frac{1}{3} - \frac{1}{2} + 2\right] - \left[\frac{8}{3} - 2 - 4\right]\right]$

$+ \left[\left[\frac{8}{3} + 2 - 4\right] - \left[\frac{1}{3} + \frac{1}{2} - 2\right]\right] = \frac{49}{6}$

18. $\text{area} = \int_{-1}^{2} [2-y^2-(-y)]\,dy = \int_{-1}^{2} (-y^2+y+2)\,dy = -\frac{y^3}{3} + \frac{y^2}{2} + 2y \Big]_{-1}^{2}$

$= \left[-\frac{8}{3} + 2 + 4 \right] - \left[\frac{1}{3} + \frac{1}{2} - 2 \right] = \frac{9}{2}$

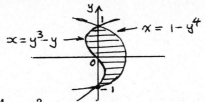

20. $\text{area} = \int_{0}^{1} [(x^3-4x^2+3x) - (x^2-x)]\,dx + \int_{1}^{4} [x^2-x - (x^3-4x^2+3x)]\,dx$

$= \int_{0}^{1} (x^3-5x^2+4x)\,dx + \int_{1}^{4} (-x^3+5x^2-4x)\,dx$

$= \frac{x^4}{4} - \frac{5}{3}x^3 + 2x^2 \Big]_{0}^{1} + \left[-\frac{x^4}{4} + \frac{5}{3}x^3 - 2x^2 \right]\Big]_{1}^{4}$

$= \left[\frac{1}{4} - \frac{5}{3} + 2 \right] - 0 + \left[-64 + \frac{320}{3} - 32 \right] - \left[-\frac{1}{4} + \frac{5}{3} - 2 \right] = \frac{71}{6}$

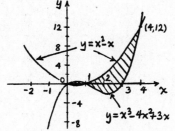

22. $\text{area} = \int_{-1}^{1} [(1-y^4) - (y^3-y)]\,dy = \int_{-1}^{1} (-y^4-y^3+y+1)\,dy$

$= -\frac{y^5}{5} - \frac{y^4}{4} + \frac{y^2}{2} + y \Big]_{-1}^{1} = \left[-\frac{1}{5} - \frac{1}{4} + \frac{1}{2} + 1 \right] - \left[\frac{1}{5} - \frac{1}{4} + \frac{1}{2} - 1 \right] = \frac{8}{5}$

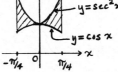

24. $\text{area} = 2\int_{0}^{\pi/4} (\sec^2 x - \cos x)\,dx = 2(\tan x - \sin x)\Big]_{0}^{\pi/4}$

$= 2(1 - 1/\sqrt{2}) - 0 = 2 - \sqrt{2}$

26. $\sin x = \sin 2x = 2 \sin x \cos x$ when $\sin x = 0$ and when $\cos x = \frac{1}{2}$;

i.e., when $x = 0$ or $\pi/3$.

area $= \int_0^{\pi/3} (\sin 2x - \sin x)dx + \int_{\pi/3}^{\pi/2} (\sin x - \sin 2x)dx$

$= -\frac{1}{2} \cos 2x + \cos x]_0^{\pi/3} + (\frac{1}{2} \cos 2x - \cos x)]_{\pi/3}^{\pi/2}$

$= [-\frac{1}{2}(-\frac{1}{2})+\frac{1}{2}] - (-\frac{1}{2}+1) + (-\frac{1}{2}-0) - [\frac{1}{2} \cdot (-\frac{1}{2})-\frac{1}{2}] = \frac{1}{2}$

28. $\sin x = \cos 2x = 1 - 2 \sin^2 x \Longleftrightarrow 2 \sin^2 x + \sin x - 1 = 0 \Longleftrightarrow$

$(2 \sin x - 1)(\sin x + 1) = 0 \Longleftrightarrow \sin x = \frac{1}{2}$ or $-1 \Longleftrightarrow x = \pi/6$

area $= \int_0^{\pi/6} (\cos 2x - \sin x)dx + \int_{\pi/6}^{\pi/4} (\sin x - \cos 2x)dx$

$= \frac{1}{2} \sin 2x + \cos x]_0^{\pi/6} - (\frac{1}{2} \sin 2x + \cos x)]_{\pi/6}^{\pi/4}$

$= \left[\frac{1}{2} \frac{\sqrt{3}}{2} + \frac{\sqrt{3}}{2}\right] - 1 - \left[\frac{1}{2} + \frac{\sqrt{2}}{2}\right] + \left[\frac{1}{2} \frac{\sqrt{3}}{2} + \frac{\sqrt{3}}{2}\right] = \frac{3\sqrt{3} - \sqrt{2} - 3}{2}$

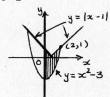

30. area $= \int_0^1 [(1-x) - (x^2-3)]dx + \int_1^2 [(x-1)-(x^2-3)]dx = -\frac{x^3}{3} - \frac{x^2}{2} + 4x]_0^1$

$+ \left[-\frac{x^3}{3} + \frac{x^2}{2} + 2x\right]\Big]_1^2 = (-\frac{1}{3}-\frac{1}{2}+4) - 0 + (-\frac{8}{3}+2+4) - (-\frac{1}{3}+\frac{1}{2}+2) = \frac{13}{3}$

32. area $= \int_{-2}^3 (x+5-|x^2-1|)dx$

$= \int_{-2}^{-1} [x+5-(x^2-1)]dx + \int_{-1}^1 [x+5-(1-x^2)]dx + \int_1^3 [x+5-(x^2-1)]dx$

$= \int_{-2}^{-1} (-x^2+x+6)dx + \int_{-1}^1 (x^2+x+4)dx + \int_1^3 (-x^2+x+6)dx$

$= \left[-\frac{x^3}{3} + \frac{x^2}{2} + 6x\right]_{-2}^{-1} + \left[\frac{x^3}{3} + \frac{x^2}{2} + 4x\right]_{-1}^1 + \left[-\frac{x^3}{3} + \frac{x^2}{2} + 6x\right]_1^3$

$= \left[\frac{1}{3}+\frac{1}{2}-6\right] - \left[\frac{8}{3}+2-12\right] + \left[\frac{1}{3}+\frac{1}{2}+4\right] - \left[-\frac{1}{3}+\frac{1}{2}-4\right] + \left[-9+\frac{9}{2}+18\right] - \left[-\frac{1}{3}+\frac{1}{2}+6\right] = \frac{109}{6}$

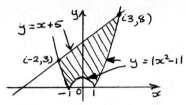

34. (a) area = $\int_1^7 \left[\left[\frac{7}{6} - \frac{x}{6}\right] - \left[2 - \sqrt{\frac{x+1}{2}}\right]\right] dx = \int_1^7 \left[\frac{-5}{6} - \frac{x}{6} + \frac{1}{\sqrt{2}}(x+1)^{1/2}\right] dx$

$= \left. -\frac{5}{6}x - \frac{x^2}{12} + \frac{1}{\sqrt{2}} \frac{2}{3} (x+1)^{3/2}\right]_1^7 = -5 - 4 + \frac{\sqrt{2}}{3}(8\sqrt{8} - 2\sqrt{2}) = \frac{1}{3}$

(b) area = $\int_0^1 [(7-6y) - \{2(y-2)^2 - 1\}] dy = \int_0^1 (-2y^2 + 2y) dy$

$= \left. -\frac{2}{3}y^3 + y^2\right]_0^1 = -\frac{2}{3} + 1 = \frac{1}{3}$

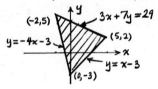

36. area = $\int_{-2}^0 \left[\left[-\frac{3}{7}x + \frac{29}{7}\right] - \left[-4x - 3\right]\right] dx + \int_0^5 \left[\left[-\frac{3}{7}x + \frac{29}{7}\right] - (x-3)\right] dx$

$= \int_{-2}^0 \left[\frac{25}{7}x + \frac{50}{7}\right] dx + \int_0^5 \left[-\frac{10}{7}x + \frac{50}{7}\right] dx = \left. \frac{25}{7}\frac{x^2}{2} + \frac{50}{7}x\right]_{-2}^0 - \left. \frac{5}{7}x^2 + \frac{50}{7}x\right]_0^5$

$= \frac{25}{7}(0-2) + \frac{50}{7}(0+2) - \frac{5}{7}(25-0) + \frac{50}{7}(5-0) = 25$

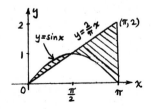

38. $\int_0^\pi |\sin x - \frac{2}{\pi}x| dx = \int_0^{\pi/2} \left[\sin x - \frac{2}{\pi}x\right] dx + \int_{\pi/2}^\pi \left[\frac{2}{\pi}x - \sin x\right] dx$

$= \left. \left[-\cos x - \frac{x^2}{\pi}\right]\right]_0^{\pi/2} + \left. \left[\frac{x^2}{\pi} + \cos x\right]\right]_{\pi/2}^\pi = -\frac{\pi}{4} + 1 + (\pi - 1) - \frac{\pi}{4} = \frac{\pi}{2}$

40. $\int_{-2}^{2} (x+x^2)dx = \int_{-2}^{2} x\, dx + \int_{-2}^{2} x^2\, dx = 0 + 2\int_{0}^{2} x^2\, dx = \frac{2}{3}x^3\Big]_{0}^{2} = \frac{16}{3}$

42. $\int_{\pi/4}^{5\pi/2} \sin x\, dx = -\cos x\Big]_{\pi/4}^{5\pi/2} = 0 + \frac{\sqrt{2}}{2} = \frac{\sqrt{2}}{2}$

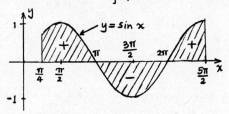

44. $A = \int_{1}^{2} \frac{1}{y}\, dy = \ln y\Big]_{1}^{2} = \ln 2 - \ln 1 = \ln 2$

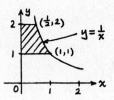

46. $A = \int_{-1}^{0}(2^x-5^x)dx + \int_{0}^{1}(5^x-2^x)dx = \left[\frac{2^x}{\ln 2} - \frac{5^x}{\ln 5}\right]\Big]_{-1}^{0} + \left[\frac{5^x}{\ln 5} - \frac{2^x}{\ln 2}\right]\Big]_{0}^{1}$

$= \left[\frac{1}{\ln 2} - \frac{1}{\ln 5}\right] - \left[\frac{1/2}{\ln 2} - \frac{1/5}{\ln 5}\right] + \left[\frac{5}{\ln 5} - \frac{2}{\ln 2}\right] - \left[\frac{1}{\ln 5} - \frac{1}{\ln 2}\right]$

$= 16/(5 \ln 5) - 1/(2 \ln 2)$

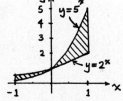

48. $A = \int_{0}^{\ln 2}\left[e^x - \frac{e^{2x}}{2}\right]dx + \int_{\ln 2}^{1}\left[\frac{e^{2x}}{2} - e^x\right]dx$

$= e^x - \frac{e^{2x}}{4}\Big]_{0}^{\ln 2} + \left[\frac{e^{2x}}{4} - e^x\right]\Big]_{\ln 2}^{1}$

$= (2-1)-\left[1-\frac{1}{4}\right]+\left[\frac{e^2}{4} - e\right]-(1-2) = \frac{e^2}{4} - e + \frac{5}{4}$

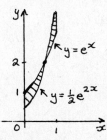

156

Exercises 5.8

2. (a) displacement $= \int_0^3 (3t-5)dt = \frac{3}{2}t^2-5t\Big]_0^3 = \frac{27}{2} - 15 = -\frac{3}{2}$ m

(b) distance traveled $= \int_0^3 |3t-5|dt = \int_0^{5/3}(5-3t)dt + \int_{5/3}^3 (3t-5)dt$

$= \left[5t-\frac{3}{2}t^2\right]_0^{5/3} + \left[\frac{3}{2}t^2-5t\right]_{5/3}^3 = \frac{25}{3} - \frac{3}{2}\frac{25}{9} + \frac{27}{2} - 15 - \left[\frac{3}{2}\frac{25}{9} - \frac{25}{3}\right] = \frac{41}{6}$ m

4. (a) displacement $= \int_0^3 \sin\left[\frac{\pi t}{4}\right]dt = \int_0^{3\pi/4} \frac{4}{\pi} \sin u\, du$ $[u = \pi t/4 \Rightarrow$

$du = (\pi/4)dt] = \frac{4}{\pi}(-\cos u)\Big]_0^{3\pi/4} = \frac{4}{\pi}(\sqrt{2}+1)$ m

(b) distance traveled $= \int_0^3 |\sin(\frac{\pi t}{4})|dt = \int_0^3 \sin(\frac{\pi t}{4})dt = \frac{4}{\pi}(\sqrt{2}+1)$ m

6. (a) displacement $= \int_1^4 (4t-t^3)dt = 2t^2-\frac{t^4}{4}\Big]_1^4 = (32-64)-(2-\frac{1}{4}) = -33.75$ m

(b) distance traveled $= \int_1^4 |4t-t^3|dt = \int_1^2 (4t-t^3)dt + \int_2^4 (t^3-4t)dt$

$= \left[2t^2-\frac{t^4}{4}\right]\Big]_1^2 + \left[\frac{t^4}{4} - 2t^2\right]\Big]_2^4 = (8-4)-(2-\frac{1}{4})+(64-32)-(4-8) = 38.25$ m

8. (a) $v'(t) = 2t+3 \Rightarrow v(t) = t^2+3t+C \Rightarrow C = v(0) = -4 \Rightarrow v(t) = t^2+3t-4$

(b) distance $= \int_0^3 |t^2+3t-4|dt = \int_0^3 |(t+4)(t-1)|dt$

$= \int_0^1 (-t^2-3t+4)dt + \int_1^3 (t^2+3t-4)dt = -\frac{t^3}{3} - \frac{3t^2}{2} +4t\Big]_0^1 + \frac{t^3}{3} + \frac{3t^2}{2} -4t\Big]_1^3$

$= \left[-\frac{1}{3}-\frac{3}{2}+4\right]+\left[9 + \frac{27}{2} - 12\right]-\left[\frac{1}{3}+\frac{3}{2}-4\right] = \frac{89}{6}$ m

10. (a) $v'(t) = (3t+1)/2\sqrt{t} = \frac{3}{2}\sqrt{t} + \frac{1}{2}t^{-1/2} \Rightarrow v(t) = t^{3/2}+t^{1/2}+C$,

where $2 = v(1) = 2+C$, so $C = 0$. $v(t) = t^{3/2}+t^{1/2}$ m/s

(b) $\int_1^4 |t^{3/2}+t^{1/2}|dt = \int_1^4 (t^{3/2}+t^{1/2})dt = \frac{2}{5}t^{5/2}+\frac{2}{3}t^{3/2}\Big]_1^4$

$= \left[\frac{2}{5}\cdot 32+\frac{2}{3}\cdot 8\right]-\left[\frac{2}{5}+\frac{2}{3}\right] = \frac{256}{15}$ m

12. $n(10)-n(4) = \int_4^{10}(200+50t)dt = 200t + 25t^2\Big]_4^{10}$

$= 2000+2500-(800+400) = 3300$

14. $R'(x) = 90-0.02x$ and $R(100) = \$8800$, so $R(200) = R(100)$

$+ \int_{100}^{200} R'(x)dx = 8800+\int_{100}^{200} (90-0.02x)dx = 8800+(90x-0.01x^2)\Big]_{100}^{200}$

$= 8800+(18000-400)-(9000-100) = \$17,500$

16. Number of calculators $= x(4)-x(2) = \int_2^4 5000[1-100(t+10)^{-2}]dt$

$= 5000[t+100(t+10)^{-1}]_2^4 = 5000[(4+100/14)-(2+100/12)] \approx 4048$

Exercises 5.9

2. $f_{ave} = \frac{1}{3-0} \int_0^3 (x^2-2x)dx = \frac{1}{3}\left[\frac{x^3}{3} - x^2\right]\Big]_0^3 = \frac{1}{3}(9-9) = 0$

4. $f_{ave} = \frac{1}{\pi-0} \int_0^\pi \sin x\, dx = \frac{1}{\pi}(-\cos x)]_0^\pi = \frac{1}{\pi}(1+1) = \frac{2}{\pi}$

6. $f_{ave} = \frac{1}{3-1} \int_1^3 (x^3-x)dx = \frac{1}{2}\left[\frac{x^4}{4} - \frac{x^2}{2}\right]\Big]_1^3 = \frac{1}{2}\left[\left[\frac{81}{4} - \frac{9}{2}\right]-\left[\frac{1}{4}-\frac{1}{2}\right]\right] = \frac{1}{2}\cdot 16 = 8$

8. $f_{ave} = \frac{1}{9-4} \int_4^9 \sqrt{x}\, dx = \frac{1}{5}\cdot\frac{2}{3} x^{3/2}\Big]_4^9 = \frac{2}{15}(27-8) = \frac{38}{15}$

10. (a) $f_{ave} = \frac{1}{2-(-1)} \int_{-1}^2 x^3\, dx = \frac{1}{3}\frac{x^4}{4}\Big]_{-1}^2 = \frac{1}{3}\left[4-\frac{1}{4}\right] = \frac{5}{4}$

 (b) $f_{ave} = f(c) \Longleftrightarrow \frac{5}{4} = c^3 \Longleftrightarrow c = \sqrt[3]{5/4} = \sqrt[3]{10}/2$

 (c)

12. (a) $f_{ave} = \frac{1}{3-0} \int_0^3 (4x-x^2)dx = \frac{1}{3}\left[2x^2 - \frac{x^3}{3}\right]\Big]_0^3 = \frac{1}{3}(18-9) = 3$

 (b) $f_{ave} = f(c) \Longleftrightarrow 3 = 4c-c^2 \Longleftrightarrow c^2-4c+3 = 0 \Longleftrightarrow c = 1 \text{ or } 3$

 (c)

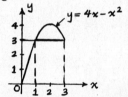

14. $T_{ave} = \frac{1}{5} \int_0^5 4x\, dx = \frac{2}{5}x^2\Big]_0^5 = 10°C$

16. $v_{ave} = \frac{1}{t_2-t_1} \int_{t_1}^{t_2} v(t)dt = \frac{1}{t_2-t_1} \int_{t_1}^{t_2} s'(t)dt = \frac{s(t_2)-s(t_1)}{t_2-t_1}$

 by the Fundamental Theorem of Calculus.

18. $v_{ave} = \frac{1}{R-0} \int_0^R v(r)dr = \frac{1}{R} \int_0^R \frac{P}{4\eta\ell}(R^2-r^2)dr = \frac{P}{4\eta\ell R}\left[R^2 r - \frac{r^3}{3}\right]\Big]_0^R$

 $= \frac{P}{4\eta\ell R}\frac{2}{3}R^3 = \frac{PR^2}{6\eta\ell}.$ Since $v(r)$ is decreasing on $[0,R]$,

 $v_{max} = v(0) = \frac{PR^2}{4\eta\ell}.$ Thus $v_{ave} = \frac{2}{3}v_{max}.$

Review Exercises for Chapter 5

2. $\displaystyle\sum_{j=1}^{5} \sin(j\pi/2) = \sin(\pi/2) + \sin \pi + \sin(3\pi/2) + \sin 2\pi + \sin(5\pi/2)$

$= 1 + 0 + (-1) + 0 + 1 = 1$

4. $\displaystyle\sum_{i=1}^{n} i(i-2) = \sum_{i=1}^{n} (i^2 - 2i) = \sum_{i=1}^{n} i^2 - 2\sum_{i=1}^{n} i$

$= n(n+1)(2n+1)/6 - 2 \cdot n(n+1)/2 = n(n+1)(2n+1)/6 - n(n+1)$

$= [n(n+1)/6][(2n+1) - 6] = n(n+1)(2n-5)/6$

6. $\displaystyle\sum_{i=1}^{n} f(x_i^*)\Delta x_i = \sum_{i=1}^{4} f\left[\frac{2i-1}{4}\right] \cdot \frac{1}{2} = \frac{1}{2}[f(1/4) + f(3/4) + f(5/4) + f(7/4)]$

$= \frac{1}{2}[5.0625 + 3.5625 + 2.5625 + 2.0625] = \frac{1}{2}[13.25] = 6.625$

$y = 2 + (x-2)^2$

8. $\displaystyle\int_1^2 (x+3x^2)\,dx = \lim_{n\to\infty} \frac{1}{n}\sum_{i=1}^{n}\left[1+\frac{i}{n}+3\left[1+\frac{i}{n}\right]^2\right]$ [by (5.12)]

$= \lim_{n\to\infty} \frac{1}{n}\sum_{i=1}^{n}\left[4 + \frac{7i}{n} + \frac{3i^2}{n^2}\right] = \lim_{n\to\infty} \frac{1}{n}\left[4n + \frac{7}{n}\frac{n(n+1)}{2} + \frac{3}{n^2}\frac{n(n+1)(2n+1)}{6}\right]$

$= \lim_{n\to\infty}\left[4 + \frac{7}{2}\left[1+\frac{1}{n}\right] + \frac{1}{2}\left[1+\frac{1}{n}\right]\left[2+\frac{1}{n}\right]\right] = 4 + \frac{7}{2} + \frac{1}{2}\cdot 1 \cdot 2 = \frac{17}{2}$

10. $\displaystyle\int_0^b (x^3+4x-1)\,dx = \lim_{n\to\infty} \frac{b}{n}\sum_{i=1}^{n}\left[\left[\frac{bi}{n}\right]^3 + 4\left[\frac{bi}{n}\right] - 1\right]$ [by (5.12)]

$= \lim_{n\to\infty}\left[\frac{b^4}{n^4}\Sigma i^3 + 4\frac{b^2}{n^2}\Sigma i - \frac{b}{n}\Sigma 1\right]$

$= \lim_{n\to\infty}\left[\frac{b^4}{n^4}\frac{n^2(n+1)^2}{4} + 4\frac{b^2}{n^2}\frac{n(n+1)}{2} - \frac{b}{n}n\right]$

$= \lim_{n\to\infty}\left[\frac{b^4}{4}\left[1+\frac{1}{n}\right]^2 + 2b^2\left[1+\frac{1}{n}\right] - b\right] = \frac{b^4}{4} + 2b^2 - b$

12. $\displaystyle\int_0^b (x^3+4x-1)\,dx = \frac{x^4}{4} + 2x^2 - x\bigg]_0^b = \frac{b^4}{4} + 2b^2 - b$

NOTE: We evaluated this integral in #10.

14. Let $u = 1-x$. Then $\int_0^1 (1-x)^9 dx = \int_1^0 u^9(-du) = \int_0^1 u^9 du = u^{10}/10 \big]_0^1 = \frac{1}{10}$

16. $\int_1^4 \frac{x^2-x+1}{\sqrt{x}}\, dx = \int_1^4 (x^{3/2}-x^{1/2}+x^{-1/2})dx = \frac{2}{5}x^{5/2}-\frac{2}{3}x^{3/2}+2x^{1/2}\big]_1^4$

$= \left[\frac{2}{5}\cdot 32 - \frac{2}{3}\cdot 8 + 4\right] - \left[\frac{2}{5}-\frac{2}{3}+2\right] = \frac{146}{15}$

18. Let $u = 16-3x$. Then $x = (16-u)/3$, $dx = -\,du/3$, so $\int_0^4 x\sqrt{16-3x}\, dx$

$= \int_{16}^4 u^{1/2}\left[\frac{16-u}{3}\right]\left[-\frac{1}{3}\right]du = \frac{1}{9}\int_4^{16}(16u^{1/2}-u^{3/2})du$

$= \frac{1}{9}\left[16\cdot\frac{2}{3}u^{3/2} - \frac{2}{5}u^{5/2}\right]_4^{16} = \frac{1}{9}\left[\frac{32}{3}\cdot 64 - \frac{2}{5}\cdot 1024 - \frac{32}{3}\cdot 8 + \frac{2}{5}\cdot 32\right] = \frac{3008}{135}$

20. $\int_0^2 \frac{x\,dx}{(x^2-1)^2}$ does not exist since the integrand has an infinite

discontinuity at 1.

22. $\int_{-1}^1 \frac{x+x^3+x^5}{1+x^2+x^4}\, dx = 0$ by (5.33) since the integrand is odd.

24. Let $u = 2x-x^2$. Then $du = 2(1-x)dx$, so $\int (1-x)\sqrt{2x-x^2}\, dx$

$= \int u^{1/2}\,\frac{1}{2}\,du = \frac{1}{2}\cdot\frac{2}{3}u^{3/2} + C = \frac{1}{3}(2x-x^2)^{3/2} + C$

26. Let $u = 1 + \sin x$. Then $du = \cos x\, dx$, so $\int \frac{\cos x\,dx}{\sqrt{1+\sin x}}$

$= \int u^{-1/2}\,du = 2u^{1/2} + C = 2\sqrt{1 + \sin x} + C$

28. Let $u = 3t$. Then $du = 3\,dt$, so $\int \csc^2 3t\, dt = \int \csc^2 u\,(1/3)du$

$= -\frac{1}{3}\cot u + C = -\frac{1}{3}\cot 3t + C$

30. Let $u = x^2+1$. Then $x^2 = u-1$ and $x\,dx = (1/2)du$, so $\int \frac{x^3\,dx}{\sqrt{x^2+1}}$

$= \int \frac{(u-1)(1/2)du}{\sqrt{u}} = \frac{1}{2}\int(u^{1/2} - u^{-1/2})du = \frac{1}{2}\left[\frac{2}{3}u^{3/2} - 2u^{1/2}\right] + C$

$= \frac{1}{3}(x^2+1)^{3/2} - (x^2+1)^{1/2} + C = \frac{1}{3}(x^2+1)^{1/2}(x^2-2) + C$

32. $\int_0^8 |x^2-6x+8|dx = \int_0^8 |(x-2)(x-4)|dx = \int_0^2 (x^2-6x+8)dx - \int_2^4 (x^2-6x+8)dx$

$+ \int_4^8 (x^2-6x+8)dx = \frac{x^3}{3} - 3x^2+8x\big]_0^2 - \left[\frac{x^3}{3} - 3x^2+8x\right]\big]_2^4 + \left[\frac{x^3}{3} - 3x^2+8x\right]\big]_4^8$

$= (\frac{8}{3}-12+16)-0-(\frac{64}{3} - 48+32)+(\frac{8}{3}-12+16)+(\frac{512}{3} - 192+64)-(\frac{64}{3} - 48+32) = \frac{136}{3}$

34. $F(x) = \int_\pi^x \tan(s^2)\, ds \Rightarrow F'(x) = \tan(x^2)$

36. $g(x) = \int_1^{\cos x} \sqrt[3]{1-t^2}\, dt$. Let $y = g(x)$ and $u = \cos x$. Then

$g'(x) = \frac{dy}{dx} = \frac{dy}{du}\frac{du}{dx} = \sqrt[3]{1-u^2}\,(-\sin x) = \sqrt[3]{1 - \cos^2 x}\,(-\sin x)$

$= -\sin x \sqrt[3]{\sin^2 x} = -(\sin x)^{5/3}$

38. $y = \int_{2x}^{3x+1} \sin(t^4)dt = \int_0^{3x+1} \sin(t^4)dt - \int_0^{2x} \sin(t^4)dt$

$y' = 3\sin[(3x+1)^4] - 2\sin[(2x)^4]$

40. area $= \int_{-1}^{4}(4+3x-x^2)dx = 4x+\frac{3}{2}x^2-\frac{x^3}{3}\Big]_{-1}^{4} = \left[16+24-\frac{64}{3}\right]-\left[-4+\frac{3}{2}+\frac{1}{3}\right] = \frac{125}{6}$

42. $12-x^2 = x^2-6 \iff x^2 = 9 \iff x = \pm 3$

By symmetry, $A = 2\int_0^5 |(12-x^2)-(x^2-6)|dx = 4\int_0^5 |9-x^2|dx$

$= 4\int_0^3 (9-x^2)dx + 4\int_3^5 (x^2-9)dx = 4\left[[9x-\frac{1}{3}x^3]_0^3 + [\frac{1}{3}x^3-9x]_3^5\right]$

$= 4[(27-\frac{27}{3})-0+(\frac{125}{3}-45)-(\frac{27}{3}-27)] = \frac{392}{3}$

44. area $= \int_1^7 [(2y-7) - (y^2-6y)]dy = \int_1^7 (-y^2+8y-7)dy$

$= (-\frac{1}{3}y^3+4y^2-7y)\Big]_1^7 = -\frac{343}{3}+196-49-(-\frac{1}{3}+4-7) = 36$

46. The curves intersect at $(1,1)$, so the area is

$A = \int_0^2 |x^3-(x^2-4x+4)|dx = \int_0^1 (-x^3+x^2-4x+4)dx + \int_1^2 (x^3-x^2+4x-4)dx$

$= -\frac{1}{4}x^4+\frac{1}{3}x^3-2x^2+4x\Big]_0^1 + \left[\frac{1}{4}x^4-\frac{1}{3}x^3+2x^2-4x\right]_1^2$

$= -\frac{1}{4}+\frac{1}{3}-2+4+4-\frac{8}{3}+8-8-\frac{1}{4}+\frac{1}{3}-2+4 = 5.5$

48. If $3 \le x \le 5$, then $4 \le x+1 \le 6$ and $\frac{1}{6} \le \frac{1}{x+1} \le \frac{1}{4}$, so

$\frac{1}{6}\cdot(5-3) \le \int_3^5 \frac{1}{x+1}dx \le \frac{1}{4}\cdot(5-3)$; that is, $\frac{1}{3} \le \int_3^5 \frac{1}{x+1}dx \le \frac{1}{2}$

50. If $0 \le x \le \sqrt{\pi}/2$, then $0 \le x^2 \le \pi/4$, so $\sin(x^2) \le \cos(x^2)$.

It follows that $\int_0^{\sqrt{\pi}/2} \sin(x^2)dx \le \int_0^{\sqrt{\pi}/2} \cos(x^2)dx$ [Property 7]

52. On the interval $[\pi/4, \pi/2]$, x is increasing and sin x is decreasing,

so $\frac{\sin x}{x}$ is decreasing. Therefore the largest value of $\frac{\sin x}{x}$ on

$[\pi/4, \pi/2]$ is $\frac{\sin(\pi/4)}{\pi/4} = \frac{\sqrt{2}/2}{\pi/4} = \frac{2\sqrt{2}}{\pi}$. By Property 8 with $M = 2\sqrt{2}/\pi$,

we get $\int_{\pi/4}^{\pi/2} \frac{\sin x}{x}dx \le \frac{2\sqrt{2}}{\pi}\left[\frac{\pi}{2} - \frac{\pi}{4}\right] = \frac{\sqrt{2}}{2} \approx .707$

54. (a) displacement $= \int_0^5 (t^2-t)dt = \frac{t^3}{3} - \frac{t^2}{2}\Big]_0^5 = \frac{125}{3} - \frac{25}{2} = \frac{175}{6}$

(b) distance $= \int_0^5 |t^2-t|dt = \int_0^5 |t(t-1)|dt = \int_0^1 (t-t^2)dt + \int_1^5 (t^2-t)dt$

$= \left[\frac{t^2}{2} - \frac{t^3}{3}\right]\Big]_0^1 + \left[\frac{t^3}{3} - \frac{t^2}{2}\right]\Big]_1^5 = \frac{1}{2}-\frac{1}{3}+\left(\frac{125}{3} -\frac{25}{2}\right)-\left(\frac{1}{3}-\frac{1}{2}\right) = 29.5$

56. $\displaystyle\lim_{n\to\infty} \frac{1}{n}\left[\left[\frac{1}{n}\right]^9 + \left[\frac{2}{n}\right]^9 + \left[\frac{3}{n}\right]^9 + \cdots + \left[\frac{n}{n}\right]^9\right] = \lim_{n\to\infty} \frac{1-0}{n} \sum_{i=1}^{n} \left[\frac{i}{n}\right]^9$

$= \int_0^1 x^9 \, dx = \frac{1}{10}x^{10}\Big]_0^1 = \frac{1}{10}$

[The limit is based on Riemann sums using right endpoints and subintervals of equal length. (Theorem 5.12)]

58. Let $u = \ln x$. Then $du = \dfrac{dx}{x}$ so $\displaystyle\int \frac{\cos(\ln x)}{x} \, dx = \int \cos u \, du$

$= \sin u + C = \sin(\ln x) + C$

60. Let $u = x^2$. Then $du = 2x \, dx$, so $\displaystyle\int \frac{x \, dx}{\sqrt{1-x^4}} = \int \frac{(1/2)du}{\sqrt{1-u^2}}$

$= \dfrac{1}{2} \sin^{-1}u + C = \dfrac{1}{2} \sin^{-1}(x^2) + C$

62. Let $u = \ln(e^x+1)$. Then $\displaystyle\int \frac{e^x \, dx}{(e^x+1)\ln(e^x+1)} = \int \frac{du}{u} = \ln|u| + C$

$= \ln(\ln(e^x+1)) + C$

NOTE: $e^x+1 > 1$, so $\ln(e^x+1) > 0$ and $|\ln(e^x+1)| = \ln(e^x+1)$.

CHAPTER SIX

Exercises 6.1

2.

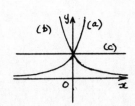

4. $y = (1.1)^x$

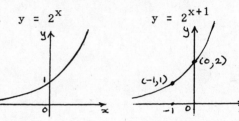

6. $y = (0.1)^x$

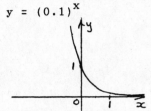

8. $y = 2^x$ $y = 2^{x+1}$

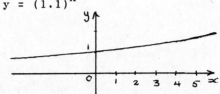

10. $y = 3^x$ $y = -3^x$

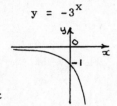

12. $y = 2^x$ $y = 2^{|x|}$

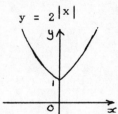

14. $y = 5^x$ $y = 5^{x-3}$

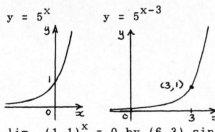

16. $y = -10^{-x}$ $y = 2+5(1-10^{-x})$

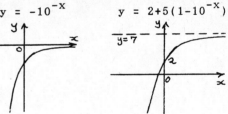

18. $\lim\limits_{x \to -\infty} (1.1)^x = 0$ by (6.3) since $1.1 > 1$

20. $\lim\limits_{x \to -\infty} \pi^{-x} = \lim\limits_{x \to -\infty} \left[\dfrac{1}{\pi}\right]^x = \infty$ by (6.3) since $0 < \dfrac{1}{\pi} < 1$

    [OR: $\lim\limits_{x \to -\infty} \pi^{-x} = \infty$ since $-x \to \infty$ as $x \to -\infty$]

22. $\lim\limits_{x \to -\infty} 2^{3x+1} = 0$ since $3x+1 \to -\infty$ as $x \to -\infty$

24. $\lim\limits_{x \to \infty} (0.8)^{x+1} = 0$ since $x+1 \to \infty$ as $x \to \infty$

163

26. $\lim\limits_{x \to \infty} \left[\frac{2\pi}{7}\right]^x = 0$ since $0 < \frac{2\pi}{7} < 1$

28. $\lim\limits_{x \to -\pi/2^+} 2^{\tan x} = 0$ since $\tan x \to -\infty$ as $x \to -\pi/2^+$

30. $\lim\limits_{x \to -\infty} 3^{1/x} = 3^0 = 1$ since $\frac{1}{x} \to 0$ as $x \to -\infty$

32. $\lim\limits_{x \to 0^-} 3^{1/x} = 0$ since $\frac{1}{x} \to -\infty$ as $x \to 0^-$

34. Divide numerator and denominator by 2^x:

$$\lim\limits_{x \to \infty} \frac{2^x - 2^{-x}}{2^x + 3 \cdot 2^{-x}} = \lim\limits_{x \to \infty} \frac{1 - 2^{-2x}}{1 + 3 \cdot 2^{-2x}} = \frac{1 - 0}{1 + 3 \cdot 0} = 1$$

36. $\lim\limits_{t \to 0^-} (3 - 2^{\csc t}) = 3 - 0 = 3$ since $\csc t \to -\infty$ as $t \to 0^-$

Section 6.2

Exercises 6.2

2. One-to-one   4. Not one-to-one   6. One-to-one

8. $f(x) = x^2 - 2x + 5 \Rightarrow f(0) = 5 = f(2)$, so f is not one-to-one.

10. $g(x) = |x| \Rightarrow g(-1) = 1 = g(1)$, so g is not one-to-one.

12. $x_1 \neq x_2 \Rightarrow x_1^4 \neq x_2^4$ (since $x \geq 0$) $\Rightarrow x_1^4 + 5 \neq x_2^4 + 5 \Rightarrow$ $h(x_1) \neq h(x_2)$, so h is one-to-one.

14. $f(x) = \frac{x-2}{x+2}$ If $f(x_1) = f(x_2)$, then $\frac{x_1 - 2}{x_1 + 2} = \frac{x_2 - 2}{x_2 + 2} \Rightarrow$

$x_1 x_2 + 2x_1 - 2x_2 - 4 = x_1 x_2 - 2x_1 + 2x_2 - 4 \Rightarrow 4x_1 = 4x_2 \Rightarrow x_1 = x_2$, so f is one-to-one. $y = \frac{x-2}{x+2} \Rightarrow xy + 2y = x - 2 \Rightarrow x(1-y) = 2(y+1) \Rightarrow$

$x = \frac{2(1+y)}{1-y}$ Interchange x and y: $y = \frac{2(1+x)}{1-x}$ So $f^{-1}(x) = \frac{2(1+x)}{1-x}$

16. $x_1 \neq x_2 \Rightarrow x_1^3 \neq x_2^3 \Rightarrow -4x_1^3 \neq -4x_2^3 \Rightarrow 5 - 4x_1^3 \neq 5 - 4x_2^3 \Rightarrow$ $f(x_1) \neq f(x_2)$, so f is one-to-one. $y = 5 - 4x^3 \Rightarrow 4x^3 = 5 - y \Rightarrow$ $x^3 = (5-y)/4 \Rightarrow x = \sqrt[3]{(5-y)/4}$. Interchange x and y: $y = \sqrt[3]{(5-x)/4}$. So $f^{-1}(x) = \sqrt[3]{(5-x)/4}$.

18. $f(x) = x^2 + x$, $x \geq -1/2$. $f'(x) = 2x + 1 > 0$ for $x > -1/2$, so f is increasing on $[-1/2, \infty)$ and hence one-to-one. [Or use the Horizontal Line Test.] $y = x^2 + x \Rightarrow x^2 + x - y = 0 \Rightarrow x = (-1 \pm \sqrt{1+4y})/2$ by the quadratic formula. But $x \geq -1/2 \Rightarrow x = (-1 + \sqrt{1+4y})/2$. Interchange x and y: $y = (-1 + \sqrt{1+4x})/2$. So $f^{-1}(x) = (-1 + \sqrt{1+4x})/2$.

20. (a) $x_1 \neq x_2 \Rightarrow -x_1 \neq -x_2 \Rightarrow 6-x_1 \neq 6-x_2 \Rightarrow f(x_1) \neq f(x_2)$, so f
    is one-to-one. (b) $f'(x) = -1$ and $g(2) = 4$ since $f(4) = 2$, so by
    Theorem 6.12, $g'(2) = 1/f'(4) = 1/(-1) = -1$. (c) $y = 6-x \Rightarrow$
    $x = 6-y$. Interchange x and y: $y = 6-x$. (e)
    So $g(x) = 6-x$. Domain = R = Range.
    (d) $g'(x) = -1$, so $g'(2) = -1$.

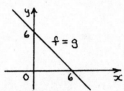

22. (a) $x_1 \neq x_2 \Rightarrow x_1-2 \neq x_2-2 \Rightarrow \sqrt{x_1-2} \neq \sqrt{x_2-2} \Rightarrow f(x_1) \neq f(x_2)$, so
    f is one-to-one. (b) $f(6) = 2$, so $g(2) = 6$. Also $f'(x) = 1/2\sqrt{x-2}$,
    so $g'(2) = 1/f'(g(2)) = 1/f'(6) = 1/(1/4) = 4$. (c) $y = \sqrt{x-2} \Rightarrow$
    $y^2 = x-2 \Rightarrow x = y^2+2$. Interchange (e)
    x and y: $y = x^2+2$. So $g(x) = x^2+2$.
    Domain = $[0,\infty)$, range = $[2,\infty)$.
    (d) $g'(x) = 2x \Rightarrow g'(2) = 4$.

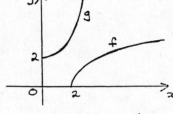

24. $f(x) = \dfrac{1}{x-1}$, $x>1$. (a) $x_1 \neq x_2 \Rightarrow x_1-1 \neq x_2-1 \Rightarrow \dfrac{1}{x_1-1} \neq \dfrac{1}{x_2-1} \Rightarrow$
    $f(x_1) \neq f(x_2)$, so f is one-to-one. (b) $g(2) = 3/2$ since $f(3/2) = 2$.
    Also $f'(x) = -1/(x-1)^2$, so $g'(2) = 1/f'(3/2) = 1/(-4) = -1/4$.
    (c) $y = \dfrac{1}{x-1} \Rightarrow x-1 = \dfrac{1}{y} \Rightarrow x = 1+\dfrac{1}{y}$ (e)
    Interchange x and y: $y = 1+\dfrac{1}{x}$.

    So $g(x) = 1+1/x$, $x>0$ (since $y>1$)
    Domain = $(0,\infty)$, range = $(1,\infty)$.
    (d) $g'(x) = -\dfrac{1}{x^2}$, so $g'(2) = -\dfrac{1}{4}$

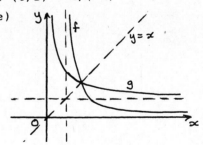

26. See Section 6.8.

Exercises 6.3

2. $\log_6 \frac{1}{36} = -2$ since $6^{-2} = \frac{1}{36}$ 4. $\log_8 4 = \frac{2}{3}$ since $8^{2/3} = 4$

6. $e^{\ln 6} = 6$ 8. $\log_3 3^{\sqrt{5}} = \sqrt{5}$

10. $\log_3 108 - \log_3 4 = \log_3 \frac{108}{4} = \log_3 27 = 3$

12. $\log_5 10 + \log_5 20 - 3 \log_5 2 = \log_5 \frac{10 \cdot 20}{2^3} = \log_5 25 = 2$

14. $e^{3 \ln 2} = e^{\ln(2^3)} = e^{\ln 8} = 8$ [Or: $e^{3 \ln 2} = (e^{\ln 2})^3 = 2^3 = 8$]

16. $\log_2 x + 5 \log_2(x+1) + \frac{1}{2} \log_2(x-1) = \log_2 x + \log_2(x+1)^5 + \log_2 \sqrt{x-1}$

    $= \log_2 [x(x+1)^5 \sqrt{x-1}]$

18. $\ln x + a \ln y - b \ln z = \ln x + \ln y^a - \ln z^b = \ln(xy^a/z^b)$

20.

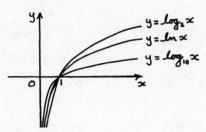

22. $y = \log_{100} x$ 24. $y = \log_{0.9} x$

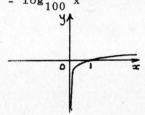   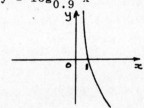

26. $y = \log_5 x$ $y = 1 + \log_5(x-1)$ 28. $y = \ln x$ $y = \ln(-x)$

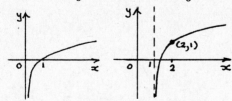   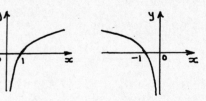

30. $y = \ln|x|$

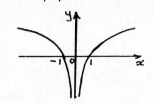

32. $y = \ln x \qquad y = \ln \frac{1}{x} = -\ln x$

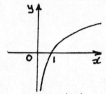 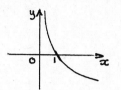

34. $y = \ln|x+3|$

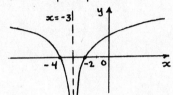

36. $y = e^{|x|} \qquad y = e^{|x-2|}$

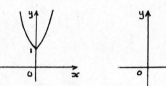 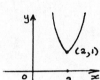

38. Note that, since $-1 \leq \sin x \leq 1$, we have $-e^{-x} \leq e^{-x}\sin x \leq e^{-x}$.

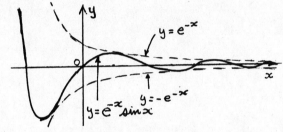

40. $x = e^{\ln \pi} = \pi$

42. $\log_{10} x^2 = A \;\Rightarrow\; x^2 = 10^A \;\Rightarrow\; x = \pm 10^{A/2}$

44. $y = e^{3x-4} \;\Rightarrow\; \ln y = 3x-4 \;\Rightarrow\; x = (\ln y + 4)/3$

46. $6 = 5^{\log_5(2x)} = 2x \;\Rightarrow\; x = 3$

48. $\ln x^2 = 2\ln 4 - 4\ln 2 = 4\ln 2 - 4\ln 2 = 0 \;\Rightarrow\; x^2 = 1 \;\Rightarrow\; x = \pm 1$

50. $\ln x + \ln(x-1) = \ln x(x-1) = 1 \;\Rightarrow\; x(x-1) = e \;\Rightarrow\; x^2 - x - e = 0$

The quadratic formula gives $x = (1 \pm \sqrt{1+4e})/2$, but we reject the minus sign since $(1-\sqrt{1+4e})/2 < 0$. So $x = (1+\sqrt{1+4e})/2$.

52. $y = \log_2(\log_3(\log_4 x)) \;\Rightarrow\; 2^y = \log_3(\log_4 x) \;\Rightarrow\; 3^{2^y} = \log_4 x$

$\Rightarrow\; x = 4^{3^{2^y}}$

54. (a) $b^{\log_b c} = c \;\Rightarrow\; \log_a c = \log_a\left[b^{\log_b c}\right] = (\log_b c)(\log_a b)$

(b) Take $c = a$ in part (a): $(\log_a b)(\log_b a) = \log_a a = 1 \;\Rightarrow\;$

$\log_a b = 1/\log_b a.$

(c) Take b = e in part (b): $\log_a e = 1/\log_e a = 1/\ln a$.

56. (a) $\log_2 5 = \dfrac{\ln 5}{\ln 2} \approx 2.321928$ (b) $\log_5 26.05 = \dfrac{\ln 26.05}{\ln 5} \approx 2.025563$

     (c) $\log_3 e = \dfrac{1}{\ln 3} \approx 0.910239$ (d) $\log_{0.7} 14 = \dfrac{\ln 14}{\ln 0.7} \approx -7.399054$

58. Let I_1 and I_2 be the intensities of the music and the mower. Then

$10 \log_{10}(I_1/I_o) = 120$ and $10 \log_{10}(I_2/I_o) = 106$, so $\log_{10}(I_1/I_2)$

$= \log_{10}\left[\dfrac{I_1/I_o}{I_2/I_o}\right] = \log_{10}(I_1/I_0) - \log_{10}(I_2/I_0) = 12-10.6 = 1.4 \Rightarrow$

$I_1/I_2 = 10^{1.4} \approx 25$.

60. $\lim\limits_{x\to 0^+} \log_{0.5}(4x) = \infty$ by (6.17) since $4x \to 0^+$ as $x \to 0^+$

62. $\lim\limits_{x\to 0^+} \ln(\sin x) = -\infty$ since $\sin x \to 0^+$ as $x \to 0^+$

64. Divide numerator and denominator by e^{-3x}:

$\lim\limits_{x\to -\infty} \dfrac{e^{3x}-e^{-3x}}{e^{3x}+e^{-3x}} = \lim\limits_{x\to -\infty} \dfrac{e^{6x}-1}{e^{6x}+1} = \dfrac{0-1}{0+1} = -1$

66. $\lim\limits_{x\to\infty} \dfrac{\ln x}{1 + \ln x} = \lim\limits_{x\to\infty} \dfrac{1}{(1/\ln x) + 1} = \dfrac{1}{0+1} = 1$

68. $\lim\limits_{x\to 1^+} e^{2/(x-1)} = \infty$ since $\dfrac{2}{x-1} \to \infty$ as $x \to 1^+$

70. As $x \to 0^-$, $\cot x = \dfrac{\cos x}{\sin x} \to -\infty$, so $e^{\cot x} \to 0$ and

$\lim\limits_{x\to 0} \dfrac{2}{1 + e^{\cot x}} = \dfrac{2}{1+0} = 2$

72. $\lim\limits_{x\to 0} (1+x)^{2/x} = \lim\limits_{x\to 0} [(1+x)^{1/x}]^2 = \left[\lim\limits_{x\to 0} (1+x)^{1/x}\right]^2 = e^2$

74. Divide numerator and denominator by e^{-x}:

$\lim\limits_{x\to -\infty} \dfrac{e^x+2e^{-x}}{e^x-3e^{-x}} = \lim\limits_{x\to -\infty} \dfrac{e^{2x}+2}{e^{2x}-3} = \dfrac{0+2}{0-3} = -\dfrac{2}{3}$

76. $g(x) = \ln(4-x^2)$ $\text{Dom}(g) = \{x \mid 4-x^2>0\} = \{x \mid |x|<2\} = (-2,2)$. Since $4-x^2 \le 4$, we have $\ln(4-x^2) \le \ln 4$. Also $\lim\limits_{x\to 2^-} g(x) = -\infty$, so range(g) $= (-\infty, \ln 4]$.

78. $G(t) = \ln(t^3-t)$ $\text{Dom}(G) = \{t \mid t^3-t>0\} = \{t \mid t(t^2-1)>0\}$ $= \{t \mid t>1 \text{ or } -1<t<0\} = (-1,0) \cup (1,\infty)$. Range(G) = R.

80. $y = 2^{10^x} \Rightarrow \log_2 y = 10^x \Rightarrow \log_{10}(\log_2 y) = x$. Interchange x and y: $y = \log_{10}(\log_2 x)$ is the inverse function.

82. $y = (\ln x)^2$, $x \geq 1$, $\Rightarrow$ $\ln x = \sqrt{y}$ $\Rightarrow$ $x = e^{\sqrt{y}}$. Interchange x and y:

$y = e^{\sqrt{x}}$ is the inverse function.

84. $y = \dfrac{1+e^x}{1-e^x}$ $\Rightarrow$ $y - ye^x = 1 + e^x$ $\Rightarrow$ $e^x(y+1) = y-1$ $\Rightarrow$ $e^x = \dfrac{y-1}{y+1}$ $\Rightarrow$

$x = \ln\left[\dfrac{y-1}{y+1}\right]$ Interchange x and y: $y = \ln\left[\dfrac{x-1}{x+1}\right]$ is the inverse

function.

86. (a) $\lim\limits_{x\to\infty} x^{\ln x} = \lim\limits_{x\to\infty} (e^{\ln x})^{\ln x} = \lim\limits_{x\to\infty} e^{(\ln x)^2} = \infty$ since $(\ln x)^2 \to \infty$

(b) $\lim\limits_{x\to 0^+} x^{-\ln x} = \lim\limits_{x\to 0^+} (e^{\ln x})^{-\ln x} = \lim\limits_{x\to 0^+} e^{-(\ln x)^2} = 0$ since

$-(\ln x)^2 \to -\infty$ as $x \to 0^+$

(c) $\lim\limits_{x\to 0^+} x^{1/x} = \lim\limits_{x\to 0^+} (e^{\ln x})^{1/x} = \lim\limits_{x\to 0^+} e^{(\ln x/x)} = 0$ since

$\dfrac{\ln x}{x} \to -\infty$ as $x \to 0^+$

(d) $\lim\limits_{x\to\infty} (\ln 2x)^{-\ln x} = \lim\limits_{x\to\infty} (e^{\ln(\ln 2x)})^{-\ln x} = \lim\limits_{x\to\infty} e^{-\ln x \, \ln(\ln 2x)}$

$= 0$ since $-\ln x \, \ln(\ln 2x) \to -\infty$ as $x \to \infty$

88. Suppose that $\log_2 5$ is a rational number. Then $\log_2 5 = \dfrac{m}{n}$ where m

and n are positive integers $\Rightarrow$ $2^{m/n} = 5$ $\Rightarrow$ $2^m = 5^n$. But this is

impossible since 2^m is even and 5^n is odd. So $\log_2 5$ is irrational.

Section 6.4

Exercises 6.4

2. $f(x) = \log_{10}(5-2x)$ $\Rightarrow$ $f'(x) = \dfrac{1}{5-2x} \log_{10} e \cdot (-2) = \dfrac{-2\log_{10} e}{5-2x}$ or

$\dfrac{-2}{(\ln 10)(5-2x)}$ Dom$(f) = \{x \mid 5-2x>0\} = \{x \mid x<\frac{5}{2}\} = (-\infty, \frac{5}{2}) =$ dom(f')

4. $f(x) = \ln \ln x$ $\Rightarrow$ $f'(x) = \dfrac{1}{\ln x} \cdot \dfrac{1}{x} = \dfrac{1}{x \ln x}$

Dom$(f) =$ dom$(f') = \{x \mid \ln x > 0\} = \{x \mid x>1\} = (1,\infty)$

6. $f(x) = \cos(\ln x)$ $\Rightarrow$ $f'(x) = -\sin(\ln x)/x$. Dom$(f) =$ dom$(f') = (0,\infty)$

8. $f(x) = \ln \ln \ln x$ $\Rightarrow$ $f'(x) = \dfrac{1}{\ln \ln x} \cdot \dfrac{1}{\ln x} \cdot \dfrac{1}{x}$

dom$(f) = \{x \mid \ln \ln x > 0\} = \{x \mid \ln x > 1\} = \{x \mid x > e\} = (e,\infty)$

dom$(f') = (e,\infty)$

10. $f(x) = \ln(\sqrt{x}-\sqrt{x-1}) \;\Rightarrow\; f'(x) = \dfrac{1}{\sqrt{x}-\sqrt{x-1}}\left[\dfrac{1}{2\sqrt{x}} - \dfrac{1}{2\sqrt{x-1}}\right]$

$= \dfrac{1}{\sqrt{x}-\sqrt{x-1}}\,\dfrac{\sqrt{x-1}-\sqrt{x}}{2\sqrt{x}\sqrt{x-1}} = \dfrac{-1}{2\sqrt{x}\sqrt{x-1}}$ $\text{Dom}(f) = \{x \mid x \geq 1\} = [1,\infty)$,

$\text{dom}(f') = \{x \mid x > 1\} = (1,\infty)$.

12. $y = \ln(ax) \;\Rightarrow\; y' = \dfrac{a}{ax} = \dfrac{1}{x} \;\Rightarrow\; y'' = -1/x^2$

14. $y = \ln(\sec x + \tan x) \;\Rightarrow\; y' = \dfrac{1}{\sec x + \tan x}(\sec x \tan x + \sec^2 x)$

$= \sec x \;\Rightarrow\; y'' = \sec x \tan x$

16. $f(x) = \log_{10}\left[\dfrac{x}{x-1}\right] = \log_{10} x - \log_{10}(x-1) \;\Rightarrow$

$f'(x) = \dfrac{1}{x}\log_{10} e - \dfrac{1}{x-1}\log_{10} e = \left[\dfrac{1}{x} - \dfrac{1}{x-1}\right]\log_{10} e$

$\left[\text{or} \; -\dfrac{1}{x(x-1)}\log_{10} e \; \text{or} \; -\dfrac{1}{x(x-1)\,\ln 10}\right]$

18. $h(x) = \ln(x+\sqrt{x^2-1}) \;\Rightarrow\; h'(x) = \dfrac{1}{x+\sqrt{x^2-1}}\left[1 + \dfrac{x}{\sqrt{x^2-1}}\right] = \dfrac{1}{\sqrt{x^2-1}}$

20. $G(x) = \sqrt{\ln x} \;\Rightarrow\; G'(x) = (1/2\sqrt{\ln x})(1/x) = 1/2x\sqrt{\ln x}$

22. $g(t) = \sin(\ln t) \;\Rightarrow\; g'(t) = \cos(\ln t)/t$

24. $k(r) = r\sin r \ln r \;\Rightarrow\; k'(r) = \sin r \ln r + r\cos r \ln r + \sin r$

26. $G(u) = \ln\sqrt{\dfrac{3u+2}{3u-2}} = \dfrac{1}{2}[\ln(3u+2) - \ln(3u-2)] \;\Rightarrow$

$G'(u) = \dfrac{1}{2}\left[\dfrac{3}{3u+2} - \dfrac{3}{3u-2}\right] = \dfrac{-6}{9u^2-4}$

28. $y = \log_3(\log_2 x) \;\Rightarrow\; y' = \dfrac{1}{(\log_2 x)(\ln 3)}\dfrac{1}{x \ln 2}$

30. $y = \ln(x\sqrt{1-x^2}\sin x) = \ln x + (1/2)\ln(1-x^2) + \ln \sin x \;\Rightarrow$

$y' = \dfrac{1}{x} + \dfrac{1}{2}\dfrac{-2x}{1-x^2} + \dfrac{\cos x}{\sin x} = \dfrac{1}{x} - \dfrac{x}{1-x^2} + \cot x$

32. $y = \ln|\tan 2x| \;\Rightarrow\; y' = \dfrac{2\sec^2 2x}{\tan 2x}$

34. $y = \tan[\ln(ax+b)] \;\Rightarrow\; y' = \sec^2[\ln(ax+b)]\dfrac{a}{ax+b}$

36. $y = \log_x e = \dfrac{1}{\ln x} \;\Rightarrow\; y' = -(\ln x)^{-2}(1/x) = -1/x(\ln x)^2$

38. $\displaystyle\int_{-e^2}^{-e} \dfrac{3}{x}\,dx = 3\ln|x|\Big]_{-e^2}^{-e} = 3\ln e - 3\ln(e^2) = 3 - 6 = -3$

40. $\displaystyle\int_4^9\left[\sqrt{x} + \dfrac{1}{\sqrt{x}}\right]^2 dx = \int_4^9\left(x + 2 + \dfrac{1}{x}\right)dx = \dfrac{1}{2}x^2 + 2x + \ln x\Big]_4^9$

$= \dfrac{81}{2} + 18 + \ln 9 - (8 + 8 + \ln 4) = \dfrac{85}{2} + \ln\dfrac{9}{4}$

42. Let $u = x^3 + 3x + 1$. Then $du = 3(x^2+1)dx$, so $\int \dfrac{x^2+1}{x^3+3x+1}\,dx = \dfrac{1}{3}\int \dfrac{du}{u}$

$= \dfrac{1}{3}\ln|u| + C = \dfrac{1}{3}\ln|x^3+3x+1| + C$

44. Let $u = \ln x$. Then $du = \dfrac{1}{x}\,dx$, so $\int \dfrac{dx}{x\,\ln x} = \int \dfrac{du}{u} = \ln|u| + C$

$= \ln|\ln x| + C$

46. Let $u = 2 - \tan x$. Then $du = -\sec^2 x\,dx$, so $\int \dfrac{\sec^2 x}{2 - \tan x}\,dx = -\int \dfrac{du}{u}$

$= -\ln|u| + C = -\ln|2 - \tan x| + C$

48. Let $u = 1 + \ln x$. Then $du = (1/x)dx$, so

$\int \dfrac{(1 + \ln x)^4}{x}\,dx = \int u^4\,du = \dfrac{1}{5}u^5 + C = \dfrac{1}{5}(1 + \ln x)^5 + C$

50. Let $u = x-2$. Then the area is $A = -\int_{-4}^{-1} \dfrac{2}{x-2}\,dx = -2\int_{-6}^{-3} \dfrac{du}{u}$

$= -2\,\ln|u|\Big]_{-6}^{-3} = -2\,\ln 3 + 2\,\ln 6 = 2\,\ln 2 \approx 1.386.$

52. $y = x^{2/5}(x^2+8)^4 e^{x^2+x} \;\Rightarrow\; \ln|y| = (2/5)\ln|x| + 4\,\ln(x^2+8) + x^2 + x \Rightarrow$

$\dfrac{y'}{y} = \dfrac{2}{5}\cdot\dfrac{1}{x} + 4\cdot\dfrac{2x}{x^2+8} + 2x+1 \Rightarrow y' = x^{2/5}(x^2+8)^4 e^{x^2+x}\left[\dfrac{2}{5x} + \dfrac{8x}{x^2+8} + 2x+1\right]$

54. $y = \sqrt{\dfrac{x^2+1}{x+1}} \;\Rightarrow\; \ln y = \dfrac{1}{2}[\ln(x^2+1) - \ln(x+1)] \;\Rightarrow\; \dfrac{y'}{y} = \dfrac{1}{2}\left[\dfrac{2x}{x^2+1} - \dfrac{1}{x+1}\right]$

$\Rightarrow\; y' = \sqrt{\dfrac{x^2+1}{x+1}}\left[\dfrac{x}{x^2+1} - \dfrac{1}{2(x+1)}\right]$

56. $y = \dfrac{(x^3+1)^4 \sin^2 x}{\sqrt[3]{x}} \;\Rightarrow\; \ln|y| = 4\,\ln|x^3+1| + 2\,\ln|\sin x| - \dfrac{1}{3}\ln|x|$

$\dfrac{y'}{y} = 4\cdot\dfrac{3x^2}{x^3+1} + 2\,\dfrac{\cos x}{\sin x} - \dfrac{1}{3x} \Rightarrow y' = \dfrac{(x^3+1)^4 \sin^2 x}{\sqrt[3]{x}}\left[\dfrac{12x^2}{x^3+1} + 2\cot x - \dfrac{1}{3x}\right]$

58. $\ln(x+y) = x^2 + y^2 \;\Rightarrow\; \dfrac{1+y'}{x+y} = 2x+2yy' \;\Rightarrow\; 1+y' = 2x^2+2xy+2xyy'+2y^2 y'$

$\Rightarrow\; y' = \dfrac{1-2x^2-2xy}{2xy+2y^2-1}$

60. $f(x) = x^2 \ln x \;\Rightarrow\; f'(x) = 2x\,\ln x + x^2(1/x) = 2x\,\ln x + x \;\Rightarrow$

$f'(1) = 2\,\ln 1 + 1 = 1$

62. $y = f(x) = \ln x \;\Rightarrow\; f'(x) = 1/x \;\Rightarrow\; f'(a) = 1/a$, so the equation of

the tangent at $(a, \ln a)$ is $y - \ln a = \dfrac{1}{a}(x-a)$ or $x - ay = a\,\ln a - a$.

64. $y = x^8 \ln x$, $D^9 y = D^8(8x^7 \ln x + x^7) = D^8(8x^7 \ln x)$

$= D^7(8\cdot 7x^6 \ln x + 8x^6) = D^7(8\cdot 7x^6 \ln x) = D^6(8\cdot 7\cdot 6x^5 \ln x) = \cdots$

$= D(8!\ln x) = 8!/x$

66. $f(x) = \cos x + 5 \ln(x+1)$, $h = f^{-1}$. $f(0) = 1 \Rightarrow h(1) = 0$ and
$f'(x) = -\sin x + 5/(x+1)$, so by Theorem 6.12, $h'(1) = 1/f'(0) = 1/5$

68. $f(x) = \sqrt{x} \ln x \Rightarrow f'(x) = (1/2)x^{-1/2}\ln x + x^{-1/2} \Rightarrow$
$f''(x) = -\frac{1}{4}x^{-3/2}\ln x + \frac{1}{2}x^{-3/2} - \frac{1}{2}x^{-3/2} = -\frac{1}{4}x^{-3/2}\ln x > 0 \Leftrightarrow \ln x < 0$
$\Leftrightarrow 0 < x < 1$. So f is CU on $(0,1)$ and CD on $(1,\infty)$. Inflection point is $(1,0)$.

70. $y = f(x) = \ln(\sin x)$ A. $D = \{x \mid \sin x > 0\} = \{x \mid 2n\pi < x < (2n+1)\pi\}$
B. x-intercepts when $\sin x = 1 \Leftrightarrow x = 2n\pi + \pi/2$, no y-intercept.
C. f is periodic with period 2π, so we determine D-G on $(0,\pi)$.
D. $\lim_{x \to 0^+} \ln(\sin x) = -\infty$, $\lim_{x \to \pi^-} \ln(\sin x) = -\infty$, so $x = 0$ and $x = \pi$ are
VA. E. $f'(x) = \frac{\cos x}{\sin x} = \cot x > 0$ for $0 < x < \pi/2$ and $f'(x) < 0$ for
$\pi/2 < x < \pi$, so f is increasing on $(0,\pi/2]$ and decreasing on $[\pi/2,\pi)$.
F. $f(\pi/2) = 0$ is a local maximum. G. $f''(x) = -\csc^2 x < 0$, so f is
CD on $(0,\pi)$.
H.
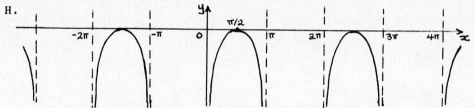

72. $y = f(x) = x^2 + \ln x$ A. $D = (0,\infty)$ B. No y-intercept C. No
symmetry D. $\lim_{x \to \infty}(x^2 + \ln x) = \infty$, no HA. $\lim_{x \to 0^+}(x^2 + \ln x) = -\infty$, so
$x = 0$ is a VA. E. $f'(x) = 2x + 1/x > 0$, so f is increasing on $(0,\infty)$
F. No extrema   H.

G. $f''(x) = 2 - \dfrac{1}{x^2} = \dfrac{2x^2 - 1}{x^2} > 0$

$\Leftrightarrow 2x^2 > 1 \Leftrightarrow x > 1/\sqrt{2}$, so f is CU
on $(1/\sqrt{2},\infty)$ and CD on $(0,1/\sqrt{2})$.
IP $(1/\sqrt{2},(1-\ln 2)/2)$

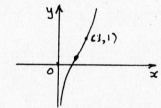

74. $y = \ln(\tan^2 x)$ A. $D = \{x \mid x \neq n\pi/2\}$ B. x-intercepts $n\pi + \pi/4$, no
y-intercept C. $f(-x) = f(x)$, so the curve is symmetric about the
y-axis. Also $f(x+\pi) = f(x)$, so f is periodic with period π and we
consider D-G only for $-\pi/2 < x < \pi/2$. D. $\lim_{x \to 0} \ln(\tan^2 x) = -\infty$ and
$\lim_{x \to \pi/2^-} \ln(\tan^2 x) = \infty$, $\lim_{x \to -\pi/2^+} \ln(\tan^2 x) = \infty$, so $x = 0$, $x = \pm\frac{\pi}{2}$ are VA.

E. $f'(x) = \dfrac{2 \tan x \sec^2 x}{\tan^2 x} = 2\dfrac{\sec^2 x}{\tan x} > 0 \Leftrightarrow \tan x > 0 \Leftrightarrow 0 < x < \dfrac{\pi}{2}$,

so f is increasing on $(0,\pi/2)$ and decreasing on $(-\pi/2,0)$.

F. No extrema G. $f'(x) = \dfrac{2}{\sin x \cos x} = \dfrac{4}{\sin 2x} \Rightarrow f''(x) = \dfrac{-8 \cos 2x}{\sin^2 2x}$

$< 0 \Leftrightarrow \cos 2x > 0 \Leftrightarrow -\pi/4 < x < \pi/4$, so f is CD on $(-\pi/4,0)$ and $(0,\pi/4)$
and CU on $(-\pi/2,-\pi/4)$ and $(\pi/4,\pi/2)$. IP are $(\pm\pi/4,0)$.

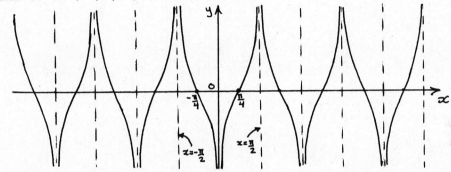

76. $y = f(x) = \ln(x^2-x)$ A. $D = \{x \mid x^2-x>0\} = \{x \mid x<0$ or $x>1\}$
$= (-\infty,0)\cup(1,\infty)$ B. x-intercepts occur when $x^2-x = 1 \Leftrightarrow x^2-x-1 = 0$
$\Leftrightarrow x = (1\pm\sqrt{5})/2$. No y-intercept. C. No symmetry.

D. $\lim\limits_{x\to\infty} \ln(x^2-x) = \infty$, no HA. $\lim\limits_{x\to 0^-} \ln(x^2-x) = -\infty$, $\lim\limits_{x\to 1^+} \ln(x^2-x) = -\infty$,

so $x = 0$ and $x = 1$ are VA. E. $f'(x) = (2x-1)/(x^2-x) > 0$ when $x>1$
and $f'(x) < 0$ when $x<0$, so f is increasing on $(1,\infty)$ and decreasing
on $(-\infty,0)$. F. No extrema G. $f''(x) = \dfrac{2(x^2-x)-(2x-1)^2}{(x^2-x)^2} = \dfrac{-2x^2+2x-1}{(x^2-x)^2}$

$\Rightarrow f''(x) < 0$ for all x since $-2x^2+2x-1$ has negative discriminant.
So f is CD on $(-\infty,0)$ and $(1,\infty)$.

H.

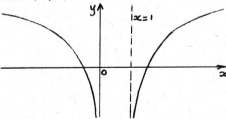

78. $f''(x) = x^{-2}$, $x>0$, $\Rightarrow f'(x) = -1/x + C \Rightarrow f(x) = -\ln x + Cx + D$.
$0 = f(1) = C+D$ and $0 = f(2) = -\ln 2 + 2C + D = -\ln 2 + 2C - C$
$= -\ln 2 + C \Rightarrow C = \ln 2$ and $D = -\ln 2$. So
$f(x) = -\ln x + (\ln 2)x - \ln 2$.

80. If $f(x) = \ln(1+x)$, then $f'(x) = 1/(1+x)$, so $f'(0) = 1$. Thus
$$\lim_{x \to 0} \frac{\ln(1+x)}{x} = \lim_{x \to 0} \frac{f(x)}{x} = \lim_{x \to 0} \frac{f(x)-f(0)}{x-0} = f'(0) = 1.$$

Section 6.5

Exercises 6.5

2. $f(x) = 10^{\sqrt{1-x}} \Rightarrow f'(x) = 10^{\sqrt{1-x}}(\ln 10)\frac{1}{2}(1-x)^{-1/2}(-1) = \dfrac{(-\ln 10)10^{\sqrt{1-x}}}{2\sqrt{1-x}}$

$\text{Dom}(f) = \{x \mid x \le 1\} = (-\infty, 1]$, $\text{dom}(f') = \{x \mid x < 1\} = (-\infty, 1)$.

4. $f(x) = \sqrt{3-2^x} \Rightarrow f'(x) = \dfrac{1}{2\sqrt{3-2^x}}(-2^x \ln 2) = -\ln 2 \, \dfrac{2^{x-1}}{\sqrt{3-2^x}}$

$\text{Dom}(f) = \{x \mid 2^x \le 3\} = \{x \mid x \le \log_2 3\} = (-\infty, \log_2 3]$,

$\text{dom}(f') = \{x \mid 2^x < 3\} = (-\infty, \log_2 3)$

6. $f(x) = (\sin x)^{\sqrt{2}} \Rightarrow f'(x) = \sqrt{2}(\sin x)^{\sqrt{2}-1}\cos x$

$\text{Dom}(f) = \text{dom}(f') = \{x \mid \sin x > 0\} = \{x \mid 2n\pi < x < (2n+1)\pi\}$

8. $f(x) = 3^{\ln(x-1)} \Rightarrow f'(x) = 3^{\ln(x-1)}(\ln 3)/(x-1)$

$\text{dom}(f) = \{x \mid x-1 > 0\} = (1, \infty) = \text{dom}(f')$

10. $y = 2^{3x} \Rightarrow y' = 2^{3x}(3 \ln 2) \Rightarrow y'' = 2^{3x}(3 \ln 2)^2 = 9(\ln 2)^2 2^{3x}$

12. $y = x^2 e^x \Rightarrow y' = 2xe^x + x^2 e^x = (2x+x^2)e^x \Rightarrow$

$y'' = (2+2x)e^x + (2x+x^2)e^x = (x^2+4x+2)e^x$

14. $f(x) = xe^{-x^2} \Rightarrow f'(x) = e^{-x^2} + xe^{-x^2}(-2x) = e^{-x^2}(1-2x^2)$

16. $G(x) = 5^{\tan x} \Rightarrow G'(x) = 5^{\tan x}(\ln 5)\sec^2 x$

18. $g(x) = 1.6^x + x^{1.6} \Rightarrow g'(x) = 1.6^x \ln(1.6) + 1.6x^{0.6}$

20. $h(\theta) = 10^{\sec\theta} \Rightarrow h'(\theta) = 10^{\sec\theta}(\ln 10)\sec\theta \tan\theta$

22. $y = e^{x \cos x} \Rightarrow y' = e^{x \cos x}(\cos x - x \sin x)$

24. $y = \dfrac{e^{-x^2}}{x} \Rightarrow y' = \dfrac{xe^{-x^2}(-2x) - e^{-x^2}}{x^2} = \dfrac{e^{-x^2}(-2x^2-1)}{x^2}$

26. $y = e^{\sin \lambda x} \Rightarrow y' = e^{\sin \lambda x}(\lambda \cos \lambda x)$

28. $y = \ln(e^{2x} + \sqrt{e^{4x}+1}) \Rightarrow y' = \dfrac{2e^{2x} + 2e^{4x}/\sqrt{e^{4x}+1}}{e^{2x} + \sqrt{e^{4x}+1}} = \dfrac{2e^{2x}}{\sqrt{e^{4x}+1}}$

30. $y = a^x x^a \Rightarrow y' = a^x(\ln a)x^a + a^x(ax^{a-1}) = (\ln a)a^x x^a + a^{x+1}x^{a-1}$

32. $y = e^x\cos(1 - \ln x) \Rightarrow y' = e^x\cos(1 - \ln x) + e^x\sin(1 - \ln x)/x$

34. $y = x^x \Rightarrow \ln y = x \ln x \Rightarrow y'/y = \ln x + x(1/x) \Rightarrow y' = x^x(\ln x + 1)$

36. $y = (\sin x)^x \Rightarrow \ln y = x \ln(\sin x) \Rightarrow \dfrac{y'}{y} = \ln(\sin x) + x \dfrac{\cos x}{\sin x}$

 $\Rightarrow y' = (\sin x)^x[\ln(\sin x) + x \cot x]$

38. $y = (x^e)^x = x^{ex} \Rightarrow \ln y = ex \ln x \Rightarrow y'/y = e \ln x + ex/x \Rightarrow$
 $y' = (x^e)^x(e \ln x + e)$

40. $y = x^{\ln x} \Rightarrow \ln y = \ln x \ln x = (\ln x)^2 \Rightarrow y'/y = 2 \ln x (1/x) \Rightarrow$
 $y' = x^{\ln x}(2 \ln x / x)$

42. $y = (\sin x)^{\cos x} \Rightarrow \ln y = \cos x \ln(\sin x) \Rightarrow$
 $y'/y = - \sin x \ln \sin x + \cos x (\cos x / \sin x) \Rightarrow$
 $y' = (\sin x)^{\cos x} (- \sin x \ln \sin x + \cos x \cot x)$

44. $y = x^{x^x} \Rightarrow \ln y = x^x \ln x \Rightarrow y'/y = x^x(\ln x + 1)\ln x + x^x(1/x)$
 [by #34] $\Rightarrow y' = x^{x^x}[x^x(\ln x + 1)\ln x + x^{x-1}]$

46. $y = \cos(x^{\sqrt{x}}) \Rightarrow y' = -\sin(x^{\sqrt{x}})\cdot x^{\sqrt{x}}\left[\dfrac{\ln x + 2}{2\sqrt{x}}\right]$ by Example 5.

48. $x^y = y^x \Rightarrow y \ln x = x \ln y \Rightarrow y'\ln x + y/x = \ln y + xy'/y \Rightarrow$
 $y' = \dfrac{\ln y - y/x}{\ln x - x/y}$

50. $f(x) = 10^x \Rightarrow f'(x) = 10^x\ln 10$, so the slope of the tangent at
 $(1,10)$ is $f'(1) = 10 \ln 10$ and the equation is $y-10 = 10 \ln 10(x-1)$
 or $y = (10 \ln 10)x + 10(1 - \ln 10)$.

52. $y = (x+1)^x \Rightarrow \ln y = x \ln(x+1) \Rightarrow y'/y = \ln(x+1) + x/(x+1) \Rightarrow$
 $y' = (x+1)^x[\ln(x+1) + x/(x+1)]$, so the slope of the tangent at
 $(1,2)$ is $f'(1) = 2(\ln 2 + 1/2) = 1 + 2 \ln 2$ and the equation is
 $y-2 = (1+2\ln2)(x-1)$ or $y = (1+2\ln2)x + 1-2\ln2$.

54. Let (a,e^{-a}) be the point where the tangent meets the curve. The
 tangent has slope $-e^{-a}$ and is perpendicular to the line $2x-y = 8$
 which has slope 2. So $-e^{-a} = -1/2 \Rightarrow e^{-a} = 1/2 \Rightarrow e^a = 2 \Rightarrow$
 $a = \ln(e^a) = \ln 2$. Thus the point on the curve is $(\ln 2,1/2)$ and
 the equation of the tangent is $y-\frac{1}{2} = -\frac{1}{2}(x-\ln2)$ or $x+2y = 1+\ln2$.

56. $y = Ae^{-x}+Bxe^{-x} \Rightarrow y' = -Ae^{-x}+Be^{-x}-Bxe^{-x} = (B-A)e^{-x}-Bxe^{-x} \Rightarrow$
 $y'' = (A-B)e^{-x}-Be^{-x}+Bxe^{-x} = (A-2B)e^{-x}+Bxe^{-x}$, so
 $y''+2y'+y = (A-2B)e^{-x}+Bxe^{-x} + 2[(B-A)e^{-x}-Bxe^{-x}] + Ae^{-x}+Bxe^{-x} = 0$

58. $f(x) = xe^{-x}$, $f'(x) = e^{-x} - xe^{-x} = (1-x)e^{-x}$, $f''(x) = -e^{-x} + (1-x)(-e^{-x})$
$= (x-2)e^{-x}$. Similarly, $f'''(x) = (3-x)e^{-x}$, $f^{(4)}(x) = (x-4)e^{-x}$, $\cdots$,
$f^{(1000)}(x) = (x-1000)e^{-x}$.

60. (a) $\lim\limits_{t\to\infty} p(t) = \lim\limits_{t\to\infty} \dfrac{1}{1+ae^{-kt}} = \dfrac{1}{1+a\cdot 0} = 1$ since $k>0 \Rightarrow -kt \to -\infty$.

(b) $\dfrac{dp}{dt} = -(1+ae^{-kt})^{-2}(-kae^{-kt}) = \dfrac{kae^{-kt}}{(1+ae^{-kt})^2}$

62. (a) As in Example 3.7.5, we have $f(t) = (2000)2^{t/k}$, where k is the
doubling period. We are given that $5000 = f(1) = (2000)2^{1/k} \Rightarrow$
$2^{1/k} = 2.5 \Rightarrow (1/k)\ln 2 = \ln 2.5 \Rightarrow k = (\ln 2)/(\ln 2.5) \approx .76$ h.
(b) $f(t) = (2000)2^{t/k} \Rightarrow f'(t) = (2000 \ln 2 /k)2^{t/k}$, so the rate of
growth after 1 h is $f'(1) = (2000 \ln 2.5)2^{1/k} = (2000 \ln 2.5)(5/2)$
≈ 4581 and, after 2h, $f'(2) = (2000 \ln 2.5)(5/2)^2 \approx 11454$.

64. $f(x) = x - e^x \Rightarrow f'(x) = 1 - e^x > 0 \Longleftrightarrow e^x < 1 \Longleftrightarrow x < 0$ and $f'(x) < 0 \Longleftrightarrow x > 0$,
so f is increasing on $(-\infty, 0]$ and decreasing on $[0, \infty)$.

66. $f(x) = e^x + x \Rightarrow f'(x) = e^x + 1$, so $x_{n+1} = x_n - (e^{x_n} + x_n)/(e^{x_n} + 1)$.
From #65 there is a root between -1 and 0, so we take $x_1 = -0.5$.
Then $x_2 \approx -0.566311$, $x_3 \approx -0.567143$, $x_4 \approx -0.567143$, so the root is
-0.567143 to 6 decimal places.

68. $\int_{\ln 3}^{\ln 6} 8e^x dx = 8e^x\Big]_{\ln 3}^{\ln 6} = 8(e^{\ln 6} - e^{\ln 3}) = 8(6-3) = 24$

70. Let $u = x^2$. Then $du = 2x\, dx \Rightarrow \int xe^{x^2} dx = (1/2)\int e^u du$
$= (1/2)e^u + C = (1/2)e^{x^2} + C$

72. Let $u = \sqrt{x}$. Then $du = \dfrac{dx}{2\sqrt{x}}$ so $\int \dfrac{10^{\sqrt{x}}}{\sqrt{x}} dx = 2\int 10^u du = 2\dfrac{10^u}{\ln 10} + C$
$= \dfrac{2}{\ln 10} 10^{\sqrt{x}} + C$

74. Let $u = e^x + 1$. Then $du = e^x dx$, so $\int \dfrac{e^x}{e^x + 1} dx = \int \dfrac{du}{u} = \ln|u| + C$
$= \ln(e^x + 1) + C$

76. Let $u = \dfrac{1}{x}$. Then $du = -\dfrac{1}{x^2} dx$, so $\int \dfrac{e^{1/x}}{x^2} dx = -\int e^u du = -e^u + C$
$= -e^{1/x} + C$

78. Let $u = e^x$. Then $du = e^x dx$, so $\int e^x \sin(e^x) dx = \int \sin u\, du$
$= -\cos u + C = -\cos(e^x) + C$

80. $A = \int_{-1}^{0}(2^x-5^x)dx + \int_{0}^{1}(5^x-2^x)dx = \frac{2^x}{\ln 2} - \frac{5^x}{\ln 5}\Big]_{-1}^{0} + \frac{5^x}{\ln 5} - \frac{2^x}{\ln 2}\Big]_{0}^{1}$

$= \left[\frac{1}{\ln 2} - \frac{1}{\ln 5}\right] - \left[\frac{1}{2\ln 2} - \frac{1}{5\ln 5}\right] + \left[\frac{5}{\ln 5} - \frac{2}{\ln 2}\right] - \left[\frac{1}{\ln 5} - \frac{1}{\ln 2}\right]$

$= \frac{16}{5\ln 5} - \frac{1}{2\ln 2} \approx 1.267$

82. $e^x = e^{2x}/2 \iff 2 = e^{2x}/e^x = e^x \iff x = \ln 2$, so

$A = \int_{0}^{\ln 2}(e^x - \frac{1}{2}e^{2x})dx + \int_{\ln 2}^{1}(\frac{1}{2}e^{2x} - e^x)dx = e^x - \frac{1}{4}e^{2x}\Big]_{0}^{\ln 2} + \frac{1}{4}e^{2x} - e^x\Big]_{\ln 2}^{1}$

$= (2-1) - (1-\frac{1}{4}) + (\frac{1}{4}e^2 - e) - (1-2) = \frac{1}{4}e^2 - e + \frac{5}{4} \approx 0.379$

84. (a) $f(x) = x^2e^x \Rightarrow f'(x) = 2xe^x + x^2e^x = (x^2+2x)e^x$. $f'(x) > 0 \iff$
$x(x+2) > 0 \iff x < -2$ or $x > 0$, $f'(x) < 0 \iff -2 < x < 0$, so f is increasing on
$(-\infty, -2]$ and $[0, \infty)$ and decreasing on $[-2, 0]$.

(b) $f''(x) = (2x+2)e^x + (x^2+2x)e^x = (x^2+4x+2)e^x = 0 \iff x^2+4x+2 = 0 \iff$
$x = -2\pm\sqrt{2}$. $f''(x) > 0$ when $x > -2+\sqrt{2}$ or $x < -2-\sqrt{2}$, so f is CU on
$(-\infty, -2-\sqrt{2})$ and $(-2+\sqrt{2}, \infty)$ and CD on $(-2-\sqrt{2}, -2+\sqrt{2})$.

(c) Inflection points: $(-2+\sqrt{2}, (6-4\sqrt{2})e^{-2+\sqrt{2}})$, $(-2-\sqrt{2}, (6+4\sqrt{2})e^{-2-\sqrt{2}})$

86. $y = f(x) = e^x + 2e^{-x}$ A. $D = R$ B. No x-intercept, y-intercept = 3.
C. No symmetry   D. $\lim\limits_{x\to\pm\infty}(e^x + 2e^{-x}) = \infty$, no asymptote.

E. $f'(x) = e^x - 2e^{-x} = 0 \iff e^x = 2e^{-x} \iff e^{2x} = 2 \iff 2x = \ln 2 \iff$
$x = (1/2)\ln 2$. $f'(x) > 0 \iff x > (1/2)\ln 2$, $f'(x) < 0 \iff 0 < x < (1/2)\ln 2$, so f
is increasing on $[(1/2)\ln 2, \infty)$ and   H.
decreasing on $(-\infty, (1/2)\ln 2]$.
F. $f(\frac{1}{2}\ln 2) = \sqrt{2} + 2/\sqrt{2} = 2\sqrt{2}$ is a

local and absolute minimum.
G. $f''(x) = e^x + 2e^{-x} > 0$ for all x,
so f is CU on $(-\infty, \infty)$.

88. $y = f(x) = e^{x/(x-2)}$ A. $D = \{x \mid x \neq 2\} = (-\infty, 2)\cup(2, \infty)$
B. No x-intercept, y-intercept = $f(0) = 1$ C. No symmetry
D. $\lim\limits_{x\to\pm\infty} e^{x/(x-2)} = \lim\limits_{x\to\pm\infty} e^{1/(1-2/x)} = e^{1/(1-0)} = e$, so $y = e$ is a HA
$\lim\limits_{x\to 2^+} e^{x/(x-2)} = \infty$, so $x = 2$ is a VA. Also, $\lim\limits_{x\to 2^-} e^{x/(x-2)} = 0$ since
$x/(x-2) \to -\infty$.   E. $f'(x) = e^{x/(x-2)}\cdot\frac{x-2-x}{(x-2)^2} = -\frac{2e^{x/(x-2)}}{(x-2)^2} < 0$, so f

is decreasing on $(-\infty, 2)$ and $(2, \infty)$ F. No extrema.
G. $f''(x) = -2\dfrac{(x-2)^2[-2e^{x/(x-2)}/(x-2)^2] - e^{x/(x-2)}2(x-2)}{(x-2)^4}$

177

$$= \frac{4e^{x/(x-2)}(x-1)}{(x-2)^4} > 0 \iff x>1, \text{ so f is CU on } (1,2) \text{ and } (2,\infty) \text{ and}$$

CD on $(-\infty,1)$. IP $(1,1/e)$

H.

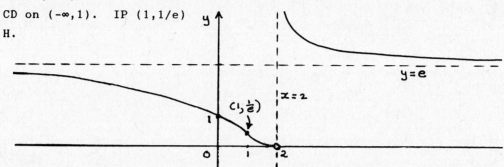

90. $y = f(x) = \ln(e^x - 2e^{-x})$ A. $D = \{x \mid e^x - 2e^{-x} > 0\}$ But $e^x > 2e^{-x} \iff e^{2x} > 2$
$\iff x > (1/2)\ln 2$, so $D = ((1/2)\ln 2, \infty)$. B. x-intercept occurs when
$\ln(e^x - 2e^{-x}) = 0 \iff e^x - 2e^{-x} = 1 \iff 0 = (e^x)^2 - e^x - 2 = (e^x + 1)(e^x - 2) \iff$
$e^x = 2 \iff x = \ln 2$ C. No symmetry D. $\lim\limits_{x \to \infty} \ln(e^x - 2e^{-x}) = \infty$, so no HA

$\lim\limits_{x \to \ln 2/2^+} \ln(e^x - 2e^{-x}) = -\infty$ since $e^x - 2e^{-x} \to 0^+$ as $x \to \frac{1}{2}\ln 2^+$, so $x = \frac{1}{2}\ln 2$

is a VA. E. $f'(x) = \dfrac{e^x + 2e^{-x}}{e^x - 2e^{-x}} > 0$ for all x, so f is increasing on D

F. No extrema.

G. $f''(x) = \dfrac{(e^x - 2e^{-x})^2 - (e^x + 2e^{-x})^2}{(e^x - 2e^{-x})^2}$

$= -\dfrac{8}{(e^x - 2e^{-x})^2} < 0$, so f is

CD on D.

H.

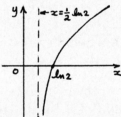

92. $y = f(x) = e^x + e^{-2x}$ A. $D = R$ B. No x-intercept, y-intercept = 2.
C. No symmetry D. $\lim\limits_{x \to \pm\infty} (e^x + e^{-2x}) = \infty$, no asymptote.

E. $f'(x) = e^x - 2e^{-2x} = e^x(1 - 2e^{-3x}) > 0 \iff e^{3x} > 2 \iff x > (1/3)\ln 2$, so f
is increasing on $[(1/3)\ln 2, \infty)$ and decreasing on $(-\infty, (1/3)\ln 2]$.

F. $f((1/3)\ln 2) = 2^{1/3} + 2^{-2/3}$

is a local minimum.

G. $f''(x) = e^x + 4e^{-2x} > 0$ for

all x, so f is CU on R.

H.

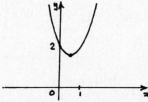

178

94. $y = f(x) = (2x)^{-\ln 3x}$ A. $D = (0,\infty)$ B. No intercepts   C. No symmetry

     D. $\lim\limits_{x\to\infty} (2x)^{-\ln 3x} = \lim\limits_{x\to\infty} (e^{\ln 2x})^{-\ln 3x} = \lim\limits_{x\to\infty} e^{-\ln 2x \, \ln 3x} = 0$, so $y = 0$

     is a HA. Also $\lim\limits_{x\to 0^+} e^{-\ln 2x \, \ln 3x} = 0$.

     E. $f'(x) = -e^{-\ln 2x \, \ln 3x} \left[\dfrac{\ln 2x + \ln 3x}{x}\right] = -(2x)^{-\ln 3x}\left[\dfrac{\ln 6x^2}{x}\right] > 0 \iff$

     $\ln 6x^2 < 0 \iff 6x^2 < 1 \iff 0 < x < 1/\sqrt{6}$, so f is increasing on $(0, 1/\sqrt{6}]$ and

     decreasing on $[1/\sqrt{6}, \infty)$.   F. $f(1/\sqrt{6}) \approx 1.04$ is a local maximum.

     G. $f''(x) = \dfrac{e^{-\ln 2x \, \ln 3x}}{x^2}(\ln(6x^2)+2)(\ln(6x^2)-1) = 0$ when $x = 1/\sqrt{6}e$ or

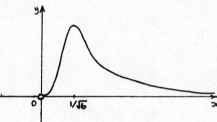

     $\sqrt{e/6}$. $f''(x) > 0 \iff 0 < x < 1/\sqrt{6}e$

     or $x > \sqrt{e/6}$, so f is CU on

     $(0, 1/\sqrt{6}e)$ and $(\sqrt{e/6}, \infty)$ and

     CD on $(1/\sqrt{6}e, \sqrt{e/6})$.

     IP when $x = 1/\sqrt{6}e$ and $\sqrt{e/6}$.

96. $f(x) = e^{1/(1-x^2)}$ A. $\text{dom}(f) = \{x \mid x \neq \pm 1\} = (-\infty, -1) \cup (-1, 1) \cup (1, \infty)$

     B. No x-intercept, y-intercept $= f(0) = e$

     C. $f(-x) = f(x)$, f is even: the curve is symmetric about the y-axis

     D. $\lim\limits_{x\to\pm\infty} e^{1/(1-x^2)} = e^0 = 1$, so $y = 1$ is a horizontal asymptote

     $\lim\limits_{x\to 1^-} e^{1/(1-x^2)} = \infty$ and $\lim\limits_{x\to -1^+} e^{1/(1-x^2)} = \infty$ since $\dfrac{1}{1-x^2} \to \infty$

     So $x = 1$ and $x = -1$ are vertical asymptotes. Also

     $\lim\limits_{x\to 1^+} e^{1/(1-x^2)} = 0$ and $\lim\limits_{x\to -1^-} e^{1/(1-x^2)} = 0$ since $\dfrac{1}{1-x^2} \to -\infty$

     E. $f'(x) = e^{1/(1-x^2)} \cdot \dfrac{2x}{(1-x^2)^2} \Rightarrow f'(x) < 0$ if $x < 0$ and $f'(x) > 0$ if $x > 0$

     So f is decreasing on $(-\infty, -1), (-1, 0]$, increasing on $[0, 1)$ and $(1, \infty)$

     F. $f(0) = e$ is a local minimum.

     G. $f''(x) = e^{1/(1-x^2)} \cdot \dfrac{4x^2}{(1-x^2)^4} + e^{1/(1-x^2)} \cdot \dfrac{2(1-x^2)^2 + 8x^2(1-x^2)}{(1-x^2)^4}$

     $= -2e^{1/(1-x^2)} \cdot \dfrac{3x^4 - 4x^2 - 1}{(1-x^2)^4} \Rightarrow f''(x) = 0$ when $x^2 = \dfrac{4 \pm \sqrt{28}}{6} = \dfrac{2 \pm \sqrt{7}}{3}$

Let $\alpha = \sqrt{(2+\sqrt{7})/3}$. Then $f''(x) > 0$ when $|x| < \alpha$ and $f''(x) < 0$ when $|x| > \alpha$. f is CD on $(-\infty, -\alpha)$ and (α, ∞) and CU on $(-\alpha, -1)$, $(-1, 1)$, and $(1, \alpha)$. There are inflection points when $x = \pm\alpha$.

H.

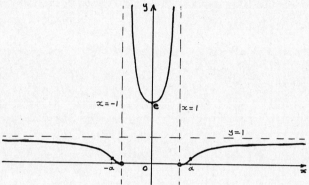

98. $f''(x) = 3e^x + 5 \sin x \Rightarrow f'(x) = 3e^x - 5 \cos x + C \Rightarrow 2 = f'(0)$
$= 3 - 5 + C \Rightarrow C = 4$, so $f'(x) = 3e^x - 5 \cos x + 4 \Rightarrow$
$f(x) = 3e^x - 5 \sin x + 4x + D \Rightarrow 1 = f(0) = 3 + D \Rightarrow D = -2$, so
$f(x) = 3e^x - 5 \sin x + 4x - 2$.

100. $f(x) = e^x - \ln x \Rightarrow f'(x) = e^x - 1/x$. $h = f^{-1}$ and $f(1) = e \Rightarrow$
$h(e) = 1$, so $h'(e) = 1/f'(1) = 1/(e-1)$.

102. $h(x) = [f(x)]^{g(x)} \Rightarrow \ln h(x) = g(x) \ln f(x) \Rightarrow$
$h'(x)/h(x) = g'(x) \ln f(x) + g(x) f'(x)/f(x) \Rightarrow$
$h'(x) = [f(x)]^{g(x)}[g'(x) \ln f(x) + g(x) f'(x)/f(x)]$

Section 6.6

Exercises 6.6

2. (a) The first figure shows that $\ln 2 = \int_1^2 \frac{1}{t} \, dt < 1$.

The second figure shows that
$$\ln 3 = \int_1^3 \frac{1}{t} \, dt > \frac{1}{4}\left[\frac{4}{5} + \frac{2}{3} + \frac{4}{7} + \frac{1}{2} + \frac{4}{9} + \frac{2}{5} + \frac{4}{11} + \frac{1}{3}\right]$$
$$= \frac{1}{5} + \frac{1}{6} + \frac{1}{7} + \frac{1}{8} + \frac{1}{9} + \frac{1}{10} + \frac{1}{11} + \frac{1}{12} > 1$$

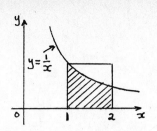
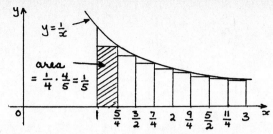

(b) From part (a), ln 2 < 1 < ln 3. Since the function exp is increasing, we have exp(ln 2) < exp(1) < exp(ln 3), so 2 < e < 3.

4. From (6.40b) and (6.48) we have $\ln(e^x/e^y) = \ln(e^x) - \ln(e^y) = x - y = \ln(e^{x-y})$. Since ln is one-to-one, we have $e^x/e^y = e^{x-y}$.

6. Using (6.52) and (6.50b) we have
$$a^{x-y} = e^{(x-y)\ln a} = e^{x \ln a - y \ln a} = \frac{e^{x \ln a}}{e^{y \ln a}} = \frac{a^x}{a^y}$$

8. (a) Let $y = \log_a x$. Then $a^y = x \Rightarrow \ln x = \ln(a^y) = \ln(e^{y \ln a})$
$= y \ln a$, so $y = \dfrac{\ln x}{\ln a}$.

(b) $\dfrac{d}{dx} \log_a x = \dfrac{d}{dx} \dfrac{\ln x}{\ln a} = \dfrac{1}{\ln a} \dfrac{d}{dx} \ln x = \dfrac{1}{x \ln a}$

Section 6.7

Exercises 6.7

2. (a) By Theorem 6.59, $y(t) = y(0)e^{kt} = 4000e^{kt} \Rightarrow y(1/2) = 4000e^{k/2}$
$= 12000 \Rightarrow e^{k/2} = 3 \Rightarrow k/2 = \ln 3 \Rightarrow k = 2\ln 3$, so
$y(t) = 4000e^{(2\ln 3)t} = 4000 \cdot 9^t$ (b) $y(1/3) = 4000 \cdot 9^{1/3} \approx 8320$
(c) $4000 \cdot 9^t = 20000 \Rightarrow 9^t = 5 \Rightarrow t \ln 9 = \ln 5 \Rightarrow t = (\ln 5)/(\ln 9)$
$\approx .73$ h ≈ 44 min

4. (a) $y(t) = y(0)e^{kt} \Rightarrow y(2) = y(0)e^{2k} = 400$, $y(6) = y(0)e^{6k} = 25600$.
Dividing these equations, we get $e^{6k}/e^{2k} = 25600/400 \Rightarrow e^{4k} = 64$
$\Rightarrow 4k = \ln 64 = 6\ln 2 \Rightarrow k = (3/2)\ln 2 = (1/2)\ln 8$.   Thus
$y(0) = 400/e^{2k} = 400/e^{\ln 8} = 400/8 = 50$.
(b) $y(t) = y(0)e^{kt} = 50e^{(\ln 8)t/2}$ (c) $y(t) = 50e^{(3\ln 2)t/2} = 100$
$\Leftrightarrow e^{(3\ln 2)t/2} = 2 \Leftrightarrow (3\ln 2)t/2 = \ln 2 \Leftrightarrow t = 2/3$ h $= 40$ min.
(d) $50e^{(\ln 8)t/2} = 100000 \Leftrightarrow e^{(\ln 8)t/2} = 2000 \Leftrightarrow (\ln 8)t/2 = \ln 2000$
$\Leftrightarrow t = (2\ln 2000)/\ln 8 \approx 7.3$ h.

6. (a) $y(t) = 450000e^{kt}$ where t is the number of years after 1980.
$y(5) = 450000e^{5k} = 500000 \Rightarrow e^{5k} = 10/9 \Rightarrow k = (1/5)\ln(10/9)$, so
$y(t) = 450000e^{\ln(10/9)t/5} = 450000(10/9)^{t/5}$ In 1990 the
population will be $y(15) = 450000(10/9)^3 \approx 617284$.
(b) In 2001 it will be $y(21) = 450000(10/9)^{21/5} \approx 700477$.

8. (a) The mass remaining after t days is $y(t) = y(0)e^{kt} = 200e^{kt}$.
Since the half-life is 140 days, $y(140) = 200e^{140k} = 100 \Rightarrow e^{140k}$
$= 1/2 \Rightarrow 140k = \ln(1/2) \Rightarrow k = -(\ln 2)/140$, so
$y(t) = 200e^{-(\ln 2)t/140} = 200 \cdot 2^{-t/140}$
(b) $y(100) = 200 \cdot 2^{-100/140} \approx 121.9$ mg
(c) $200e^{-(\ln 2)t/140} = 10 \Longleftrightarrow -(\ln 2)t/140 = \ln(1/20) = -\ln 20 \Longleftrightarrow$
$t = 140(\ln 20)/(\ln 2) \approx 605$ days

10. (a) If $y(t)$ is the mass after t days and $y(0) = A$, then $y(t) = Ae^{kt}$
$\Rightarrow y(3) = Ae^{3k} = .58A \Rightarrow e^{3k} = .58 \Rightarrow k = (1/3)\ln(.58)$. Then
$Ae^{\ln(.58)t/3} = A/2 \Longleftrightarrow \ln(.58)t/3 = \ln(1/2)$, so the half-life is
$t = -3\ln 2/\ln(.58) \approx 3.82$ days. (b) $Ae^{\ln(.58)t/3} = A/10 \Longleftrightarrow$
$\ln(.58)t/3 = \ln(1/10) \Longleftrightarrow t = -3\ln 10/\ln(.58) \approx 12.68$ days.

12. (a) Let $y(t) = $ temperature after t minutes. Newton's Law of
Cooling $\Rightarrow \dfrac{dy}{dt} = k(y-5)$. Let $u(t) = y(t)-5$. Then $\dfrac{du}{dt} = ku$, so
$u(t) = u(0)e^{kt} = 15e^{kt} \Rightarrow y(t) = 5+15e^{kt} \Rightarrow y(1) = 5+15e^k = 12 \Rightarrow$
$e^k = 7/15 \Rightarrow k = \ln(7/15)$, so $y(t) = 5+15e^{\ln(7/15)t}$ and
$y(2) = 5+15e^{2\ln(7/15)} \approx 8.3°$
(b) $5+15e^{\ln(7/15)t} = 6$ when $e^{\ln(7/15)t} = 1/15 \Rightarrow \ln(7/15)t = $
$\ln(1/15) = -\ln 15 \Rightarrow t = \dfrac{-\ln 15}{\ln(7/15)} \approx 3.6$ min

14. With the notation of Example 4, $A_0 = 500$, $i = .14$, and $t = 2$.
(a) $n = 1$: $A = 500(1.14)^2 = \$649.80$
(b) $n = 4$: $A = 500(1+.14/4)^8 = \$658.40$
(c) $n = 12$: $A = 500(1+.14/12)^{24} = \$660.49$
(d) $n = 365$: $A = 500(1+.14/365)^{2 \cdot 365} = \$661.53$
(e) $n = 365 \cdot 24$: $A = 500(1+.14/(365)(24))^{2 \cdot 365 \cdot 24} = \$661.56$
(f) continuously: $A = 500e^{(.14)2} = \$661.56$

16. $A_0 e^{.10t} = 2A_0 \Longleftrightarrow e^{.10t} = 2 \Longleftrightarrow .10t = \ln 2 \Longleftrightarrow t = 10\ln 2$, so the
investment will double in about 6.93 years.

18. (a) If $y(t)$ is the amount of salt at time t, then $y(0) = 1500(.3)$
$= 450$ kg. The rate of change of y is

182

$$\frac{dy}{dt} = \left[.1\ \frac{kg}{L}\right]\left[20\frac{L}{min}\right] - \left[\frac{y(t)}{1500}\ \frac{kg}{L}\right]\left[20\frac{L}{min}\right] = 2 - \frac{1}{75}y(t) = -\frac{1}{75}[y(t)-150]$$

Let $u(t) = y(t)-150$. Then $du/dt = -(1/75)u(t) \Rightarrow u(t) = u(0)e^{-t/75}$
$= 300e^{-t/75} \Rightarrow y(t) = 150+300e^{-t/75}$, so $y(30) = 150+300e^{-.4} \approx 351$ kg

(b) When the concentration is .2 kg/L, the amount of salt is
$(0.2)(1500) = 300$ kg. So $y(t) = 150+300e^{-t/75} = 300 \Rightarrow 300e^{-t/75}$
$= 150 \Rightarrow e^{-t/75} = 1/2 \Rightarrow -t/75 = -\ln2 \Rightarrow t = 75\ \ln2 \approx 52$ min.

Section 6.8

Exercises 6.8

2. $\sin^{-1}(0.5) = \pi/6$ since $\sin\ \pi/6 = 0.5$

4. $\arctan(-1) = -\pi/4$ since $\tan(-\pi/4) = -1$

6. $\arcsin\ 1 = \pi/2$ since $\sin\ \pi/2 = 1$

8. $\cos^{-1}(\sqrt{3}/2) = \pi/6$ since $\cos\ \pi/6 = \sqrt{3}/2$

10. $\sec^{-1}2 = \pi/3$ since $\sec\ \pi/3 = 2$

12. $\arccos(-0.5) = 2\pi/3$ since $\cos\ 2\pi/3 = -0.5$

14. $\sin^{-1}(\sin\ 1) = 1$ since $-\pi/2 \leq 1 \leq \pi/2$

16. $\tan^{-1}(\tan\ 4\pi/3) = \tan^{-1}\sqrt{3} = \pi/3$

18. $\tan(\cos^{-1}0.5) = \tan\ \pi/3 = \sqrt{3}$

20. Let $\theta = \arctan\ 2$, so $\tan\theta = 2 \Rightarrow \sec^2\theta = 1 + \tan^2\theta = 1+4 = 5 \Rightarrow$
    $\sec\theta = \sqrt{5} \Rightarrow \sec(\arctan\ 2) = \sec\theta = \sqrt{5}$

22. Let $\theta = \sin^{-1}3/5$. Then $\sin\theta = 3/5 \Rightarrow \cos\theta = \sqrt{1-(3/5)^2} = 4/5$, so
    $\sin(2\ \sin^{-1}3/5) = \sin2\theta = 2\ \sin\theta\ \cos\theta = 2(3/5)(4/5) = 24/25$.

24. Let $y = \sin^{-1}x$. Then $\sin\ y = x$, so $\cos(2\ \sin^{-1}x) = \cos\ 2y$
    $= 1 - 2\ \sin^2y = 1-2x^2$.

26. Let $x = \sin^{-1}(3/4)$ and $y = \cos^{-1}(1/4)$. Then $\sin\ x = 3/4$, $\cos\ x =$
    $\sqrt{1-(3/4)^2} = \sqrt{7}/4$, $\cos\ y = 1/4$, $\sin\ y = \sqrt{1-(1/4)^2} = \sqrt{15}/4$, so
    $\cos[\sin^{-1}(3/4)+\cos^{-1}(1/4)] = \cos(x+y) = \cos\ x\ \cos\ y - \sin\ x\ \sin\ y$
    $= (\sqrt{7}/4)(1/4)-(3/4)(\sqrt{15}/4) = (\sqrt{7}-3\sqrt{15})/16$.

28. Let $y = \sin^{-1}x$. Then $\sin\ y = x$,
    so from the triangle we see that
    $\tan(\sin^{-1}x) = \tan\ y = \dfrac{x}{\sqrt{1-x^2}}$

183

30. Let $y = \cos^{-1}x$. Then $\cos y = x \implies \sin y = \sqrt{1-x^2}$ since $0 \leq y \leq \pi$. So

$\sin(2\cos^{-1}x) = \sin 2y = 2\sin y \cos y = 2x\sqrt{1-x^2}$.

32. (a) Let $a = \sin^{-1}x$ and $b = \cos^{-1}x$. Then $\cos a = \sqrt{1-\sin^2 a} = \sqrt{1-x^2}$

since $\cos a \geq 0$ for $-\pi/2 \leq a \leq \pi/2$. Similarly, $\sin b = \sqrt{1-x^2}$. So

$\sin[\sin^{-1}x + \cos^{-1}x] = \sin(a+b) = \sin a \cos b + \cos a \sin b$

$= x \cdot x + \sqrt{1-x^2}\sqrt{1-x^2} = x^2 + (1-x^2) = 1$. But $\pi/2 \leq \sin^{-1}x + \cos^{-1}x \leq \pi/2$

and so $\sin^{-1}x + \cos^{-1}x = \pi/2$.

(b) $\dfrac{d}{dx}\cos^{-1}x = \dfrac{d}{dx}(\dfrac{\pi}{2} - \sin^{-1}x) = 0 - \dfrac{d}{dx}\sin^{-1}x = -\dfrac{1}{\sqrt{1-x^2}}$

34. Let $y = \sec^{-1}x$. Then $\sec y = x$ and $y \in (0, \pi/2] \cup (\pi, 3\pi/2]$.

Differentiate with respect to x: $\sec y \tan y \,(dy/dx) = 1 \implies$

$\dfrac{dy}{dx} = \dfrac{1}{\sec y \tan y} = \dfrac{1}{\sec y \sqrt{\sec^2 y - 1}} = \dfrac{1}{x\sqrt{x^2-1}}$

(Note that $\tan^2 y = \sec^2 y - 1 \implies \tan y = \sqrt{\sec^2 y - 1}$ since $\tan y > 0$

when $0 < y < \pi/2$ or $\pi < y < 3\pi/2$.)

36. $f(x) = \sin^{-1}(2x-1) \implies f'(x) = \dfrac{1}{\sqrt{1-(2x-1)^2}}(2) = \dfrac{1}{\sqrt{x-x^2}}$

38. $y = (\sin^{-1}x)^2 \implies y' = 2\sin^{-1}x \,/\, \sqrt{1-x^2}$

40. $G(x) = \sin^{-1}(x/a) \implies G'(x) = \dfrac{1/a}{\sqrt{1-(x/a)^2}} = \dfrac{1}{a\sqrt{1-x^2/a^2}} = \dfrac{1}{\sqrt{a^2-x^2}}$

42. $h(x) = \arcsin x \ln x \implies h'(x) = \dfrac{\ln x}{\sqrt{1-x^2}} + \dfrac{\arcsin x}{x}$

44. $f(t) = \dfrac{\cos^{-1}t}{t} \implies f'(t) = \dfrac{t/(-1/\sqrt{1-t^2}) - \cos^{-1}t}{t^2} = -\dfrac{\cos^{-1}t}{t^2} - \dfrac{1}{t\sqrt{1-t^2}}$

46. $F(t) = \sqrt{1-t^2} + \sin^{-1}t \implies F'(t) = \dfrac{-2t}{2\sqrt{1-t^2}} + \dfrac{1}{\sqrt{1-t^2}} = \dfrac{1-t}{\sqrt{1-t^2}}$

48. $y = \tan^{-1}\left[\dfrac{x}{a}\right] + \dfrac{1}{2}\ln(x-a) - \dfrac{1}{2}\ln(x+a) \implies y' = \dfrac{a}{x^2+a^2} + \dfrac{1/2}{x-a} - \dfrac{1/2}{x+a}$

$= \dfrac{a}{x^2+a^2} + \dfrac{a}{x^2-a^2} = \dfrac{2ax^2}{x^4-a^4}$

50. $y = x\cos^{-1}x - \sqrt{1-x^2} \implies y' = \cos^{-1}x - \dfrac{x}{\sqrt{1-x^2}} + \dfrac{x}{\sqrt{1-x^2}} = \cos^{-1}x$

52. $y = \sin^{-1}\left[\dfrac{\cos x}{1+\sin x}\right] \Rightarrow y' = \dfrac{1}{\sqrt{1-[\cos x/(1+\sin x)]^2}} \cdot \dfrac{-\sin x(1+\sin x)-\cos^2 x}{(1+\sin x)^2}$

$= \dfrac{1}{\sqrt{(1+2\sin x+\sin^2 x-\cos^2 x)/(1+\sin x)^2}} \cdot \dfrac{-(1+\sin x)}{(1+\sin x)^2} = -\dfrac{1}{\sqrt{2\sin x+2\sin^2 x}}$

54. $y = \left[\arcsin\sqrt{x^2+2x}\right]^{1/4} \Rightarrow y' = \dfrac{1}{4}\left[\arcsin\sqrt{x^2+2x}\right]^{-3/4} \cdot \dfrac{1}{\sqrt{1-x^2-2x}} \cdot \dfrac{2x+2}{2\sqrt{x^2+2x}}$

$= \dfrac{1}{4}\left[\arcsin\sqrt{x^2+2x}\right]^{-3/4} \dfrac{x+1}{\sqrt{1-x^2-2x}\sqrt{x^2+2x}}$

56. $y = \tan^{-1}(x-\sqrt{x^2+1}) \Rightarrow y' = \dfrac{1}{1+(x-\sqrt{x^2+1})^2}\left[1 - \dfrac{x}{\sqrt{x^2+1}}\right]$

$= \dfrac{\sqrt{x^2+1}-x}{2(1+x^2-x\sqrt{x^2+1})\sqrt{x^2+1}} = \dfrac{\sqrt{x^2+1}-x}{2(1+x^2)(\sqrt{x^2+1}-x)} = \dfrac{1}{2(1+x^2)}$

58. $y = x \sin x \csc^{-1}x \Rightarrow$

$y' = \sin x \csc^{-1}x + x \cos x \csc^{-1}x - (x \sin x)/x\sqrt{x^2-1}$

$= \sin x \csc^{-1}x + x \cos x \csc^{-1}x - (\sin x)/\sqrt{x^2-1}$

60. $f(x) = \cos^{-1}(\sin^{-1}x) \Rightarrow f'(x) = -\dfrac{1}{\sqrt{1-(\sin^{-1}x)^2}} \cdot \dfrac{1}{\sqrt{1-x^2}}$

$\text{dom}(f) = \{x|-1\leq\sin^{-1}x\leq 1\} = \{x|\sin(-1)\leq x\leq\sin 1\} = [-\sin 1, \sin 1]$

$\text{dom}(f') = \{x|-1<\sin^{-1}x<1\} = (-\sin 1, \sin 1)$

62. $h(x) = x \sec^{-1}(3x^2) \Rightarrow$

$h'(x) = \sec^{-1}(3x^2) + x \dfrac{6x}{3x^2\sqrt{(3x^2)^2-1}} = \sec^{-1}(3x^2) + \dfrac{2}{\sqrt{9x^4-1}}$

$\text{Dom}(h) = \{x| 3x^2\geq 1\} = \{x| |x|\leq 1/\sqrt{3}\} = (-\infty,-1/\sqrt{3}] \cup [1/\sqrt{3},\infty)$

$\text{dom}(h') = \{x| 3x^2>1\} = (-\infty,-1/\sqrt{3}) \cup (1/\sqrt{3},\infty)$

64. $F(x) = \sqrt{\sin^{-1}(2/x)} \Rightarrow$

$F'(x) = \dfrac{1}{2\sqrt{\sin^{-1}(2/x)}} \cdot \dfrac{1}{\sqrt{1-(2/x)^2}}\left[-\dfrac{2}{x^2}\right] = -\dfrac{1}{x^2\sqrt{\sin^{-1}(2/x)}\sqrt{1-4/x^2}}$

$\text{Dom}(F) = \{x| -1\leq 2/x\leq 1 \text{ and } \sin^{-1}(2/x)\geq 0\} = \{x| 0<2/x\leq 1\} = \{x| x\geq 2\}$

$= [2,\infty), \quad \text{dom}(F') = \{x| x>2\} = (2,\infty).$

66. $R(t) = \arcsin(2^t) \Rightarrow R'(t) = \dfrac{1}{\sqrt{1-(2^t)^2}} (2^t\ln 2) = \dfrac{2^t\ln 2}{\sqrt{1-4^t}}$

$\text{Dom}(R) = \{t| -1\leq 2^t\leq 1\} = \{t| t\leq 0\} = (-\infty,0], \text{ dom}(R') = (-\infty,0).$

68. $f(x) = x \tan^{-1}x \Rightarrow f'(x) = \tan^{-1}x + \dfrac{x}{1+x^2} \Rightarrow f'(1) = \dfrac{\pi}{4} + \dfrac{1}{2}$

70. $h(x) = (3 \tan^{-1}x)^4 \Rightarrow h'(x) = 4(3 \tan^{-1}x)^3(3/(1+x^2)) \Rightarrow$
    $h'(3) = 4(3 \tan^{-1}3)^3(3/10) = (162/5)(\tan^{-1}3)^3$

72. $\lim\limits_{x \to \infty} \sin^{-1}\left[\dfrac{x+1}{2x+1}\right] = \sin^{-1}\left[\lim\limits_{x \to \infty} \dfrac{x+1}{2x+1}\right] = \sin^{-1}(1/2) = \pi/6$

74. $\lim\limits_{x \to \infty} \sec^{-1}x = \dfrac{\pi}{2}$ since $\sec x \to \infty$ as $x \to \dfrac{\pi-}{2}$ (or see Figure 6.41)

76. $\lim\limits_{x \to \infty} \tan^{-1}(x^2) = \dfrac{\pi}{2}$ since $x^2 \to \infty$ as $x \to \infty$

78. $\lim\limits_{x \to \infty} \tan^{-1}(x-x^2) = -\dfrac{\pi}{2}$ since $x-x^2 = x(1-x) \to -\infty$ as $x \to \infty$

80. $\lim\limits_{x \to \infty} \dfrac{\tan^{-1}x}{x} = 0$ since $\lim\limits_{x \to \infty} \tan^{-1}x = \dfrac{\pi}{2}$ and $\lim\limits_{x \to \infty} x = \infty$

    [Or use $0 < \dfrac{\tan^{-1}x}{x} < \dfrac{\pi/2}{x}$ and the Squeeze Theorem.]

82. Let x be the distance from the observer to the wall. Then, from
    Figure 6.44, $\theta = \tan^{-1}\left[\dfrac{h+d}{x}\right] - \tan^{-1}\left[\dfrac{d}{x}\right]$, x>0, $\Rightarrow$
    $\dfrac{d\theta}{dx} = \dfrac{1}{1+[(h+d)/x]^2}\left[-\dfrac{h+d}{x^2}\right] - \dfrac{1}{1+(d/x)^2}\left[-\dfrac{d}{x^2}\right] = -\dfrac{h+d}{x^2+(h+d)^2} + \dfrac{d}{x^2+d^2}$
    $= \dfrac{d[x^2+(h+d)^2]-(h+d)(x^2+d^2)}{[x^2+(h+d)^2](x^2+d^2)} = \dfrac{h^2d+hd^2-hx^2}{[x^2+(h+d)^2](x^2+d^2)} = 0 \Longleftrightarrow$
    $hx^2 = h^2d+hd^2 \Longleftrightarrow x^2 = hd+d^2 \Longleftrightarrow x = \sqrt{d(h+d)}$. since $d\theta/dx>0$ for all
    $x<\sqrt{d(h+d)}$ and $d\theta/dx<0$ for all $x>\sqrt{d(h+d)}$, the absolute maximum
    occurs when $x = \sqrt{d(h+d)}$.

84. $y = f(x) = \tan^{-1}\left[\dfrac{x-1}{x+1}\right]$ A. $D = \{x \mid x \neq -1\}$ B. x-intercept = 1,
    y-intercept = $f(0) = \tan^{-1}(-1) = -\pi/4$ C. No symmetry.
    D. $\lim\limits_{x \to \pm\infty} \tan^{-1}\left[\dfrac{x-1}{x+1}\right] = \lim\limits_{x \to \pm\infty} \tan^{-1}\left[\dfrac{1-1/x}{1+1/x}\right] = \tan^{-1}1 = \dfrac{\pi}{4}$, so $y = \dfrac{\pi}{4}$ is a
    HA. Also $\lim\limits_{x \to -1^+} \tan^{-1}\left[\dfrac{x-1}{x+1}\right] = -\dfrac{\pi}{2}$ and $\lim\limits_{x \to -1^-} \tan^{-1}\left[\dfrac{x-1}{x+1}\right] = \dfrac{\pi}{2}$
    E. $f'(x) = \dfrac{1}{1+[(x-1)/(x+1)]^2} \cdot \dfrac{(x+1)-(x-1)}{(x+1)^2} = \dfrac{2}{(x+1)^2+(x-1)^2} = \dfrac{1}{x^2+1} > 0$,
    so f is increasing on $(-\infty,-1)$ and $(-1,\infty)$. F. No extrema.
    G. $f''(x) = -2x/(x^2+1)^2 > 0 \Longleftrightarrow x<0$, so f is CU on $(-\infty,-1)$ and $(-1,0)$
    and CD on $(0,\infty)$. IP is $(0,-\pi/4)$.

H.

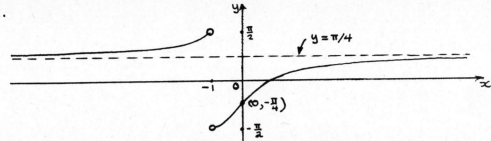

86. $y = f(x) = \arctan(\tan x)$ $D = \{x \mid x \neq (2n+1)\pi/2\}$. Since tan is
     periodic with period π, so is f. For $-\pi/2 < x < \pi/2$, $f(x) = x$. These
     two facts enable us to draw the graph.

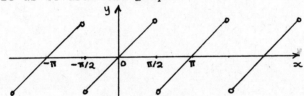

88. $y = f(x) = \tan^{-1}(e^x)$ A. $D = R$ B. y-intercept = $f(0) = \tan^{-1}1$
     $= \pi/4$, no x-intercept. C. No symmetry D. $\lim\limits_{x \to \infty} \tan^{-1}(e^x) = \frac{\pi}{2}$ and

     $\lim\limits_{x \to -\infty} \tan^{-1}(e^x) = \tan^{-1}0 = 0$, so $y = \frac{\pi}{2}$ and $y = 0$ are HA.

     E. $f'(x) = \dfrac{e^x}{1+e^{2x}} > 0$, so f is increasing on R. F. No extrema

     G. $f''(x) = \dfrac{(1+e^{2x})e^x - e^x(2e^{2x})}{(1+e^{2x})^2} = \dfrac{e^x(1-e^{2x})}{(1+e^{2x})^2} > 0 \Leftrightarrow e^{2x} < 1 \Leftrightarrow x < 0$, so f

     is CU on $(-\infty,0)$ and CD on $(0,\infty)$. IP is $(0,\pi/4)$.

     H.

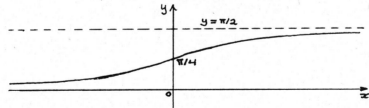

90. $y = \tan^{-1}(\ln x)$ A. $D = (0,\infty)$ B. No y-intercept, x-intercept
     occurs when $\tan^{-1}(\ln x) = 0 \Leftrightarrow \ln x = 0 \Leftrightarrow x = 1$. C. No symmetry
     D. $\lim\limits_{x \to \infty} \tan^{-1}(\ln x) = \frac{\pi}{2}$ so $y = \frac{\pi}{2}$ is a HA. Also $\lim\limits_{x \to 0^+} \tan^{-1}(\ln x) = -\frac{\pi}{2}$

     E. $f'(x) = \dfrac{1}{x[1+(\ln x)^2]} > 0$, so f is increasing on $(0,\infty)$.

187

F. No extrema

G. $f''(x) = \dfrac{-[1+(\ln x)^2+x(2\ln x/x)]}{x^2[1+(\ln x)^2]^2}$

$= -\dfrac{(1 + \ln x)^2}{x^2[1+(\ln x)^2]^2} < 0$, so f is

CD on $(0,\infty)$.

H.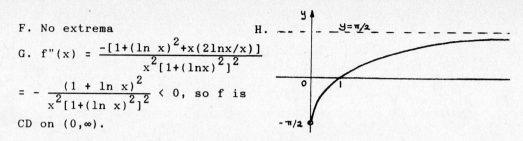

92. $f'(x) = 4-3(1+x^2)^{-1} \Rightarrow f(x) = 4x - 3\tan^{-1}x + C \Rightarrow f(\pi/4) = \pi-3+C$

$= 0 \Rightarrow C = 3-\pi$, so $f(x) = 4x - 3\tan^{-1}x + 3 - \pi$.

94. $\displaystyle\int_0^{0.5} \dfrac{dx}{\sqrt{1-x^2}} = \sin^{-1}x\Big]_0^{0.5} = \sin^{-1}(1/2) - \sin^{-1}0 = \dfrac{\pi}{6}$

96. Let $u = \tan^{-1}x$. Then $du = dx/(1+x^2)$, so $\displaystyle\int \dfrac{\tan^{-1}x}{1+x^2} = \int u\,du = \frac{1}{2}u^2+C$

$= (1/2)(\tan^{-1}x)^2 + C$

98. Let $u = \cos x$. Then $du = -\sin x\,dx$, so $\displaystyle\int \dfrac{\sin x}{1 + \cos^2 x}\,dx = -\int \dfrac{1}{1+u^2}du$

$= -\tan^{-1}u + C = -\tan^{-1}(\cos x) + C$

100. Let $u = \dfrac{x}{2}$. Then $du = \frac{1}{2}dx \Rightarrow \displaystyle\int \dfrac{dx}{x\sqrt{x^2-4}} = \int \dfrac{dx}{2x\sqrt{(x/2)^2-1}} = \int \dfrac{2\,du}{4u\sqrt{u^2-1}}$

$= \frac{1}{2} \displaystyle\int \dfrac{du}{u\sqrt{u^2-1}} = \frac{1}{2}\sec^{-1}u + C = \frac{1}{2}\sec^{-1}(x/2) + C$

102. Let $u = e^{2x}$. Then $du = 2e^{2x}dx \Rightarrow \displaystyle\int \dfrac{e^{2x}dx}{\sqrt{1-e^{4x}}} = \frac{1}{2}\int \dfrac{du}{\sqrt{1-u^2}}$

$= (1/2)\sin^{-1}u + C = (1/2)\sin^{-1}(e^{2x}) + C$

104. Let $u = \ln x$. Then $du = (1/x)dx \Rightarrow \displaystyle\int \dfrac{dx}{x[4 + (\ln x)^2]} = \int \dfrac{du}{4+u^2}$

$= \frac{1}{2}\tan^{-1}\left[\dfrac{u}{2}\right] + C = \frac{1}{2}\tan^{-1}(\frac{1}{2}\ln x) + C$

106. (a) $f(x) = \sin(\sin^{-1}x)$ (b) $g(x) = \sin^{-1}(\sin x)$

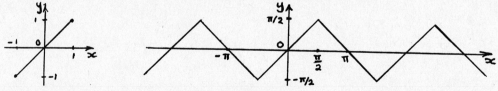

(c) $g'(x) = \dfrac{d}{dx}\sin^{-1}(\sin x) = \dfrac{1}{\sqrt{1 - \sin^2 x}} \cos x = \dfrac{\cos x}{\sqrt{\cos^2 x}} = \dfrac{\cos x}{|\cos x|}$

(d) $h(x) = \cos^{-1}(\sin x)$

$$h'(x) = -\frac{\cos x}{\sqrt{1 - \sin^2 x}}$$

$$= -\frac{\cos x}{|\cos x|}$$

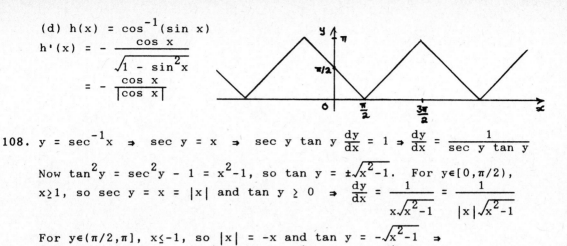

108. $y = \sec^{-1} x \Rightarrow \sec y = x \Rightarrow \sec y \tan y \dfrac{dy}{dx} = 1 \Rightarrow \dfrac{dy}{dx} = \dfrac{1}{\sec y \tan y}$

Now $\tan^2 y = \sec^2 y - 1 = x^2 - 1$, so $\tan y = \pm\sqrt{x^2-1}$. For $y \in [0, \pi/2)$,

$x \geq 1$, so $\sec y = x = |x|$ and $\tan y \geq 0 \Rightarrow \dfrac{dy}{dx} = \dfrac{1}{x\sqrt{x^2-1}} = \dfrac{1}{|x|\sqrt{x^2-1}}$

For $y \in (\pi/2, \pi]$, $x \leq -1$, so $|x| = -x$ and $\tan y = -\sqrt{x^2-1} \Rightarrow$

$\dfrac{dy}{dx} = \dfrac{1}{\sec y \tan y} = \dfrac{1}{x(-\sqrt{x^2-1})} = \dfrac{1}{(-x)\sqrt{x^2-1}} = \dfrac{1}{|x|\sqrt{x^2-1}}$

Section 6.9

Exercises 6.9

2. $\cosh(-x) = \frac{1}{2}(e^{-x} + e^{-(-x)}) = \frac{1}{2}(e^{-x} + e^{x}) = \frac{1}{2}(e^{x} + e^{-x}) = \cosh x$

4. $\cosh x - \sinh x = \frac{1}{2}(e^{x} + e^{-x}) - \frac{1}{2}(e^{x} - e^{-x}) = \frac{1}{2}(2e^{-x}) = e^{-x}$

6. $\cosh x \cosh y + \sinh x \sinh y$

$= (1/2)(e^{x}+e^{-x})(1/2)(e^{y}+e^{-y}) + (1/2)(e^{x}-e^{-x})(1/2)(e^{y}-e^{-y})$

$= (1/4)[(e^{x+y}+e^{x-y}+e^{-x+y}+e^{-x-y}) + (e^{x+y}-e^{x-y}-e^{-x+y}+e^{-x-y})]$

$= (1/4)(2e^{x+y}+2e^{-x-y}) = (1/2)(e^{x+y}+e^{-(x+y)}) = \cosh(x+y)$

8. $\tanh(x+y) = \dfrac{\sinh(x+y)}{\cosh(x+y)} = \dfrac{\sinh x \cosh y + \cosh x \sinh y}{\cosh x \cosh y + \sinh x \sinh y}$

$= \dfrac{\dfrac{\sinh x \cosh y}{\cosh x \cosh y} + \dfrac{\cosh x \sinh y}{\cosh x \cosh y}}{\dfrac{\cosh x \cosh y}{\cosh x \cosh y} + \dfrac{\sinh x \sinh y}{\cosh x \cosh y}} = \dfrac{\tanh x + \tanh y}{1 + \tanh x \tanh y}$

10. Putting $y = x$ in Exercise 6, we have $\cosh 2x = $

$\cosh(x+x) = \cosh x \cosh x + \sinh x \sinh x = \cosh^2 x + \sinh^2 x$

12. From Exercise 10 we have $\cosh 2y = \cosh^2 y + \sinh^2 y = 2\cosh^2 y - 1$

$\Rightarrow \cosh^2 y = (\cosh 2y + 1)/2 \Rightarrow \cosh y = \sqrt{(\cosh 2y + 1)/2}$ (since

$\cosh y > 0$). Put $x = 2y$. Then $\cosh(x/2) = \sqrt{(\cosh x + 1)/2}$.

14. $\dfrac{1 + (\sinh x)/\cosh x}{1 - (\sinh x)/\cosh x} = \dfrac{\cosh x + \sinh x}{\cosh x - \sinh x} = \dfrac{(1/2)(e^x+e^{-x})+(1/2)(e^x-e^{-x})}{(1/2)(e^x+e^{-x})-(1/2)(e^x-e^{-x})}$

$= \dfrac{e^x+e^{-x}+e^x-e^{-x}}{e^x+e^{-x}-e^x+e^{-x}} = \dfrac{2e^x}{2e^{-x}} = e^{2x}$

16. $\sinh x = 3/4 \Rightarrow \operatorname{csch} x = 1/\sinh x = 4/3$. $\cosh^2 x = \sinh^2 x + 1$

$= (9/16)+1 = 25/16 \Rightarrow \cosh x = 5/4$ (since $\cosh x > 0$).

$\operatorname{sech} x = 1/\cosh x = 4/5$. $\tanh x = \sinh x/\cosh x = (3/4)/(5/4) = 3/5$

and $\coth x = 1/\tanh x = 5/3$.

18.

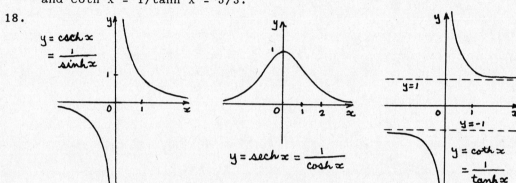

$y = \operatorname{csch} x = \dfrac{1}{\sinh x}$

$y = \operatorname{sech} x = \dfrac{1}{\cosh x}$

$y = \coth x = \dfrac{1}{\tanh x}$

20. (a) $\dfrac{d}{dx} \cosh x = \dfrac{d}{dx}\left[\dfrac{1}{2}(e^x+e^{-x})\right] = \dfrac{1}{2}(e^x-e^{-x}) = \sinh x$

(b) $\dfrac{d}{dx} \tanh x = \dfrac{d}{dx}\left[\dfrac{\sinh x}{\cosh x}\right] = \dfrac{\cosh x \cosh x - \sinh x \sinh x}{\cosh^2 x}$

$= \dfrac{\cosh^2 x - \sinh^2 x}{\cosh^2 x} = \dfrac{1}{\cosh^2 x} = \operatorname{sech}^2 x$

(c) $\dfrac{d}{dx} \operatorname{csch} x = \dfrac{d}{dx}\left[\dfrac{1}{\sinh x}\right] = - \dfrac{\cosh x}{\sinh^2 x} = - \dfrac{1}{\sinh x}\dfrac{\cosh x}{\sinh x}$

$= - \operatorname{csch} x \coth x$

(d) $\dfrac{d}{dx} \operatorname{sech} x = \dfrac{d}{dx}\left[\dfrac{1}{\cosh x}\right] = - \dfrac{\sinh x}{\cosh^2 x} = - \dfrac{1}{\cosh x}\dfrac{\sinh x}{\cosh x}$

$= - \operatorname{sech} x \tanh x$

(e) $\dfrac{d}{dx} \coth x = \dfrac{d}{dx}\left[\dfrac{\cosh x}{\sinh x}\right] = \dfrac{\sinh x \sinh x - \cosh x \cosh x}{\sinh^2 x}$

$= \dfrac{\sinh^2 x - \cosh^2 x}{\sinh^2 x} = - \dfrac{1}{\sinh^2 x} = - \operatorname{csch}^2 x$

22. Let $y = \cosh^{-1} x$. Then $\cosh y = x$ and $y \geq 0$, so $\sinh y = \sqrt{\cosh^2 y - 1}$

$= \sqrt{x^2-1}$. So, by Exercise 3, $e^y = \cosh y + \sinh y = x+\sqrt{x^2-1} \Rightarrow$

$y = \ln(x+\sqrt{x^2-1})$. [Another method: Write $x = \cosh y = (1/2)(e^y+e^{-y})$

and solve a quadratic equation as in Example 3.]

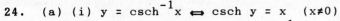

24. (a) (i) $y = \text{csch}^{-1}x \iff \text{csch } y = x \quad (x \neq 0)$

(ii) We sketch the graph of csch^{-1}
  by reflecting the graph of csch
  (see Exercise 18) in the line
  $y = x$.

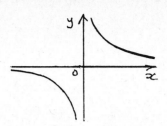

(iii) Let $y = \text{csch}^{-1}x$. Then $x = \text{csch } y = 2/(e^y - e^{-y}) \Rightarrow xe^y - xe^{-y} = 2$
$\Rightarrow x(e^y)^2 - 2e^y - x = 0 \Rightarrow e^y = (1 \pm \sqrt{x^2+1})/x$. But $e^y > 0$, so for $x > 0$,
$e^y = (1 + \sqrt{x^2+1})/x$ and for $x < 0$, $e^y = (1 - \sqrt{x^2+1})/x$. Thus

$$\text{csch}^{-1}x = \ln\left[\frac{1}{x} + \frac{\sqrt{x^2+1}}{|x|}\right]$$

(b) (i) $y = \text{sech}^{-1}x \iff \text{sech } y = x$ and $y > 0$

(ii) We sketch the graph of sech^{-1}
  by reflecting the graph of sech
  (see Exercise 18) in the line
  $y = x$.

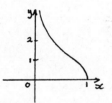

(iii) Let $y = \text{sech}^{-1}x$. Then $x = \text{sech } y = 2/(e^y + e^{-y}) \Rightarrow xe^y + xe^{-y} = 2$
$\Rightarrow x(e^y)^2 - 2e^y + x = 0 \Rightarrow e^y = (1 \pm \sqrt{1-x^2})/x$. But $y > 0 \Rightarrow e^y > 1$. This
rules out the minus sign because $(1 - \sqrt{1-x^2})/x > 1 \iff 1 - \sqrt{1-x^2} > x \iff$
$1 - x > \sqrt{1-x^2} \iff 1 - 2x + x^2 > 1 - x^2 \iff x^2 > x \iff x > 1$, but $x = \text{sech } y \leq 1$.

Thus $e^y = (1 + \sqrt{1-x^2})/x \Rightarrow \text{sech}^{-1}x = \ln\left[\frac{1 + \sqrt{1-x^2}}{x}\right]$

(c) (i) $y = \text{coth}^{-1} x \iff \text{coth } y = x$

(ii) We sketch the graph of coth^{-1}
  by reflecting the graph of coth
  (see Exercise 18) in the line
  $y = x$.

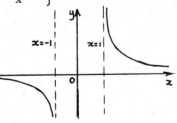

(iii) Let $y = \text{coth}^{-1}x$. Then $x = \text{coth } y = (e^y + e^{-y})/(e^y - e^{-y}) \Rightarrow$
$xe^y - xe^{-y} = e^y + e^{-y} \Rightarrow (x-1)e^y = (x+1)e^{-y} \Rightarrow e^{2y} = (x+1)/(x-1) \Rightarrow$
$2y = \ln\left[\frac{x+1}{x-1}\right] \Rightarrow \text{coth}^{-1}x = \frac{1}{2}\ln\left[\frac{x+1}{x-1}\right]$

26. $f(x) = e^x\sinh x \Rightarrow f'(x) = e^x\sinh x + e^x\cosh x$

28. $g(x) = \cosh^4 x \Rightarrow g'(x) = 4\cosh^3 x \sinh x$

30. $F(x) = e^{\coth 2x} \Rightarrow F'(x) = e^{\coth 2x}(-\text{csch}^2 2x)(2)$

32. $f(t) = \ln(\sinh t) \Rightarrow f'(t) = \dfrac{1}{\sinh t} \cdot \cosh t = \coth t$

34. $y = \cos(\sinh x) \Rightarrow y' = -\sin(\sinh x) \cosh x$

36. $y = e^{\tanh x} \cosh(\cosh x) \Rightarrow$

    $y' = e^{\tanh x} \operatorname{sech}^2 x \cosh(\cosh x) + e^{\tanh x} \sinh(\cosh x) \sinh x$

38. $y = \sqrt{x} \sinh^{-1} \sqrt{x} \Rightarrow$

    $y' = \dfrac{1}{2\sqrt{x}} \sinh^{-1}\sqrt{x} + \sqrt{x}\,\dfrac{1}{\sqrt{1+(\sqrt{x})^2}}\,\dfrac{1}{2\sqrt{x}} = \dfrac{1}{2\sqrt{x}}\sinh^{-1}\sqrt{x} + \dfrac{1}{2\sqrt{1+x}}$

40. $y = x\tanh^{-1}x + \ln\sqrt{1-x^2} = x\tanh^{-1}x + (1/2)\ln(1-x^2) \Rightarrow$

    $y' = \tanh^{-1}x + \dfrac{x}{1-x^2} + \dfrac{1}{2}\dfrac{1}{1-x^2}(-2x) = \tanh^{-1}x$

42. $y = x\sinh^{-1}\left[\dfrac{x}{3}\right] - \sqrt{9+x^2} \Rightarrow y' = \sinh^{-1}\left[\dfrac{x}{3}\right] + x\,\dfrac{1/3}{\sqrt{1+(x/3)^2}} - \dfrac{2x}{2\sqrt{9+x^2}}$

    $= \sinh^{-1}\left[\dfrac{x}{3}\right] + \dfrac{x}{\sqrt{9+x^2}} - \dfrac{x}{\sqrt{9+x^2}} = \sinh^{-1}\left[\dfrac{x}{3}\right]$

44. $y = \operatorname{sech}^{-1}\sqrt{1-x^2} \Rightarrow y' = -\dfrac{1}{\sqrt{1-x^2}\,\sqrt{1-(1-x^2)}} \cdot \dfrac{-2x}{2\sqrt{1-x^2}} = \dfrac{x}{(1-x^2)|x|}$

46. $\int \operatorname{sech}^2 x\,dx = \tanh x + C$

48. Let $u = \cosh x$. Then $du = \sinh x\,dx \Rightarrow \int \tanh x\,dx = \int \dfrac{\sinh x}{\cosh x}\,dx$

    $= \int \dfrac{du}{u} = \ln|u| + C = \ln(\cosh x) + C$

50. Let $u = 1 + \cosh x$. Then $du = \sinh x\,dx \Rightarrow \int \dfrac{\sinh x}{1+\cosh x}\,dx$

    $= \int \dfrac{du}{u} = \ln|u| + C = \ln(1 + \cosh x) + C$

52. $\int_2^3 \dfrac{1}{\sqrt{x^2-1}}\,dx = \cosh^{-1}x\Big]_2^3 = \cosh^{-1}3 - \cosh^{-1}2$ Using Equation 6.81,

    we could write this as $\ln(3+2\sqrt{2}) - \ln(2+\sqrt{3}) = \ln[(3+2\sqrt{2})/(2+\sqrt{3})]$.

54. $\lim\limits_{x\to\infty} \dfrac{\sinh x}{e^x} = \lim\limits_{x\to\infty} \dfrac{e^x - e^{-x}}{2e^x} = \lim\limits_{x\to\infty} \dfrac{1 - e^{-2x}}{2} = \dfrac{1-0}{2} = \dfrac{1}{2}$

56. (a) $y = A\sinh mx + B\cosh mx \Rightarrow y' = mA\cosh mx + mB\sinh mx$

    $\Rightarrow y'' = m^2 A\sinh mx + m^2 B\cosh x = m^2 y$

    (b) From (a) a solution of $y'' = 9y$ is $y(x) = A\sinh 3x + B\cosh 3x$.

    Then $-4 = y(0) = A\sinh 0 + B\cosh 0 = B$, so $B = -4$. Now

    $y'(x) = 3A\cosh 3x - 12\sinh 3x \Rightarrow 6 = y'(0) = 3A \Rightarrow A = 2$, so

    $y = 2\sinh 3x - 4\cosh 3x$.

Exercises 6.10

NOTE: The use of l'Hospital's Rule is indicated by H (above the equal sign).

2. $\displaystyle\lim_{x\to1}\frac{x^2+3x-4}{x-1} = \lim_{x\to1}\frac{(x-1)(x+4)}{x-1} = \lim_{x\to1}(x+4) = 5$

4. $\displaystyle\lim_{x\to1}\frac{x^a-1}{x^b-1} \overset{H}{=} \lim_{x\to1}\frac{ax^{a-1}}{bx^{b-1}} = \frac{a}{b}$ 6. $\displaystyle\lim_{x\to1}\frac{\ln x}{x-1} \overset{H}{=} \lim_{x\to1}\frac{1/x}{1} = 1$

8. $\displaystyle\lim_{x\to\pi}\frac{\tan x}{x} = \frac{\tan\pi}{\pi} = \frac{0}{\pi} = 0$

10. $\displaystyle\lim_{x\to3\pi/2}\frac{\cos x}{x-3\pi/2} \overset{H}{=} \lim_{x\to3\pi/2}\frac{-\sin x}{1} = -\sin(3\pi/2) = 1$

12. $\displaystyle\lim_{x\to0^+}\frac{\ln x}{\sqrt{x}} = -\infty$ since $\ln x \to -\infty$ and $\sqrt{x} \to 0^+$

14. $\displaystyle\lim_{x\to\infty}\frac{(\ln x)^3}{x^2} \overset{H}{=} \lim_{x\to\infty}\frac{3(\ln x)^2(1/x)}{2x} = \lim_{x\to\infty}\frac{3(\ln x)^2}{2x^2} \overset{H}{=} \lim_{x\to\infty}\frac{6(\ln x)(1/x)}{4x}$

$\displaystyle = \lim_{x\to\infty}\frac{3\ln x}{2x^2} \overset{H}{=} \lim_{x\to\infty}\frac{3/x}{4x} = \lim_{x\to\infty}\frac{3}{4x^2} = 0$

16. $\displaystyle\lim_{x\to0}\frac{6^x-2^x}{x} \overset{H}{=} \lim_{x\to0}\frac{6^x(\ln 6) - 2^x(\ln 2)}{1} = \ln 6 - \ln 2 = \ln\frac{6}{2} = \ln 3$

18. $\displaystyle\lim_{x\to0}\frac{e^x-1-x-x^2/2}{x^3} \overset{H}{=} \lim_{x\to0}\frac{e^x-1-x}{3x^2} \overset{H}{=} \lim_{x\to0}\frac{e^x-1}{6x} \overset{H}{=} \lim_{x\to0}\frac{e^x}{6} = \frac{1}{6}$

20. $\displaystyle\lim_{x\to0}\frac{\sin^2 x}{\tan(x^2)} \overset{H}{=} \lim_{x\to0}\frac{2\sin x\cos x}{2x\sec^2(x^2)} = \lim_{x\to0}\frac{\sin x}{x}\lim_{x\to0}\frac{\cos x}{\sec^2(x^2)} = 1\cdot1 = 1$

22. $\displaystyle\lim_{x\to0}\frac{\sin x - x}{x^3} \overset{H}{=} \lim_{x\to0}\frac{\cos x - 1}{3x^2} \overset{H}{=} \lim_{x\to0}\frac{-\sin x}{6x} \overset{H}{=} \lim_{x\to0}\frac{-\cos x}{6} = -\frac{1}{6}$

24. $\displaystyle\lim_{x\to0}\frac{\sin x}{\sinh x} \overset{H}{=} \lim_{x\to0}\frac{\cos x}{\cosh x} = \frac{1}{1} = 1$

26. $\displaystyle\lim_{x\to\infty}\frac{\ln(1+e^x)}{5x} \overset{H}{=} \lim_{x\to\infty}\frac{e^x/(1+e^x)}{5} = \lim_{x\to\infty}\frac{e^x}{5(1+e^x)} \overset{H}{=} \lim_{x\to\infty}\frac{e^x}{5e^x} = \frac{1}{5}$

28. $\displaystyle\lim_{x\to0}\frac{x}{\sin^{-1}(3x)} \overset{H}{=} \lim_{x\to0}\frac{1}{3/\sqrt{1-(3x)^2}} = \lim_{x\to0}\frac{1}{3}\sqrt{1-9x^2} = \frac{1}{3}$

30. $\displaystyle\lim_{x\to0}\frac{\sin mx}{\sin nx} \overset{H}{=} \lim_{x\to0}\frac{m\cos mx}{n\cos nx} = \frac{m}{n}$

32. $\displaystyle\lim_{x\to0}\frac{\sin^{10} x}{\sin(x^{10})} \overset{H}{=} \lim_{x\to0}\frac{10\sin^9 x\cos x}{10x^9\cos(x^{10})} = \left[\lim_{x\to0}\frac{\sin x}{x}\right]^9\lim_{x\to0}\frac{\cos x}{\cos(x^{10})}$

$= 1^9\cdot1 = 1$

34. $\displaystyle\lim_{x\to 0} \frac{2x - \sin^{-1}x}{2x + \cos^{-1}x} = \frac{2(0)-0}{2(0)+\pi/2} = 0$

36. $\displaystyle\lim_{x\to 0} \frac{2x - \sin^{-1}x}{2x + \tan^{-1}x} \overset{H}{=} \lim_{x\to 0} \frac{2-1/\sqrt{1-x^2}}{2+1/(1+x^2)} = \frac{2-1}{2+1} = \frac{1}{3}$

38. $\displaystyle\lim_{x\to 0} \frac{\cos mx - \cos nx}{x^2} \overset{H}{=} \lim_{x\to 0} \frac{-m \sin mx + n \sin nx}{2x}$

    $\displaystyle\overset{H}{=} \lim_{x\to 0} \frac{-m^2\cos mx + n^2\cos nx}{2} = \frac{-m^2+n^2}{2}$

40. $\displaystyle\lim_{x\to -\infty} xe^x = \lim_{x\to -\infty} \frac{x}{e^{-x}} \overset{H}{=} \lim_{x\to -\infty} \frac{1}{-e^{-x}} = \lim_{x\to -\infty} -e^x = 0$

42. $\displaystyle\lim_{x\to \pi/2^-} \sec 7x \cos 3x = \lim_{x\to \pi/2^-} \frac{\cos 3x}{\cos 7x} \overset{H}{=} \lim_{x\to \pi/2^-} \frac{-3 \sin 3x}{-7 \sin 7x} = \frac{3(-1)}{7(-1)} = \frac{3}{7}$

44. $\displaystyle\lim_{x\to 0^+} \sqrt{x} \sec x = 0\cdot 1 = 0$

46. $\displaystyle\lim_{x\to 1^+}(x-1)\tan(\pi x/2) = \lim_{x\to 1^+} \frac{x-1}{\cot(\pi x/2)} \overset{H}{=} \lim_{x\to 1^+} \frac{1}{-\csc^2(\pi x/2)(\pi/2)} = -\frac{2}{\pi}$

48. $\displaystyle\lim_{x\to 0}(\csc x - \cot x) = \lim_{x\to 0}\left[\frac{1}{\sin x} - \frac{\cos x}{\sin x}\right] = \lim_{x\to 0} \frac{1 - \cos x}{\sin x}$

    $\displaystyle\overset{H}{=} \lim_{x\to 0} \frac{\sin x}{\cos x} = 0$

50. $\displaystyle\lim_{x\to 1}\left[\frac{1}{\ln x} - \frac{1}{x-1}\right] = \lim_{x\to 1} \frac{x - 1 - \ln x}{(x-1)\ln x} \overset{H}{=} \lim_{x\to 1} \frac{1 - 1/x}{\ln x + (x-1)(1/x)}$

    $\displaystyle= \lim_{x\to 1} \frac{x - 1}{x \ln x + x - 1} \overset{H}{=} \lim_{x\to 1} \frac{1}{\ln x + 1 + 1} = \frac{1}{0+2} = \frac{1}{2}$

52. $\displaystyle\lim_{x\to \infty} (\sqrt{x^2+x+1} - \sqrt{x^2-x}) = \lim_{x\to \infty} (\sqrt{x^2+x+1} - \sqrt{x^2-x})\frac{\sqrt{x^2+x+1} + \sqrt{x^2-x}}{\sqrt{x^2+x+1} + \sqrt{x^2-x}}$

    $\displaystyle= \lim_{x\to \infty} \frac{(x^2+x+1)-(x^2-x)}{\sqrt{x^2+x+1} + \sqrt{x^2-x}} = \lim_{x\to \infty} \frac{2x+1}{\sqrt{x^2+x+1}+\sqrt{x^2-x}} = \lim_{x\to \infty} \frac{2+1/x}{\sqrt{1+1/x+1/x^2}+\sqrt{1-1/x}}$

    $\displaystyle= \frac{2}{1+1} = 1$

54. $\displaystyle\lim_{x\to \infty} (xe^{1/x}-x) = \lim_{x\to \infty} x(e^{1/x}-1) = \lim_{x\to \infty} \frac{e^{1/x}-1}{1/x} \overset{H}{=} \lim_{x\to \infty} \frac{e^{1/x}(-1/x^2)}{-1/x^2}$

    $\displaystyle= \lim_{x\to \infty} e^{1/x} = e^0 = 1$

56. Let $y = (\sin x)^{\tan x}$. Then $\ln y = \tan x \ln(\sin x) \Rightarrow \lim\limits_{x \to 0^+} \ln y$

$= \lim\limits_{x \to 0^+} \tan x \ln(\sin x) = \lim\limits_{x \to 0^+} \dfrac{\ln(\sin x)}{\cot x} \overset{H}{=} \lim\limits_{x \to 0^+} \dfrac{(\cos x)/\sin x}{-\csc^2 x}$

$= \lim\limits_{x \to 0^+}(-\sin x \cos x) = 0$, so $\lim\limits_{x \to 0^+}(\sin x)^{\tan x} = \lim\limits_{x \to 0^+} e^{\ln y} = e^0 = 1$

58. Let $y = x^{-1/\sqrt{-\ln x}}$. Then $\ln y = (-1/\sqrt{-\ln x})\ln x = \dfrac{-\ln x}{\sqrt{-\ln x}} = \sqrt{-\ln x}$,

so $\lim\limits_{x \to 0^+} \ln y = \lim\limits_{x \to 0^+} \sqrt{-\ln x} = \infty \Rightarrow \lim\limits_{x \to 0^+} x^{-1/\sqrt{-\ln x}} = \lim\limits_{x \to 0^+} e^{\ln y} = \infty$

60. Let $y = (1+a/x)^{bx}$. Then $\ln y = bx \ln(1+a/x) \Rightarrow \lim\limits_{x \to \infty} \ln y =$

$\lim\limits_{x \to \infty} \dfrac{b \ln(1+a/x)}{1/x} \overset{H}{=} \lim\limits_{x \to \infty} \dfrac{b[1/(1+a/x)](-a/x^2)}{-1/x^2} = \lim\limits_{x \to \infty} \dfrac{ab}{1+a/x} = ab$, so

$\lim\limits_{x \to \infty} \left[1 + \dfrac{a}{x}\right]^{bx} = \lim\limits_{x \to \infty} e^{\ln y} = e^{ab}$

62. Let $y = (1+1/x^2)^x$. Then $\ln y = x \ln(1+1/x^2) \Rightarrow \lim\limits_{x \to \infty} \ln y$

$= \lim\limits_{x \to \infty} x \ln(1+1/x^2) = \lim\limits_{x \to \infty} \dfrac{\ln(1+1/x^2)}{1/x} \overset{H}{=} \lim\limits_{x \to \infty} \dfrac{(-2/x^3)/(1+1/x^2)}{-1/x^2}$

$= \lim\limits_{x \to \infty} \dfrac{2/x}{1+1/x^2} = 0$, so $\lim\limits_{x \to \infty} (1+1/x^2)^x = \lim\limits_{x \to \infty} e^{\ln y} = e^0 = 1$

64. Let $y = (e^x+x)^{1/x}$. Then $\ln y = \dfrac{1}{x} \ln(e^x+x) \Rightarrow$

$\lim\limits_{x \to \infty} \ln y = \lim\limits_{x \to \infty} \dfrac{\ln(e^x+x)}{x} \overset{H}{=} \lim\limits_{x \to \infty} \dfrac{e^x+1}{e^x+x} \overset{H}{=} \lim\limits_{x \to \infty} \dfrac{e^x}{e^x+1} \overset{H}{=} \lim\limits_{x \to \infty} \dfrac{e^x}{e^x} = 1 \Rightarrow$

$\lim\limits_{x \to \infty} (e^x+x)^{1/x} = \lim\limits_{x \to \infty} e^{\ln y} = e^1 = e$

66. Let $y = (1+1/x)^{x^2}$. Then $\ln y = x^2 \ln(1+1/x) \Rightarrow \lim\limits_{x \to \infty} \ln y$

$= \lim\limits_{x \to \infty} x^2 \ln(1+1/x) = \lim\limits_{x \to \infty} \dfrac{\ln(1+1/x)}{1/x^2} \overset{H}{=} \lim\limits_{x \to \infty} \dfrac{(-1/x^2)/(1+1/x)}{-2/x^3}$

$= \lim\limits_{x \to \infty} \dfrac{x}{2(1+1/x)} = \infty \Rightarrow \lim\limits_{x \to \infty} (1+1/x)^{x^2} = \lim\limits_{x \to \infty} e^{\ln y} = \infty$

68. Let $y = (\cos 3x)^{5/x}$. Then $\ln y = \dfrac{5}{x} \ln(\cos 3x) \Rightarrow \lim\limits_{x \to 0} \ln y =$

$5 \lim\limits_{x \to 0} \dfrac{\ln(\cos 3x)}{x} \overset{H}{=} 5 \lim\limits_{x \to 0} \dfrac{-3 \tan 3x}{1} = 0$, so $\lim\limits_{x \to 0} (\cos 3x)^{5/x} = e^0 = 1$

70. Let $y = (-\ln x)^x$. Then $\ln y = x \ln(-\ln x)$ $\Rightarrow$ $\lim\limits_{x \to 0^+} \ln y$

$$= \lim\limits_{x \to 0^+} x \ln(-\ln x) = \lim\limits_{x \to 0^+} \frac{\ln(-\ln x)}{1/x} \overset{H}{=} \lim\limits_{x \to 0^+} \frac{(1/-\ln x)(-1/x)}{-1/x^2}$$

$$= \lim\limits_{x \to 0^+} \frac{-x}{\ln x} = 0 \Rightarrow \lim\limits_{x \to 0^+} (-\ln x)^x = e^0 = 1$$

72. Let $y = \left[\frac{2x-3}{2x+5}\right]^{2x+1}$. Then $\ln y = (2x+1)\ln\left[\frac{2x-3}{2x+5}\right]$ $\Rightarrow$ $\lim\limits_{x \to \infty} \ln y =$

$$\lim\limits_{x \to \infty} \frac{\ln(2x-3) - \ln(2x+5)}{1/(2x+1)} \overset{H}{=} \lim\limits_{x \to \infty} \frac{2/(2x-3) - 2/(2x+5)}{-2/(2x+1)^2} = \lim\limits_{x \to \infty} \frac{-8(2x+1)^2}{(2x-3)(2x+5)}$$

$$= \lim\limits_{x \to \infty} \frac{-8(2+1/x)^2}{(2-3/x)(2+5/x)} = -8 \Rightarrow \lim\limits_{x \to \infty} \left[\frac{2x-3}{2x+5}\right]^{2x+1} = e^{-8}$$

74. $\lim\limits_{x \to \infty} x[\ln(x+5) - \ln x] = \lim\limits_{x \to \infty} \frac{\ln(x+5) - \ln x}{1/x} \overset{H}{=} \lim\limits_{x \to \infty} \frac{1/(x+5) - 1/x}{-1/x^2}$

$$= \lim\limits_{x \to \infty} \frac{5x^2}{x(x+5)} = 5$$

76. $\lim\limits_{x \to 0} \frac{1 - \cos 2x + \tan^2 x}{x \sin x} \overset{H}{=} \lim\limits_{x \to 0} \frac{2 \sin 2x + 2 \tan x \sec^2 x}{\sin x + x \cos x} \overset{H}{=}$

$$\lim\limits_{x \to 0} \frac{4 \cos 2x + 2 \sec^4 x + 4 \sec^2 x \tan^2 x}{2 \cos x - x \sin x} = \frac{4+2+0}{2-0} = 3 \quad \text{[Another}$$

method: Use $\cos 2x = 1 - 2 \sin^2 x$ and the fact that $(\sin x)/x \to 1$.]

78. $\lim\limits_{x \to -\infty} (\sqrt{x^2+1} - \sqrt{x^2-4x}) = \lim\limits_{x \to -\infty} (\sqrt{x^2+1} - \sqrt{x^2-4x}) \dfrac{\sqrt{x^2+1} + \sqrt{x^2-4x}}{\sqrt{x^2+1} + \sqrt{x^2-4x}}$

$$= \lim\limits_{x \to -\infty} \frac{x^2+1-(x^2-4x)}{\sqrt{x^2+1} + \sqrt{x^2-4x}} = \lim\limits_{x \to -\infty} \frac{4x+1}{\sqrt{x^2+1} + \sqrt{x^2-4x}} = \lim\limits_{x \to -\infty} \frac{4+1/x}{-\sqrt{1+1/x^2} - \sqrt{1-4/x}}$$

$$= \frac{4-0}{-1-1} = -2$$

80. $y = f(x) = x^2 e^{-x}$ A. $D = R$ B. Intercepts are 0 C. No symmetry

D. $\lim\limits_{x \to \infty} x^2 e^{-x} = \lim\limits_{x \to \infty} \frac{x^2}{e^x} \overset{H}{=} \lim\limits_{x \to \infty} \frac{2x}{e^x} \overset{H}{=} \lim\limits_{x \to \infty} \frac{2}{e^x} = 0$, so $y = 0$ is a HA.

Also $\lim\limits_{x \to -\infty} x^2 e^{-x} = \infty$. E. $f'(x) = 2xe^{-x} - x^2 e^{-x} = x(2-x)e^{-x} > 0$ when

$0 < x < 2$, so f is increasing on $[0,2]$ and decreasing on $(-\infty,0]$, $[2,\infty)$.

F. $f(0) = 0$ is a local minimum, $f(2) = 4e^{-2}$ is a local maximum.

G. $f''(x) = (2-2x)e^{-x} - (2x-x^2)e^{-x} = (x^2-4x+2)e^{-x} = 0$ when $x^2-4x+2 = 0$

$\iff x = 2 \pm \sqrt{2}$. $f''(x) > 0 \iff x < 2 - \sqrt{2}$ or $x > 2 + \sqrt{2}$, so f is CU on $(-\infty, 2-\sqrt{2})$

and $(2+\sqrt{2},\infty)$ and CD on $(2-\sqrt{2}, 2+\sqrt{2})$. IP $(2 \pm \sqrt{2}, (6 \pm 4\sqrt{2})e^{\sqrt{2} \pm 2})$

H.

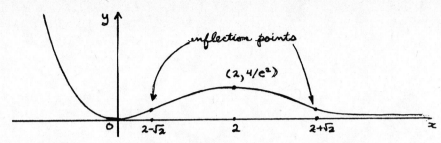

inflection points

$(2, 4/e^2)$

$2-\sqrt{2}$ 2 $2+\sqrt{2}$

82. $f(x) = (\ln x)/x$ A. domain $= (0,\infty)$ B. x-intercept $= 1$

C. No symmetry   D. $\lim\limits_{x\to\infty} \dfrac{\ln x}{x} \overset{H}{=} \lim\limits_{x\to\infty} \dfrac{1/x}{1} = 0$, so y = 0 is a

horizontal asymptote. Also $\lim\limits_{x\to 0^+} \dfrac{\ln x}{x} = -\infty$ since $\ln x \to -\infty$ and

$x \to 0^+$, so x = 0 is a vertical asymptote.

E. $f'(x) = \dfrac{1 - \ln x}{x^2} = 0$ when $\ln x = 1 \Longleftrightarrow x = e$. $f'(x) > 0 \Longleftrightarrow$

$1 - \ln x > 0 \Longleftrightarrow \ln x < 1 \Longleftrightarrow 0 < x < e$. $f'(x) < 0 \Longleftrightarrow x > e$.
So f is increasing on (0,e] and decreasing on [e,∞).

F. Thus f(e) = 1/e is a local (and absolute) maximum.

G. $f''(x) = \dfrac{(-1/x)x^2 - (1-\ln x)(2x)}{x^4} = \dfrac{2\ln x - 3}{x^3}$ $f''(x) > 0 \Longleftrightarrow$

$2\ln x - 3 > 0 \Longleftrightarrow \ln x > 3/2 \Longleftrightarrow x > e^{3/2}$. $f''(x) < 0 \Longleftrightarrow$
$0 < x < e^{3/2}$. So f is CU on $(e^{3/2}, \infty)$ and CD on $(0, e^{3/2})$.
Inflection point: $(e^{3/2}, (3/2)e^{-3/2})$

H.

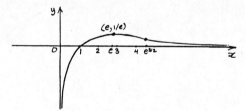

(e, 1/e)

1   2 e 3   4 e^{3/2}

84. $y = f(x) = x(\ln x)^2$ A. D $= (0,\infty)$ B. x-intercept 1, no y-intercept

C. No symmetry D. $\lim\limits_{x\to\infty} x(\ln x)^2 = \infty$, $\lim\limits_{x\to 0^+} x(\ln x)^2 = \lim\limits_{x\to 0^+} \dfrac{(\ln x)^2}{1/x}$

$\overset{H}{=} \lim\limits_{x\to 0^+} \dfrac{2(\ln x)(1/x)}{-1/x^2} = \lim\limits_{x\to 0^+} \dfrac{2\ln x}{-1/x} \overset{H}{=} \lim\limits_{x\to 0^+} \dfrac{2/x}{1/x^2} = \lim\limits_{x\to 0^+} 2x = 0$, no

asymptote. E. $f'(x) = (\ln x)^2 + 2\ln x = (\ln x)(\ln x + 2) = 0$ when

$\ln x = 0 \Longleftrightarrow x = 1$ and when $\ln x = -2 \Longleftrightarrow x = e^{-2}$. $f'(x) > 0$ when

$0 < x < e^{-2}$ and when x > 1, so f is increasing on $(0, e^{-2}]$ and $[1,\infty)$ and

197

decreasing on $[e^{-2},1]$. F. $f(e^{-2}) = 4e^{-2}$ is a local maximum, $f(1) = 0$ is a local minimum.　　　　H.

G. $f''(x) = 2(\ln x)(1/x) + 2/x$

$= (2/x)(\ln x + 1) = 0$ when

$\ln x = -1 \Leftrightarrow x = e^{-1}$.　$f''(x) > 0$

$\Leftrightarrow x > 1/e$, so f is CU on $(1/e,\infty)$,

CD on $(0,1/e)$.　IP $(1/e,1/e)$.

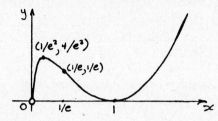

86.　$y = f(x) = x^2 e^{-x^2}$　A. $D = R$　B. Intercepts are 0

C. $f(-x) = f(x)$, so the graph is symmetric about the y-axis.

D. $\lim\limits_{x\to\pm\infty} x^2 e^{-x^2} = \lim\limits_{x\to\pm\infty} \dfrac{x^2}{e^{x^2}} \overset{H}{=} \lim\limits_{x\to\pm\infty} \dfrac{2x}{2xe^{x^2}} = \lim\limits_{x\to\pm\infty} e^{-x^2} = 0$, so $y = 0$ is

a HA.　E. $f'(x) = 2xe^{-x^2} - 2x^3 e^{-x^2} = 2x(1-x^2)e^{-x^2} > 0 \Leftrightarrow 0 < x < 1$ or $x < -1$,

so f is increasing on $[0,1]$ and $(-\infty,-1]$ and decreasing on $[-1,0]$

and $[1,\infty)$.　F. $f(0) = 0$ is a local minimum, $f(\pm 1) = 1/e$ are maxima.

G. $f''(x) = 2e^{-x^2}(2x^4 - 5x^2 + 1) = 0$ when $x^2 = (5\pm\sqrt{17})/4$.　Let $\alpha, \beta =$

$\sqrt{5\pm\sqrt{17}}/2$.　Then $f''(x) > 0 \Leftrightarrow |x| > \alpha$ or $|x| < \beta$, so f is CU on $(-\infty,-\alpha)$,

$(-\beta,\beta)$, and (α,∞), and CD on $(-\alpha,-\beta)$ and (β,α).　IP when $x = \pm\alpha, \pm\beta$.

H.

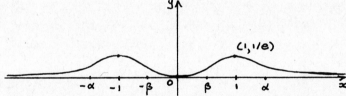

88.　$y = f(x) = e^x/x^2$　A. $D = \{x \mid x \neq 0\}$　B. No intercept　C. No symmetry

D. $\lim\limits_{x\to\infty} \dfrac{e^x}{x^2} \overset{H}{=} \lim\limits_{x\to\infty} \dfrac{e^x}{2x} \overset{H}{=} \lim\limits_{x\to\infty} \dfrac{e^x}{2} = \infty$, $\lim\limits_{x\to-\infty} \dfrac{e^x}{x^2} = 0$, so $y = 0$ is a HA.

$\lim\limits_{x\to 0} \dfrac{e^x}{x^2} = \infty$, so $x = 0$ is a VA.　E. $f'(x) = \dfrac{x^2 e^x - 2xe^x}{x^4} = \dfrac{(x-2)e^x}{x^3} > 0$

$\Leftrightarrow x < 0$ or $x > 2$, so f is increasing on $(-\infty,0)$ and $[2,\infty)$ and

decreasing on $(0,2]$.　F. $f(2) = e^2/4$ is a local minimum.

G. $f''(x) = \dfrac{x^3 e^x(x-1)-3x^2 e^x(x-2)}{x^6}$ H.

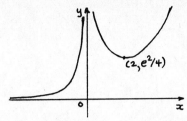

$= \dfrac{e^x(x^2-4x+6)}{x^4} > 0$ for all x since

x^2-4x+6 has positive discriminant,

so f is CU on $(-\infty,0)$ and $(0,\infty)$.

90. $y = f(x) = e^{1/x}/x$ A. $D = \{x| \; x\neq 0\}$ B. No intercept   C. No symmetry

D. $\lim\limits_{x\to\pm\infty} \dfrac{e^{1/x}}{x} = 0$, so $y = 0$ is a HA. $\lim\limits_{x\to 0^+} \dfrac{e^{1/x}}{x} = \infty$, so $x = 0$ is a

VA.   Also $\lim\limits_{x\to 0^-} \dfrac{e^{1/x}}{x} = \lim\limits_{x\to 0^-} \dfrac{1/x}{e^{-1/x}} \overset{H}{=} \lim\limits_{x\to 0^-} \dfrac{-1/x^2}{e^{-1/x}(1/x^2)} = \lim\limits_{x\to 0^-} -e^{1/x} = 0$

E. $f'(x) = \dfrac{xe^{1/x}(-1/x^2)-e^{1/x}}{x^2} = -\dfrac{e^{1/x}(x+1)}{x^3} > 0 \iff -1<x<0$, so f is

increasing on $[-1,0)$ and decreasing on $(-\infty,-1]$ and $(0,\infty)$.

F. $f(-1) = -1/e$ is a local (and absolute) minimum.

G. $f''(x) = \dfrac{e^{1/x}(2x^2+4x+1)}{x^5} = 0$ when $x = -1\pm\sqrt{2}/2$. $f''(x)>0 \iff x>0$ or

$-1-\sqrt{2}/2<x<-1+\sqrt{2}/2$, so f is CU on $(-1-\sqrt{2}/2,-1+\sqrt{2}/2)$ and $(0,\infty)$, and

CD on $(-\infty,-1-\sqrt{2}/2)$ and $(-1+\sqrt{2}/2,0)$.   IP when $x = -1\pm\sqrt{2}/2$.

H.

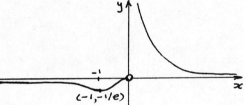

92. $y = f(x) = x^2 e^{-1/x}$ A. $D = \{x|x\neq 0\}$ B. No intercept   C. No symmetry

D. $\lim\limits_{x\to\pm\infty} x^2 e^{-1/x} = \infty$. $\lim\limits_{x\to 0^+} x^2 e^{-1/x} = 0$, $\lim\limits_{x\to 0^-} x^2 e^{-1/x} = \lim\limits_{x\to 0^-} \dfrac{e^{-1/x}}{1/x^2}$

$\overset{H}{=} \lim\limits_{x\to 0^-} \dfrac{e^{-1/x}(1/x^2)}{-2/x^3} = \lim\limits_{x\to 0^-} \dfrac{e^{-1/x}}{-2/x} \overset{H}{=} \lim\limits_{x\to 0^-} \dfrac{e^{-1/x}(1/x^2)}{2/x^2} = \lim\limits_{x\to 0^-} \dfrac{1}{2}e^{-1/x}$

$= \infty$, so $x = 0$ is a VA.   E. $f'(x) = 2xe^{-1/x} + x^2 e^{-1/x}(1/x^2)$

$= e^{-1/x}(2x+1) > 0$ if $x>-1/2$, so f is increasing on $[-1/2,0)$, $(0,\infty)$,

and decreasing on $(-\infty,-1/2]$.

F. $f(-\frac{1}{2}) = \frac{1}{4}e^2$ is a local minimum.

G. $f''(x) = e^{-1/x}(1/x^2)(2x+1) + 2e^{-1/x}$
$= e^{-1/x}(2x^2+2x+1)/x^2 > 0$ for all x
since $2x^2+2x+1$ has positive
discriminant, so f is CU on $(-\infty,0)$
and $(0,\infty)$.

H.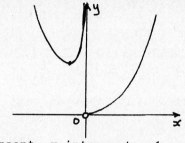

94. $y = f(x) = e^x - x$ A. $D = R$ B. No x-intercept, y-intercept = 1.

C. No symmetry D. $\lim_{x \to -\infty} (e^x - x) = \infty$, $\lim_{x \to \infty} (e^x - x) = \lim_{x \to \infty} x(\frac{e^x}{x} - 1) = \infty$

since $\lim_{x \to \infty} \frac{e^x}{x} \overset{H}{=} \lim_{x \to \infty} \frac{e^x}{1} = \infty$. y = -x is a slant asymptote since

$(e^x - x) - (-x) = e^x \to 0$ as $x \to -\infty$. E. $f'(x) = e^x - 1 > 0 \iff e^x > 1 \iff x > 0$, so f

is increasing on $[0,\infty)$ and
decreasing on $(-\infty,0]$.

F. $f(0) = 1$ is a local (and
absolute) minimum.

G. $f''(x) = e^x > 0$ for all x,
so f is CU on R.

H.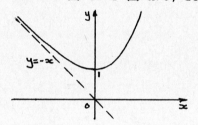

96. $y = f(x) = e^x - 3e^{-x} - 4x$ A. $D = R$ B. y-intercept = -2 C. No

symmetry D. $\lim_{x \to \infty} (e^x - 3e^{-x} - 4x) = \lim_{x \to \infty} x(\frac{e^x}{x} - 3\frac{e^{-x}}{x} - 4) = \infty$, since

$\lim_{x \to \infty} \frac{e^x}{x} \overset{H}{=} \lim_{x \to \infty} \frac{e^x}{1} = \infty$. Similarly, $\lim_{x \to -\infty} (e^x - 3e^{-x} - 4x) = -\infty$.

E. $f'(x) = e^x + 3e^{-x} - 4 = e^{-x}(e^{2x} - 4e^x + 3) = e^{-x}(e^x - 3)(e^x - 1) > 0 \iff e^x > 3$

or $e^x < 1 \iff x > \ln 3$ or $x < 0$. So f is increasing on $(-\infty,0]$ and

$[\ln 3, \infty)$ and decreasing on $[0, \ln 3]$. F. $f(0) = -2$ is a local maximum

and $f(\ln 3) = 2 - 4\ln 3$ is a local

minimum. G. $f''(x) = e^x - 3e^{-x}$

$= e^{-x}(e^{2x} - 3) > 0 \iff e^{2x} > 3 \iff$

$x > \frac{1}{2}\ln 3$, so f is CU on $(\frac{1}{2}\ln 3, \infty)$

and CD on $(-\infty, \frac{1}{2}\ln 3)$.

IP when $x = (1/2)\ln 3$.

H.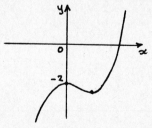

98. $y = f(x) = (2x)^{3x}$ A. $D = (0,\infty)$ B. No intercept C. No symmetry

D. $\lim_{x \to \infty} (2x)^{3x} = \infty$. $\ln y = 3x \ln(2x) \Rightarrow \lim_{x \to 0^+} \ln y = \lim_{x \to 0^+} 3x \ln(2x)$

$$= \lim_{x \to 0^+} \frac{\ln(2x)}{1/3x} \overset{H}{=} \lim_{x \to 0^+} \frac{1/x}{-1/3x^2} = \lim_{x \to 0^+} -3x = 0 \Rightarrow \lim_{x \to 0^+} (2x)^{3x} = e^0 = 1$$

E. $\ln y = 3x \ln(2x) \Rightarrow y'/y = 3 \ln(2x) + 3 \Rightarrow f'(x) = (2x)^{3x}(1+\ln 2x)$
$> 0 \Leftrightarrow \ln 2x > -1 \Leftrightarrow 2x > e^{-1} \Leftrightarrow x > 1/2e$, so f is increasing on
$[1/2e, \infty)$ and decreasing on
$(0, 1/2e]$. F. $f(1/2e) = (1/e)^{3/2e}$
is a local (and absolute) minimum.
G. $f''(x) = 9(2x)^{3x}(1+\ln 2x)^2$
$+ 3(2x)^{3x}(1/x) > 0$, so f is
CU on $(0, \infty)$.

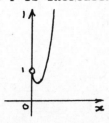

100. $y = f(x) = x^{1/x}$ A. $D = (0, \infty)$ B. No intercept C. No symmetry

D. $\lim_{x \to \infty} \ln y = \lim_{x \to \infty} \frac{\ln x}{x} \overset{H}{=} \lim_{x \to \infty} \frac{1/x}{1} = 0 \Rightarrow \lim_{x \to \infty} x^{1/x} = e^0 = 1$, so

$y = 1$ is a HA. $\lim_{x \to 0^+} x^{1/x} = \lim_{x \to 0^+} (e^{\ln x})^{1/x} = \lim_{x \to 0^+} e^{\ln x/x} = 0$ since

$\frac{\ln x}{x} \to -\infty$ as $x \to 0^+$. E. $\ln y = \frac{\ln x}{x} \Rightarrow \frac{y'}{y} = \frac{1 - \ln x}{x^2} \Rightarrow$

$f'(x) = x^{1/x}(1 - \ln x)/x^2 > 0 \Leftrightarrow \ln x < 1 \Leftrightarrow x < e$, so f is
increasing on $(0, e]$ and decreasing on $[e, \infty)$. F. $f(e) = e^{1/e}$ is a
local (and absolute) maximum.

H.

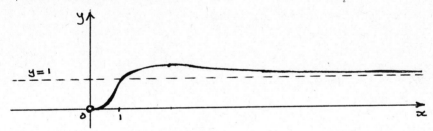

102. $y = f(x) = (\sin x)^{\sin x}$ A. $D = \{x \mid \sin x > 0\} = \{x \mid 2n\pi < x < (2n+1)\pi\}$
B. No intercept C. f has period 2π, so in D-G we treat f only for

$0 < x < \pi$. D. $\lim_{x \to 0^+} \ln y = \lim_{x \to 0^+} \sin x \ln \sin x = \lim_{x \to 0^+} \frac{\ln \sin x}{\csc x} \overset{H}{=}$

$\lim_{x \to 0^+} \frac{\cot x}{- \csc x \cot x} = \lim_{x \to 0^+} -\sin x = 0 \Rightarrow \lim_{x \to 0^+} (\sin x)^{\sin x} = e^0 = 1$

Similarly, $\lim_{x \to \pi^-} (\sin x)^{\sin x} = 1$. E. $\ln y = \sin x \ln \sin x \Rightarrow$

$\frac{y'}{y} = \cos x \ln \sin x + \sin x \frac{\cos x}{\sin x} = \cos x (1 + \ln \sin x) \Rightarrow$

$y' = (\sin x)^{\sin x} \cos x (1 + \ln \sin x) = 0$ when $\cos x = 0$ or
$\ln \sin x = -1 \Leftrightarrow x = \pi/2$ or $\sin x = 1/e$. Let $\alpha = \sin^{-1}(1/e)$. Then

$f'(x)>0 \iff \alpha<x<\pi/2$ or $\pi-\alpha<x<\pi$, so f is increasing on $[\alpha,\pi/2]$ and $[\pi-\alpha,\pi)$, and decreasing on $(0,\alpha]$ and $[\pi/2,\pi-\alpha]$. F. $f(\pi/2) = 1$ is a local maximum, $f(\alpha) = f(\pi-\alpha) = (1/e)^{1/e}$ are local minima.

H.

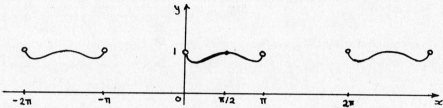

104. $y = f(x) = (2^x-1)/x$ A. $D = \{x|\ x\neq0\}$ B. No intercept C No symmetry D. $\lim\limits_{x\to\infty} \dfrac{2^x-1}{x} \overset{H}{=} \lim\limits_{x\to\infty} \dfrac{2^x\ln2}{1} = \infty$, $\lim\limits_{x\to-\infty} \dfrac{2^x-1}{x} = 0$, so $y = 0$ is a

HA. $\lim\limits_{x\to0} \dfrac{2^x-1}{x} \overset{H}{=} \lim\limits_{x\to0} \dfrac{2^x\ln2}{1} = \ln2$. E. $f'(x) = \dfrac{x2^x\ln2-(2^x-1)}{x^2}$

$= \dfrac{1+2^x(x\ln2 - 1)}{x^2}$. Let $g(x) = 1+2^x(x\ln2 - 1)$. Then $g'(x) = x2^x(\ln2)^2$

>0 for $x>0$, $g'(x)<0$ for $x<0$, and $g(0) = 0 \Rightarrow g(x)>0$ for $x\neq0$. Thus $f'(x)>0$ for $x\neq0$, so f is increasing on its domain. F. No extrema.

H.

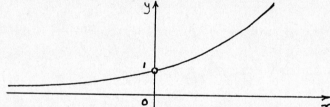

106. $\lim\limits_{x\to\infty} \dfrac{\ln x}{x^p} \overset{H}{=} \lim\limits_{x\to\infty} \dfrac{1/x}{px^{p-1}} = \lim\limits_{x\to\infty} \dfrac{1}{px^p} = 0$ since $p>0$.

108. Using l'Hospital's Rule and the Fundamental Theorem of Calculus, Part 1, we have $\lim\limits_{x\to0} \dfrac{\int_0^x \sin(t^2)dt}{x^3} = \lim\limits_{x\to0} \dfrac{\frac{d}{dx}\int_0^x \sin(t^2)dt}{3x^2}$

$= \lim\limits_{x\to0} \dfrac{\sin(x^2)}{3x^2} = \dfrac{1}{3} \lim\limits_{x\to0} \dfrac{\sin(x^2)}{x^2} = \dfrac{1}{3}\cdot1 = \dfrac{1}{3}$

Review Exercises for Chapter 6

2. $y = (0.7)^x$

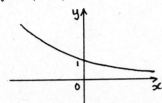

4. $y = \pi^{-x} = (1/\pi)^x$

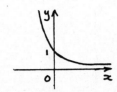

6. $y = \ln x \qquad y = \ln(x-1)$

8. $y = e^x \cos x$

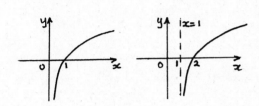 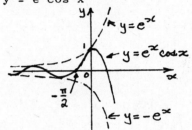

10. $\ln x = 2 \Rightarrow x = e^{\ln x} = e^2$

12. $e^{e^x} = 2 \Rightarrow \ln 2 = \ln e^{e^x} = e^x \Rightarrow x = \ln e^x = \ln \ln 2$

14. $1 = \ln(x+1) - \ln(x) = \ln\left[\frac{x+1}{x}\right] \Rightarrow \frac{x+1}{x} = e \Rightarrow ex = x+1 \Rightarrow x = \frac{1}{e-1}$

16. $\sin^{-1} x = 1 \Rightarrow x = \sin 1$

18. $y = \sqrt{2}^x \Rightarrow y' = \sqrt{2}^x \ln\sqrt{2} = \sqrt{2}^x (\ln 2)/2$

20. $y = \ln(\csc 5x) \Rightarrow y' = \frac{-5\csc 5x \cot 5x}{\csc 5x} = -5\cot 5x$

22. $y = \sin^{-1}(e^x) \Rightarrow y' = e^x/\sqrt{1-e^{2x}}$

24. $y = \ln(x^2 e^x) = 2\ln|x| + x \Rightarrow y' = 2/x + 1$

26. $y = \ln|\csc 3x + \cot 3x| \Rightarrow y' = \frac{-3\csc 3x \cot 3x - 3\csc^2 3x}{\csc 3x + \cot 3x} = -3\csc 3x$

28. $y = x^r e^{sx} \Rightarrow y' = rx^{r-1}e^{sx} + sx^r e^{sx}$

30. $y = 5^{x\tan x} \Rightarrow y' = 5^{x\tan x}(\ln 5)(\tan x + x\sec^2 x)$

32. $xe^y = y-1 \Rightarrow e^y + xe^y y' = y' \Rightarrow y' = e^y/(1-xe^y)$

34. $y = e^{\cos x} + \cos(e^x) \Rightarrow y' = -\sin x\, e^{\cos x} - e^x \sin(e^x)$

36. $y = \ln|x^2-4| - \ln|2x+5| \Rightarrow y' = \frac{2x}{x^2-4} - \frac{2}{2x+5}$

38. $y = \log_3 \sqrt{(1+cx^a)^s} = \frac{s}{2}\log_3|1+cx^a| \Rightarrow y' = \frac{sacx^{a-1}}{2(1+cx^a)}\log_3 e$

40. $y = x \tanh^{-1}\sqrt{x} \Rightarrow y' = \tanh^{-1}\sqrt{x} + x \dfrac{1}{1-(\sqrt{x})^2} \dfrac{1}{2\sqrt{x}} = \tanh^{-1}\sqrt{x} + \dfrac{\sqrt{x}}{2(1-x)}$

42. $y = (c/x)^x \Rightarrow \ln y = x \ln(c/x) = x \ln c - x \ln x \Rightarrow$
$y'/y = \ln c - \ln x - 1 \Rightarrow y' = (c/x)^x[\ln(c/x)-1]$

44. $y = \arctan(\arcsin\sqrt{x}) \Rightarrow y' = \dfrac{1}{1+(\arcsin\sqrt{x})^2} \cdot \dfrac{1}{\sqrt{1-x}} \cdot \dfrac{1}{2\sqrt{x}}$

46. $y = \dfrac{x}{\sqrt{a^2-1}} - \dfrac{2}{\sqrt{a^2-1}} \arctan \dfrac{\sin x}{a + \sqrt{a^2-1} + \cos x}$ Let $k = a+\sqrt{a^2-1}$. Then

$y' = \dfrac{1}{\sqrt{a^2-1}} - \dfrac{2}{\sqrt{a^2-1}} \dfrac{1}{1 + \sin^2 x/(k + \cos x)^2} \cdot \dfrac{\cos x (k + \cos x) + \sin^2 x}{(k + \cos x)^2}$

$= \dfrac{1}{\sqrt{a^2-1}} - \dfrac{2}{\sqrt{a^2-1}} \cdot \dfrac{k \cos x + \cos^2 x + \sin^2 x}{(k + \cos x)^2 + \sin^2 x} =$

$\dfrac{1}{\sqrt{a^2-1}} - \dfrac{2}{\sqrt{a^2-1}} \cdot \dfrac{k \cos x + 1}{k^2 + 2k \cos x + 1} = \dfrac{k^2 + 2k \cos x + 1 - 2k \cos x - 2}{\sqrt{a^2-1}(k^2 + 2k \cos x + 1)}$

$= \dfrac{k^2-1}{\sqrt{a^2-1}(k^2 + 2k \cos x + 1)}$ But $k^2 = 2a^2+2a\sqrt{a^2-1}-1 = 2a(a+\sqrt{a^2-1})-1$

$= 2ak-1$, so $k^2+1 = 2ak$, $k^2-1 = 2(ak-1)$

So $y' = \dfrac{2(ak-1)}{\sqrt{a^2-1}(2ak + 2k \cos x)} = \dfrac{ak-1}{\sqrt{a^2-1} \, k(a + \cos x)}$

But $ak-1 = a^2+a\sqrt{a^2-1}-1 = k\sqrt{a^2-1}$, so $y' = \dfrac{1}{a + \cos x}$.

48. $f(x) = \ln(2x) = \ln 2 + \ln x \Rightarrow f'(x) = x^{-1}$, $f''(x) = -x^{-2}$,
$f'''(x) = 2x^{-3}$, $f^{(4)}(x) = -2\cdot 3 x^{-4}$, $\cdots$, $f^{(n)}(x) = (-1)^{n-1}(n-1)! x^{-n}$

50. $y = f(x) = x \ln x \Rightarrow f'(x) = \ln x + 1$, so the slope of the tangent
at (e,e) is $f'(e) = 2$ and the equation is $y-e = 2(x-e)$ or $y = 2x-e$.

52. The line $x-4y = 1$ has slope $1/4$. A tangent to $y = e^x$ has slope $1/4$
when $y' = e^x = 1/4 \Rightarrow x = \ln(1/4) = -\ln 4$, so the equation is
$y-(1/4) = (1/4)(x+\ln 4)$ or $x-4y+1+\ln 4 = 0$.

54. $\lim\limits_{x\to\infty} \dfrac{4^x}{4^x-1} = \lim\limits_{x\to\infty} \dfrac{1}{1-4^{-x}} = \dfrac{1}{1-0} = 1$

56. $-e^{x/2} \le e^{x/2}\cos x \le e^{x/2}$ and $\lim\limits_{x\to-\infty} (-e^{x/2}) = 0 = \lim\limits_{x\to-\infty} e^{x/2}$, so
$\lim\limits_{x\to-\infty} e^{x/2}\cos x = 0$ by the Squeeze Theorem.

58. $\lim\limits_{x\to-1^+} e^{\tanh^{-1}x} = 0$ since $\tanh^{-1}x \to -\infty$ as $x \to -1^+$

60. $\lim\limits_{x\to-\infty} \tan^{-1}(x^4) = \dfrac{\pi}{2}$ since $x^4 \to \infty$ as $x \to -\infty$

62. $\lim\limits_{x\to 0} \dfrac{e^{ax}-e^{bx}}{x} \overset{H}{=} \lim\limits_{x\to 0} \dfrac{ae^{ax}-be^{bx}}{1} = a-b$

64. $\lim\limits_{x\to 0} \dfrac{1 + \sin x - \cos x}{1 - \sin x - \cos x} \overset{H}{=} \lim\limits_{x\to 0} \dfrac{\cos x + \sin x}{-\cos x + \sin x} = \dfrac{1+0}{-1+0} = -1$

66. $\lim\limits_{x\to \pi/2} \left[\dfrac{\pi}{2} - x\right]\tan x = \lim\limits_{x\to \pi/2} \dfrac{\pi/2 - x}{\cot x} \overset{H}{=} \lim\limits_{x\to \pi/2} \dfrac{-1}{-\csc^2 x} = \lim\limits_{x\to \pi/2} \sin^2 x = 1$

68. $\lim\limits_{x\to 0} (\csc^2 x - x^{-2}) = \lim\limits_{x\to 0} \left[\dfrac{1}{\sin^2 x} - \dfrac{1}{x^2}\right] = \lim\limits_{x\to 0} \dfrac{x^2 - \sin^2 x}{x^2\sin^2 x}$

$\overset{H}{=} \lim\limits_{x\to 0} \dfrac{2x - \sin 2x}{2x \sin^2 x + x^2\sin 2x} \overset{H}{=} \lim\limits_{x\to 0} \dfrac{2 - 2\cos 2x}{2\sin^2 x + 4x\sin 2x + 2x^2\cos 2x}$

$\overset{H}{=} \lim\limits_{x\to 0} \dfrac{4\sin 2x}{6\sin 2x + 12x\cos 2x - 4x^2\sin 2x}$

$\overset{H}{=} \lim\limits_{x\to 0} \dfrac{8\cos 2x}{24\cos 2x - 32x\sin 2x - 8x^2\cos 2x} = \dfrac{8}{24} = \dfrac{1}{3}$

70. Let $y = x^{1/(1-x)}$. Then $\ln y = (\ln x)/(1-x)$, so

$\lim\limits_{x\to 1} \ln y = \lim\limits_{x\to 1} \dfrac{\ln x}{1-x} \overset{H}{=} \lim\limits_{x\to 1} \dfrac{1/x}{-1} = -1 \;\Rightarrow\; \lim\limits_{x\to 1} x^{1/(1-x)} = e^{-1}$

72. $\lim\limits_{x\to \infty} \dfrac{\sqrt{x}}{\ln x} \overset{H}{=} \lim\limits_{x\to \infty} \dfrac{1/2\sqrt{x}}{1/x} = \lim\limits_{x\to \infty} \dfrac{\sqrt{x}}{2} = \infty$, so $\lim\limits_{x\to \infty} \tan^{-1}\left[\dfrac{\sqrt{x}}{\ln x}\right] = \dfrac{\pi}{2}$

74. $y = f(x) = \sin^{-1}(1/x)$ A. $D = \{x \mid -1 \leq 1/x \leq 1\} = (-\infty,-1] \cup [1,\infty)$

B. No intercept C. $f(-x) = -f(x)$, symmetric about the origin.

D. $\lim\limits_{x\to \pm\infty} \sin^{-1}(1/x) = \sin^{-1}(0) = 0$, so $y = 0$ is a HA.

E. $f'(x) = \dfrac{1}{\sqrt{1-(1/x)^2}}\left[-\dfrac{1}{x^2}\right] = \dfrac{-1}{\sqrt{x^4-x^2}} < 0$, so f is decreasing on

$(-\infty,-1]$ and $[1,\infty)$. F. No local extrema, but $f(1) = \pi/2$ is the

absolute maximum and $f(-1) = -\pi/2$ is the absolute minimum.

G. $f''(x) = \dfrac{4x^3-2x}{2(x^4-x^2)^{3/2}} = \dfrac{x(2x^2-1)}{(x^4-x^2)^{3/2}} > 0$ for $x>1$ and $f''(x) < 0$ for

$x<-1$, so f is CU on $(1,\infty)$ and CD on $(-\infty,-1)$.

H.

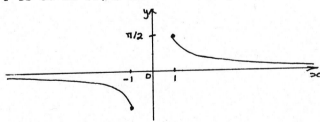

76. $y = f(x) = e^{2x-x^2}$ A. $D = R$ B. No x-intercept, y-intercept = 1.
C. No symmetry   D. $\lim\limits_{x\to\pm\infty} e^{2x-x^2} = 0$, so $y = 0$ is a HA.

E. $f'(x) = 2(1-x)e^{2x-x^2} > 0 \Leftrightarrow x<1$, so f is increasing on $(-\infty,1]$
and decreasing on $[1,\infty)$.   F. $f(1) = e$ is a local and absolute
maximum.   G. $f''(x) = 2(2x^2-4x+1)e^{2x-x^2} = 0 \Leftrightarrow x = 1\pm\sqrt{2}/2$. $f''(x)>0$
$\Leftrightarrow x<1-\sqrt{2}/2$ or $x>1+\sqrt{2}/2$, so f is CU on $(-\infty,1-\sqrt{2}/2)$ and $(1+\sqrt{2}/2,\infty)$,
and CD on $(1-\sqrt{2}/2,1+\sqrt{2}/2)$.   IP when $x = 1\pm\sqrt{2}/2$.
H.

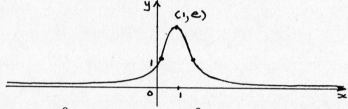

78. $y = f(x) = \ln(x^2-1)$ A. $D = \{x\mid x^2>1\} = (-\infty,-1) \cup (1,\infty)$
B. No y-intercept, x-intercepts occur when $x^2-1 = 1 \Leftrightarrow x = \pm\sqrt{2}$
C. $f(-x) = f(x)$, so the graph is symmetric about the y-axis.
D. $\lim\limits_{x\to\pm\infty} \ln(x^2-1) = \infty$, $\lim\limits_{x\to1^+} \ln(x^2-1) = -\infty$, $\lim\limits_{x\to-1^-} \ln(x^2-1) = -\infty$, so
$x = 1$ and $x = -1$ are VA.   E. $f'(x) = 2x/(x^2-1) > 0$ for $x>1$ and
$f'(x)<0$ for $x<-1$, so f is increasing on $(1,\infty)$ and decreasing on
$(-\infty,-1)$.   F. No extrema.   H.
G. $f''(x) = -2(x^2+1)/(x^2-1)^2 < 0$,
so f is CD on $(-\infty,-1)$ and $(1,\infty)$.

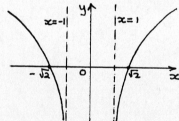

80. $y = f(x) = e^{-1/x^2}$ A. $D = \{x\mid x\neq0\}$ B. No intercept
C. $f(-x) = f(x)$, so the graph is symmetric about the y-axis.
D. $\lim\limits_{x\to\pm\infty} e^{-1/x^2} = e^0 = 1$, so $y = 1$ is a HA. $\lim\limits_{x\to0} e^{-1/x^2} = 0$.

E. $f'(x) = e^{-1/x^2}(2/x^3) > 0 \Leftrightarrow x>0$, so f is increasing on $(0,\infty)$ and
decreasing on $(-\infty,0)$.   F. No extrema   G. $f''(x) = 2(2-3x^2)e^{-1/x^2}/x^6$
$> 0 \Leftrightarrow 3x^2<2 \Leftrightarrow |x|<\sqrt{2/3}$, so f is CU on $(-\sqrt{2/3},0)$ and $(0,\sqrt{2/3})$, and
CD on $(-\infty,-\sqrt{2/3})$ and $(\sqrt{2/3},\infty)$.   IP are $(\pm\sqrt{2/3},e^{-3/2})$.

H.

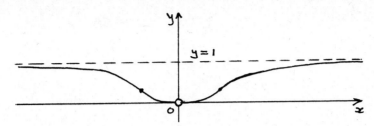

82. (a) If $y(t)$ is the mass remaining after t years, then
$y(t) = y(0)e^{kt} = 18e^{kt}$ ➠ $y(25) = 18e^{25k} = 9$ ➠ $e^{25k} = 1/2$ ➠
$25k = -\ln 2$ ➠ $k = -(\ln 2)/25$ ➠ $y(t) = 18e^{-(\ln 2)t/25} = 18 \cdot 2^{-t/25}$.
(b) $18 \cdot 2^{-t/25} = 2$ ➠ $2^{-t/25} = 1/9$ ➠ $-(t/25)\ln 2 = -\ln 9$ ➠
$t = 25(\ln 9)/(\ln 2) \approx 79$ years.

84. $f(x) = g(e^x)$ ➠ $f'(x) = g'(e^x)e^x$

86. $f(x) = g(\ln x)$ ➠ $f'(x) = g'(\ln x)/x$

88. Let $u = 2-3x$. Then $du = -3\ dx$ ➠ $\int_1^2 \frac{1}{2-3x}\ dx = -\frac{1}{3}\int_{-1}^{-4}\frac{du}{u}$

$= -\frac{1}{3}\ \ln|u|\Big]_{-1}^{-4} = -\frac{1}{3}\ \ln 4$

90. $\int_0^1 e^{\pi t}dt = \frac{1}{\pi}\ e^{\pi t}\Big]_0^1 = \frac{1}{\pi}(e^{\pi}-1)$

92. Let $u = \ln x$. Then $du = \frac{1}{x}\ dx$ ➠ $\int \frac{\cos(\ln x)}{x}\ dx = \int \cos u\ du$

$= \sin u + C = \sin(\ln x) + C$

94. Let $u = x^2$. Then $du = 2x\ dx$ ➠ $\int \frac{x}{\sqrt{1-x^4}}\ dx = \frac{1}{2}\int \frac{du}{\sqrt{1-u^2}}$

$= \frac{1}{2}\ \sin^{-1}u + C = \frac{1}{2}\ \sin^{-1}(x^2) + C$

96. Let $u = \ln(e^x+1)$. Then $du = [e^x/(e^x+1)]dx$ ➠

$\int \frac{e^x}{(e^x+1)\ln(e^x+1)}\ dx = \int \frac{du}{u} = \ln|u| + C = \ln\ \ln(e^x+1) + C$

98. Let $u = \sqrt{x}$. Then $du = dx/2\sqrt{x}$ ➠ $\int \frac{1}{\sqrt{x}(1+x)}\ dx = 2\int \frac{du}{1+u^2}$

$= 2\ \tan^{-1}u + C = 2\ \tan^{-1}\sqrt{x} + C$

100. Let $u = -x^3$. Then $du = -3x^2 dx$ ➠ $\int x^2 2^{-x^3}dx = -\frac{1}{3}\int 2^u du$

$= -\frac{1}{3}\ \frac{2^u}{\ln 2} + C = -\frac{1}{3\ln 2}\ 2^{-x^3} + C$

102. $1+e^{2x} > e^{2x}$ ➠ $\sqrt{1+e^{2x}} > \sqrt{e^{2x}} = e^x$ ➠ $\int_0^1 \sqrt{1+e^{2x}}dx \geq \int_0^1 e^x dx = e^x\Big]_0^1$

$= e-1$

104. For $0 \leq x \leq 1$, $0 \leq \sin^{-1}x \leq \pi/2$, so $\int_0^1 x \sin^{-1}x\,dx \leq \int_0^1 x(\pi/2)dx$

$= \frac{\pi}{4}x^2\Big]_0^1 = \frac{\pi}{4}$

106. $f'(x) = \frac{d}{dx}\int_{\ln x}^{2x} e^{-t^2}dt = -\frac{d}{dx}\int_0^{\ln x} e^{-t^2}dt + \frac{d}{dx}\int_0^{2x} e^{-t^2}dt$

$= -e^{-(\ln x)^2}(1/x) + e^{-(2x)^2}(2) = -e^{-(\ln x)^2}/x + 2e^{-4x^2}$

108. $A = \int_{-2}^0 (e^{-x}-e^x)dx + \int_0^1 (e^x-e^{-x})dx = (-e^{-x}-e^x)\Big]_{-2}^0 + (e^x+e^{-x})\Big]_0^1$

$= (-1-1)-(-e^2-e^{-2})+(e+e^{-1})-(1+1) = e^2+e+e^{-1}+e^{-2}-4$

110. Using Theorem 5.12 with $a = 0$ $b = 1$, we have $\int_0^1 e^x dx = \lim_{n\to\infty}\frac{1}{n}\sum_{i=1}^n e^{i/n}$

This series is a geometric series with $a = r = e^{1/n}$, so

$$\sum_{i=1}^n e^{i/n} = e^{1/n}\frac{e^{n/n}-1}{e^{1/n}-1} = e^{1/n}\frac{e-1}{e^{1/n}-1} \Rightarrow$$

$\int_0^1 e^x dx = \lim_{n\to\infty}\frac{1}{n}\sum_{i=1}^n e^{i/n} = \lim_{n\to\infty}(e-1)e^{1/n}\frac{1/n}{e^{1/n}-1}$ As $n\to\infty$, $1/n\to 0^+$, so

$e^{1/n}\to e^0 = 1$. Let $t = 1/n$. Then $e^{1/n}-1 = e^t-1\to 0^+$, so l'Hospital's

Rule gives $\lim_{t\to 0}\frac{t}{e^t-1} = \lim_{t\to 0}\frac{1}{e^t} = 1$ and we have

$$\int_0^1 e^x dx = \lim_{t\to 0^+}(e-1)e^t \cdot \lim_{t\to 0^+}\frac{t}{e^t-1} = e-1$$

CHAPTER SEVEN

Exercises 7.1

2. Let $u = x$, $dv = \cos x\, dx$ $\Rightarrow$ $du = dx$, $v = \sin x$. Then by (7.2),
    $\int x \cos dx = x \sin x - \int \sin x\, dx = x \sin x + \cos x + C$

4. Let $u = \ln x$, $dv = x\, dx$ $\Rightarrow$ $du = dx/x$, $v = \frac{1}{2}x^2$. Then $\int x \ln x\, dx$
    $= \frac{1}{2}x^2 \ln x - \int \frac{1}{2}x^2 \frac{1}{x}\, dx = \frac{1}{2}x^2 \ln x - \frac{1}{4}x^2 + C$

6. Let $u = x^2$, $dv = \sin 2x\, dx$ $\Rightarrow$ $du = 2x\, dx$, $v = -\frac{1}{2}\cos 2x$. Then
    $I = \int x^2 \sin 2x\, dx = -\frac{1}{2}x^2 \cos 2x - \int -\frac{1}{2}\cos 2x \cdot 2x\, dx$
    $= -\frac{1}{2}x^2 \cos 2x + \int x \cos 2x\, dx$. Next let $U = x$, $dV = \cos 2x\, dx$,
    $\Rightarrow$ $dU = dx$, $V = \frac{1}{2}\sin 2x$ to get $\int x \cos 2x\, dx$
    $= \frac{1}{2}x \sin 2x - \frac{1}{2}\int \sin 2x\, dx = \frac{1}{2}x \sin 2x + \frac{1}{4}\cos 2x + C$.
    Substituting in the previous formula, we obtain
    $I = -\frac{1}{2}x^2 \cos 2x + \frac{1}{2}x \sin 2x + \frac{1}{4}\cos 2x + C$

8. Let $u = \sin^{-1}x$, $dv = dx$ $\Rightarrow$ $du = dx/\sqrt{1-x^2}$, $v = x$. Then
    $\int \sin^{-1}x\, dx = x \sin^{-1}x - \int \frac{x}{\sqrt{1-x^2}}\, dx$. Setting $t = 1 - x^2$, we get
    $dt = -2x\, dx$, so $-\int \frac{x\, dx}{\sqrt{1-x^2}} = \int t^{-1/2} \cdot \frac{1}{2}\, dt = t^{1/2} + C = \sqrt{1-x^2} + C$.
    Hence $\int \sin^{-1}x\, dx = x \sin^{-1}x + \sqrt{1-x^2} + C$

10. Let $u = \theta$, $dv = \sec^2\theta\, d\theta$ $\Rightarrow$ $du = d\theta$, $v = \tan\theta$. Then
    $\int \theta \sec^2\theta\, d\theta = \theta \tan\theta - \int \tan\theta\, d\theta = \theta \tan\theta - \ln|\sec\theta| + C$

12. Let $u = t^3$, $dv = e^t\, dt$ $\Rightarrow$ $du = 3t^2$, $v = e^t$. Then $I = \int t^3 e^t\, dt$
    $= t^3 e^t - \int 3t^2 e^t\, dt$. Integrate by parts twice more with
    $dv = e^t\, dt$. $I = t^3 e^t - (3t^2 e^t - \int 6t e^t\, dt) = t^3 e^t - 3t^2 e^t + 6t e^t -$
    $\int 6 e^t\, dt = t^3 e^t - 3t^2 e^t + 6t e^t - 6 e^t + C = (t^3 - 3t^2 + 6t - 6)e^t + C$
    More generally, if $p(t)$ is a polynomial of degree n in t, then
    repeated integration by parts shows that $\int p(t)e^t\, dt$
    $= [p(t) - p'(t) + p''(t) - p'''(t) + \cdots + (-1)^n p^{(n)}(t)]e^t + C$

14. Let $u = \cos 3\theta$, $dv = e^{-\theta}d\theta$ $\Rightarrow$ $du = -3\sin 3\theta\, d\theta$, $v = -e^{-\theta}$. Then
    $I = \int e^{-\theta} \cos 3\theta\, d\theta = -e^{-\theta} \cos 3\theta - 3\int e^{-\theta} \sin 3\theta\, d\theta$. Integrate
    by parts again: $I = -e^{-\theta} \cos 3\theta + 3e^{-\theta} \sin 3\theta - \int e^{-\theta} 9 \cos 3\theta\, d\theta$

so $10 \int e^{-\theta} \cos 3\theta \, d\theta = e^{-\theta}(3 \sin 3\theta - \cos 3\theta) + C_1$ and

$I = \frac{1}{10} e^{-\theta}(3 \sin 3\theta - \cos 3\theta) + C$, where $C = C_1/10$

16. Let $u = y$, $dv = \cosh ay \Rightarrow du = dy$, $v = \frac{1}{a} \sinh ay$. Then

$\int y \cosh ay \, dy = \frac{1}{a}y \sinh ay - \frac{1}{a} \int \sinh ay \, dy$

$= (1/a)y \sinh ay - (1/a^2)\cosh ay + C$

18. Let $u = \ln t$, $dv = \sqrt{t} \, dt \Rightarrow du = dt/t$, $v = \frac{2}{3}t^{3/2}$. By (7.6),

$\int_1^4 \sqrt{t} \ln t \, dt = \frac{2}{3} t^{3/2} \ln t \Big]_1^4 - \frac{2}{3} \int_1^4 \sqrt{t} \, dt$

$= \frac{2}{3} \cdot 8 \cdot \ln 4 - 0 - \frac{2}{3} \cdot \frac{2}{3} t^{3/2} \Big]_1^4 = \frac{16}{3} \ln 4 - \frac{4}{9}(8-1) = \frac{32}{3} \ln 2 - \frac{28}{9}$

20. Let $u = x^2$, $dv = e^{-x}dx \Rightarrow du = 2x \, dx$, $v = -e^{-x}$. Then
$I = \int_0^1 x^2 e^{-x} \, dx = - x^2 e^{-x} \Big]_0^1 + \int_0^1 2xe^{-x} \, dx = -\frac{1}{e} + \int_0^1 2xe^{-x} \, dx$.

Use parts again with $u = 2x$, $dv = e^{-x}$. Then $I = -\frac{1}{e} - 2xe^{-x} \Big]_0^1$

$+ \int_0^1 2e^{-x} \, dx = -\frac{1}{e} - \frac{2}{e} - 2e^{-x} \Big]_0^1 = -\frac{3}{e} - \frac{2}{e} + 2 = 2 - \frac{5}{e}$

22. Let $u = x$, $dv = \csc^2 x \, dx \Rightarrow du = dx$, $v = -\cot x$. Then
$\int_{\pi/4}^{\pi/2} x \csc^2 x \, dx = - x \cot x \Big]_{\pi/4}^{\pi/2} + \int_{\pi/4}^{\pi/2} \cot x \, dx$

$= -\frac{\pi}{2} \cdot 0 + \frac{\pi}{4} \cdot 1 + \ln|\sin x| \Big]_{\pi/4}^{\pi/2} = \frac{\pi}{4} + \ln 1 - \ln(1/\sqrt{2}) = \frac{\pi}{4} + \frac{1}{2} \ln 2$

24. $I = \int \sin 2x \sin 4x \, dx = \int \sin 2x \, (2 \sin 2x \cos 2x)dx$
$= \int \sin^2 2x \, (2 \cos 2x)dx = \frac{1}{3}\sin^3 2x + C$

[Alternate method I: Integrate by parts twice as in Exercise 23.
This gives $I = (1/6)(- 2 \sin 2x \cos 4x + \cos 2x \sin 4x) + C$
Alternate method II: Write $\sin 2x \sin 4x = (1/2)(\cos 2x - \cos 6x)$
as in Section 7.2. This gives $I = (1/4)\sin 2x - (1/12)\sin 6x + C$.]

26. Substitute $t = x^2 \Rightarrow dt = 2x \, dx$. Then use parts: $u = t$,

$dv = e^t dt \Rightarrow du = dt$, $v = e^t$. Thus $\int x^3 e^{x^2} \, dx = \frac{1}{2} \int te^t \, dt$

$= \frac{1}{2}te^t - \frac{1}{2} \int e^t \, dt = \frac{1}{2}te^t - \frac{1}{2}e^t + C = \frac{1}{2}e^{x^2}(x^2-1) + C$

28. Let $u = x$, $dv = 5^x \, dx \Rightarrow du = dx$, $v = (5^x/\ln 5)dx$. Then
$\int x5^x \, dx = (1/\ln 5)(x5^x - \int 5^x \, dx)$
$= (1/\ln 5)(x5^x - 5^x/\ln 5) + C = (5^x/\ln 5)(x - 1/\ln 5) + C$

30. Let $w = \sqrt{x}$, so that $x = w^2$ and $dx = 2w \, dw$. Then use $u = 2w$,
$dv = e^w \, dw$. So $\int_1^4 e^{\sqrt{x}} \, dx = \int_1^2 e^w \, 2w \, dw = 2we^w \Big]_1^2 - 2 \int_1^2 e^w \, dw$
$= 4e^2 - 2e - 2(e^2 - e) = 2e^2$

32. Let $w = \ln x$, so that $x = e^w$ and $dx = e^w\, dw$. Then

$\int \sin(\ln x)dx = \int e^w \sin w\, dw = (1/2)e^w(\sin w - \cos w) + C$

[*by Example 4*] $= (1/2)x[\sin(\ln x) - \cos(\ln x)] + C$

34. Substitute $t = x^3 \Rightarrow dt = 3x^2\, dx$. Then use parts with $u = t$,

$dv = \cos t\, dt$. Thus $\int x^5 \cos(x^3)dx = \frac{1}{3} \int x^3 \cos(x^3)\cdot 3x^2 dx$

$= \frac{1}{3} \int t \cos t\, dt = \frac{1}{3} t \sin t - \frac{1}{3} \int \sin t\, dt$

$= \frac{1}{3} t \sin t + \frac{1}{3} \cos t + C = \frac{1}{3} x^3 \sin(x^3) + \frac{1}{3} \cos(x^3) + C$

36. Let $u = \tan^{-1}x$, $dv = x\, dx \Rightarrow du = dx/(1+x^2)$, $v = \frac{1}{2}x^2$. Then

$\int x \tan^{-1}x\, dx = \frac{1}{2}x^2 \tan^{-1}x - \frac{1}{2} \int \frac{x^2 dx}{1+x^2}$. But $\int \frac{x^2 dx}{1+x^2}$

$= \int \frac{(1+x^2) - 1}{1+x^2} dx = \int 1\, dx - \int \frac{dx}{1+x^2} = x - \tan^{-1}x + C_1$

$\Rightarrow \int x \tan^{-1}x\, dx = \frac{1}{2}x^2 \tan^{-1}x + \frac{1}{2} \tan^{-1}x - \frac{1}{2}x + C$

38. (a) Let $u = \cos^{n-1}x$, $dv = \cos x\, dx \Rightarrow$

$du = - (n-1)\cos^{n-2}x \sin x\, dx$, $v = \sin x$ in (7.2) to get

$\int \cos^n x\, dx = \cos^{n-1}x \sin x + (n-1) \int \cos^{n-2}x \sin^2 x\, dx$

$= \cos^{n-1}x \sin x + (n-1) \int \cos^{n-2}x (1 - \cos^2 x)dx$

$= \cos^{n-1}x \sin x + (n-1) \int \cos^{n-2}x\, dx - (n-1) \int \cos^n x\, dx$

Rearranging terms gives

$n \int \cos^n x\, dx = \cos^{n-1}x \sin x + (n-1) \int \cos^{n-2}x\, dx$ or

$\int \cos^n x\, dx = \frac{1}{n} \cos^{n-1}x \sin x + \frac{n-1}{n} \int \cos^{n-2}x\, dx$

(b) Take $n = 2$ in (a) to get

$\int \cos^2 x\, dx = \frac{1}{2} \cos x \sin x + \frac{1}{2} \int 1\, dx = \frac{x}{2} + \frac{\sin 2x}{4} + C$

(c) $\int \cos^4 x\, dx = \frac{1}{4} \cos^3 x \sin x + \frac{3}{4} \int \cos^2 x\, dx$

$= \frac{1}{4} \cos^3 x \sin x + \frac{3}{8}x + \frac{3}{16} \sin 2x + C$

40. For n even, let $m = n/2$. Then the formula becomes

$\int_0^{\pi/2} \sin^{2m}x\, dx = \frac{1\cdot 3\cdot 5\cdots(2m-1)}{2\cdot 4\cdot 6\cdots(2m)}\cdot\frac{\pi}{2}$ $(m{\geq}1)$. The formula holds for

$m = 1$ because $\int_0^{\pi/2} \sin^2 x\, dx = \frac{1}{2}\left[x - \frac{1}{2} \sin 2x\right]_0^{\pi/2} = \frac{\pi}{4} = \frac{1}{2}\cdot\frac{\pi}{2}$.

Assume it holds for some $m \geq 1$. Then by the reduction formula in

Ex. 6, $\int_0^{\pi/2} \sin^{2(m+1)}x\, dx = \frac{2m+1}{2m+2} \int_0^{\pi/2}\sin^{2m}x\, dx = \frac{1\cdot 3\cdot 5\cdots(2m+1)}{2\cdot 4\cdot 6\cdots(2m+2)}\cdot\frac{\pi}{2}$,

so the formula holds for $m+1$. By induction, the formula holds for

all $m \geq 1$, that is, for all even $n \geq 2$.

42. Let $u = x^n$, $dv = e^x dx$ ➔ $du = nx^{n-1}dx$, $v = e^x$. Then
$\int x^n e^x dx = x^n e^x - n \int x^{n-1} e^x dx$ by (7.2).

44. Let $u = \sec^{n-2} x$, $dv = \sec^2 x \, dx$ ➔ $du = (n-2)\sec^{n-3} x \sec x \tan x \, dx$,
$v = \tan x$. Then by (7.2), $\int \sec^n x \, dx$
$= \tan x \sec^{n-2} x - (n-2) \int \sec^{n-2} x \tan^2 x \, dx$
$= \tan x \sec^{n-2} x - (n-2) \int \sec^{n-2} x (\sec^2 x - 1) dx$
$= \tan x \sec^{n-2} x - (n-2) \int \sec^n x \, dx + (n-2) \int \sec^{n-2} x \, dx$, so
$(n-1) \int \sec^n x \, dx = \tan x \sec^{n-2} x + (n-2) \int \sec^{n-2} x \, dx$. If $n-1 \neq 0$,
then $\int \sec^n x \, dx = \dfrac{\tan x \sec^{n-2} x}{n-1} + \dfrac{n-2}{n-1} \int \sec^{n-2} x \, dx$

46. Take $n = 4$ in #42 to get $\int x^4 e^x dx = x^4 e^x - 4 \int x^3 e^x dx$
$= x^4 e^x - 4(x^3 - 3x^2 + 6x - 6)e^x + C$ [by #12] $= e^x(x^4 - 4x^3 + 12x^2 - 24x + 24) + C$
OR: Instead of using #12, apply #42 with $n = 3$, then $n = 2$, etc.

48. Let $u = x$, $dv = e^{-x}dx$ ➔ $du = dx$, $v = -e^{-x}$. Then area $= \int_0^5 xe^{-x} dx$
$= -xe^{-x}\Big]_0^5 + \int_0^5 e^{-x} dx = -5e^{-5} + 0 - e^{-x}\Big]_0^5 = -5e^{-5} - e^{-5} + 1 = 1 - 6e^{-5}$

50. The curves intersect when $(x-5)\ln x = 0$; i.e., when $x = 1$ or $x = 5$.
For $1 < x < 5$, we have $5 \ln x > x \ln x$ since $\ln x > 0$. Thus area $=$
$\int_1^5 \Big[5 \ln x - x \ln x\Big]dx$. Let $u = \ln x$, $dv = (5-x)dx$ ➔ $du = dx/x$,
$v = 5x - \frac{1}{2}x^2$. Then area $= (\ln x)\Big[5x - \frac{1}{2}x^2\Big]\Big]_1^5 - \int_1^5 (5x - \frac{1}{2}x^2) \frac{1}{x} dx$
$= (\ln 5)(25/2) - 0 - \int_1^5 \Big[5 - \frac{1}{2}x\Big]dx = \frac{25}{2} \ln 5 - \Big[5x - \frac{1}{4}x^2\Big]_1^5$
$= \frac{25}{2} \ln 5 - \Big[\Big[25 - \frac{25}{4}\Big] - \Big[5 - \frac{1}{4}\Big]\Big] = \frac{25}{2} \ln 5 - 14$

52. Suppose $f(0) = g(0) = 0$ and put $u = f(x)$, $dv = g''(x)dx$ ➔
$du = f'(x)dx$, $v = g'(x)$. Then $\int_0^a f(x)g''(x)dx$
$= f(x)g'(x)\Big]_0^a - \int_0^a f'(x)g'(x)dx = f(a)g'(a) - \int_0^a f'(x)g'(x)dx$.

Now put $U = f'(x)$, $dV = g'(x)dx$ ➔ $dU = f''(x)dx$ and $V = g(x)$, so
$\int_0^a f'(x)g'(x)dx = f'(x)g(x)\Big]_0^a - \int_0^a f''(x)g(x)dx$
$= f'(a)g(a) - \int_0^a f''(x)g(x)dx$. Combining the two results, we get
$\int_0^a f(x)g''(x)dx = f(a)g'(a) - f'(a)g(a) + \int_0^a f''(x)g(x)dx$

54. By # 53, $\int_a^b f(x)dx = bf(b) - af(a) - \int_a^b xf'(x)dx$. Now let
$y = f(x)$, so that $x = g(y)$ and $dy = f'(x)dx$. Then $\int_a^b xf'(x)dx$
$= \int_{f(a)}^{f(b)} g(y)dy$. The result follows.

56. Exercise 54 says that area of region ABFC

    = area of rectangle OBFE - area of rectangle OACD

      - area of region DCFE

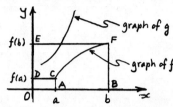

Section 7.2

Exercises 7.2

2. $\int_0^{\pi/2} \cos^2 x \, dx = \int_0^{\pi/2} \frac{1}{2}(1 + \cos 2x)dx = \left[\frac{x}{2} + \frac{\sin 2x}{4}\right]_0^{\pi/2} = \frac{\pi}{4}$

4. $\int \sin^3 x \, dx = \int (1 - \cos^2 x)\sin x \, dx = \int \sin x \, dx + \int \cos^2 x(-\sin x)dx$

    $= -\cos x + \frac{1}{3}\cos^3 x + C$ (Let $u = \cos x$ in $\int \cos^2 x(-\sin x)dx$.)

6. $\int \sin^4 x \cos^3 x \, dx = \int \sin^4 x(1 - \sin^2 x)\cos x \, dx = \int (u^4 - u^6)du$

    $[u = \sin x, \; du = \cos x \, dx] = \frac{u^5}{5} - \frac{u^7}{7} + C = \frac{1}{5}\sin^5 x - \frac{1}{7}\sin^7 x + C$

8. $\int_0^{\pi/2} \sin^2 x \cos^2 x \, dx = \frac{1}{4}\int_0^{\pi/2} \sin^2 2x \, dx = \frac{1}{8}\int_0^{\pi/2}(1 - \cos 4x)dx$

    $= \frac{1}{8}\left[x - \frac{\sin 4x}{4}\right]_0^{\pi/2} = \frac{1}{8}\left[\frac{\pi}{2}\right] = \frac{\pi}{16}$

10. $\int \sin(x + \frac{\pi}{6})\cos x \, dx = \int (\sin x \frac{\sqrt{3}}{2} + \cos x \cdot \frac{1}{2})\cos x \, dx$

    $= \frac{\sqrt{3}}{4}\int \sin 2x \, dx + \frac{1}{4}\int (1 + \cos 2x)dx = -\frac{\sqrt{3}}{8}\cos 2x + \frac{x}{4} + \frac{\sin 2x}{8} + C$

12. $\int \sin^6 x \, dx = \int \left[\frac{1}{2}(1 - \cos 2x)\right]^3 dx$

    $= \frac{1}{8}\int (1 - 3\cos 2x + 3\cos^2 2x - \cos^3 2x)dx$

    $= \frac{1}{8}\int [1 - 3\cos 2x + \frac{3}{2}(1 + \cos 4x) - (1 - \sin^2 2x)\cos 2x] \, dx$

    $= \frac{1}{8}\int \left\{\frac{5}{2} - 4\cos 2x + \frac{3}{2}\cos 4x + \sin^2 2x \cos 2x\right\} dx$

    $= \frac{1}{8}\left[\frac{5}{2}x - 2\sin 2x + \frac{3}{8}\sin 4x + \frac{1}{6}\sin^3 2x\right] + C$

14. $\int \sin^5 2x \cos^4 2x \, dx = \int \cos^4 2x(1 - \cos^2 2x)^2 \sin 2x \, dx$

    $= \int u^4(1 - u^2)^2(-\frac{1}{2}du)$ [*where* $u = \cos 2x$, $du = -2\sin 2x \, dx$]

$$= -\frac{1}{2} \int (u^4 - 2u^6 + u^8)\,du = -\frac{1}{2}\left[\frac{u^9}{9} - \frac{2u^7}{7} + \frac{u^5}{5}\right] + C$$

$$= -\frac{1}{2}\left[\frac{\cos^9 2x}{9} - \frac{2\cos^7 2x}{7} + \frac{\cos^5 2x}{5}\right] + C$$

16. $\int \sin^4 x \cos^4 x\,dx = \int (\frac{1}{2}\sin 2x)^4\,dx = \frac{1}{16}\int \sin^4 2x\,dx$

$$= \frac{1}{16}\int \left[\frac{1}{2}(1 - \cos 4x)\right]^2 dx = \frac{1}{64}\int (1 - 2\cos 4x + \cos^2 4x)\,dx$$

$$= \frac{1}{64}\left[x - \frac{\sin 4x}{2}\right] + \frac{1}{128}\int (1 + \cos 8x)\,dx = \frac{1}{64}(x - \frac{1}{2}\sin 4x)$$

$$+ \frac{1}{128}(x + \frac{1}{8}\sin 8x) + C = \frac{3x}{128} - \frac{\sin 4x}{128} + \frac{\sin 8x}{1024} + C$$

18. $\int \frac{\cos^3 x}{\sqrt{\sin x}}\,dx = \int \frac{(1-u^2)\,du}{u^{1/2}}$ *[where $u = \sin x$, $du = \cos x\,dx$]*

$$= \int (u^{-1/2} - u^{3/2})\,du = 2u^{1/2} - \frac{2}{5}u^{5/2} + C = 2u^{1/2}(1 - \frac{1}{5}u^2) + C$$

$$= 2(1 - \frac{1}{5}\sin^2 x)\sqrt{\sin x} + C$$

20. Let $u = x^2$, $du = 2x\,dx$. Then $\int x\sin^3(x^2)\,dx = \int \sin^3 u \cdot \frac{1}{2}\,du$

$$= \frac{1}{2}(-\cos u + \frac{1}{3}\cos^3 u) + C \;[by\; \#4] = -\frac{1}{2}\cos(x^2) + \frac{1}{6}\cos^3(x^2) + C$$

22. $\int \cot^5 x \sin^2 x\,dx = \int \frac{\cos^5 x}{\sin^3 x}\,dx = \int \frac{(1-u^2)^2}{u^3}\,du$ *[where $u = \sin x$,*

$du = \cos x\,dx$] $\;= \int (u^{-3} - 2u^{-1} + u)\,du = -\frac{1}{2}u^{-2} - 2\ln|u| + \frac{1}{2}u^2 + C$

$$= \frac{1}{2}\sin^2 x - \frac{1}{2}\csc^2 x - 2\ln|\sin x| + C$$

24. $\int \frac{dx}{1 - \sin x} = \int \frac{1 + \sin x}{1 - \sin^2 x}\,dx = \int \frac{1 + \sin x}{\cos^2 x}\,dx$

$$= \int (\sec^2 x + \sec x \tan x)\,dx = \tan x + \sec x + C$$

26. $\int \tan^4 x\,dx = \int \tan^2 x(\sec^2 x - 1)\,dx = \int \tan^2 x \sec^2 x\,dx - \int \tan^2 x\,dx$

$= \frac{1}{3}\tan^3 x - \tan x + x + C$ [Set $u = \tan x$ in the first integral and

use #25 for the second.]

28. $\int \sec^6 x\,dx = \int (\tan^2 x + 1)^2 \sec^2 x\,dx$

$$= \int \tan^4 x \sec^2 x\,dx + 2\int \tan^2 x \sec^2 x\,dx + \int \sec^2 x\,dx$$

$$= \frac{1}{5}\tan^5 x + \frac{2}{3}\tan^3 x + \tan x + C$$

30. $\int_0^{\pi/4} \tan^2 x \sec^4 x\,dx = \int_0^1 u^2(u^2+1)\,du$ *[where $u = \tan x$]*

$$= \int_0^1 (u^4 + u^2)\,du = \left[\frac{u^5}{5} + \frac{u^3}{3}\right]_0^1 = \frac{1}{5} + \frac{1}{3} = \frac{8}{15}$$

32. $\int \tan^3 x \sec^3 x\,dx = \int \sec^2 x \tan^2 x \sec x \tan x\,dx = \int u^2(u^2-1)\,du$

[where $u = \sec x$, $du = \sec x \tan x\,dx$]

$$= \int (u^4 - u^2)\,du = \frac{1}{5}u^5 - \frac{1}{3}u^3 + C = \frac{1}{5}\sec^5 x - \frac{1}{3}\sec^3 x + C$$

34. $\int \tan^6 x \, dx = \int \tan^4 x \, (\sec^2 x - 1)dx = \int \tan^4 x \, \sec^2 x \, dx - \int \tan^4 x \, dx$

$= (1/5) \tan^5 x - \int \tan^2 x \, (\sec^2 x - 1)dx$

$= (1/5) \tan^5 x - \int \tan^2 x \, \sec^2 x \, dx + \int (\sec^2 x - 1)dx$

$= (1/5) \tan^5 x - (1/3) \tan^3 x + \tan x - x + C$

36. $\int_0^{\pi/3} \tan^5 x \, \sec^3 x \, dx = \int_0^{\pi/3} (\sec^2 x - 1)^2 \sec^2 x \, \sec x \tan x \, dx$

$= \int_1^2 (u^2 - 1)^2 u^2 \, du$ [*where* $u = \sec x$, $du = \sec x \tan x \, dx$]

$= \int_1^2 (u^6 - 2u^4 + u^2)du = \left[\dfrac{u^7}{7} - \dfrac{2u^5}{5} + \dfrac{u^3}{3}\right]_1^2 = \left(\dfrac{128}{7} - \dfrac{64}{5} + \dfrac{8}{3}\right) - \left(\dfrac{1}{7} - \dfrac{2}{5} + \dfrac{1}{3}\right) = \dfrac{848}{105}$

38. $\int \tan^3 x \, \sec^6 x \, dx = \int (\sec^2 x - 1) \sec^5 x \cdot \sec x \tan x \, dx = \int (u^2 - 1)u^5 \, du$

[*where* $u = \sec x$] $= \int (u^7 - u^5)du = \dfrac{1}{8}u^8 - \dfrac{1}{6}u^6 + C = \dfrac{1}{8} \sec^8 x - \dfrac{1}{6} \sec^6 x + C$

OR: $\int \tan^3 x \, \sec^6 x \, dx = \int \tan^3 x \, (\tan^2 x + 1)^2 \sec^2 x \, dx$

$= \int v^3 (v^2 + 1)^2 dv$ [*where* $v = \tan x$] $= \int (v^7 + 2v^5 + v^3)dv$

$= \dfrac{1}{8}v^8 + \dfrac{1}{3}v^6 + \dfrac{1}{4}v^4 + C_1 = \dfrac{1}{8} \tan^2 x + \dfrac{1}{3} \tan^6 x + \dfrac{1}{4} \tan^4 x + C_1$

40. $\int \tan^2 x \, \sec x \, dx = \int (\sec^2 x - 1) \sec x \, dx = \int \sec^3 x \, dx - \int \sec x \, dx$

$= (1/2) (\sec x \tan x + \ln|\sec x + \tan x|) - \ln|\sec x + \tan x| + C$

[*by Examples 9 and 8 respectively*]

$= (1/2)(\sec x \tan x - \ln|\sec x + \tan x|) + C$

42. $\int_{\pi/4}^{\pi/2} \cot^3 x \, dx = \int_{\pi/4}^{\pi/2} \cot x \, (\csc^2 x - 1)dx$

$= \int_{\pi/4}^{\pi/2} \cot x \, \csc^2 x \, dx - \int_{\pi/4}^{\pi/2} \dfrac{\cos x}{\sin x} dx = \left[-\dfrac{1}{2} \cot^2 x - \ln|\sin x|\right]_{\pi/4}^{\pi/2}$

$= (0 - \ln 1) - \left[-\dfrac{1}{2} - \ln(1/\sqrt{2})\right] = \dfrac{1}{2} + \ln(1/\sqrt{2}) = \dfrac{1 - \ln 2}{2}$

44. $\int \cot^3 x \, \csc^4 x \, dx = \int \cot^3 x \, (\cot^2 x + 1) \csc^2 x \, dx$

$= \int u^3 (u^2 + 1)(-du)$ [*where* $u = \cot x$, $du = -\csc^2 x \, dx$]

$= -\dfrac{1}{6}u^6 - \dfrac{1}{4}u^4 + C = -\dfrac{1}{6} \cot^6 x - \dfrac{1}{4} \cot^4 x + C$

46. Let $u = \csc x$, $dv = \csc^2 x \, dx$. Then $du = -\csc x \cot x$, $v = -\cot x$

$\Rightarrow \int \csc^3 x \, dx = -\csc x \cot x - \int \csc x \cot^2 x \, dx = -\csc x \cot x -$

$\int \csc x \, (\csc^2 x - 1)dx = -\csc x \cot x + \int \csc x \, dx - \int \csc^3 x \, dx$

Solving for $\int \csc^3 x \, dx$ and using #45, we get

$\int \csc^3 x \, dx = -(1/2) \csc x \cot x + (1/2) \int \csc x \, dx$

$= -(1/2) \csc x \cot x + (1/2) \ln|\csc x - \cot x| + C$

48. $\int \dfrac{dx}{\sin^4 x} = \int \csc^4 x \, dx = \int (\cot^2 x + 1) \csc^2 x \, dx = \int (u^2 + 1)(-du)$

[*where* $u = \cot x$] $= -(1/3)u^3 - u + C = -(1/3) \cot^3 x - \cot x + C$

50. $\int \sin 3x \cos x \, dx = \int (1/2)[\sin(3x+x) + \sin(3x-x)]dx$

$= \frac{1}{2} \int (\sin 4x + \sin 2x)dx = -\frac{1}{8} \cos 4x - \frac{1}{4} \cos 2x + C$

52. $\int \sin 3x \sin 6x \, dx = \int (1/2)[\cos(3x-6x) - \cos(3x+6x)]dx$

$= \frac{1}{2} \int (\cos 3x - \cos 9x)dx = \frac{1}{6} \sin 3x - \frac{1}{18} \sin 9x + C$

54. $\int \cos x \cos 2x \cos 3x \, dx = \int \cos x \cdot \frac{1}{2}\Big[\cos(2x-3x) + \cos(2x+3x)\Big]dx$

$= \frac{1}{2} \int \cos^2 x \, dx + \frac{1}{2} \int \cos x \cos 5x \, dx = \frac{1}{4} \int (1 + \cos 2x)dx$

$+ \frac{1}{2} \int \frac{1}{2}\Big[\cos(x-5x) + \cos(x+5x)\Big]dx = \frac{1}{4}x + \frac{1}{8} \sin 2x +$

$\frac{1}{4} \int (\cos 4x + \cos 6x)dx = \frac{1}{4}x + \frac{1}{8} \sin 2x + \frac{1}{16} \sin 4x + \frac{1}{24} \sin 6x + C$

56. $\int \frac{\cos x + \sin x}{\sin 2x} \, dx = \frac{1}{2} \int \frac{\cos x + \sin x}{\sin x \cos x} \, dx = \frac{1}{2} \int (\csc x + \sec x)dx$

$= \frac{1}{2}\Big[\ln|\csc x - \cot x| + \ln|\sec x + \tan x|\Big] + C$

58. (a) Let $u = \cos x$. Then $du = -\sin x \, dx \Rightarrow \int \sin x \cos x \, dx$

$= \int u(-du) = -\frac{1}{2}u^2 + C = -\frac{1}{2} \cos^2 x + C_1$

(b) Let $u = \sin x$. Then $du = \cos x \, dx \Rightarrow \int \sin x \cos x \, dx$

$= \int u \, du = \frac{1}{2}u^2 + C = \frac{1}{2} \sin^2 x + C_2$

(c) $\int \sin x \cos x \, dx = \int \frac{1}{2} \sin 2x \, dx = -\frac{1}{4} \cos 2x + C_3$

(d) Let $u = \sin x$, $dv = \cos x \, dx$. Then $du = \cos x \, dx$, $v = \sin x$
so $\int \sin x \cos x \, dx = \sin^2 x - \int \sin x \cos dx$ by (7.2), so
$\int \sin x \cos x \, dx = \frac{1}{2} \sin^2 x + C_4$

The answers differ from one another by constants. Since
$\cos 2x = 1 - 2 \sin^2 x = 2 \cos^2 x - 1$, we find that
$-\frac{1}{4} \cos 2x = \frac{1}{2} \sin^2 x - \frac{1}{4} = -\frac{1}{2} \cos^2 x + \frac{1}{4}$.

60. $\sin x > 0$ for $0 < x < \pi/2$, so the sign of $2 \sin^2 x - \sin x$ [which
equals $2 \sin x(\sin x - \frac{1}{2})$] is the same as that of $\sin x - \frac{1}{2}$. Thus
$2 \sin^2 x - \sin x$ is positive on $(\pi/6, \pi/2)$ and negative on $(0, \pi/6)$.
The desired area is
$\int_0^{\pi/6} (\sin x - 2 \sin^2 x)dx + \int_{\pi/6}^{\pi/2} (2 \sin^2 x - \sin x)dx$

$= \int_0^{\pi/6} (\sin x - 1 + \cos 2x)dx + \int_{\pi/6}^{\pi/2} (1 - \cos 2x - \sin x)dx$

$= \Big[-\cos x - x + \frac{1}{2} \sin 2x\Big]_0^{\pi/6} + \Big[x - \frac{1}{2} \sin 2x + \cos x\Big]_{\pi/6}^{\pi/2}$

$= -\frac{\sqrt{3}}{2} - \frac{\pi}{6} + \frac{\sqrt{3}}{4} - (-1) + \frac{\pi}{2} - (\frac{\pi}{6} - \frac{\sqrt{3}}{4} + \frac{\sqrt{3}}{2}) = 1 + \frac{\pi}{6} - \frac{\sqrt{3}}{2}$

62. Just note that the integrand is odd $[f(-x) = -f(x)]$.   OR:

Calculate $\int_{-\pi}^{\pi} \sin mx \cos nx\ dx = \int_{-\pi}^{\pi} \frac{1}{2}[\sin(m-n)x + \sin(m+n)x]dx$

$= \frac{1}{2}\left[-\frac{1}{m-n}\cos(m-n)x - \frac{1}{m+n}\cos(m+n)x\right]_{-\pi}^{\pi} = 0$

(If $m = n$, the first term in each set of brackets is zero.)

64. $\int_{-\pi}^{\pi} \cos mx \cos nx\ dx = \int_{-\pi}^{\pi} \frac{1}{2}[\cos(m-n)x + \cos(m+n)x]dx$.   If $m \neq n$,

this $= \frac{1}{2}\left[\frac{1}{m-n}\sin(m-n)x + \frac{1}{m+n}\sin(m+n)x\right]_{-\pi}^{\pi} = 0$.   If $m = n$, we get

$\int_{-\pi}^{\pi} \frac{1}{2}[1 + \cos(m+n)x]dx = \frac{x}{2}\Big]_{-\pi}^{\pi} + \frac{1}{2(m+n)}\sin(m+n)x\Big]_{-\pi}^{\pi} = \pi + 0 = \pi$

Section 7.3

Exercises 7.3

2. Let $x = 2\sin\theta$, where $-\pi/2 \leq \theta \leq \pi/2$. Then $dx = 2\cos\theta\ d\theta$ and

$\sqrt{4-x^2} = |2\cos\theta| = 2\cos\theta$, so $\int_0^2 x^3\sqrt{4-x^2}\ dx$

$= \int_0^{\pi/2} 8\sin^3\theta\ 2\cos\theta\ 2\cos\theta\ d\theta$

$= 32\int_0^{\pi/2}\cos^2\theta\ (1-\cos^2\theta)\sin\theta\ d\theta = 32\int_1^0 u^2(1-u^2)(-du)$ [where

$u = \cos\theta$] $= 32\int_0^1(u^2-u^4)du = 32\left[\frac{1}{3}u^3 - \frac{1}{5}u^5\right]_0^1 = 32\left[\frac{1}{3} - \frac{1}{5}\right] = \frac{64}{15}$

4. Let $u = 4-x^2$. Then $du = -2x\ dx \Rightarrow \int x\sqrt{4-x^2}\ dx = -(1/2)\int\sqrt{u}\ du$

$= -\frac{1}{2}\cdot\frac{2}{3}u^{3/2} + C = -\frac{1}{3}(4-x^2)^{3/2} + C$

6. Let $x = 2\tan\theta$, where $-\pi/2 < \theta < \pi/2$. Then $dx = 2\sec^2\theta\ d\theta$ and

$\sqrt{x^2+4} = 2\sec\theta$, so $\int_0^2 \frac{x^3}{\sqrt{x^2+4}}\ dx = \int_0^{\pi/4} \frac{8\tan^3\theta}{2\sec\theta}\ 2\sec^2\theta\ d\theta$

$= 8\int_0^{\pi/4}(\sec^2\theta - 1)\sec\theta\tan\theta\ d\theta = 8\left(\frac{1}{3}\sec^3\theta - \sec\theta\right)\Big]_0^{\pi/4}$

$= 8\left[\frac{1}{3}\cdot2\sqrt{2} - \sqrt{2}\right] - 8\left[\frac{1}{3} - 1\right] = \frac{8}{3}(2-\sqrt{2})$

8. Let $x = \tan\theta$, where $\pi/2 < \theta < \pi/2$. Then $dx = \sec^2\theta\ d\theta$ and

$\sqrt{x^2+1} = \sec\theta$, so $\int\sqrt{x^2+1}\ dx = \int\sec\theta\ \sec^2\theta\ d\theta = \int\sec^3\theta\ d\theta$

$= \frac{1}{2}(\sec\theta\tan\theta + \ln|\sec\theta + \tan\theta|) + C$ [by Example 7.2.9]

$= \frac{1}{2}\left\{x\sqrt{x^2+1} + \ln\left[x+\sqrt{x^2+1}\right]\right\} + C.$ [We can drop the

absolute value sign because $\sqrt{x^2+1} > |x|$ for all x.]

10. Let $x = a\sec\theta$, where $0 \le \theta < \pi/2$ or $\pi \le \theta < 3\pi/2$. Then

$dx = a\sec\theta\tan\theta\,d\theta$ and $\sqrt{x^2-a^2} = a\tan\theta$.

$\displaystyle\int \frac{\sqrt{x^2-a^2}}{x^4}\,dx = \int \frac{a\tan\theta}{a^4\sec^4\theta}\, a\sec\theta\tan\theta\,d\theta = \frac{1}{a^2}\int\sin^2\theta\cos\theta\,d\theta$

$\displaystyle= \frac{1}{3a^2}\sin^3\theta + C = \frac{(x^2-a^2)^{3/2}}{3a^2x^3} + C$

12. Let $4x = 3\sec\theta$, where $0 \le \theta < \pi/2$ or $\pi \le \theta < 3\pi/2$. Then

$dx = (3/4)\sec\theta\tan\theta\,d\theta$ and $\sqrt{16x^2-9} = 3\tan\theta$, so

$\displaystyle\int \frac{dx}{x^2\sqrt{16x^2-9}} = \int \frac{(3/4)\sec\theta\tan\theta\,d\theta}{(3/4)^2\sec^2\theta\,3\tan\theta} = \frac{4}{9}\int\cos\theta\,d\theta = \frac{4}{9}\sin\theta + C$

$\displaystyle= \frac{4}{9}\frac{\sqrt{16x^2-9}}{4x} + C = \frac{\sqrt{16x^2-9}}{9x} + C$

14. Let $x = \sqrt{5}\sin\theta$, where $-\pi/2 \le \theta \le \pi/2$. Then $\displaystyle\int \frac{x^2}{\sqrt{5-x^2}}\,dx$

$\displaystyle= \int \frac{5\sin^2\theta}{\sqrt{5}\cos\theta}\sqrt{5}\cos\theta\,d\theta = 5\int\sin^2\theta\,d\theta = \frac{5}{2}\int(1-\cos 2\theta)$

$\displaystyle= \frac{5}{2}(\theta - \frac{1}{2}\sin 2\theta) + C = \frac{5}{2}(\theta - \sin\theta\cos\theta) + C$

$\displaystyle= \frac{5}{2}\left[\sin^{-1}\left[\frac{x}{\sqrt{5}}\right] - \frac{x}{\sqrt{5}}\frac{\sqrt{5-x^2}}{\sqrt{5}}\right] + C = \frac{5}{2}\sin^{-1}\left[\frac{x}{\sqrt{5}}\right] - \frac{1}{2}x\sqrt{5-x^2} + C$

16. Let $u = x^2+4$, $du = 2x\,dx$. Then $\displaystyle\int \frac{x\,dx}{(x^2+4)^{5/2}} = \frac{1}{2}\int u^{-5/2}\,du$

$\displaystyle= \frac{1}{2}(-\frac{2}{3})u^{-3/2} + C = (-1/3)u^{-3/2} + C = (-1/3)(x^2+4)^{-3/2} + C$

18. Let $x = 3\sin\theta$, where $-\pi/2 \le \theta \le \pi/2$. Then

$\displaystyle\int_0^3 x^2\sqrt{9-x^2}\,dx = \int_0^{\pi/2} 9\sin^2\theta\,3\cos\theta\,3\cos\theta\,d\theta = \frac{81}{4}\int_0^{\pi/2}\sin^2 2\theta\,d\theta$

$\displaystyle= \frac{81}{8}\int_0^{\pi/2}(1-\cos 4\theta)d\theta = \frac{81}{8}\left[\theta - \frac{1}{4}\sin 4\theta\right]_0^{\pi/2} = \frac{81\pi}{16}$

20. Let $2x = 5\sec\theta$, where $0 \le \theta < \pi/2$ or $\pi \le \theta < 3\pi/2$. Then

$\displaystyle\int \frac{dx}{(4x^2-25)^{3/2}} = \int \frac{(5/2)\sec\theta\tan\theta\,d\theta}{125\tan^3\theta} = \frac{1}{50}\int \frac{\cos\theta}{\sin^2\theta}\,d\theta$

$- 1/(50\sin\theta) + C = (-1/50)(2x/\sqrt{4x^2-25}) + C$

$\displaystyle= -\frac{x}{25\sqrt{4x^2-25}} + C$

218

22. Let $x = \tan\theta$, where $-\pi/2 < \theta < \pi/2$. Then $\displaystyle\int \frac{dx}{(1+x^2)^2}$

$$= \int \frac{\sec^2\theta \, d\theta}{\sec^4\theta} = \int \cos^2\theta \, d\theta = \frac{1}{2}\int (1 + \cos 2\theta)d\theta$$

$$= \frac{1}{2}\left[\theta + \frac{1}{2}\sin 2\theta\right] + C = \frac{1}{2}(\theta + \sin\theta\cos\theta) + C$$

$$= (1/2)[\tan^{-1}x + x/(1+x^2)] + C$$

24. $x^2+4x+8 = (x+2)^2+4$. Let $u = x+2$, $du = dx$. Then let $u = 2\tan\theta$.

$$\int \frac{dx}{\sqrt{x^2+4x+8}} = \int \frac{du}{\sqrt{u^2+4}} = \int \frac{2\sec^2\theta \, d\theta}{2\sec\theta} = \int \sec\theta \, d\theta$$

$$= \ln|\sec\theta + \tan\theta| + C_1 = \ln\left[\frac{\sqrt{u^2+4} + u}{2}\right] + C_1$$

$$= \ln\left[\sqrt{u^2+4} + u\right] + C = \ln\left[\sqrt{x^2+4x+8} + x + 2\right] + C$$

26. $4x-x^2 = -(x^2-4x+4)+4 = 4-(x-2)^2$, so let $u = x-2$. Then $x = u+2$ and

$dx = du$, so $\displaystyle\int \frac{x^2 \, dx}{\sqrt{4x-x^2}} = \int \frac{(u+2)^2 du}{\sqrt{4-u^2}} = \int \frac{(2\sin\theta + 2)^2}{2\cos\theta} 2\cos\theta \, d\theta =$

$[u = 2\sin\theta]$

$$4\int(\sin^2\theta + 2\sin\theta + 1)d\theta = 2\int(1 - \cos 2\theta)d\theta + 8\int \sin\theta \, d\theta + 4\int d\theta$$

$$= 2\theta - \sin 2\theta - 8\cos\theta + 4\theta + C = 6\theta - 8\cos\theta - 2\sin\theta\cos\theta + C$$

$$= 6\sin^{-1}(u/2) - 4\sqrt{4-u^2} - \frac{1}{2}u\sqrt{4-u^2} + C$$

$$= 6\sin^{-1}\left[\frac{x-2}{2}\right] - 4\sqrt{4x-x^2} - \left[\frac{x-2}{2}\right]\sqrt{4x-x^2} + C$$

28. $5-4x-x^2 = -(x^2+4x+4)+9 = 9-(x+2)^2$. Let $u = x+2$, $du = dx$. Then

$$\int \frac{dx}{(5-4x-x^2)^{5/2}} = \int \frac{du}{(9-u^2)^{5/2}} = \int \frac{3\cos\theta \, d\theta}{(3\cos\theta)^5}$$

[*where $u = 3\sin\theta$, $du = 3\cos\theta \, d\theta$, and $\sqrt{9-u^2} = 3\cos\theta$*]

$$= \frac{1}{81}\int \sec^4\theta \, d\theta = \frac{1}{81}\int(\tan^2\theta + 1)\sec^2\theta \, d\theta$$

$$= \frac{1}{81}\left[\frac{1}{3}\tan^3\theta + \tan\theta\right] + C = \frac{1}{243}\left[u^3/(9-u^2)^{3/2} + 3u/\sqrt{9-u^2}\right] + C$$

$$= (1/243)\left[(x+2)^3/(5-4x-x^2)^{3/2} + 3(x+2)/\sqrt{5-4x-x^2}\right] + C$$

30. Let $u = e^t$. Then $t = \ln u$ and $dt = du/u$. Hence

$$I = \int \sqrt{e^{2t}-9} \, dt = \int \frac{\sqrt{u^2-9}}{u} \, du. \text{ Now let } u = 3\sec\theta, \text{ where}$$

$0 \le \theta < \pi/2$ or $\pi \le \theta < 3\pi/2$. Then $\sqrt{u^2-9} = 3\tan\theta$ and

$du = 3\sec\theta\tan\theta \, d\theta$, so $I = \displaystyle\int \frac{3\tan\theta}{3\sec\theta} 3\sec\theta\tan\theta \, d\theta$

$= 3 \int \tan^2\theta \, d\theta = 3 \int (\sec^2\theta - 1) d\theta = 3(\tan\theta - \theta) + C$

$= 3\left[\sqrt{u^2-9}/3 - \sec^{-1}(u/3)\right] + C = \sqrt{e^{2t}-9} - 3\sec^{-1}(e^t/3) + C$

32. (a) Let $x = a\tan\theta$, $-\pi/2 < \theta < \pi/2$. Then $I = \int \dfrac{x^2}{(x^2+a^2)^{3/2}} dx$

$\displaystyle = \int \frac{a^2 \tan^2\theta}{a^3 \sec^3\theta} \, a\sec^2\theta \, d\theta = \int \frac{\tan^2\theta}{\sec\theta} d\theta = \int \frac{\sec^2\theta - 1}{\sec\theta} d\theta$

$\displaystyle = \int (\sec\theta - \cos\theta) d\theta = \ln|\sec\theta + \tan\theta| - \sin\theta + C$

$\displaystyle = \ln\left|\frac{\sqrt{x^2+a^2}}{a} + \frac{x}{a}\right| - \frac{x}{\sqrt{x^2+a^2}} + C = \ln\left[x+\sqrt{x^2+a^2}\right] - \frac{x}{\sqrt{x^2+a^2}} + C_1$

(b) Let $x = a\sinh t$. Then $I = \displaystyle\int \frac{a^2 \sinh^2 t}{a^3 \cosh^3 t} \, a\cosh t \, dt$

$\displaystyle = \int \tanh^2 t \, dt = \int (1 - \text{sech}^2 t) dt = t - \tanh t + C$

$= \sinh^{-1}(x/a) - x/\sqrt{a^2+x^2} + C$

34. $9x^2 - 4y^2 = 36 \Rightarrow y = \pm\frac{3}{2}\sqrt{x^2-4} \Rightarrow \text{area} = 2\int_2^3 \frac{3}{2}\sqrt{x^2-4} \, dx$

$= 3\int_2^3 \sqrt{x^2-4} \, dx = 3\int_0^\alpha 2\tan\theta \, 2\sec\theta\tan\theta \, d\theta$ *[where $x = 2\sec\theta$,*

$dx = 2\sec\theta\tan\theta \, d\theta$, $\alpha = \sec^{-1}(3/2)$] $= 12\int_0^\alpha (\sec^2\theta - 1)\sec\theta \, d\theta$

$= 12\int_0^\alpha (\sec^3\theta - \sec\theta) d\theta = 12\left[\frac{1}{2}(\sec\theta\tan\theta + \ln|\sec\theta + \tan\theta|)\right.$

$\left. - \ln|\sec\theta + \tan\theta|\right]_0^\alpha = 6\left[\sec\theta\tan\theta - \ln|\sec\theta + \tan\theta|\right]_0^\alpha$

$= 6\left[\frac{3\sqrt{5}}{4} - \ln(\frac{3}{2} + \frac{\sqrt{5}}{2})\right] = \frac{9\sqrt{5}}{2} - 6\ln\left[\frac{3+\sqrt{5}}{2}\right]$

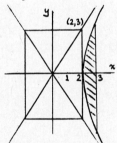

Exercises 7.4

2. $\dfrac{x}{(x+3)(2x-5)} = \dfrac{A}{x+3} + \dfrac{B}{2x-5}$

4. $\dfrac{7}{(2x-3)(x+4)} = \dfrac{A}{2x-3} + \dfrac{B}{x+4}$

6. $\dfrac{x^3-x^2}{(x-6)(5x+3)^3} = \dfrac{A}{x-6} + \dfrac{B}{5x+3} + \dfrac{C}{(5x+3)^2} + \dfrac{D}{(5x+3)^3}$

8. $\dfrac{1+x+x^2}{(x+1)(x+2)^2(x+3)^3} = \dfrac{A}{x+1} + \dfrac{B}{x+2} + \dfrac{C}{(x+2)^2} + \dfrac{D}{x+3} + \dfrac{E}{(x+3)^2} + \dfrac{F}{(x+3)^3}$

10. $\dfrac{x^4+x^3-x^2-x+1}{x^3-x} = x + 1 + \dfrac{1}{x(x+1)(x-1)} = x + 1 + \dfrac{A}{x} + \dfrac{B}{x+1} + \dfrac{C}{x-1}$

12. $\dfrac{x^3-4x^2+2}{(x^2+1)(x^2+2)} = \dfrac{Ax+B}{x^2+1} + \dfrac{Cx+D}{x^2+2}$

14. $\dfrac{1+16x}{(2x-3)(x+5)^2(x^2+x+1)} = \dfrac{A}{2x-3} + \dfrac{B}{x+5} + \dfrac{C}{(x+5)^2} + \dfrac{Dx+E}{x^2+x+1}$

16. $\dfrac{19x}{(x-1)^3(4x^2+5x+3)^2} = \dfrac{A}{x-1} + \dfrac{B}{(x-1)^2} + \dfrac{C}{(x-1)^3} + \dfrac{Dx+E}{4x^2+5x+3} + \dfrac{Fx+G}{(4x^2+5x+3)^2}$

18. $\dfrac{1}{x^6-x^3} = \dfrac{1}{x^3(x^3-1)} = \dfrac{1}{x^3(x-1)(x^2+x+1)} = \dfrac{A}{x} + \dfrac{B}{x^2} + \dfrac{C}{x^3} + \dfrac{D}{x-1} + \dfrac{Ex+F}{x^2+x+1}$

20. $\displaystyle\int \dfrac{x}{x-5}\,dx = \int \dfrac{(x-5)+5}{x-5}\,dx = \int \left(1 + \dfrac{5}{x-5}\right)dx = x + 5\ln|x-5| + C$

22. $\dfrac{1}{(x+1)(x-2)} = \dfrac{A}{x+1} + \dfrac{B}{x-2} \Rightarrow 1 = A(x-2) + B(x+1)$. Taking $x = -1$,

then $x = 2$ gives $A = -1/3$, $B = 1/3$. Hence

$\displaystyle\int_3^7 \dfrac{dx}{(x+1)(x-2)} = \dfrac{1}{3}\int_3^7 \left[\dfrac{1}{x-2} - \dfrac{1}{x+1}\right]dx = \dfrac{1}{3}\left[\ln|x-2| - \ln|x+1|\right]_3^7$

$= \dfrac{1}{3}(\ln 5 - \ln 8 - \ln 1 + \ln 4) = \dfrac{1}{3}\ln 2.5$

24. If $a \neq b$, $\dfrac{1}{(x+a)(x+b)} = \dfrac{1}{b-a}\left[\dfrac{1}{x+a} - \dfrac{1}{x+b}\right]$, so $\displaystyle\int \dfrac{dx}{(x+a)(x+b)}$

$= \dfrac{1}{b-a}(\ln|x+a| - \ln|x+b|) + C = \dfrac{1}{b-a}\ln\left|\dfrac{x+a}{x+b}\right| + C$

If $a = b$, $\displaystyle\int \dfrac{dx}{(x+a)^2} = -\dfrac{1}{x+a} + C$

26. $\dfrac{x^3+x^2-12x+1}{x^2+x-12} = x + \dfrac{1}{x^2+x-12} = x + \dfrac{1}{(x-3)(x+4)} = x + \dfrac{1}{7}\left[\dfrac{1}{x-3} - \dfrac{1}{x+4}\right]$

$\displaystyle\int_0^2 \dfrac{x^3+x^2-12x+1}{x^2+x-12}\,dx = \left[\dfrac{x^2}{2} + \dfrac{1}{7}(\ln|x-3| - \ln|x+4|)\right]_0^2 = 2 + \dfrac{1}{7}\ln\dfrac{2}{9}$

28. $\dfrac{1}{(x-1)(x-2)(x-3)} = \dfrac{A}{x-1} + \dfrac{B}{x-2} + \dfrac{C}{x-3}$. Multiply by $x-1$ to get

$\dfrac{1}{(x-2)(x-3)} = A + \dfrac{B(x-1)}{x-2} + \dfrac{C(x-1)}{x-3}$; then set $x = 1$ to get $A = 1/2$.

Similarly, multiply by $x-2$ and set $x = 2$ to get $B = -1$; then

multiply by $x-3$ and set $x = 3$ to get $C = 1/2$.

Now $\int \frac{dx}{(x-1)(x-2)(x-3)} = \int \left[\frac{1/2}{x-1} - \frac{1}{x-2} + \frac{1/2}{x-3}\right]dx$

$= \frac{1}{2} \ln|x-1| - \ln|x-2| + \frac{1}{2} \ln|x-3| + C = \frac{1}{2} \ln \frac{|(x-1)(x-3)|}{(x-2)^2} + C$

30. $\frac{3x^2-6x+2}{2x^3-3x^2+x} = \frac{A}{x} + \frac{B}{x-1} + \frac{C}{2x-1}$. Multiply by x to get $\frac{3x^2-6x+2}{(x-1)(2x-1)}$

$= A + x\left[\frac{B}{x-1} + \frac{C}{2x-1}\right]$. Set x = 0 to get A = 2. Similarly, find

B = -1 and C = 1. Then $\int \frac{3x^2-6x+2}{2x^3-3x^2+x} dx = \int\left[\frac{2}{x} - \frac{1}{x-1} + \frac{1}{2x-1}\right]dx$

$= 2 \ln|x| - \ln|x-1| + (1/2) \ln|2x-1| + C$

32. $\frac{x}{x^2+4x+4} = \frac{A}{x+2} + \frac{B}{(x+2)^2} \Rightarrow x = A(x+2) + B$. Set x = -2 to get

B = -2 and equate coefficients of x to get A = 1.
Then $\int_0^1 \frac{x\, dx}{x^2+4x+4} = \int_0^1 \left[\frac{1}{x+2} - \frac{2}{(x+2)^2}\right]dx = \left[\ln(x+2) + \frac{2}{x+2}\right]_0^1$

$= \ln 3 + 2/3 - (\ln 2 + 1) = \ln(3/2) - 1/3$

34. $\int \frac{x^2}{(x-3)(x+2)^2} dx = \int \left[\frac{9/25}{x-3} + \frac{16/25}{x+2} - \frac{4/5}{(x+2)^2}\right]dx$

$= (9/25)\ln|x-3| + (16/25)\ln|x+2| + (4/5)/(x+2) + C$

36. $\int \frac{18-2x-4x^2}{x^3+4x^2+x-6} dx = \int \frac{18-2x-4x^2}{(x-1)(x+2)(x+3)} dx = \int \left[\frac{1}{x-1} - \frac{2}{x+2} - \frac{3}{x+3}\right]dx$

$= \ln|x-1| - 2 \ln|x+2| - 3 \ln|x+3| + C$

38. $\int \frac{2x^4-3x^3-10x^2+2x+11}{x^3-x^2-5x-3} dx = \int \left[2x - 1 + \frac{-x^2+3x+8}{(x+1)^2(x-3)}\right]dx$

$= \int \left[2x - 1 - \frac{3/2}{x+1} - \frac{1}{(x+1)^2} + \frac{1/2}{x-3}\right]dx$

$= x^2 - x - (3/2)\ln|x+1| + 1/(x+1) + (1/2)\ln|x-3| + C$

40. $\frac{1}{x^2(x-1)^2} = \frac{A}{x} + \frac{B}{x^2} + \frac{C}{x-1} + \frac{D}{(x-1)^2}$. Multiply by x^2 and set x = 0 to

get $B = \frac{1}{(x-1)^2}\Big|_{x=0} = 1$. Multiply by $(x-1)^2$ and set x = 1 to get

D = 1. Multiply by x and let $x \to \infty$ to get 0 = A+C. We now have
$\frac{1}{x^2(x-1)^2} = A\left[\frac{1}{x} - \frac{1}{x-1}\right] + \frac{1}{x^2} + \frac{1}{(x-1)^2}$. Taking x = 2, we get

$\frac{1}{4} = A\left[-\frac{1}{2}\right] + \frac{1}{4} + 1$, so A = 2. Now $\int \frac{dx}{x^2(x-1)^2}$

$= \int\left[\frac{2}{x} + \frac{1}{x^2} - \frac{2}{x-1} + \frac{1}{(x-1)^2}\right]dx = 2 \ln|x| - \frac{1}{x} - 2 \ln|x-1| - \frac{1}{x-1} + C$

42. $\dfrac{1}{2x^4+x^3} = \dfrac{1}{x^3(2x+1)} = \dfrac{A}{x} + \dfrac{B}{x^2} + \dfrac{C}{x^3} + \dfrac{D}{2x+1}$. Multiply by x^3 and set

$x = 0$ to get $C = 1$. Multiply by $2x+1$ and set $x = -1/2$ to get $D = -8$. Multiply by x and let $x \to \infty$ to get $0 = A + \frac{1}{2}D$, so that $A = 4$.

Finally take $x = -1$ to get $1 = -4+B-1+8$, so that $B = -2$. Now

$\displaystyle\int \dfrac{dx}{2x^4+x^3} = \int \left[\dfrac{4}{x} - \dfrac{2}{x^2} + \dfrac{1}{x^3} - \dfrac{8}{2x+1}\right]dx = 4\,\ln|x| + 2/x - 1/(2x^2)$

$- \; 4\,\ln|2x+1| + C = 4\,\ln|x/(2x+1)| + 2/x - 1/(2x^2) + C$

44. $\dfrac{x}{x+1} = \dfrac{(x+1)-1}{x+1} = 1 - \dfrac{1}{x+1}$, so $\dfrac{x^3}{(x+1)^3} = \left[1 - \dfrac{1}{x+1}\right]^3$

$= 1 - \dfrac{3}{x+1} + \dfrac{3}{(x+1)^2} - \dfrac{1}{(x+1)^3}$. Thus $\displaystyle\int \dfrac{x^3}{(x+1)^3}\,dx$

$= \displaystyle\int \left[1 - \dfrac{3}{x+1} + \dfrac{3}{(x+1)^2} - \dfrac{1}{(x+1)^3}\right]dx = x - 3\,\ln|x+1| - \dfrac{3}{x+1} + \dfrac{1}{2(x+1)^2} + C$

46. $\dfrac{1}{x^5+2x^4+x^3} = \dfrac{1}{x^3(x^2+2x+1)} = \dfrac{1}{x^3(x+1)^2} = \dfrac{A}{x} + \dfrac{B}{x^2} + \dfrac{C}{x^3} + \dfrac{D}{x+1} + \dfrac{E}{(x+1)^2}$.

Multiply by x^3 and set $x = 0$ to get $C = 1$. Multiply by $(x+1)^2$ and

set $x = -1$ to get $E = -1$. Multiply by x and let $x \to \infty$ to get

$0 = A+D$. We now have $\dfrac{1}{x^3(x+1)^2} = \dfrac{A}{x} + \dfrac{B}{x^2} + \dfrac{1}{x^3} - \dfrac{A}{x+1} - \dfrac{1}{(x+1)^2}$. Take

$x = 1$ to get $\dfrac{1}{4} = A+B+1-\dfrac{A}{2}-\dfrac{1}{4}$; i.e., $A+2B = -1$. Take $x = -2$ to get

$-\dfrac{1}{8} = -\dfrac{A}{2}+\dfrac{B}{4}-\dfrac{1}{8}+A-1$; i.e., $A+\dfrac{1}{2}B = 2$. The two equations in A and B give

$A = 3$ and $B = -2$. Thus $\dfrac{1}{x^3(x+1)^2} = \dfrac{3}{x} - \dfrac{2}{x^2} + \dfrac{1}{x^3} - \dfrac{3}{x+1} - \dfrac{1}{(x+1)^2}$ and

$\displaystyle\int \dfrac{dx}{x^3(x+1)^2} = 3\,\ln|x| + \dfrac{2}{x} - \dfrac{1}{2x^2} - 3\,\ln|x+1| + \dfrac{1}{x+1} + C$

48. Let $u = x^4-x^2+1$. Then $du = (4x^3-2x)dx \Rightarrow \displaystyle\int \dfrac{2x^3-x}{x^4-x^2+1}\,dx$

$= \displaystyle\int \dfrac{(1/2)du}{u} = \dfrac{1}{2}\,\ln|x^4-x^2+1| + C = \dfrac{1}{2}\,\ln(x^4-x^2+1) + C$

50. $\displaystyle\int_0^1 \dfrac{x-1}{x^2+2x+2}\,dx = \int_0^1 \dfrac{x+1}{x^2+2x+2}\,dx - \int_0^1 \dfrac{2}{x^2+2x+2}\,dx = \dfrac{1}{2}\,\ln(x^2+2x+2)\Big]_0^1$

$- \; 2\displaystyle\int_0^1 \dfrac{dx}{(x+1)^2+1} = \dfrac{1}{2}(\ln 5 - \ln 2) - 2\left[\tan^{-1}(x+1)\right]_0^1$

$= \dfrac{1}{2}\,\ln\left[\dfrac{5}{2}\right] - 2\,\tan^{-1}2 + \dfrac{\pi}{4}$ [OR: Complete the square and let $u = x+1$]

52. $\displaystyle\int_{-1/2}^{1/2} \dfrac{4x^2+5x+7}{4x^2+4x+5}\,dx = \int_{-1/2}^{1/2} \left[1 + \dfrac{x+2}{4x^2+4x+5}\right]dx$

$= x\Big]_{-1/2}^{1/2} + \displaystyle\int_{-1/2}^{1/2} \dfrac{x+1/2}{4x^2+4x+5}\,dx + \int_{-1/2}^{1/2} \dfrac{3/2}{4x^2+4x+5}\,dx$

$$= 1 + \left[\frac{1}{8}\ln(4x^2+4x+5)\right]_{-1/2}^{1/2} + \frac{3}{2}\int_{-1/2}^{1/2}\frac{dx}{(2x+1)^2+4}$$

$$= 1 + \frac{1}{8}(\ln 8 - \ln 4) + \frac{3}{2}\int_0^2 \frac{(1/2)du}{u^2+4} \quad [u = 2x+1, \quad du = 2\,dx]$$

$$= 1 + (\ln 2)/8 + \frac{3}{4}\left[\frac{1}{2}\tan^{-1}(u/2)\right]_0^2 = 1 + (\ln 2)/8 + 3\pi/32$$

54. $\dfrac{2x+3}{x(x^2+3)} = \dfrac{A}{x} + \dfrac{Bx+C}{x^2+3} \;\Rightarrow\; 2x+3 = A(x^2+3) + (Bx+C)x$

$= (A+B)x^2 + Cx + 3A \;\Rightarrow\; A = 1, \; C = 2, \; B = -A = -1.$ Hence

$$\int \frac{2x+3}{x^3+3x}\,dx = \int\left[\frac{1}{x} + \frac{-x+2}{x^2+3}\right]dx = \ln|x| - \frac{1}{2}\int\frac{2x\,dx}{x^2+3} + 2\int\frac{dx}{x^2+3}$$

$$= \ln|x| - \frac{1}{2}\ln(x^2+3) + \frac{2}{\sqrt{3}}\tan^{-1}(x/\sqrt{3}) + C$$

56. $\dfrac{4x+1}{(x-3)(x^2+6x+12)} = \dfrac{A}{x-3} + \dfrac{Bx+C}{x^2+6x+12} \;\Rightarrow\; 4x+1$

$= A(x^2+6x+12) + (Bx+C)(x-3).$ Take $x = 3$ to get $13 = 39A$; i.e.

$A = 1/3.$ Equate the terms of degree 2 and degree 0 to get

$0 = 1/3+B$ and $1 = 4-3C$; i.e., $B = -1/3$ and $C = 1.$ Now

$$\int \frac{(4x+1)dx}{(x-3)(x^2+6x+12)} = \int\frac{(1/3)dx}{x-3} - \frac{1}{3}\int\frac{x-3}{x^2+6x+12}\,dx = \frac{1}{3}\ln|x-3|$$

$$-\frac{1}{3}\int\frac{x+3}{x^2+6x+12}\,dx + \frac{1}{3}\int\frac{6\,dx}{x^2+6x+12} = \frac{1}{3}\ln|x-3| - \frac{1}{6}\ln(x^2+6x+12)$$

$$+ 2\int\frac{dx}{(x+3)^2+3} = \frac{1}{3}\ln|x-3| - \frac{1}{6}\ln(x^2+6x+12) + \frac{2}{\sqrt{3}}\tan^{-1}\left[\frac{x+3}{\sqrt{3}}\right] + C$$

58. $\dfrac{x^3}{x^3+1} = 1 - \dfrac{1}{x^3+1} = 1 - \dfrac{1/3}{x+1} + \dfrac{(1/3)x-2/3}{x^2-x+1},$ so

$$\int \frac{x^3}{x^3+1}\,dx = x - \frac{1}{3}\ln|x+1| + \frac{1}{6}\int\frac{2x-1}{x^2-x+1}\,dx - \frac{1}{2}\int\frac{dx}{(x-1/2)^2+3/4}$$

$$= x - (1/3)\ln|x+1| + (1/6)\ln(x^2-x+1) - (1/\sqrt{3})\tan^{-1}[(2x-1)/\sqrt{3}] + C$$

60. $\dfrac{x^4}{x^4-1} = 1 + \dfrac{1}{x^4-1}$ and $\dfrac{1}{x^4-1} = \dfrac{1}{(x-1)(x+1)(x^2+1)} = \dfrac{A}{x-1} + \dfrac{B}{x+1} + \dfrac{Cx+D}{x^2+1}$

Multiply by $x-1$ and set $x = 1$ to get $A = 1/4.$ Multiply by $x+1$ and

set $x = -1$ to get $B = -1/4.$ Take $x = 0$ to get $-1 = -A+B+D = D-1/2,$

so that $D = -1/2.$ Finally, multiply by x and let $x \to \infty$ to get

$0 = A+B+C = C.$ Now

$$\int \frac{x^4\,dx}{x^4-1} = \int\left[1 + \frac{1/4}{x-1} - \frac{1/4}{x+1} - \frac{1/2}{x^2+1}\right]dx = x + \frac{1}{4}\ln\left|\frac{x-1}{x+1}\right| - \frac{1}{2}\tan^{-1}x + C$$

62. $\dfrac{x^3-2x^2+x+1}{x^4+5x^2+4} = \dfrac{x^3-2x^2+x+1}{(x^2+1)(x^2+4)} = \dfrac{Ax+B}{x^2+1} + \dfrac{Cx+D}{x^2+4} \;\Rightarrow$

$x^3-2x^2+x+1 = (Ax+B)(x^2+4) + (Cx+D)(x^2+1) \;\Rightarrow\; A+C = 1, \; B+D = -2,$

224

$4A+C = 1$, $4B+D = 1$ $\Rightarrow$ $A = 0$, $C = 1$, $B = 1$, $D = -3$. Now

$$\int \frac{x^3-2x^2+x+1}{x^4+5x^2+4} \, dx = \int \frac{dx}{x^2+1} + \int \frac{x-3}{x^2+4} \, dx$$

$$= \tan^{-1}x + (1/2)\ln(x^2+4) - (3/2)\tan^{-1}(x/2) + C$$

64. $\dfrac{1}{(x^2+4x+4)(x^2+4x+8)} = \dfrac{1}{(x+2)^2(x^2+4x+8)} = \dfrac{A}{x+2} + \dfrac{B}{(x+2)^2} + \dfrac{Cx+D}{x^2+4x+8}$ $\Rightarrow$

$1 = A(x+2)(x^2+4x+8) + B(x^2+4x+8) + (Cx+D)(x+2)^2$ $\Rightarrow$

$A+C = 0$, $6A+B+4C+D = 0$, $16A+4B+4C+4D = 0$, and $16A+8B+4D = 1$ $\Rightarrow$

$C = -A$, so $2A+B+D = 0$, $3A+B+D = 0$, and $4A+2B+D = 1/4$ $\Rightarrow$ $A = C = 0$,

$B = -D = 1/4$. Now we have

$$\int \frac{dx}{(x^2+4x+4)(x^2+4x+8)} = \int \frac{1/4}{(x+2)^2} \, dx - \int \frac{(1/4)dx}{(x+2)^2+4}$$

$$= -1/[4(x+2)] - (1/8)\tan^{-1}[(x+2)/2] + C$$

66. $\displaystyle\int \frac{x+1}{(x^2+x+2)^2} \, dx = \frac{1}{2} \int \frac{2x+1}{(x^2+x+2)^2} \, dx + \frac{1}{2} \int \frac{dx}{[(x+1/2)^2+7/4]^2}$

$$= -\frac{1}{2(x^2+x+2)} + \frac{1}{2} \int \frac{du}{(u^2+7/4)^2} \qquad [u = x+1/2]$$

$$= -\frac{1}{2(x^2+x+2)} + \frac{1}{2} \int \frac{(\sqrt{7}/2)\sec^2\theta \, d\theta}{(49/16)\sec^4\theta} \qquad [u = (\sqrt{7}/2)\tan\theta]$$

$$= -\frac{1}{2(x^2+x+2)} + \frac{4\sqrt{7}}{49} \int \cos^2\theta \, d\theta = -\frac{1}{2(x^2+x+2)} + \frac{2\sqrt{7}}{49}(\theta + \sin\theta \cos\theta)$$

$$+ C = -\frac{1}{2(x^2+x+2)} + \frac{2\sqrt{7}}{49} \tan^{-1}\left[\frac{2x+1}{\sqrt{7}}\right] + \frac{2x+1}{14(x^2+x+2)} + C$$

$$= \frac{x-3}{7(x^2+x+2)} + \frac{2\sqrt{7}}{49} \tan^{-1}\left[\frac{2x+1}{\sqrt{7}}\right] + C$$

68. $\dfrac{3x^4-2x^3+20x^2-5x+34}{(x-1)(x^2+4)^2} = \dfrac{A}{x-1} + \dfrac{Bx+C}{x^2+4} + \dfrac{Dx+E}{(x^2+4)^2}$. Multiply by $x-1$ and set

$x = 1$ to get $A = 2$. Then equate coefficients to get $B = 1$, $C = -1$,

$D = -1$, $E = 2$. So $\displaystyle\int \frac{3x^4-2x^3+20x^2-5x+34}{(x-1)(x^2+4)^2} \, dx = 2 \int \frac{dx}{x-1} + \int \frac{x}{x^2+4} \, dx$

$$- \int \frac{dx}{x^2+4} - \int \frac{x}{(x^2+4)^2} \, dx + 2 \int \frac{dx}{(x^2+4)^2} = 2 \ln|x-1| + \frac{1}{2} \ln(x^2+4)$$

$$- \frac{1}{2} \tan^{-1}\left(\frac{x}{2}\right) + \frac{1}{2(x^2+4)} + \frac{1}{8}\left[\tan^{-1}\left(\frac{x}{2}\right) + \frac{2x}{x^2+4}\right] + C$$

where the last integral is evaluated by substituting $x = 2 \tan\theta$ as
in Example 7.4.8.

70. $\dfrac{x^3-6x^2+13x+2}{(x^2-6x+10)^2} = \dfrac{Ax+B}{x^2-6x+10} + \dfrac{Cx+D}{(x^2-6x+10)^2}$ ⇒

$x^3-6x^2+13x+12 = (Ax+B)(x^2-6x+10)+Cx+D$ ⇒ $A = 1$, $-6A+B = -6$,

$10A-6B+C = 13$, $10B+D = 2$ ⇒ $A = 1$, $B = 0$, $C = 3$, and $D = 2$. Hence

$\displaystyle\int \dfrac{x^3-6x^2+13x+2}{(x^2-6x+10)^2}\,dx = \int \dfrac{x\,dx}{x^2-6x+10} + \int \dfrac{(3x+2)\,dx}{(x^2-6x+10)^2}$

$= \dfrac{1}{2}\displaystyle\int \dfrac{(2x-6)\,dx}{x^2-6x+10} + 3 \int \dfrac{dx}{(x-3)^2+1} + \dfrac{3}{2}\int \dfrac{(2x-6)\,dx}{(x^2-6x+10)^2} + 11\int \dfrac{dx}{[(x-3)^2+1]^2}$

$= (1/2)\ln(x^2-6x+10) + 3\,\tan^{-1}(x-3) - 3/[2(x^2-6x+10)]$

$\qquad + (11/2)\tan^{-1}(x-3) + 11(x-3)/[2(x^2-6x+10)] + C$

$= (1/2)\ln(x^2-6x+10) + (17/2)\tan^{-1}(x-3) + (11x-36)/[2(x^2-6x+10)] + C$

72. Let $u = x^3+3x$. Then $\displaystyle\int \dfrac{(x^2+1)\,dx}{(x^3+3x)^2} = \dfrac{1}{3}\int u^{-2}\,du = -\dfrac{1}{3u} + C$

$= -\dfrac{1}{3(x^3+3x)} + C$

74. Let $u = \cos x$, then $du = -\sin x\,dx$ ⇒ $\displaystyle\int \dfrac{\sin x \cos^2 x}{5 + \cos^2 x}\,dx$

$= \displaystyle\int \dfrac{-u^2\,du}{5+u^2} = -\int\left[1 - \dfrac{5}{u^2+5}\right]du = -u + \dfrac{5}{\sqrt{5}}\tan^{-1}\left[\dfrac{u}{\sqrt{5}}\right] + C$

$= -\cos x + \sqrt{5}\,\tan^{-1}[(\cos x)/\sqrt{5}] + C$

76. $\displaystyle\int \dfrac{dx}{x^2+2x-3} = \int \dfrac{dx}{(x+1)^2-4} = \int \dfrac{du}{u^2-4}$ $[u = x+1]$ $= \dfrac{1}{4}\ln\left|\dfrac{u-2}{u+2}\right| + C$

$[by\ (7.20)]$ $= \dfrac{1}{4}\ln\left|\dfrac{x-1}{x+3}\right| + C$

78. $\displaystyle\int \dfrac{(2x+1)\,dx}{4x^2+12x-7} = \dfrac{1}{4}\int \dfrac{(8x+12)\,dx}{4x^2+12x-7} - \int \dfrac{2\,dx}{(2x+3)^2-16}$

$= (1/4)\ln|4x^2+12x-7| - \displaystyle\int \dfrac{du}{u^2-16}$ $[u = 2x+3]$

$= (1/4)\ln|4x^2+12x-7| - (1/8)\ln|(u-4)/(u+4)| + C$ $[by\ (7.20)]$

$= (1/4)\ln|4x^2+12x-7| - (1/8)\ln|(2x-1)/(2x+7)| + C$

80. $x^2-6x+8 = (x-3)^2-1$ is positive for $5 \le x \le 10$, so

area $= \displaystyle\int_5^{10} \dfrac{dx}{(x-3)^2-1} = \int_2^7 \dfrac{du}{u^2-1}$ $[u = x-3\ ] = \dfrac{1}{2}\ln\left|\dfrac{u-1}{u+1}\right|\Big]_2^7$

$= \dfrac{1}{2}\ln \dfrac{3}{4} - \dfrac{1}{2}\ln \dfrac{1}{3} = \dfrac{1}{2}(\ln 3 - 2\ln 2 + \ln 3) = \ln 3 - \ln 2 = \ln \dfrac{3}{2}$

82. $x^2-2x+10 = (x-1)^2+9 > 0$ for all x, so the curve lies below the

x-axis on $[-1, 0)$ and above it on $(0, 2]$. The desired area is

$-\displaystyle\int_{-1}^{0} \dfrac{x\,dx}{x^2-2x+10} + \int_0^2 \dfrac{x\,dx}{x^2-2x+10}$. Since $\displaystyle\int \dfrac{x\,dx}{x^2-2x+10}$

$= \dfrac{1}{2}\displaystyle\int \dfrac{(2x-2)\,dx}{x^2-2x+10} + \int \dfrac{dx}{(x-1)^2+9} = \dfrac{1}{2}\ln(x^2-2x+10) + \dfrac{1}{3}\tan^{-1}[(x-1)/3] + C,$

the area is $-\left[(1/2)\ln(x^2-2x+10) + (1/3)\tan^{-1}[(x-1)/3]\right]_{-1}^{0}$

$\qquad + \left[(1/2)\ln(x^2-2x+10) + (1/3)\tan^{-1}[(x-1)/3]\right]_{0}^{2}$

$= -[(1/2)\ln 10 + (1/3)\tan^{-1}(-1/3) - (1/2)\ln 13 - (1/3)\tan^{-1}(-2/3)]$

$\qquad + [(1/2)\ln 10 + (1/3)\tan^{-1}(1/3) - (1/2)\ln 10 - (1/3)\tan^{-1}(-1/3)]$

$= (1/2)\ln(13/10) + (1/3)\tan^{-1}(2/3) + \tan^{-1}(1/3)$

$\qquad$ *[since $\tan^{-1}(-x) = -\tan^{-1}x$]*

$= (1/2)\ln 1.3 + \tan^{-1}(1/3) - (1/3)\tan^{-1}(2/3)$

Section 7.5

Exercises 7.5

2. Let $u = \sqrt[3]{x}$. Then $x = u^3$, $dx = 3u^2\,du$ $\Rightarrow$ $\int_0^1 \dfrac{x}{1+\sqrt[3]{x}}\,dx = \int_0^1 \dfrac{3u^2\,du}{1+u}$

$= \int_0^1 (3u - 3 + \dfrac{3}{1+u})du = \left[\dfrac{3}{2}u^2 - 3u + 3\ln(1+u)\right]_0^1 = 3(\ln 2 - \dfrac{1}{2})$

4. Let $u = \sqrt{x+1}$. Then $x = u^2-1$, $dx = 2u\,du$ $\Rightarrow$

$\int \dfrac{dx}{x\sqrt{x+1}} = \int \dfrac{2u\,du}{(u^2-1)u} = 2\int \dfrac{du}{u^2-1} = \ln\left|\dfrac{u-1}{u+1}\right| + C = \ln\left|\dfrac{\sqrt{x+1}-1}{\sqrt{x+1}+1}\right| + C$

6. Let $u = \sqrt{x+2}$. Then $x = u^2-2$, $dx = 2u\,du$ $\Rightarrow$ $I = \int \dfrac{dx}{x-\sqrt{x+2}} = \int \dfrac{2u\,du}{u^2-2-u}$

$= 2\int \dfrac{u\,du}{u^2-u-2}$ and $\dfrac{u}{u^2-u-2} = \dfrac{A}{u-2} + \dfrac{B}{u+1}$ $\Rightarrow$ $u = A(u+1)+B(u-2)$ $\Rightarrow$

$A = \dfrac{2}{3}$, $B = \dfrac{1}{3}$, so $I = \dfrac{2}{3}\int\left[\dfrac{2}{u-2} + \dfrac{1}{u+1}\right]du = \dfrac{2}{3}(2\ln|u-2| + \ln|u+1|) + C$

$= (2/3)[2\ln|\sqrt{x+2}-2| + \ln(\sqrt{x+2}+1)] + C$

8. Let $u = \sqrt{x-1}$. Then $x = u^2+1$, $dx = 2u\,du$ $\Rightarrow$ $\int_1^3 \dfrac{\sqrt{x-1}}{x+1}\,dx$

$= \int_0^{\sqrt{2}} \dfrac{u}{u^2+2}\,2u\,du = 2\int_0^{\sqrt{2}}\left[1 - \dfrac{2}{u^2+2}\right]du = \left[2u - \dfrac{4}{\sqrt{2}}\tan^{-1}\left[\dfrac{u}{\sqrt{2}}\right]\right]_0^{\sqrt{2}}$

$= 2\sqrt{2} - 2\sqrt{2}\tan^{-1}1 = 2\sqrt{2}(1 - \pi/4)$

10. Let $u = \sqrt{x}$. Then $x = u^2$, $dx = 2u\,du$ $\Rightarrow$ $\int_{1/3}^3 \dfrac{\sqrt{x}}{x^2+x}\,dx$

$= \int_{1/\sqrt{3}}^{\sqrt{3}} \dfrac{u\cdot 2u\,du}{u^4+u^2} = 2\int_{1/\sqrt{3}}^{\sqrt{3}} \dfrac{du}{u^2+1} = 2\tan^{-1}u\Big]_{1/\sqrt{3}}^{\sqrt{3}} = 2(\dfrac{\pi}{3} - \dfrac{\pi}{6}) = \dfrac{\pi}{3}$

12. Let $u = \sqrt[3]{x}$. Then $x = u^3$, $dx = 3u^2\,du$ $\Rightarrow$ $\displaystyle\int \frac{\sqrt[3]{x} + 1}{\sqrt[3]{x} - 1}\,dx$

$= \displaystyle\int \frac{u+1}{u-1}\,3u^2\,du = 3\int (u^2 + 2u + 2 + \frac{2}{u-1})\,du = u^3 + 3u^2 + 6u$

$+\ 6\ln|u-1| + C = x + 3x^{2/3} + 6\sqrt[3]{x} + 6\ln|\sqrt[3]{x} - 1| + C$

14. Let $u = \sqrt[3]{x^2}$. Then $x^2 = u^3$, $2x\,dx = 3u^2\,du$ $\Rightarrow$ $\displaystyle\int \frac{x\,dx}{x^2 - \sqrt[3]{x^2}}$

$= \dfrac{3}{2}\displaystyle\int \frac{u^2\,du}{u^3 - u} = \dfrac{3}{4}\int \frac{2u}{u^2-1}\,du = \dfrac{3}{4}\ln|u^2-1| + C = \dfrac{3}{4}\ln|x^{4/3}-1| + C$

16. Let $u = \sqrt[6]{x}$. Then $x = u^6$, $dx = 6u^5\,du$, $\sqrt{x} = u^3$, and $\sqrt[3]{x} = u^2$, so

$\displaystyle\int \frac{\sqrt{x}\,dx}{\sqrt{x} - \sqrt[3]{x}} = \int \frac{u^3 \cdot 6u^5\,du}{u^3 - u^2} = 6\int \frac{u^6\,du}{u-1} = \int (u^5 + u^4 + u^3 + u^2 + u + 1 + \frac{1}{u-1})\,du$

$= u^6 + (6/5)u^5 + (3/2)u^4 + 2u^3 + 3u^2 + 6u + 6\ln|u-1| + C$

$= x + (6/5)x^{5/6} + (3/2)x^{2/3} + 2\sqrt{x} + 3\sqrt[3]{x} + 6\sqrt[6]{x} + 6\ln|\sqrt[6]{x}-1| + C$

18. Let $u = \sqrt[12]{x}$. Then $x = u^{12}$, $dx = 12u^{11}\,du$ $\Rightarrow$ $\displaystyle\int \frac{dx}{\sqrt[3]{x} + \sqrt[4]{x}}$

$= \displaystyle\int \frac{12u^{11}\,du}{u^4 + u^3} = 12\int \frac{u^8\,du}{u+1} = 12\int (u^7 - u^6 + u^5 - u^4 + u^3 - u^2 + u - 1 + \frac{1}{u+1})\,du$

$= (3/2)u^8 - (12/7)u^7 + 2u^6 - (12/5)u^5 + 3u^4 - 4u^3 + 6u^2 - 12u + 12\ln|u+1| + C$

$= \dfrac{3}{2}x^{2/3} - \dfrac{12}{7}x^{7/12} + 2\sqrt{x} - \dfrac{12}{5}x^{5/12} + 3\sqrt[3]{x} - 4\sqrt[4]{x} + 6\sqrt[6]{x} - 12\sqrt[12]{x} + 12\ln(\sqrt[12]{x}+1) + C$

20. Let $u = \sqrt{x}$. Then $x = u^2$, $dx = 2u\,du$ $\Rightarrow$ $\displaystyle\int \frac{dx}{(1+\sqrt{x})^3} = \int \frac{2u\,du}{(1+u)^3}$

$= 2\displaystyle\int \left[\frac{1}{(1+u)^2} - \frac{1}{(1+u)^3}\right]du = -\frac{2}{1+u} + \frac{1}{(1+u)^2} + C$

$= -2/(1+\sqrt{x}) + 1/(1+\sqrt{x})^2 + C$

22. Let $u = \sqrt{x}$. Then $x = u^2$, $dx = 2u\,du$ $\Rightarrow$ $\displaystyle\int \frac{\sqrt[3]{1+\sqrt{x}}}{x}\,dx = \int \frac{\sqrt[3]{1+u}}{u^2}\,2u\,du$

$= 2\displaystyle\int \frac{\sqrt[3]{1+u}}{u}\,du = 2\int \frac{v}{v^3 - 1}\,3v^2\,dv \quad [v = \sqrt[3]{1+u}] \quad = 6\int \frac{v^3}{v^3 - 1}\,dv$

$= 6\displaystyle\int \left[1 + \frac{1}{v^3 - 1}\right]dv = 6v + 6\int \frac{dv}{v^3 - 1} = 6v + 2\ln|v-1| - \ln(v^2 + v + 1) - $

$2\sqrt{3}\tan^{-1}\left[\dfrac{2v+1}{\sqrt{3}}\right] + C \text{ [by Exercise 7.4.57]} = 6\sqrt[3]{1+\sqrt{x}} + \ln\dfrac{[\sqrt[3]{1+\sqrt{x}}-1]^3}{\sqrt{x}}$

$-\ 2\sqrt{3}\tan^{-1}[(2\sqrt[3]{1+\sqrt{x}}+1)/\sqrt{3}] + C \quad [\text{since } (v^2+v+1)(v-1) = v^3-1]$

24. Let $u = \sqrt{x}$. Then $x = u^2$, $dx = 2u\,du$ $\Rightarrow$ $\displaystyle\int \sqrt{\frac{x-1}{x}}\,du = \int \frac{\sqrt{u^2-1}}{u}\,2u\,du$

$= 2\displaystyle\int \sqrt{u^2-1}\,du = 2\int \tan\theta\,\sec\theta\,\tan\theta\,d\theta \quad [u = \sec\theta]$

$= 2 \int (\sec^2 \theta - 1)\sec \theta \, d\theta = 2(\int \sec^3 \theta \, d\theta - \int \sec \theta \, d\theta)$

$= \sec \theta \tan \theta + \ln|\sec \theta + \tan \theta| - 2 \ln|\sec \theta + \tan \theta| + C$

    [by Examples 8 and 9 of 7.2]

$= \sec \theta \tan \theta - \ln|\sec \theta + \tan \theta| + C$

$= \sqrt{x(x-1)} - \ln(\sqrt{x}+\sqrt{x-1}) + C$

26. Let $u = \cos x$. Then $du = -\sin x \, dx$ $\Rightarrow$ $\int \dfrac{\sin x \, dx}{\cos^2 x + \cos x - 6}$

$= -\int \dfrac{du}{u^2+u-6} = -\int \dfrac{du}{(u-2)(u+3)} = -\frac{1}{5} \int \left[\dfrac{1}{u-2} - \dfrac{1}{u+3}\right] du = \frac{1}{5} \ln\left|\dfrac{u+3}{u-2}\right| + C$

$= (1/5)\ln|(\cos x + 3)/(\cos x - 2)| + C$

28. Let $u = e^x$. Then $x = \ln u$, $dx = du/u$ $\Rightarrow$ $\int \dfrac{dx}{\sqrt{1+e^x}} = \int \dfrac{du/u}{\sqrt{1+u}}$

$= \int \dfrac{2v \, dv}{v(v^2-1)}$ $[v = \sqrt{1+u},\ u = v^2-1,\ du = 2v \, dv]$ $= 2 \int \dfrac{dv}{v^2-1}$

$= \ln\left|\dfrac{v-1}{v+1}\right| + C = \ln|(\sqrt{1+e^x}-1)/(\sqrt{1+e^x}+1)| + C$

30. Let $u = e^x$. Then $x = \ln u$, $dx = du/u$ $\Rightarrow$ $\int \dfrac{e^{3x} \, dx}{e^{2x}-1} = \int \dfrac{u^3(du/u)}{u^2-1}$

$= \int \dfrac{u^2 \, du}{u^2-1} = \int \left[1 + \dfrac{1}{u^2-1}\right] du = u + \frac{1}{2} \ln\left|\dfrac{u-1}{u+1}\right| + C$

$= e^x + (1/2)\ln|(e^x-1)/(e^x+1)| + C$

32. Let $t = \tan(x/2)$. Then $dx = 2dt/(1+t^2)$, $\sin x = 2t/(1+t^2)$ $\Rightarrow$

$\int \dfrac{dx}{3 - 5 \sin x} = \int \dfrac{2dt/(1+t^2)}{3-10t/(1+t^2)} = \int \dfrac{2 \, dt}{3(1+t^2)-10t} = 2 \int \dfrac{dt}{3t^2-10t+3}$

$= \frac{1}{4} \int \left[\dfrac{1}{t-3} - \dfrac{3}{3t-1}\right] dt = \frac{1}{4}[\ln|t-3| - \ln|3t-1|] + C$

$= (1/4)\ln|(\tan(x/2)-3)/(3\tan(x/2)-1)| + C$

34. Let $t = \tan(x/2)$. Then, by (7.25), $\displaystyle\int_{\pi/3}^{\pi/2} \dfrac{dx}{1 + \sin x - \cos x}$

$= \int_{1/\sqrt{3}}^{1} \dfrac{2dt/(1+t^2)}{1+2t/(1+t^2)-(1-t^2)/(1+t^2)} = \int_{1/\sqrt{3}}^{1} \dfrac{2dt}{1+t^2+2t-1+t^2}$

$= \int_{1/\sqrt{3}}^{1} \left[\dfrac{1}{t} - \dfrac{1}{t+1}\right] dt = \left[\ln t - \ln(t+1)\right]_{1/\sqrt{3}}^{1}$

$= \ln(1/2) - \ln(1/(\sqrt{3}+1)) = \ln((\sqrt{3}+1)/2)$

36. Let $t = \tan(x/2)$. Then $\int \dfrac{dx}{\sin x + \tan x} = \int \dfrac{2dt/(1+t^2)}{2t/(1+t^2)+2t/(1-t^2)}$

$= \int \dfrac{2(1-t^2)dt}{2t(1-t^2)+2t(1+t^2)} = \int \dfrac{1-t^2}{2t} \, dt = \frac{1}{2} \int \left[\dfrac{1}{t} - t\right] dt$

$= (1/2)(\ln|t|-(1/2)t^2) + C = (1/2)\ln|\tan(x/2)| - (1/4)\tan^2(x/2) + C$

38. Let $t = \tan(x/2)$. Then $\int \dfrac{\sec x \, dx}{1 + \sin x} = \int \dfrac{\dfrac{1+t^2}{1-t^2}\dfrac{2dt}{1+t^2}}{1+2t/(1+t^2)} = \int \dfrac{2dt/(1-t^2)}{1+2t/(1+t^2)}$

$= \int \dfrac{2(1+t^2)dt}{(1-t^2)(1+t^2+2t)} = 2 \int \dfrac{(t^2+1)dt}{(1-t)(1+t)^3}$

$= 2 \int \left[\dfrac{1/4}{1-t} + \dfrac{1/4}{1+t} - \dfrac{1/2}{(1+t)^2} + \dfrac{1}{(1+t)^3}\right] dt$

$= -\dfrac{1}{2} \ln|1-t| + \dfrac{1}{2} \ln|1+t| + 1/(1+t) - 1/(1+t)^2 + C$

$= \dfrac{1}{2} \ln|[1+\tan(x/2)]/[1-\tan(x/2)]| + 1/[1+\tan(x/2)] - 1/[1+\tan(x/2)]^2 + C$

40. Then $\int \dfrac{dx}{a^2\sin^2 x + b^2\cos^2 x} = \int \dfrac{dx}{(a^2/2)(1-\cos 2x)+(b^2/2)(1+\cos 2x)}$

$= \int \dfrac{dx}{\frac{1}{2}(b^2+a^2)+\frac{1}{2}(b^2-a^2)\cos 2x} = \int \dfrac{dX}{(b^2+a^2)+(b^2-a^2)\cos X}$ [where $X = 2x$]

$= \int \dfrac{2dt/(1+t^2)}{(b^2+a^2)+(b^2-a^2)(1-t^2)/(1+t^2)}$ [$t = \tan(X/2)$]

$= \int \dfrac{2dt}{(b^2+a^2)(1+t^2)+(b^2-a^2)(1-t^2)} = \int \dfrac{2dt}{2a^2t^2+2b^2} = \int \dfrac{dt}{a^2t^2+b^2}$

$= \dfrac{1}{a} \int \dfrac{du}{u^2+b^2}$ [$u = at$, $dt = \frac{1}{a} du$]

$= \dfrac{1}{ab} \tan^{-1}(\dfrac{u}{b}) + C = \dfrac{1}{ab} \tan^{-1}(\dfrac{at}{b}) + C = \dfrac{1}{ab} \tan^{-1}[(a \tan x)/b] + C$

42. Let $t = \tan(x/2)$. Then $\int \csc x \, dx = \int \dfrac{dx}{\sin x} = \int \dfrac{2dt}{2t}$

$= \ln|t| + C = \ln|\tan(x/2)| + C$

Section 7.6

Exercises 7.6

2. $\int \dfrac{\sin x - \cos x}{\sin x + \cos x} \, dx = -\int \dfrac{(\cos x - \sin x)dx}{\sin x + \cos x} = -\ln|\sin x + \cos x| + C$

4. Integrate by parts with $u = \ln x$, $dv = x^3 dx \Rightarrow du = dx/x$, $v = x^4/4$:

$\int_1^2 x^3 \ln x \, dx = (x^4 \ln x)/4]_1^2 - \dfrac{1}{4} \int_1^2 x^3 \, dx = 4 \ln 2 - \dfrac{1}{16}\left[x^4\right]_1^2$

$= 4 \ln 2 - 15/16$

6. $\int \dfrac{x \, dx}{(x+2)^2} = \int \dfrac{(x+2)-2}{(x+2)^2} \, dx = \int\left[\dfrac{1}{x+2} - \dfrac{2}{(x+2)^2}\right]dx = \ln|x+2| + \dfrac{2}{x+2} + C$

8. Let $u = \ln x$. Then $du = dx/x \Rightarrow \int \dfrac{\sqrt{1 + \ln x}}{x \ln x} \, dx = \int \dfrac{\sqrt{1+u}}{u} \, du$

$= \int \dfrac{v}{v^2-1} 2v \, dv$ [$v = \sqrt{1+u}$, $u = v^2-1$, $du = 2v \, dv$] $= 2 \int\left[1 + \dfrac{1}{v^2-1}\right]dv$

$= 2v + \ln\left|\dfrac{v-1}{v+1}\right| + C = 2\sqrt{1 + \ln x} + \ln[(\sqrt{1+\ln x} - 1)/(\sqrt{1+\ln x} + 1)] + C$

10. Let $u = \tan x$. Then $\int_0^{\pi/4} \tan^3 x \sec^4 x \, dx$

$= \int_0^{\pi/4} \tan^3 x (\tan^2 x + 1)\sec^2 x \, dx = \int_0^1 u^3(u^2+1)du = \int_0^1 (u^5+u^3)du$

$= \left[\dfrac{u^6}{6} + \dfrac{u^4}{4}\right]_0^1 = \dfrac{1}{6} + \dfrac{1}{4} = \dfrac{5}{12}$

12. Integrate by parts: $u = \sin^{-1}x$, $dv = x \, dx$ $\Rightarrow$ $du = (1/\sqrt{1-x^2})dx$,

$v = x^2/2$, so $\int x \sin^{-1}x \, dx = \dfrac{1}{2}x^2\sin^{-1}x - \dfrac{1}{2}\int \dfrac{x^2 \, dx}{\sqrt{1-x^2}} = \dfrac{1}{2}x^2\sin^{-1}x$

$\qquad - \dfrac{1}{2}\int \dfrac{\sin^2\theta \, \cos\theta \, d\theta}{\cos\theta}$ $[x = \sin\theta, \, -\pi/2 \le \theta \le \pi/2]$

$= \dfrac{1}{2}x^2\sin^{-1}x - \dfrac{1}{4}\int(1 - \cos 2\theta)d\theta = \dfrac{1}{2}x^2\sin^{-1}x - \dfrac{1}{4}(\theta - \sin\theta\cos\theta) + C$

$= \dfrac{1}{2}x^2\sin^{-1}x - \dfrac{1}{4}\left[\sin^{-1}x - x\sqrt{1-x^2}\right] + C = \dfrac{1}{4}\left[(2x^2-1)\sin^{-1}x + x\sqrt{1-x^2}\right] + C$

14. $\int \dfrac{x}{x^2+3x+2} \, dx = \int \left[\dfrac{-1}{x+1} + \dfrac{2}{x+2}\right]dx = \ln[(x+2)^2/|x+1|] + C$

16. $\int \dfrac{x^3+x+1}{x^4+2x^2+4x} \, dx = \dfrac{1}{4}\ln|x^4+2x^2+4x| + C$

18. Let $u = \sqrt{x}$. Then $x = u^2$, $dx = 2u \, du$ $\Rightarrow$ $\int \cos\sqrt{x} \, dx = \int \cos u \cdot 2u \, du$

$= 2u \sin u - \int 2\sin u \, du$ [by parts]

$= 2u \sin u + 2\cos u + C = 2(\sqrt{x}\sin\sqrt{x} + \cos\sqrt{x}) + C$

20. Let $u = e^x$. Then $x = \ln u$, $dx = du/u$ $\Rightarrow$ $\int \dfrac{e^{2x}}{1+e^x} \, dx = \int \dfrac{u^2}{1+u} \dfrac{du}{u}$

$= \int \dfrac{u}{1+u} \, du = \int \left[1 - \dfrac{1}{1+u}\right]du = u - \ln|1+u| + C = e^x - \ln(1+e^x) + C$

22. $\int \cos 3x \cos 5x \, dx = \int \dfrac{1}{2}[\cos 8x + \cos 2x]dx$

$= (1/16) \sin 8x + (1/4) \sin 2x + C$ OR: Use integration by parts.

24. Integrate by parts with $u = \ln(1+x)$, $dv = x^2dx$ $\Rightarrow$ $du = dx/(1+x)$,

$v = \dfrac{1}{3}x^3$: $\int x^2\ln(1+x)dx = \dfrac{1}{3}x^3\ln(1+x) - \int \dfrac{x^3 \, dx}{3(1+x)}$

$= \dfrac{1}{3}x^3\ln(1+x) - \dfrac{1}{3}\int\left[x^2 - x + 1 - \dfrac{1}{x+1}\right]dx$

$= (1/3)x^3\ln(1+x) - x^3/9 + x^2/6 - x/3 + (1/3)\ln(1+x) + C$

26. $\int \tan^2 4x \, dx = \int(\sec^2 4x - 1)dx = \dfrac{1}{4}\tan 4x - x + C$

28. Integrate by parts with $u = \tan^{-1}x$, $dv = x^2dx$ $\Rightarrow$ $du = dx/(1+x^2)$,

$v = \dfrac{1}{3}x^3$: $\int x^2\tan^{-1}x \, dx = \dfrac{1}{3}x^3\tan^{-1}x - \int \dfrac{x^3}{3} \dfrac{dx}{1+x^2}$

$= \dfrac{1}{3}x^3\tan^{-1}x - \dfrac{1}{3}\int\left[x - \dfrac{x}{x^2+1}\right]dx = \dfrac{1}{3}x^3\tan^{-1}x - \dfrac{1}{6}x^2 + \dfrac{1}{6}\ln(x^2+1) + C$

30. Let $u = e^x$. Then $x = \ln u$, $dx = du/u$ $\Rightarrow$ $\int \dfrac{dx}{e^x - e^{-x}} = \int \dfrac{e^x \, dx}{e^{2x} - 1}$

$= \int \dfrac{u}{u^2 - 1} \dfrac{du}{u} = \int \dfrac{du}{u^2 - 1} = \dfrac{1}{2} \ln \left| \dfrac{u-1}{u+1} \right| + C = \dfrac{1}{2} \ln[|e^x - 1| / (e^x + 1)] + C$

32. Let $u = \sqrt[3]{x}$. Then $x = u^3$, $dx = 3u^2 \, du$ $\Rightarrow$ $\int \dfrac{dx}{x + \sqrt[3]{x}} = \int \dfrac{3u^2 \, du}{u^3 + u}$

$= \dfrac{3}{2} \int \dfrac{2u \, du}{u^2 + 1} = \dfrac{3}{2} \ln(u^2 + 1) + C = \dfrac{3}{2} \ln(x^{2/3} + 1) + C$

34. Let $u = x+2$. Then $du = dx$ $\Rightarrow$ $\int \dfrac{dx}{\sqrt{5 - 4x - x^2}} = \int \dfrac{dx}{\sqrt{9 - (x+2)^2}} = \int \dfrac{du}{\sqrt{9 - u^2}}$

$= \sin^{-1}(u/3) + C = \sin^{-1}[(x+2)/3] + C$

36. $\int \dfrac{1 + \cos x}{\sin x} \, dx = \int (\csc x + \cot x) dx = \ln|\csc x - \cot x|$

$+ \ln|\sin x| + C = \ln|1 - \cos x| + C$ OR: $\int \dfrac{1 + \cos x}{\sin x} \, dx =$

$\int \dfrac{1 - \cos^2 x}{\sin x (1 - \cos x)} \, dx = \int \dfrac{\sin x \, dx}{1 - \cos x} = \ln|1 - \cos x| + C$

38. $\int \dfrac{dx}{x^3 - 8} = \int \left[\dfrac{1/12}{x-2} - \dfrac{x/12 + 1/3}{x^2 + 2x + 4} \right] dx = \dfrac{1}{12} \int \left[\dfrac{1}{x-2} - \dfrac{x+4}{x^2 + 2x + 4} \right] dx$

$= \dfrac{1}{12} \ln|x-2| - \dfrac{1}{24} \int \dfrac{2x+2}{x^2 + 2x + 4} \, dx - \dfrac{1}{4} \int \dfrac{dx}{(x+1)^2 + 3}$

$= (1/12)\ln|x-2| - (1/24)\ln(x^2 + 2x + 4) - \{\tan^{-1}[(x+1)/\sqrt{3}]\}/(4\sqrt{3}) + C$

40. Let $u = \tan x$. Then $\int_{\pi/4}^{\pi/3} \dfrac{\ln(\tan x) dx}{\sin x \cos x} = \int_{\pi/4}^{\pi/3} \dfrac{\ln(\tan x)}{\tan x} \sec^2 x \, dx$

$= \int_1^{\sqrt{3}} \dfrac{\ln u}{u} \, du = \dfrac{1}{2}(\ln u)^2 \Big]_1^{\sqrt{3}} = \dfrac{1}{2}(\ln \sqrt{3})^2 = \dfrac{1}{8}(\ln 3)^2$

42. Let $u = \sin \theta$. Then $\int_0^{\pi/4} \cos^5 \theta \, d\theta = \int_0^{\pi/4} (1 - \sin^2 \theta)^2 \cos \theta \, d\theta$

$= \int_0^{1/\sqrt{2}} (1 - u^2)^2 \, du = \int_0^{1/\sqrt{2}} (u^4 - 2u^2 + 1) du = [u^5/5 - (2/3)u^3 + u]_0^{1/\sqrt{2}}$

$= \dfrac{1}{20\sqrt{2}} - \dfrac{1}{3\sqrt{2}} + \dfrac{1}{\sqrt{2}} = \dfrac{43\sqrt{2}}{120}$

44. Let $u = e^x$. Then $x = \ln u$, $dx = du/u$ $\Rightarrow$ $\int \dfrac{1 + e^x}{1 - e^x} \, dx = \int \dfrac{(1+u) du}{(1-u) u}$

$= -\int \dfrac{(u+1) du}{(u-1) u} = -\int \left[\dfrac{2}{u-1} - \dfrac{1}{u} \right] du = \ln|u| - 2 \ln|u-1| + C$

$= \ln e^x - 2 \ln|e^x - 1| + C = x - 2 \ln|e^x - 1| + C$

46. If $t = \tan(x/2)$, then $\int \dfrac{dx}{4 - 5 \sin x} = \int \dfrac{2dt/(1+t^2)}{4 - 10t/(1+t^2)} = \int \dfrac{dt}{2(1+t^2) - 5t}$

$= \int \dfrac{dt}{(t-2)(2t-1)} = \int \left[\dfrac{1/3}{t-2} - \dfrac{2/3}{2t-1} \right] dt = (1/3)\ln|t-2| - (1/3)\ln|2t-1| + C$

$= (1/3)\ln|[\tan(x/2) - 2]/[2 \tan(x/2) - 1]| + C$

48. Let $u = \sqrt[3]{x}$. Then $x = u^3 \Rightarrow \int e^{\sqrt[3]{x}}\,dx = \int e^u \cdot 3u^2\,du$

$= e^u(3u^2 - 6u + 6) + C$ [by parts twice; see the solution to Ex. 7.1.12]

$= 3e^{\sqrt[3]{x}}(x^{2/3} - 2\sqrt[3]{x} + 2) + C$

50. $\int \dfrac{x^3+1}{x^3-x^2}\,dx = \int\left[1 + \dfrac{x^2+1}{(x-1)x^2}\right]dx = x + \int\left[\dfrac{2}{x-1} - \dfrac{1}{x} - \dfrac{1}{x^2}\right]dx$

$= x + 2\ln|x-1| - \ln|x| + 1/x + C$

52. Let $u = \cos x$. Then $du = -\sin x\,dx \Rightarrow \int \sin x \cos(\cos x)\,dx$

$= -\int \cos u\,du = -\sin u + C = -\sin(\cos x) + C$

54. Let $u = x+1$. Then $du = dx \Rightarrow \int \dfrac{x^3}{(x+1)^{10}}\,dx = \int \dfrac{(u-1)^3}{u^{10}}\,du$

$= \int (u^{-7} - 3u^{-8} + 3u^{-9} - u^{-10})\,du$

$= -(1/6)u^{-6} + (3/7)u^{-7} - (3/8)u^{-8} + (1/9)u^{-9} + C$

$= (x+1)^{-9}[-(1/6)(x+1)^3 + (3/7)(x+1)^2 - (3/8)(x+1) + 1/9] + C$

56. $\int (x + \sin x)^2\,dx = \int (x^2 + 2x\sin x + \sin^2 x)\,dx$

$= x^3/3 + 2(\sin x - x\cos x) + \dfrac{1}{2}(x - \sin x\cos x) + C$

$= \dfrac{x^3}{3} + \dfrac{x}{2} + 2\sin x - \dfrac{1}{2}\sin x\cos x - 2x\cos x + C$

58. Let $u = x^2$. Then $du = 2x\,dx \Rightarrow \int \dfrac{dx}{x(x^4+1)} = \int \dfrac{x\,dx}{x^2(x^4+1)}$

$= \dfrac{1}{2}\int \dfrac{du}{u(u^2+1)} = \dfrac{1}{2}\int\left[\dfrac{1}{u} - \dfrac{u}{u^2+1}\right]du = \dfrac{1}{2}\ln|u| - \dfrac{1}{4}\ln(u^2+1) + C$

$= \dfrac{1}{2}\ln(x^2) - \dfrac{1}{4}\ln(x^4+1) + C = \dfrac{1}{4}[\ln(x^4) - \ln(x^4+1)] + C$

$= (1/4)\ln[x^4/(x^4+1)] + C$

[Another method: Write $I = \int \dfrac{x^3\,dx}{x^4(x^4+1)}$ and let $u = x^4$.]

60. Let $u = \sqrt[6]{t}$. Then $t = u^6$, $dt = 6u^5\,du \Rightarrow \int \dfrac{\sqrt{t}\,dt}{1+\sqrt[3]{t}} = \int \dfrac{u^3 \cdot 6u^5\,du}{1+u^2}$

$= 6\int \dfrac{u^8}{u^2+1}\,du = 6\int\left[u^6 - u^4 + u^2 - 1 + \dfrac{1}{u^2+1}\right]du$

$= 6(u^7/7 - u^5/5 + u^3/3 - u + \tan^{-1}u) + C$

$= 6(t^{7/6}/7 - t^{5/6}/5 + t^{1/2}/3 - t^{1/6} + \tan^{-1} t^{1/6}) + C$

62. $\int_1^3 |\ln(x/2)|\,dx = -\int_1^2 \ln(x/2)\,dx + \int_2^3 \ln(x/2)\,dx$ Let $u = x/2$. Then

$x = 2u$, $dx = 2\,du \Rightarrow \int \ln(x/2)\,dx = 2\int \ln u\,du$

$= 2(u\ln u - u) + C = x\ln(x/2) - x + C$, so $\int_1^3 |\ln(x/2)|\,dx$

233

$= [x - x \ln(x/2)]_1^2 + [x \ln(x/2) - x]_2^3 = 2 - [1 - \ln(1/2)]$

$+ [3 \ln(3/2) - 3] - (-2) = 3 \ln 3 - 4 \ln 2 = \ln \dfrac{27}{16}$

64. Let $t = \sqrt{x^2-1}$. Then $dt = (x/\sqrt{x^2-1})dx$, $x^2-1 = t^2$, $x = \sqrt{t^2+1}$, so

$I = \displaystyle\int \dfrac{x \ln x}{\sqrt{x^2-1}} dx = \int \ln\sqrt{t^2+1}\, dt = \dfrac{1}{2} \int \ln(t^2+1)dt$

Now use parts with $u = \ln(t^2+1)$, $dv = dt$: $I = \dfrac{1}{2}t \ln(t^2+1)$

$- \displaystyle\int \dfrac{t^2}{t^2+1} dt = \dfrac{1}{2}t \ln(t^2+1) - \int\left[1 - \dfrac{1}{t^2+1}\right]dt = \dfrac{1}{2}t \ln(t^2+1) - t +$

$\tan^{-1}t + C = \sqrt{x^2-1} \ln x - \sqrt{x^2-1} + \tan^{-1}\sqrt{x^2-1} + C$ [Another method:

First integrate by parts with $u = \ln x$, $dv = (x/\sqrt{x^2-1})dx$ and then

use substitution $(x = \sec \theta$ or $u = \sqrt{x^2-1})$.]

66. Let $u = \cot 4x$. Then $du = - 4 \csc^2 4x\, dx$ $\Rightarrow$ $\displaystyle\int \csc^4 4x\, dx$

$= \displaystyle\int(\cot^2 4x + 1)\csc^2 4x\, dx = \int(u^2+1)(-\dfrac{1}{4} du) = - (1/4)(u^3/3 + u) + C$

$= - (1/12)(\cot^3 4x + 3 \cot 4x) + C$

68. Let $x - 1/2 = (\sqrt{5}/2)u$. Then $dx = (\sqrt{5}/2)du$, $u = (2x-1)/\sqrt{5}$ $\Rightarrow$

$\displaystyle\int \sqrt{1+x-x^2}\, dx = \int \sqrt{5/4 - (x-1/2)^2}\, dx = (5/4) \int \sqrt{1-u^2}\, du$

$= (5/4) \displaystyle\int \cos \theta \cdot \cos \theta\, d\theta = (5/8)(\theta + \sin \theta \cos \theta) + C$

$= \dfrac{5}{8}\left[\sin^{-1}\left[\dfrac{2x-1}{\sqrt{5}}\right] + \dfrac{2x-1}{\sqrt{5}}\cdot\dfrac{2}{\sqrt{5}} \sqrt{1+x-x^2}\right] + C$

$= (5/8) \sin^{-1}[(2x-1)/\sqrt{5}] + (1/4)(2x-1)\sqrt{1+x-x^2} + C$

70. $\displaystyle\int \dfrac{x+2}{x^2+x+2} dx = \dfrac{1}{2} \int \dfrac{2x+1}{x^2+x+2} dx + \dfrac{3}{2} \int \dfrac{dx}{(x+\frac{1}{2})^2+\frac{7}{4}}$

$= \dfrac{1}{2} \ln(x^2+x+2) + \dfrac{3}{2} \dfrac{2}{\sqrt{7}} \tan^{-1}\left[\dfrac{2}{\sqrt{7}} (x + \dfrac{1}{2})\right] + C$

$= \ln \sqrt{x^2+x+2} + (3/\sqrt{7}) \tan^{-1}[(2x+1)/\sqrt{7}] + C$

72. Let $u = x^2$. Then $du = 2x\, dx$ $\Rightarrow$ $\displaystyle\int \dfrac{x\, dx}{x^4-a^4} = \int \dfrac{(1/2)du}{u^2-(a^2)^2}$

$= \dfrac{1}{4a^2} \ln\left|\dfrac{u-a^2}{u+a^2}\right| + C = \dfrac{1}{4a^2} \ln\left|\dfrac{x^2-a^2}{x^2+a^2}\right| + C$

74. Let $u = e^x$. Then $x = \ln u$, $dx = du/u$ $\Rightarrow$ $\displaystyle\int \dfrac{dx}{1+2e^x-e^{-x}} = \int \dfrac{du/u}{1+2u-1/u}$

$= \displaystyle\int \dfrac{du}{2u^2+u-1} = \int \left[\dfrac{2/3}{2u-1} - \dfrac{1/3}{u+1}\right]du = \dfrac{1}{3} \ln|2u-1| - \dfrac{1}{3} \ln|u+1| + C$

$= \dfrac{1}{3} \ln|(2e^x-1)/(e^x+1)| + C$

76. Use parts with $u = \ln(x+1)$, $dv = dx/x^2$: $\int \dfrac{\ln(x+1)}{x^2}\, dx$

$= -(1/x)\,\ln(x+1) + \int \dfrac{dx}{x(x+1)} = -(1/x)\ln(x+1) + \int\left[\dfrac{1}{x} - \dfrac{1}{x+1}\right]dx$

$= -(1/x)\ln(x+1) + \ln|x| - \ln(x+1) + C = -(1+1/x)\ln(x+1) + \ln|x| + C$

78. $\int e^{-x}\sinh x\, dx = \int e^{-x}\cdot\dfrac{1}{2}\left[e^x - e^{-x}\right]dx = \int\left[\dfrac{1}{2} - \dfrac{1}{2}e^{-2x}\right]dx$

$= x/2 + (1/4)e^{-2x} + C$

80. $\int \dfrac{1 + \cos^2 x}{1 - \cos^2 x}\, dx = \int \dfrac{1 + \cos^2 x}{\sin^2 x}\, dx = \int (\csc^2 x + \cot^2 x)\, dx$

$= \int (2\csc^2 x - 1)\, dx = -2\cot x - x + C$

Section 7.7

Exercises 7.7

NOTATION: T = Trapezoidal approximation, S = Simpson's approximation

2. $\int_0^2 e^x\, dx = e^x\Big]_0^2 = e^2 - 1 \approx 6.389056.$ $f(x) = e^x,$ $\Delta x = \dfrac{2-0}{8} = 1/4$

(a) $T = \dfrac{1/4}{2}\,[e^0 + 2e^{1/4} + 2e^{1/2} + 2e^{3/4} + 2e^1 + 2e^{5/4} + 2e^{3/2} + 2e^{7/4} + e^2]$

≈ 6.422298

(b) $S = \dfrac{1/4}{3}\,[e^0 + 4e^{1/4} + 2e^{1/2} + 4e^{3/4} + 2e^1 + 4e^{5/4} + 2e^{3/2} + 4e^{7/4} + e^2]$

≈ 6.389194

4. $\int_0^1 \dfrac{dx}{1+x^2} = \tan^{-1}x\Big]_0^1 = \pi/4 \approx 0.785398.$ $\Delta x = 1/10$

(a) $T = \dfrac{0.1}{2}\left[1 + \dfrac{2}{1.01} + \dfrac{2}{1.04} + \dfrac{2}{1.09} + \dfrac{2}{1.16} + \dfrac{2}{1.25} + \dfrac{2}{1.36} + \dfrac{2}{1.49}\right.$

$\left. + \dfrac{2}{1.64} + \dfrac{2}{1.81} + \dfrac{1}{2}\right] \approx 0.784981$

(b) $S = \dfrac{0.1}{3}\left[1 + \dfrac{4}{1.01} + \dfrac{2}{1.04} + \dfrac{4}{1.09} + \dfrac{2}{1.16} + \dfrac{4}{1.25} + \dfrac{2}{1.36} + \dfrac{4}{1.49}\right.$

$\left. + \dfrac{2}{1.64} + \dfrac{4}{1.81} + \dfrac{1}{2}\right] \approx 0.785398$

6. $\int_{-1}^2 xe^x\, dx = \left[xe^x - e^x\right]_{-1}^2 = \left[(x-1)e^x\right]_{-1}^2 = e^2 - (-2e^{-1})$

$= e^2 + 2/e \approx 8.124815.$ $\Delta x = \dfrac{2-(-1)}{12} = 1/4$

(a) $T = (.25/2)\,[-e^{-1} + 2(-.75e^{-.75}) + 2(-.5e^{-.5}) + 2(-.25e^{-.25})$

$+ 2\cdot 0 + 2(.25e^{.25}) + 2(.5e^{.5}) + 2(.75e^{.75}) + 2e + 2(1.25e^{1.25})$

$+ 2(1.5e^{1.5}) + 2(1.75e^{1.75}) + 2e^2] \approx 8.240073$

(b) $S = (.25/3) [-e^{-1} + 4(-.75e^{-.75}) + 2(-.5e^{-.5}) + 4(-.25e^{-.25})$

$+ 2 \cdot 0 + 4(.25e^{.25}) + 2(.5e^{.5}) + 4(.75e^{.75}) + 2e + 4(1.25e^{1.25})$

$+ 2(1.5e^{1.5}) + 4(1.75e^{1.75}) + 2e^2] \approx 8.125593$

8. $f(x) = \cos(x^2)$, $\Delta x = \dfrac{1-0}{4} = 1/4$

(a) $T = (.25/2) [f(0) + 2f(1/4) + 2f(1/2) + 2f(3/4) + f(1)]$

≈ 0.895759

(b) $S = (.25/3) [f(0) + 4f(1/4) + 2f(1/2) + 4f(3/4) + f(1)]$

≈ 0.904501

10. $f(x) = x \tan x$, $\Delta x = (\pi/4-0)/6 = \pi/24$

(a) $T = (\pi/48) [f(0) + 2f(\pi/24) + 2f(\pi/12) + \cdots + 2f(5\pi/24)$

$+ f(\pi/4)] \approx 0.189445$

(b) $S = (\pi/72) [f(0) + 4f(\pi/24) + 2f(\pi/12) + 4f(\pi/8) + 2f(\pi/6)$

$+ 4f(5\pi/24) + f(\pi/4)] \approx 0.185822$

12. $f(x) = 1/\sqrt{1+x^3}$, $\Delta x = (2-0)/10 = 1/5$

(a) $T = (.2/2) [f(0) + 2f(.2) + 2f(.4) + \cdots + 2f(1.6) + 2f(1.8)$

$+ f(2)] \approx 1.401435$

(b) $S = (.2/3) [f(0) + 4f(.2) + 2f(.4) + 4f(.6) + 2f(.8) + 4f(1)$

$+ 2f(1.2) + 4f(1.4) + 2f(1.6) + 4f(1.8) + f(2)] \approx 1.402206$

14. $f(x) = 1/\ln x$, $\Delta x = (3-2)/10 = 1/10$

(a) $T = (.1/2) [f(2) + 2f(2.1) + 2f(2.2) + \cdots + 2f(2.9) + f(3)]$

≈ 1.119061

(b) $S = (.1/3) [f(2) + 4f(2.1) + 2f(2.2) + 4f(2.3) + 2f(2.4)$

$+ 4f(2.5) + 2f(2.6) + 4f(2.7) + 2f(2.8) + 4f(2.9) + f(3)]$

≈ 1.118428

16. $f(x) = \ln(1+e^x)$, $\Delta x = (1-0)/8 = 1/8$

(a) $T = (1/16)[f(0) + 2f(1/8) + 2f(1/4) + 2f(3/8) + 2f(1/2)$

$+ 2f(5/8) + 2f(3/4) + 2f(7/8) + f(1)] \approx 0.984120$

(b) $S = \dfrac{1/8}{3} [f(0) + 4f(1/8) + 2f(1/4) + 4f(3/8) + 2f(1/2) + 4f(5/8)$

$+ 2f(3/4) + 4f(7/8) + f(1)] \approx 0.983819$

NOTATION FOR EXERCISES 18-24: E_T AND E_S DENOTE THE ERROR INVOLVED

IN USING THE TRAPEZOIDAL RULE AND SIMPSON'S RULE.

18. (a) $f(x) = \cos(x^2)$, $f'(x) = -2x \sin(x^2)$, $f''(x) = -2 \sin(x^2)$

$- 4x^2\cos(x^2)$. For $0 \leq x \leq 1$, sin and cos are positive, so $|f''(x)|$

$= 2 \sin(x^2) + 4x^2\cos(x^2) \leq 2 \cdot 1 + 4 \cdot 1 \cdot 1 = 6$ since $\sin(x^2) \leq 1$ and

$\cos(x^2) \leq 1$ for all x and $x^2 \leq 1$ for $0 \leq x \leq 1$. So, taking M = 6, a = 0, b = 1, n = 4, in (7.30), we get $E_T \leq 6 \cdot 1^3/12(4)^2 = 1/32 = 0.03125$.

[A slightly better estimate is obtained by noting that $0 \leq x \leq 1 \Rightarrow \sin(x^2) \leq \sin 1$, so we can take M = 4 + 2 sin 1 $\Rightarrow$ $E_T < .03$.]

(b) $f'''(x) = -12x \cos(x^2) + 8x^3 \sin(x^2)$, $f^{(4)}(x) = 48x^2 \sin(x^2) + (16x^4 - 12)\cos(x^2)$. By the triangle inequality, $|f^{(4)}(x)| \leq 48x^2 |\sin(x^2)| + |16x^4 - 12||\cos(x^2)|$. For $0 \leq x \leq 1$, $-12 \leq 16x^4 - 12 \leq 4 \Rightarrow |16x^4 - 12| \leq 12 \Rightarrow |f^{(4)}(x)| \leq 48 \cdot 1 \cdot 1 + 12 \cdot 1 = 60$. Taking M = 60, a = 0, b = 1, n = 4 in (7.32), we get $E_S \leq 60 \cdot 1^5/180(4)^4 = 1/768 \approx .0013$. [Or use M = 12 + 48 sin 1 $\Rightarrow$ $E_T < .00114$.]

20. (a) $f(x) = \ln(1 + e^x) \Rightarrow f'(x) = e^x/(1 + e^x) = 1 - 1/(1 + e^x) \Rightarrow f''(x) = e^x/(1 + e^x)^2$. A crude estimate is obtained by noting that e^x and $(1 + e^x)^2$ are increasing, so for $0 \leq x \leq 1$ we have

$$|f''(x)| = \frac{e^x}{(1 + e^x)^2} \leq \frac{e^1}{(1 + e^0)^2} = \frac{e}{4} \Rightarrow E_T \leq \frac{(e/4) \cdot 1^3}{12 \cdot 8^2} \leq 0.00088$$

For a better estimate, note that $f'''(x) = (e^x - e^{2x})/(1 + e^x)^3 < 0$ for x > 0, so f'' is positive and decreasing $\Rightarrow$ $|f''(x)| \leq f(0) = 1/4$. This gives $E_T \leq (1/4) \cdot 1^3/12 \cdot 8^2 = 1/3072 < .00033$.

(b) $f^{(4)}(x) = (e^x - 4e^{2x} + e^{3x})/(1 + e^x)^4$, so by the Triangle Inequality,

$$|f^{(4)}(x)| = \frac{|e^x - 4e^{2x} + e^{3x}|}{(1 + e^x)^4} \leq \frac{e^x + 4e^{2x} + e^{3x}}{(1 + e^x)^4} \leq \frac{e^1 + 4e^2 + e^3}{(1 + e^0)^2} < 3.28 \Rightarrow$$

$E_S < (3.28) \cdot 1^5/180 \cdot 8^4 \approx .0000044$.

22. From # 17(b), we know that we can take M = 28. Then $\frac{28}{180n^4} < .00001$

$\Leftrightarrow n^4 > 2800000/180 = 140000/9 \Leftrightarrow n > \sqrt[4]{140000/9} \approx 11.2$, so n = 12 will ensure the desired accuracy. [If we take M = 12, we get $n^4 > 20000/3 \Rightarrow n > \sqrt[4]{20000/3} \approx 9$, so n = 10 actually suffices.]

24. $f(x) = xe^{x^3}$, $f'(x) = (3x^3 + 1)e^{x^3}$, $f''(x) = (9x^5 + 12x^2)e^{x^3}$. f'' is increasing on [0,1], so $|f''(x)| \leq f(1) = 21e$. Taking M = 21e, we have $E_T < .01$ if $21e/12n^2 < .01 \Leftrightarrow n^2 > 2100e/12 \Leftrightarrow n > \sqrt{2100e/12} \approx 21.8$. Taking n = 22, we can calculate T ≈ 0.78.

If we use Simpson's Rule, we need $f'''(x) = (27x^7 + 81x^4 + 24x)e^{x^3}$,

237

$f^{(4)}(x) = (81x^9 + 432x^6 + 396x^3 + 24)e^{x^3}$. Taking $M = f^{(4)}(1) = 933e$, we have $E_S < .01$ if $933e/180n^4 < .01 \iff n^4 > 93300e/180 \iff n > \sqrt[4]{93300e/180} \approx 6.1$. Taking $n = 8$, we can calculate $S \approx 0.78$.

26. $\int_2^6 y\, dx \approx \frac{.5}{3}[9.22 + 4(9.01) + 2(8.76) + 4(8.30) + 2(7.52) + 4(6.83)$
$\qquad\qquad + 2(7.32) + 4(7.69) + 7.91] \approx 31.94$

28. If x = distance from left end of pool and $w = w(x)$ = width at x, then Simpson's Rule with $n = 8$ and $\Delta x = 2$ gives
area $= \int_0^{16} w\, dx \approx \frac{2}{3}[0 + 4(6.2) + 2(7.2) + 4(6.8) + 2(5.6) + 4(5.0)$
$\qquad + 2(4.8) + 4(4.8) + 0] \approx 84\ m^2$

Section 7.8

Exercises 7.8

2. $\int_2^\infty \dfrac{dx}{(x+3)^{3/2}} = \lim_{t \to \infty} \int_2^t \dfrac{dx}{(x+3)^{3/2}} = \lim_{t \to \infty} (-2)\left[(x+3)^{-1/2}\right]_2^t$

$= \lim_{t \to \infty} \left[\dfrac{-2}{\sqrt{t+3}} + \dfrac{2}{\sqrt 5}\right] = \dfrac{2}{\sqrt 5}$

4. $\int_{-\infty}^{-1} \dfrac{dx}{\sqrt[3]{x-1}} = \lim_{t \to -\infty} \int_t^{-1} (x-1)^{-1/3} dx = \lim_{t \to -\infty} \left[\dfrac{3}{2}(x-1)^{2/3}\right]_t^{-1}$

$= \lim_{t \to -\infty} \left[\dfrac{3}{2}\sqrt[3]{4} - \dfrac{3}{2}(t-1)^{2/3}\right] = -\infty$. Divergent.

6. $\int_{-\infty}^{\infty}(2x^2 - x + 3)dx = \int_{-\infty}^{0}(2x^2 - x + 3)dx + \int_0^\infty(2x^2 - x + 3)dx$.

$\int_{-\infty}^{0}(2x^2 - x + 3)dx = \lim_{t \to -\infty} \left[\dfrac{2}{3}x^3 - \dfrac{1}{2}x^2 + 3x\right]_t^0 = \lim_{t \to -\infty} \left[-\dfrac{2}{3}t^3 + \dfrac{1}{2}t^2 - 3t\right]$

$= \infty$. Divergent.

8. $\int_{-\infty}^{0} e^{3x}\, dx = \lim_{t \to -\infty} \int_t^0 e^{3x}\, dx = \lim_{t \to -\infty} \left[\dfrac{1}{3}e^{3x}\right]_t^0 = \lim_{t \to -\infty} \left[\dfrac{1}{3} - \dfrac{1}{3}e^{3t}\right] = \dfrac{1}{3}$

10. $\int_{-\infty}^{\infty} x^2 e^{-x^3}\, dx = \int_{-\infty}^{0} x^2 e^{-x^3}\, dx + \int_0^\infty x^2 e^{-x^3}\, dx$. $\int_{-\infty}^{0} x^2 e^{-x^3}\, dx$

$= \lim_{t \to -\infty} \left[(-1/3)e^{-x^3}\right]_t^0 = -\dfrac{1}{3} + \dfrac{1}{3}\lim_{t \to -\infty} e^{-t^3} = \infty$. Divergent.

12. $\int_0^\infty \dfrac{x\, dx}{(x+2)(x+3)} = \lim_{t \to \infty} \int_0^t \left[\dfrac{-2}{x+2} + \dfrac{3}{x+3}\right]dx = \lim_{t \to \infty} \left[3\ln(x+3) - 2\ln(x+2)\right]_0^t$

$= \lim_{t \to \infty} \left[\ln \dfrac{(t+3)^3}{(t+2)^2} - \ln \dfrac{27}{4}\right] = \infty$. Divergent.

14. $\int_1^\infty \sin \pi x \, dx = \lim_{t\to\infty} (-1/\pi) \left[\cos \pi x\right]_1^t = (-1/\pi) \lim_{t\to\infty} (\cos \pi t + 1)$, which

does not exist. Divergent.

16. $\int_{-\infty}^3 \dfrac{dx}{x^2+9} = \lim_{t\to-\infty} \left[\dfrac{1}{3} \tan^{-1}(\dfrac{x}{3})\right]_t^3 = \lim_{t\to-\infty} \dfrac{1}{3}\left[\dfrac{\pi}{4} - \tan^{-1}(\dfrac{t}{3})\right] = \dfrac{1}{3}\left[\dfrac{\pi}{4} + \dfrac{\pi}{2}\right] = \dfrac{\pi}{4}$

18. $\int_0^\infty xe^{-x}dx = \lim_{t\to\infty} \left[-xe^{-x} - e^{-x}\right]_0^t = \lim_{t\to\infty} [1-(t+1)e^{-t}] = 1 - \lim_{t\to\infty} \dfrac{t+1}{e^t}$

$\overset{H}{=} 1 - \lim_{t\to\infty} \dfrac{1}{e^t} = 1-0 = 1$

20. $\int_e^\infty \dfrac{dx}{x(\ln x)^2} = \lim_{t\to\infty} \int_e^t \dfrac{dx}{x(\ln x)^2} = \lim_{t\to\infty} \left[- \dfrac{1}{\ln x}\right]_e^t = \lim_{t\to\infty} \left[1 - \dfrac{1}{\ln t}\right] = 1$

22. $\int_{-\infty}^\infty e^{-|x|}dx = \int_{-\infty}^0 e^x \, dx + \int_0^\infty e^{-x} \, dx.$ $\int_{-\infty}^0 e^x \, dx = \lim_{t\to-\infty} \left[e^x\right]_t^0$

$= \lim_{t\to-\infty} (1-e^t) = 1.$ $\int_0^\infty e^{-x} \, dx = \lim_{t\to\infty} \left[-e^{-x}\right]_0^t = \lim_{t\to\infty} (1-e^{-t}) = 1.$

Therefore $\int_{-\infty}^\infty e^{-|x|} \, dx = 1 + 1 = 2$

24. $\int_{-\infty}^\infty \dfrac{dx}{x^2+4x+6} = \int_{-\infty}^0 \dfrac{dx}{(x+2)^2+2} + \int_0^\infty \dfrac{dx}{(x+2)^2+2}.$ $\int_{-\infty}^0 \dfrac{dx}{(x+2)^2+2}$

$= \lim_{t\to-\infty} \dfrac{1}{\sqrt{2}} \left[\tan^{-1}\left[\dfrac{x+2}{\sqrt{2}}\right]\right]_t^0 = \lim_{t\to-\infty} \dfrac{1}{\sqrt{2}}\left[\tan^{-1}\sqrt{2} - \tan^{-1}\left[\dfrac{t+2}{\sqrt{2}}\right]\right]$

$= \dfrac{1}{\sqrt{2}} \left[\tan^{-1}\sqrt{2} + \dfrac{\pi}{2}\right]$ $\int_0^\infty \dfrac{dx}{(x+2)^2+2} = \lim_{t\to\infty} \dfrac{1}{\sqrt{2}} \left[\tan^{-1}\left[\dfrac{x+2}{\sqrt{2}}\right]\right]_0^t$

$= \dfrac{1}{\sqrt{2}}\left[\dfrac{\pi}{2} - \tan^{-1}\sqrt{2}\right].$ Therefore $\int_{-\infty}^\infty \dfrac{dx}{x^2+4x+6} = \int_{-\infty}^0 + \int_0^\infty = \dfrac{\pi}{\sqrt{2}}$

26. Integrate by parts with $u = \ln x$, $dv = dx/x^3$, $du = dx/x$, $v = -1/2x^2$

$\int_1^\infty \dfrac{\ln x}{x^3} \, dx = \lim_{t\to\infty} \int_1^t \dfrac{\ln x}{x^3} = \lim_{t\to\infty} \left[-\dfrac{1}{2x^2} \ln x\right]_1^t + \dfrac{1}{2} \int_1^t \dfrac{1}{x^3} \, dx\right]$

$= \lim_{t\to\infty} \left[-\dfrac{1}{2} \dfrac{\ln t}{t^2} + 0 - \dfrac{1}{4t^2} + \dfrac{1}{4}\right] = \dfrac{1}{4}$

since, by l'Hospital's Rule, $\lim_{t\to\infty} \dfrac{\ln t}{t^2} = \lim_{t\to\infty} \dfrac{1/t}{2t} = \lim_{t\to\infty} \dfrac{1}{2t^2} = 0$

28. $\int_0^3 \dfrac{dx}{x\sqrt{x}} = \lim_{t\to0^+} \int_t^3 \dfrac{dx}{x^{3/2}} = \lim_{t\to0^+} \left[\dfrac{-2}{\sqrt{x}}\right]_t^3 = \dfrac{-2}{\sqrt{3}} + \lim_{t\to0^+} \dfrac{2}{\sqrt{t}} = \infty.$ Divergent.

30. $\int_1^9 \dfrac{dx}{\sqrt[3]{x-9}} = \lim_{t\to9^-} \int_1^t \dfrac{dx}{\sqrt[3]{x-9}} = \lim_{t\to9^-} \left[\dfrac{3}{2}(x-9)^{2/3}\right]_1^t = \lim_{t\to9^-} \left[\dfrac{3}{2}(t-9)^{2/3}-6\right] = -6$

32. $\int_0^2 \dfrac{dx}{4x-5} = \int_0^{5/4} \dfrac{dx}{4x-5} + \int_{5/4}^2 \dfrac{dx}{4x-5}.$ $\int_0^{5/4} \dfrac{dx}{4x-5}$

$= \lim_{t\to5/4^-} \left[\dfrac{1}{4} \ln|4x-5|\right]_0^t = \lim_{t\to5/4^-} \dfrac{1}{4}\left[\ln|4t-5| - \ln 5\right] = -\infty$ Divergent.

34. $\int_{\pi/4}^{\pi/2} \sec^2 x \, dx = \lim_{t\to\pi/2^-}[\tan x]_{\pi/4}^t = \lim_{t\to\pi/2^-}(\tan t - 1) = \infty.$

Divergent.

239

36. $\int_0^{\pi/4} \frac{\cos x\, dx}{\sqrt{\sin x}} = \lim_{t\to 0^+} \int_t^{\pi/4} \frac{\cos x\, dx}{\sqrt{\sin x}} = \lim_{t\to 0^+} \left[2\sqrt{\sin x}\right]_t^{\pi/4}$

$= \lim_{t\to 0^+} (2\sqrt{1/\sqrt{2}} - 2\sqrt{\sin t}) = 2\sqrt{1/\sqrt{2}} = \frac{2}{2^{1/4}} = 2^{3/4}$

38. $\int_0^9 \frac{dx}{(x+9)\sqrt{x}} = \lim_{t\to 0^+} \int_t^9 \frac{dx}{(x+9)\sqrt{x}} = \lim_{t\to 0^+} \int_{\sqrt{t}}^3 \frac{2u\, du}{(u^2+9)u}$ $[u = \sqrt{x} \Rightarrow x = u^2,$

$dx = 2u\, du] = \lim_{t\to 0^+} \int_{\sqrt{t}}^3 \frac{2\, du}{u^2+9} = \lim_{t\to 0^+} \frac{2}{3} \tan^{-1}(\frac{u}{3})\Big]_{\sqrt{t}}^3 = \frac{2}{3}(\frac{\pi}{4}) = \frac{\pi}{6}$

40. $\int_0^4 \frac{dx}{x^2+x-6} = \int_0^4 \frac{dx}{(x+3)(x-2)} = \int_0^2 \frac{dx}{(x-2)(x+3)} + \int_2^4 \frac{dx}{(x-2)(x+3)}.$

$\int_0^2 \frac{dx}{(x-2)(x+3)} = \lim_{t\to 2^-} \int_0^t \left[\frac{1/5}{x-2} - \frac{1/5}{x+3}\right]dx = \lim_{t\to 2^-} \left[\frac{1}{5} \ln\left|\frac{x-2}{x+3}\right|\right]_0^t$

$= \lim_{t\to 2^-} \frac{1}{5}\left[\ln\left|\frac{t-2}{t+3}\right| - \ln\frac{2}{3}\right] = -\infty.$ **Divergent.**

42. $\int_{\pi/4}^{3\pi/4} \tan x\, dx = \int_{\pi/4}^{\pi/2} \tan x\, dx + \int_{\pi/2}^{3\pi/4} \tan x\, dx.$ $\int_{\pi/4}^{\pi/2} \tan x\, dx$

$= \lim_{t\to \pi/2^-} [\ln|\sec x|]_{\pi/4}^t = \lim_{t\to \pi/2^-} \left[\ln(\sec t) - \ln\sqrt{2}\right] = \infty.$ **Divergent.**

44. $\int_0^2 \frac{x-3}{2x-3}\, dx = \int_0^{3/2} \frac{x-3}{2x-3}\, dx + \int_{3/4}^2 \frac{x-3}{2x-3}\, dx.$ $\int \frac{x-3}{2x-3}\, dx = \frac{1}{2} \int \frac{2x-6}{2x-3}\, dx$

$= \frac{1}{2} \int \left[1 - \frac{3}{2x-3}\right]dx = x/2 - (3/4)\ln|2x-3| + C,$ so $\int_0^{3/2} \frac{x-3}{2x-3}\, dx$

$= \lim_{t\to 3/2^-} \frac{1}{4}\left[2x - 3\ln|2x-3|\right]_0^t = \infty.$ **Divergent.**

46. Integrate by parts with $u = \ln x$, $dv = dx/\sqrt{x} \Rightarrow du = dx/x$, $v =$

$2\sqrt{x}:$ $\int_0^1 \frac{\ln x}{\sqrt{x}}\, dx = \lim_{t\to 0^+} \int_t^1 \frac{\ln x}{\sqrt{x}}\, dx = \lim_{t\to 0^+} \left\{2\sqrt{x}\ln x\Big]_t^1 - 2\int_t^1 dx/\sqrt{x}\right\}$

$= \lim_{t\to 0^+} \left\{-2\sqrt{t}\ln t - 4[\sqrt{x}]_t^1\right\} = \lim_{t\to 0^+} (-2\sqrt{t}\ln t - 4 + 4\sqrt{t}) = -4,$

since, by l'Hospital's Rule, $\lim_{t\to 0^+} \sqrt{t}\ln t = \lim_{t\to 0^+} \frac{\ln t}{t^{-1/2}}$

$= \lim_{t\to 0^+} \frac{1/t}{-(1/2)t^{-3/2}} = \lim_{t\to 0^+} (-2\sqrt{t}) = 0$

48.

Area $= \int_{-2}^\infty e^{-x/2}\, dx = -2 \lim_{t\to\infty} [e^{-x/2}]_{-2}^t$

$= -2 \lim_{t\to\infty} e^{-t/2} + 2e = 2e$

50.

Area $= \int_0^\infty \frac{dx}{\sqrt{x+1}} = \lim_{t\to\infty} [2\sqrt{x+1}]_0^t = \infty,$ so the

area is infinite.

240

52.

$$\text{Area} = \int_3^7 \frac{dx}{\sqrt{x-3}} = \lim_{t \to 3^+} \left[2\sqrt{x-3} \right]_t^7$$

$$= 4 - 2 \lim_{t \to 3^+} 2\sqrt{t-3} = 4-0 = 4$$

54. $$\int_2^\infty \frac{dx}{x\sqrt{x^2-4}} = \int_2^3 \frac{dx}{x\sqrt{x^2-4}} + \int_3^\infty \frac{dx}{x\sqrt{x^2-4}} = \lim_{t \to 2^+} \int_t^3 \frac{dx}{x\sqrt{x^2-4}} + \lim_{t \to \infty} \int_3^t \frac{dx}{x\sqrt{x^2-4}}$$

$$\int \frac{dx}{x\sqrt{x^2-4}} = \int \frac{2 \sec \theta \tan \theta \, d\theta}{2 \sec \theta \cdot 2 \tan \theta} \quad [x = 2 \sec \theta] \quad = \frac{1}{2}\theta + C = \frac{1}{2}\sec^{-1}(\frac{x}{2})$$

$$+ C, \text{ so } \int_2^\infty \frac{dx}{x\sqrt{x^2-4}} = \lim_{t \to 2^+} \left[\frac{1}{2} \sec^{-1}(\frac{x}{2}) \right]_t^3 + \lim_{t \to \infty} \left[\frac{1}{2} \sec^{-1}\left[\frac{x}{2}\right] \right]_3^t$$

$$= \frac{1}{2} \sec^{-1}(\frac{3}{2}) - 0 + \frac{1}{2}(\frac{\pi}{2}) - \frac{1}{2} \sec^{-1}(\frac{3}{2}) = \frac{\pi}{4}$$

56. Let $u = \ln x$. Then $du = dx/x \Rightarrow \int_e^\infty \frac{dx}{x(\ln x)^p} = \int_1^\infty \frac{du}{u^p}$. By Ex. 4,

this converges to $1/(p-1)$ if $p > 1$ and diverges otherwise.

58. For n a nonnegative integer, integration by parts with $u = x^{n+1}$,

dv = $e^{-x}dx$, gives $\int x^{n+1}e^{-x} \, dx = -x^{n+1}e^{-x} + (n+1)\int x^n e^{-x} \, dx$, so

$\int_0^\infty x^{n+1}e^{-x} \, dx = \lim_{t \to \infty} \int_0^t x^{n+1}e^{-x} \, dx = \lim_{t \to \infty} [-x^{n+1}e^{-x}]_0^t$

$+ (n+1)\int_0^\infty x^n e^{-x} \, dx = \lim_{t \to \infty} \frac{-t^{n+1}}{e^t} + (n+1)\int_0^\infty x^n e^{-x} \, dx$

$= (n+1)\int_0^\infty x^n e^{-x} \, dx$. Now $\int_0^\infty x^0 e^{-x} \, dx = \lim_{t \to \infty} \int_0^t e^{-x} \, dx = \lim_{t \to \infty} [-e^{-x}]_0^t$

$= 1$, so $\int_0^\infty x^1 e^{-x} \, dx = 1 \cdot 1 = 1$, $\int_0^\infty x^2 e^{-x} \, dx = 2 \cdot 1 = 2$, and

$\int_0^\infty x^3 e^{-x} \, dx = 3 \cdot 2 = 6$. In general, we guess that $\int_0^\infty x^n e^{-x} \, dx = n!$

$= 1 \cdot 2 \cdot 3 \cdots n$ when n is a positive integer. (Since $0! = 1$, our guess

holds for $n = 0$ too.) Our guess works for $n \leq 3$.

Suppose that $\int_0^\infty x^n e^{-x} \, dx = n!$ for some positive integer n. Then

$\int_0^\infty x^{n+1}e^{-x} \, dx = (n+1)n! = (n+1)!$, so the formula holds for n+1. By

induction, the formula holds for all integers $n \geq 0$.

60. Assume without loss of generality that $a < b$. Then

$\int_{-\infty}^a f(x)dx + \int_a^\infty f(x)dx = \lim_{t \to -\infty} \int_t^a f(x)dx + \lim_{u \to \infty} \int_a^u f(x)dx$

$= \lim_{t \to -\infty} \int_t^a f(x)dx + \lim_{u \to \infty} \left\{ \int_a^b f(x)dx + \int_b^u f(x)dx \right\} = \lim_{t \to -\infty} \int_t^a f(x)dx$

$+ \int_a^b f(x)dx + \lim_{u \to \infty} \int_b^u f(x)dx$

$$= \lim_{t \to -\infty} \left\{ \int_t^a f(x)dx + \int_a^b f(x)dx \right\} + \int_b^\infty f(x)dx$$

$$= \lim_{t \to -\infty} \int_t^b f(x)dx + \int_b^\infty f(x)dx = \int_{-\infty}^b f(x)dx + \int_b^\infty f(x)dx$$

62. $\dfrac{\sqrt{1+\sqrt{x}}}{\sqrt{x}} > \dfrac{1}{\sqrt{x}}$ on $[1, \infty)$. $\int_1^\infty \dfrac{dx}{\sqrt{x}}$ is divergent by Ex. 4, so $\displaystyle\int_1^\infty \dfrac{\sqrt{1+\sqrt{x}}}{\sqrt{x}}\, dx$

is divergent by the Comparison Theorem.

64. $\dfrac{1}{\sqrt{x^3+1}} \le \dfrac{1}{x^{3/2}}$ on $[1, \infty)$. $\int_1^\infty \dfrac{dx}{x^{3/2}}$ converges by Ex. 4, so

$\displaystyle\int_1^\infty \dfrac{dx}{\sqrt{x^3+1}}$ converges by the Comparison Theorem.

Section 7.9

Exercises 7.9

2. Let $u = \dfrac{x}{2}$ and use Formula 72: $\int \csc^3(\dfrac{x}{2})dx = 2 \int \csc^3 u\, du$

$= -\csc u \cot u + \ln|\csc u - \cot u| + C$

$= -\csc(x/2) \cot(x/2) + \ln|\csc(x/2) - \cot(x/2)| + C$

4. By Formula 32, $\int \dfrac{\sqrt{4-3x^2}}{x}\, dx = \int \dfrac{\sqrt{4-u^2}}{u/\sqrt{3}} \dfrac{du}{\sqrt{3}}$ $\quad [u = \sqrt{3}x]$

$= \int \dfrac{\sqrt{4-u^2}}{u}\, du = \sqrt{4-u^2} - 2\ln\left|\dfrac{2 + \sqrt{4-u^2}}{u}\right| + C_1 = \sqrt{4-3x^2}$

$- 2\ln\left|\dfrac{2 + \sqrt{4-3x^2}}{\sqrt{3}x}\right| + C_1 = \sqrt{4-3x^2} - 2\ln|(2 + \sqrt{4-3x^2})/x| + C$

6. Let $u = \sin x$. Then $du = \cos x\, dx$, so $\int \dfrac{\sin x \cos x}{\sqrt{1 + \sin x}}\, dx$

$= \int \dfrac{u\, du}{\sqrt{1+u}} = \dfrac{2}{3}(u-2)\sqrt{1+u} + C$ $\quad$ [Formula 55]

$= -\dfrac{2}{3}(2 - \sin x)\sqrt{1 + \sin x} + C$

8. Let $u = x^2$. Then $du = 2x\, dx$, so $\int x^3 \sin^{-1}(x^2)dx$

$= \dfrac{1}{2}\int u \sin^{-1}u\, du = \dfrac{2u^2-1}{8}\sin^{-1}u + \dfrac{u\sqrt{1-u^2}}{8} + C$ $\quad$ [Formula 90]

$$= \frac{2x^4-1}{8} \sin^{-1}(x^2) + \frac{x^2\sqrt{1-x^4}}{8} + C$$

10. Let u = 3x. Then du = 3 dx, so $\int x^2 \cos 3x\, dx$

$$= \frac{1}{27} \int u^2 \cos u\, du = \frac{1}{27}(u^2 \sin u - 2\int u \sin u\, du) \quad \text{[Formula 85]}$$

$$= \frac{1}{3} x^2 \sin 3x - \frac{2}{27}(\sin 3x - 3x \cos 3x) + C \quad \text{[Formula 82]}$$

$$= \frac{1}{27}[(9x^2-2) \sin 3x + 6x \cos 3x] + C$$

12. Let $u = x^2$. Then du = 2x dx, so by Formula 48, $\int \frac{x^5\, dx}{x^2+\sqrt{2}}$

$$= \frac{1}{2} \int \frac{u^2}{u+\sqrt{2}}\, du = \frac{1}{2}\cdot\frac{1}{2}[(u+\sqrt{2})^2 - 4\sqrt{2}(u+\sqrt{2}) + 4\ln|u+\sqrt{2}|] + C$$

$$= \frac{1}{4}[(x^2+\sqrt{2})^2 - 4\sqrt{2}(x^2+\sqrt{2}) + 4\ln(x^2+\sqrt{2})] + C$$

$$= (1/4)x^4 - (1/\sqrt{2})x^2 + \ln(x^2+\sqrt{2}) + K \quad [\text{OR: Let } u = x^2+\sqrt{2}.]$$

14. Let u = 2x. Then du = 2 dx, so $\int \sin^6 2x\, dx = \frac{1}{2} \int \sin^6 u\, du$

$$= \frac{1}{2} \left(- \frac{1}{6}\sin^5 u \cos u + \frac{5}{6} \int \sin^4 u\, du\right) \text{ [Formula 73]}$$

$$= \frac{-1}{12} \sin^5 u \cos u + \frac{5}{12}\left[\frac{-1}{4}\sin^3 u \cos u + \frac{3}{4} \int \sin^2 u\, du\right] \text{ [Formula 73]}$$

$$= \frac{-1}{12}\sin^5 u \cos u - \frac{5}{48}\sin^3 u \cos u + \frac{5}{16}\left[\frac{1}{2}u - \frac{1}{4}\sin 2u\right] + C \text{ [Formula 63]}$$

$$= \frac{-1}{12} \sin^5 2x \cos 2x - \frac{5}{48} \sin^3 2x \cos 2x - \frac{5}{64} \sin 4x + \frac{5}{16} x + C$$

16. Let $u = e^x$. Then x = ln u, dx = du/u, so $\int \frac{dx}{e^x(1+2e^x)} = \int \frac{du/u}{u(1+2u)}$

$$= \int \frac{du}{u^2(1+2u)} = \frac{-1}{u} + 2\ln\left|\frac{1+2u}{u}\right| + C \quad \text{[Formula 50]}$$

$$= - e^{-x} + 2\ln(e^{-x} + 2) + C$$

18. Let u = x-2. Then $\int \frac{x\, dx}{\sqrt{x^2-4x}} = \int \frac{(x-2) + 2}{\sqrt{(x-2)^2-4}}\, dx = \int \frac{u\, du}{\sqrt{u^2-4}} + 2 \int \frac{du}{\sqrt{u^2-4}}$

$$= \frac{1}{2} \int v^{-1/2}dv + 2 \int \frac{du}{\sqrt{u^2-4}} \quad [v = u^2-4]$$

$$= v^{1/2} + 2\ln|u + \sqrt{u^2-4}| + C \quad \text{[Formulas 2 and 43]}$$

$$= \sqrt{x^2-4x} + 2\ln|x - 2 + \sqrt{x^2-4x}| + C$$

20. $\int_0^\infty x^4 e^{-x}\, dx = \lim_{t\to\infty} \int_0^t x^4 e^{-x}\, dx$. Since $\int x^4 e^{-x}\, dx$

$$= - x^4 e^{-x} + 4 \int x^3 e^{-x}\, dx \quad \text{[Formula 97]}$$

$$= - x^4 e^{-x} + 4(- x^3 e^{-x} + 3 \int x^2 e^{-x}\, dx) \quad \text{[Formula 97]}$$

$$= - (x^4 + 4x^3)e^{-x} + 12(- x^2 e^{-x} + 2 \int xe^{-x}\, dx) \quad \text{[Formula 97]}$$

$$= - (x^4 + 4x^3 + 12x^2)e^{-x} + 24[(- x - 1)e^{-x}] + C \quad \text{[Formula 96]}$$

$$= - (x^4 + 4x^3 + 12x^2 + 24x + 24)e^{-x} + C, \text{ we find that } \int_0^\infty x^4 e^{-x} \, dx$$

$$= - \lim_{t \to \infty} (t^4 + 4t^3 + 12t^2 + 24t + 24)e^{-t} + 24e^0 = 0 + 24 = 24$$

Chapter 7 Review

Review Exercises for Chapter 7

2. Let $u = \cos x$. Then $\int \frac{\sin^3 x}{\cos x} \, dx = \int \frac{(1-\cos^2 x)\sin x}{\cos x} \, dx = - \int \frac{1-u^2}{u} \, du$

$= \int (u - \frac{1}{u}) du = \frac{u^2}{2} - \ln|u| + C = \frac{1}{2} \cos^2 x - \ln|\cos x| + C$

4. Integrate by parts twice, first with $u = x^2$, $dv = e^{-3x} dx \Rightarrow du = 2x \, dx$, $v = -\frac{1}{3}e^{-3x}$: $\int x^2 e^{-3x} \, dx = - \frac{1}{3}x^2 e^{-3x} + \frac{2}{3} \int xe^{-3x} \, dx$

$= -\frac{1}{3}x^2 e^{-3x} \, dx + \frac{2}{3}\left[-\frac{1}{3}xe^{-3x} + \frac{1}{3} \int e^{-3x} \, dx\right] = -\left[\frac{1}{3}x^2 + \frac{2}{9}x + \frac{2}{27}\right]e^{-3x} + C$

6. $\int \frac{x^2+1}{x-1} \, dx = \int (x + 1 + \frac{2}{x-1}) dx = \frac{1}{2}x^2 + x + 2 \ln|x-1| + C$

8. Let $u = \tan \theta$. Then $\int \frac{\sec^2 \theta \, d\theta}{1 - \tan \theta} = \int \frac{du}{1-u} = - \ln|1-u| + C$

$= - \ln|1 - \tan \theta| + C$

10. Let $u = 2x$. Then $\int x \sin^2 x \, dx = \frac{1}{2} \int x(1 - \cos 2x) dx$

$= \frac{x^2}{4} - \frac{1}{8} \int 2x \cos 2x \, 2 \, dx = \frac{x^2}{4} - \frac{1}{8} \int u \cos u \, du$

$= \frac{x^2}{4} - \frac{1}{8}(u \sin u + \cos u) + C = \frac{x^2}{4} - \frac{x}{4} \sin 2x - \frac{1}{8} \cos 2x + C$

12. $\int \frac{dt}{\sin^2 t + \cos 2t} = \int \frac{dt}{\sin^2 t + (\cos^2 t - \sin^2 t)} = \int \frac{dt}{\cos^2 t}$

$= \int \sec^2 t \, dt = \tan t + C$

14. Let $u = x-1$. Then $\int \frac{dx}{\sqrt{8+2x-x^2}} = \int \frac{dx}{\sqrt{9-(x-1)^2}} = \int \frac{du}{\sqrt{9-u^2}}$

$= \sin^{-1}(\frac{u}{3}) + C = \sin^{-1}\left[\frac{x-1}{3}\right] + C$

16. Let $u = \tan^{-1} x$. Then $x = \tan u$, $dx = \sec^2 u \, du$, so $\int x(\tan^{-1} x)^2 dx$

$= \int (\tan u)u^2 \sec^2 u \, du = \int u^2 \, d(\frac{1}{2} \tan^2 u) = \frac{u^2}{2} \tan^2 u - \int u \tan^2 u \, du$

$$= \frac{u^2}{2} \tan^2 u - \int u \, d(\tan u - u) = \frac{u^2}{2} \tan^2 u - u(\tan u - u)$$

$$+ \int (\tan u - u) du = \frac{u^2}{2} \tan^2 u + u^2 - u \tan u + \ln|\sec u| - \frac{1}{2} u^2 + C$$

$$= \frac{u^2}{2} (\tan^2 u + 1) - u \tan u + \ln|\sec u| + C$$

$$= \frac{1}{2}(x^2+1)(\tan^{-1}x)^2 - x \tan^{-1}x + \ln\sqrt{x^2+1} + C$$

or $\frac{1}{2}(x^2+1)(\tan^{-1}x)^2 - x \tan^{-1}x + \frac{1}{2} \ln(x^2+1) + C$

18. $\displaystyle \int \frac{dx}{x^3-2x^2+x} = \int \frac{dx}{(x-1)^2 x} = \int \left[\frac{-1}{x-1} + \frac{1}{(x-1)^2} + \frac{1}{x} \right] dx$

$$= -1/(x-1) + \ln|x/(x-1)| + C$$

20. Let $x = \tan \theta$, $-\pi/2 < \theta < \pi/2$. Then $\displaystyle \int \frac{dx}{x^2\sqrt{1+x^2}} = \int \frac{\sec^2\theta \, d\theta}{\tan^2\theta \, \sec \theta}$

$$= \int \frac{\sec \theta \, d\theta}{\tan^2\theta} = \int \frac{\cos \theta \, d\theta}{\sin^2\theta} = \int \frac{du}{u^2} \quad [u = \sin \theta]$$

$$= -1/u + C = -1/\sin \theta + C = - \frac{\sqrt{1+x^2}}{x} + C$$

22. Let $u = e^x$. Then $x = \ln u$, $dx = du/u$, so $\displaystyle \int \frac{dx}{1+e^x} = \int \frac{du/u}{1+u}$

$$= \int \left[\frac{1}{u} - \frac{1}{u+1} \right] du = \ln u - \ln(u+1) + C$$

$$= \ln e^x - \ln(1+e^x) + C = x - \ln(1+e^x) + C$$

24. Let $t = \tan(x/2)$. Then $\displaystyle \int \frac{dx}{5 - 3 \cos x} = \int \frac{2dt/(1+t^2)}{5-3(1-t^2)/(1+t^2)}$

$$= \int \frac{2 \, dt}{5(1+t^2)-3(1-t^2)} = \int \frac{2 \, dt}{8t^2+2} = \frac{1}{2} \int \frac{2 \, dt}{(2t)^2+1} = \frac{1}{2} \int \frac{du}{u^2+1} \quad [u = 2t]$$

$$= \frac{1}{2} \tan^{-1}u + C = \frac{1}{2} \tan^{-1}(2t) + C = \frac{1}{2} \tan^{-1}[2 \tan(x/2)] + C$$

26. $\displaystyle \int \sqrt{1 + \cos x} \, dx = \int \sqrt{2 \cos^2(x/2)} \, dx = \sqrt{2} \int |\cos(x/2)| dx$

On an interval where $\cos(x/2) \geq 0$, this $= 2\sqrt{2} \sin(x/2) + C$

On an interval where $\cos(x/2) < 0$, this $= -2\sqrt{2} \sin(x/2) + C$

28. Let $u = x+1$. Then $\displaystyle \int \frac{x^3}{(x+1)^{10}} \, dx = \int \frac{(u-1)^3}{u^{10}} \, dx = \int \frac{u^3-3u^2+3u-1}{u^{10}} \, du$

$$= \int (u^{-7}-3u^{-8}+3u^{-9}-u^{-10}) du = \frac{u^{-6}}{-6} - 3 \frac{u^{-7}}{-7} + 3 \frac{u^{-8}}{-8} - \frac{u^{-9}}{-9} + C$$

$$= \frac{-1}{6(x+1)^6} + \frac{3}{7(x+1)^7} - \frac{3}{8(x+1)^8} + \frac{1}{9(x+1)^9} + C$$

30. Integrate by parts twice, first with $u = (\arcsin x)^2$, $dv = dx$:

$$\int (\arcsin x)^2 \, dx = x(\arcsin x)^2 - \int x \cdot 2 \arcsin x \cdot \frac{dx}{\sqrt{1-x^2}}$$

$$= x(\arcsin x)^2 + 2\int \arcsin x \, d\left[\sqrt{1-x^2}\right] = x(\sin^{-1}x)^2 + 2\sqrt{1-x^2}\,\sin^{-1}x$$

$$- 2 \int \sqrt{1-x^2}\,\frac{dx}{\sqrt{1-x^2}} = x(\arcsin x)^2 + 2\sqrt{1-x^2}\,\arcsin x - 2x + C$$

32. $\displaystyle\int \frac{\sin x}{1 + \sin x}\, dx = \int \frac{\sin x\,(1 - \sin x)}{1 - \sin^2 x}\, dx = \int \frac{\sin x - \sin^2 x}{\cos^2 x}\, dx$

$\displaystyle = \int (\sec x \tan x - \tan^2 x)\,dx = \sec x - \int (\sec^2 x - 1)\,dx$

$= \sec x - \tan x + x + C$

34. $\displaystyle\int_{-1}^{1} \frac{dx}{2x+1} = \int_{-1}^{-1/2} \frac{dx}{2x+1} + \int_{-1/2}^{1} \frac{dx}{2x+1}. \quad \int_{-1/2}^{1} \frac{dx}{2x+1} = \lim_{t \to -1/2^+} \int_{t}^{1} \frac{dx}{2x+1}$

$\displaystyle = \lim_{t \to -1/2^+} \frac{1}{2}\ln|2x+1|\Big]_{t}^{1} = \infty$, so $\displaystyle\int_{-1}^{1} \frac{dx}{2x+1}$ is divergent

36. Let $x = 2\theta$. Then $\displaystyle\int_{0}^{\pi/4} \cos^5(2\theta)\,d\theta = \frac{1}{2}\int_{0}^{\pi/2} \cos^5 x \, dx$

$\displaystyle = \frac{1}{2}\int_{0}^{\pi/2}(1 - \sin^2 x)^2 \cos x \, dx = \frac{1}{2}\int_{0}^{1}(1-u^2)^2 du \quad [u = \sin x]$

$\displaystyle = \frac{1}{2}\int_{0}^{1}(u^4 - 2u^2 + 1)\,du = \frac{1}{2}[u^5/5 - 2u^3/3 + u]_{0}^{1} = \frac{1}{2}\left[\frac{1}{5} - \frac{2}{3} + 1\right] = \frac{4}{15}$

38. Let $u = \sqrt{y-2}$. Then $y = u^2 + 2$, so $\displaystyle\int \frac{y\,dy}{\sqrt{y-2}} = \int \frac{(u^2+2)\,2u\,du}{u}$

$\displaystyle = 2 \int (u^2 + 2)\,du = 2\left[\frac{u^3}{3} + 2u\right] + C$, so $\displaystyle\int_{2}^{6} \frac{y\,dy}{\sqrt{y-2}} = \lim_{t \to 2^+} \int_{t}^{6} \frac{y\,dy}{\sqrt{y-2}}$

$\displaystyle = \lim_{t \to 2^+}\left[\frac{2}{3}(y-2)^{3/2} + 4\sqrt{y-2}\right]_{t}^{6} = \lim_{t \to 2^+}\left[\frac{16}{3} + 8 - \frac{2}{3}(t-2)^{3/2} - 4\sqrt{t-2}\right] = \frac{40}{3}$

40. Let $u = 1/x$. Then $du = -\frac{1}{x^2}\,dx$, so $\displaystyle\int_{1}^{4} \frac{e^{1/x}}{x^2}\, dx = \int_{1/4}^{1} e^u \, du$

$\displaystyle = e^u\Big]_{1/4}^{1} = e - e^{1/4}$

42. $\displaystyle\int_{0}^{\infty} \frac{dx}{(x+1)^2(x+2)} = \lim_{t \to \infty}\int_{0}^{t}\left\{\frac{1}{x+2} - \frac{1}{x+1} + \frac{1}{(x+1)^2}\right\}dx$

$\displaystyle = \lim_{t \to \infty}\left[\ln\left[\frac{x+2}{x+1}\right] - 1/(x+1)\right]_{0}^{t} = 1 - \ln 2$

44. $\displaystyle\int_{-3}^{3} x\sqrt{1+x^4}\, dx = 0$ since the integrand is an odd function.

46. Let $u = \ln x$. Then $du = dx/x$, so $\displaystyle\int_{1}^{e} \frac{dx}{x[1+(\ln x)^2]} = \int_{0}^{1} \frac{du}{1+u^2}$

$\displaystyle = \left[\tan^{-1} u\right]_{0}^{1} = \pi/4 - 0 = \frac{\pi}{4}$

48. $\int_{-1}^{1}(x^{-1/3}+x^{-4/3})dx = \int_{-1}^{0}(x^{-1/3}+x^{-4/3})dx + \int_{0}^{1}(x^{-1/3}+x^{-4/3})dx$

$\int_{0}^{1}(x^{-1/3}+x^{-4/3})dx = \lim_{t\to0^+}\int_{t}^{1}(x^{-1/3}+x^{-4/3})dx = \lim_{t\to0^+}\left[\frac{3}{2}x^{2/3}-3x^{-1/3}\right]_{t}^{1}$

$= \lim_{t\to0^+}\left[\frac{3}{2} - 3 - \frac{3}{2}t^{2/3} + 3t^{-1/3}\right] = \infty.$ Divergent.

50. $\int_{1}^{\infty}\frac{\tan^{-1}x}{x^2}dx = \lim_{t\to\infty}\int_{1}^{t}\frac{\tan^{-1}x}{x^2}dx.$ Integrate by parts: $\int\frac{\tan^{-1}x}{x^2}dx$

$= \frac{-\tan^{-1}x}{x} + \int\frac{1}{x}\frac{dx}{1+x^2} = \frac{-\tan^{-1}x}{x} + \int\left[\frac{1}{x} - \frac{x}{x^2+1}\right]dx = \frac{-\tan^{-1}x}{x} + \ln|x|$

$- \frac{1}{2}\ln(x^2+1) + C = \frac{-\tan^{-1}x}{x} + \frac{1}{2}\ln\frac{x^2}{x^2+1} + C,$ so $\int_{1}^{\infty}\frac{\tan^{-1}x}{x^2}dx$

$= \lim_{t\to\infty}\left[-\frac{\tan^{-1}x}{x} + \frac{1}{2}\ln\frac{x^2}{x^2+1}\right]_{1}^{t} = \lim_{t\to\infty}\left[-\frac{\tan^{-1}t}{t} + \frac{1}{2}\ln\frac{t^2}{t^2+1} + \frac{\pi}{4} - \frac{1}{2}\ln\frac{1}{2}\right]$

$= 0 + \frac{1}{2}\ln 1 + \frac{\pi}{4} + \frac{1}{2}\ln 2 = \frac{\pi}{4} + \frac{1}{2}\ln 2$

52. $\int\tan^5 x\,dx = \frac{1}{4}\tan^4 x - \int\tan^3 x\,dx$ [Formula 75 with n = 5]

$= \frac{1}{4}\tan^4 x - \frac{1}{2}\tan^2 x - \ln|\cos x| + C$ [Formula 69]

54. Let u = sin x. Then du = cos x dx, so $\int\frac{\cot x\,dx}{\sqrt{1 + 2\sin x}} = \int\frac{du}{u\sqrt{1+2u}}$

$= \ln\left|\frac{\sqrt{1+2u} - 1}{\sqrt{1+2u} + 1}\right| + C$ [Formula 57 with a = 1 and b = 2]

$= \ln\left|\frac{\sqrt{1 + 2\sin x} - 1}{\sqrt{1 + 2\sin x} + 1}\right| + C$

56. $f(x) = \sqrt{\sin x}$, $\Delta x = (\pi/2-0)/10 = \pi/20$.

(a) $T = \frac{\pi}{20}[\frac{1}{2}f(0) + f(\pi/20) + f(\pi/10) + f(3\pi/20) + f(\pi/5) + f(\pi/4)$

$+ f(3\pi/10) + f(7\pi/20) + f(2\pi/5) + f(9\pi/20) + \frac{1}{2}f(\pi/2)] \approx 1.185197$

(b) $S = \frac{\pi/20}{3}[f(0) + 4f(\pi/20) + 2f(\pi/10) + 4f(3\pi/20) + 2f(\pi/5)$

$+ 4f(\pi/4) + 2f(3\pi/10) + 4f(7\pi/20) + 2f(2\pi/5) + 4f(9\pi/20)$

$+ f(\pi/2)] \approx 1.193089$

58. $f(x) = 1/\ln x$, $f'(x) = -(\ln x)^{-2}(1/x) = -1/[x(\ln x)^2]$,

$f''(x) = \frac{2}{x^2(\ln x)^3} + \frac{1}{x^2(\ln x)^2}$, $f'''(x) = -\frac{6}{x^3(\ln x)^4} - \frac{6}{x^3(\ln x)^3}$

$- \frac{2}{x^3(\ln x)^2}$, $f^{(4)}(x) = \frac{24}{x^4(\ln x)^5} + \frac{36}{x^4(\ln x)^4} + \frac{22}{x^4(\ln x)^3}$

$+ \frac{6}{x^4(\ln x)^2}$. On [2,4], we have x ≥ 2 and ln x ≥ ln 2, so $\frac{1}{x^4} \leq \frac{1}{16}$

and $\dfrac{1}{(\ln x)^k} \le \dfrac{1}{(\ln 2)^k}$ $\Rightarrow$ $|f^{(4)}(x)| \le \dfrac{24}{16 \cdot (\ln 2)^5} + \dfrac{36}{16 \cdot (\ln 2)^4}$

$+ \dfrac{22}{16 \cdot (\ln 2)^3} + \dfrac{6}{16 \cdot (\ln 2)^2} = 24.031396\ldots$. We take $M = 24.0314$.

Then $\dfrac{M(b-a)^5}{180n^4} < .005 \iff .9n^4 > (24.0314)2^5 \iff n^4 > 854.44977\ldots$

$\iff n \ge 6$. Taking $n = 6$, we estimate $\displaystyle\int_2^4 \dfrac{dx}{\ln x} \approx \dfrac{(4-2)/6}{3}\left[\dfrac{1}{\ln 2}\right.$

$+ \dfrac{4}{\ln(7/3)} + \dfrac{2}{\ln(8/3)} + \dfrac{4}{\ln 3} + \dfrac{2}{\ln(10/3)} + \dfrac{4}{\ln(11/3)} + \left.\dfrac{1}{\ln 4}\right] \approx 1.92$

60. The line $y = 3$ intersects the hyperbola $y^2 - x^2 = 1$ at two points on its upper branch, namely $(-2\sqrt{2}, 3)$ and $(2\sqrt{2}, 3)$. The desired area is

$A = \displaystyle\int_{-2\sqrt{2}}^{2\sqrt{2}} \left[3 - \sqrt{x^2+1}\right]dx = 2 \int_0^{2\sqrt{2}} \left[3 - \sqrt{x^2+1}\right]dx$

$= 2\left[3x - \dfrac{x}{2}\sqrt{x^2+1} - \dfrac{1}{2}\ln\left[x + \sqrt{x^2+1}\right]\right]_0^{2\sqrt{2}}$ [Formula 21]

$= \left[6x - x\sqrt{x^2+1} - \ln\left[x + \sqrt{x^2+1}\right]\right]_0^{2\sqrt{2}} = 12\sqrt{2} - 2\sqrt{2}\cdot 3 - \ln(2\sqrt{2}+3)$

$= 6\sqrt{2} - \ln(3+2\sqrt{2})$

[Another method: $A = 2\displaystyle\int_1^3 \sqrt{y^2-1}\,dy$ and use Formula 39.]

62. The curves $y = 1/(2\pm\sqrt{x})$ are defined for $x \ge 0$. For $x > 0$, $1/(2-\sqrt{x}) > 1/(2+\sqrt{x})$. Thus the required area is $\displaystyle\int_0^1 \left[\dfrac{1}{2-\sqrt{x}} - \dfrac{1}{2+\sqrt{x}}\right]dx$

$= \displaystyle\int_0^1 \left[\dfrac{1}{2-u} - \dfrac{1}{2+u}\right]2u\,du$ $[u = \sqrt{x}]$ $= 2\int_0^1 \left[-\dfrac{u}{u-2} - \dfrac{u}{u+2}\right]du$

$= 2\displaystyle\int_0^1 \left[-1 - \dfrac{2}{u-2} - 1 + \dfrac{2}{u+2}\right]du = 2\left[2\ln|(u+2)/(u-2)| - 2u\right]_0^1$

$= 4\ln 3 - 4$

64. If n is a positive integer, then $\displaystyle\int (\ln x)^n\,dx$

$= x(\ln x)^n - \displaystyle\int x\cdot n(\ln x)^{n-1}\cdot\dfrac{1}{x}\,dx$ [integration by parts]

$= x(\ln x)^n - n\displaystyle\int (\ln x)^{n-1}\,dx$, so $\displaystyle\int_0^1 (\ln x)^n\,dx$

$= \displaystyle\lim_{t\to 0^+} \int_t^1 (\ln x)^n\,dx = \lim_{t\to 0^+} \left[x(\ln x)^n\right]_t^1 - n\lim_{t\to 0^+} \int_t^1 (\ln x)^{n-1}\,dx$

$= -\displaystyle\lim_{t\to 0^+} \dfrac{(\ln t)^n}{1/t} - n\int_0^1 (\ln x)^{n-1}\,dx = -n\int_0^1 (\ln x)^{n-1}\,dx$

[by repeated application of l'Hospital's rule]

We want to prove that $\int_0^1 (\ln x)^n \, dx = (-1)^n \, n!$ for every positive integer n. For n = 1, we have $\int_0^1 (\ln x)^1 \, dx = (-1) \int_0^1 (\ln x)^0 \, dx$

$= - \int_0^1 dx = -1 \left[\text{or } \int_0^1 \ln x \, dx = \lim_{t \to 0^+} \left[x \ln x - x \right]_t^1 = -1 \right]$.

Assuming that the formula holds for the integer n, we find that

$\int_0^1 (\ln x)^{n+1} \, dx = -(n+1) \int_0^1 (\ln x)^n \, dx = -(n+1)(-1)^n \, n!$

$= (-1)^{n+1} (n+1)!$ This is the formula for n+1. Thus the formula holds for all positive integers n by induction.

CHAPTER 8

Exercises 8.1   ABBREVIATION: V = Volume

2. $V = \int_0^4 \pi(x^{3/2})^2 dx = \pi\left[\dfrac{x^4}{4}\right]_0^4 = 64\pi$

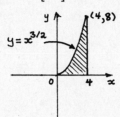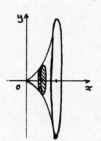

4. $V = \int_{\pi/2}^{\pi} \pi \sin^2 x \, dx = \pi\left[\dfrac{x}{2} - \dfrac{1}{4}\sin 2x\right]_{\pi/2}^{\pi} = \pi\left(\dfrac{\pi}{2} - 0 - \dfrac{\pi}{4} + 0\right) = \dfrac{\pi^2}{4}$

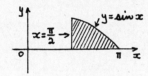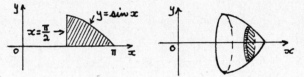

6. $V = \int_0^1 \pi(y-y^2)^2 dy = \pi\int_0^1 (y^4 - 2y^3 + y^2)\,dy = \pi\left[\dfrac{y^5}{5} - \dfrac{y^4}{2} + \dfrac{y^3}{3}\right]_0^1$

$= \pi\left(\dfrac{1}{5} - \dfrac{1}{2} + \dfrac{1}{3}\right) = \dfrac{\pi}{30}$

8. $V = \pi\int_{-1}^1 \left[(3-x^2)^2 - (x^2+1)^2\right] dx = \pi\int_{-1}^1 (8-8x^2)\,dx = 2\pi\int_0^1 (8-8x^2)\,dx$

$= 2\pi\left[8x - \dfrac{8}{3}x^3\right]_0^1 = 2\pi\left(8 - \dfrac{8}{3}\right) = \dfrac{32\pi}{3}$

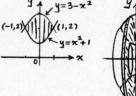

10. $V = \pi\int_0^1 \left[1^2 - (1-\sqrt{1-y})^2\right] dy = \pi\int_0^1 (2\sqrt{1-y} - 1 + y)\,dy$

$= \pi\left[-\dfrac{4}{3}(1-y)^{3/2} - y + \dfrac{y^2}{2}\right]_0^1 = \pi\left[\left(0 - 1 + \dfrac{1}{2}\right) - \left(-\dfrac{4}{3} - 0 + 0\right)\right] = \dfrac{5\pi}{6}$

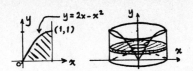 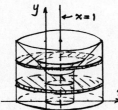

12. $V = \pi \int_0^2 (3^2 - 1^2) dy + \pi \int_2^4 \left[3^2 - (y-1)^2 \right] dy = \pi \left[8y \right]_0^2 + \pi \int_2^4 (8 + 2y - y^2) dy$

$= 16\pi + \pi \left[8y + y^2 - \frac{y^3}{3} \right]_2^4 = 16\pi + \pi \left[(32 + 16 - \frac{64}{3}) - (16 + 4 - \frac{8}{3}) \right] = \frac{76\pi}{3}$

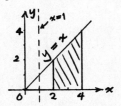 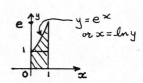

14. $V = \pi \int_0^2 \left[8^2 - (4y)^2 \right] dy = \pi \left[64y - \frac{16y^3}{3} \right]_0^2 = \pi (128 - \frac{128}{3}) = \frac{256\pi}{3}$

16. $V = \pi \int_0^8 \left[2^2 - (2 - \frac{x}{4})^2 \right] dx = \pi \int_0^8 (x - \frac{x^2}{16}) dx = \pi \left[\frac{x^2}{2} - \frac{x^3}{48} \right]_0^8 = \pi (32 - \frac{32}{3})$

$= \frac{64\pi}{3}$

18. $V = \pi \int_0^2 \left[(4y)^2 - (y^3)^2 \right] dy = \pi \int_0^2 (16y^2 - y^6) dy = \pi \left[\frac{16}{3} y^3 - \frac{y^7}{7} \right]_0^2$

$= \pi (\frac{128}{3} - \frac{128}{7}) = \frac{512\pi}{21}$

20. $V = \pi \int_0^2 \left[(8 - y^3)^2 - (8 - 4y)^2 \right] dy = \pi \int_0^2 (-16y^3 + y^6 + 64y - 16y^2) dy$

$= \pi \left[-4y^4 + \frac{y^7}{7} + 32y^2 - \frac{16}{3} y^3 \right]_0^2 = \pi (-64 + \frac{128}{7} + 128 - \frac{128}{3}) = \frac{832\pi}{21}$

22. $V = \pi \int_0^2 (y^3)^2 dy = \pi \left[\frac{y^7}{7} \right]_0^2 = \frac{128\pi}{7}$

24. $V = \pi \int_0^2 \left[8^2 - (8 - y^3)^2 \right] dy = \pi \int_0^2 (16y^3 - y^6) dy = \pi \left[4y^4 - \frac{y^7}{7} \right]_0^2$

$= \pi (64 - \frac{128}{7}) = \frac{320\pi}{7}$

26. $V = \pi \int_1^3 \left[\frac{1}{x} \right]^2 dx = \pi \left[\frac{-1}{x} \right]_1^3 = \pi (-\frac{1}{3} + 1) = \frac{2\pi}{3}$

28. $V = \pi \int_0^1 1^2 dy + \pi \int_1^e \left[1^2 - (\ln y)^2 \right] dy$

$= \pi + \pi \left[y - y(\ln y)^2 + 2y \ln y - 2y \right]_1^e$

[by Exercise 7.1.7]

$= \pi + \pi [(e - e + 2e - 2e) - (-1)] = 2\pi$

30. $V = \pi \int_0^{\pi/4} (\cos^2 x - \sin^2 x) dx = \frac{\pi}{2} \int_0^{\pi/4} \cos 2x \, 2dx = \frac{\pi}{2} \left[\sin 2x \right]_0^{\pi/4}$

$= \frac{\pi}{2} (1 - 0) = \frac{\pi}{2}$

32. $V = \pi \int_0^1 \left[\left(\frac{\pi}{2}\right)^2 - (\sin^{-1}x)^2 \right]dx = \frac{\pi^3}{4} - \pi\left[x(\sin^{-1}x)^2 - 2x + 2\sqrt{1-x^2}\sin^{-1}x \right]_0^1$

[by Rev. Exer. 30 for Ch. 7] $= \frac{\pi^3}{4} - \pi\left[1\cdot\left(\frac{\pi}{2}\right)^2 - 2 + 2\cdot 0\cdot\left(\frac{\pi}{2}\right) \right] = 2\pi$

34. $V = \pi \int_0^{1/e} 1^2 dy + \pi \int_{1/e}^1 \left(\sqrt{-\ln y}\right)^2 dy$

$= \frac{\pi}{e} - \pi \int_{1/e}^1 \ln y \, dy = \frac{\pi}{e} - \pi\left[y \ln y - y \right]_{1/e}^1$

$= \frac{\pi}{e} - \pi\left[(-1) - \left(-\frac{1}{e} - \frac{1}{e}\right) \right] = \pi\left(1 - \frac{1}{e}\right)$

36. $V = \pi \int_0^{\pi/2} \left[1^2 - (1 - \cos x)^2 \right]dx = \pi \int_0^{\pi/2} (2\cos x - \cos^2 x)dx$

$= \pi\left[2\sin x - \frac{x}{2} - \frac{\sin 2x}{4} \right]_0^{\pi/2} = \pi\left[\left(2 - \frac{\pi}{4} - 0\right) - 0 \right] = 2\pi - \frac{\pi^2}{4}$

38. $V = \pi \int_0^1 \left[(e+1)^2 - (e^y+1)^2 \right]dy = \pi \int_0^1 (e^2 + 2e - e^{2y} - 2e^y)dy$

$= \pi(e^2 + 2e) - \pi\left[\frac{1}{2}e^{2y} + 2e^y \right]_0^1 = \pi\left[e^2 + 2e - \frac{1}{2}e^2 - 2e + \frac{1}{2} + 2 \right] = \pi(e^2 + 5)/2$

40. $V = \pi \int_1^2 1^2 dx + \pi \int_2^3 2^2 dx + \pi \int_3^4 3^2 dx + \pi \int_4^5 4^2 dx + \pi \int_5^6 5^2 dx$

$= \pi\cdot 1 + \pi\cdot 4 + \pi\cdot 9 + \pi\cdot 16 + \pi\cdot 25 = 55\pi$

42. $V = \pi \int_0^1 \left(\frac{1}{2}\right)^2 dx + \pi \int_1^2 (x^2 - 2x + 2)^2 dx = \frac{\pi}{4} + \pi \int_1^2 (x^4 - 4x^3 + 8x^2 - 8x + 4)dx$

$= \frac{\pi}{4} + \pi\left[\frac{x^5}{5} - x^4 + \frac{8}{3}x^3 - 4x^2 + 4x \right]_1^2 = \frac{\pi}{4} + \pi\left[\left(\frac{32}{5} - 16 + \frac{64}{3} - 16 + 8\right) - \left(\frac{1}{5} - 1 + \frac{8}{3} - 4 + 4\right) \right]$

$= \frac{127\pi}{60}$

44. $V = \pi \int_0^h \left(R - \frac{R-r}{h}y\right)^2 dy = \pi \int_0^h \left[R^2 - \frac{2R(R-r)}{h}y + \left(\frac{R-r}{h}\right)^2 y^2 \right]dy$

$= \pi\left[R^2 y - \frac{R(R-r)}{h}y^2 + \frac{1}{3}\left(\frac{R-r}{h}\right)^2 y^3 \right]_0^h$

$= \pi\left[R^2 h - R(R-r)h + \frac{1}{3}(R-r)^2 h \right]$

$= \pi\left[Rrh + \frac{1}{3}(R^2 - 2Rr + r^2)h \right] = \frac{1}{3}\pi h(R^2 + Rr + r^2)$

ALTERNATE SOLUTION:

$\frac{H}{R} = \frac{H-h}{r}$ by similar triangles. Therefore

$Hr = HR - hR$ and $hR = H(R-r)$, so $H = \frac{hR}{R-r}$

Now $V = \frac{1}{3}\pi R^2 H - \frac{1}{3}\pi r^2(H-h)$ [by #43]

252

$$= \frac{1}{3}\pi R^2 \frac{hR}{R-r} - \frac{1}{3}\pi r^2 \frac{rh}{R-r} = \frac{\pi h}{3} \frac{R^3-r^3}{R-r} = \frac{1}{3}\pi h(R^2+Rr+r^2)$$

$$= \frac{1}{3}\left[\pi R^2+\pi r^2+\sqrt{(\pi R^2)(\pi r^2)}\right]h = \frac{1}{3}(A_1+A_2+\sqrt{A_1A_2})h, \text{ where } A_1 \text{ and } A_2 \text{ are}$$

the areas of the bases of the frustum.

46. $V = \int_0^h A(y)dy = \int_0^h \left[\frac{a-b}{h}y + b\right]^2 dy$

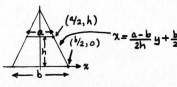

$$= \int_0^h \left[\frac{(a-b)^2}{h^2}y^2 + \frac{2b(a-b)}{h}y + b^2\right]dy$$

$$= \left[\frac{(a-b)^2}{3h^2}y^3 + \frac{b(a-b)}{h}y^2 + b^2y\right]_0^h$$

$$= \frac{(a-b)^2}{3}h + b(a-b)h + b^2h = \frac{1}{3}(a^2-2ab+b^2+3ab)h = \frac{1}{3}(a^2+ab+b^2)h$$

[Note that this can be written as $\frac{1}{3}(A_1+A_2+\sqrt{A_1A_2})h$ as in #44.]

48. A typical cross section at height y above the base has side

$a(1 - \frac{y}{h})$ and area $A(y) = \frac{a^2(1-y/h)^2}{4}\sqrt{3}$, so $V = \int_0^h A(y)dy$

$$= \frac{a^2\sqrt{3}}{4} \int_0^h (1 - \frac{y}{h})^2 dy = \frac{a^2\sqrt{3}}{4} \cdot \frac{h}{3} \text{ [as in #47]} = \sqrt{3}a^2h/12$$

50. Area of cross section at height z is

$A(z) = \frac{1}{2}\cdot 3(1 - \frac{z}{5})\cdot 4(1 - \frac{z}{5}) = 6(1 - \frac{z}{5})^2$, so

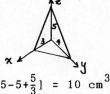

$V = \int_0^5 A(z)dz = 6 \int_0^5 (1 - \frac{z}{5})^2 dz$

$$= 6 \int_0^5 (1 - \frac{2z}{5} + \frac{z^2}{25})dz = 6\left[z - \frac{z^2}{5} + \frac{z^3}{75}\right]_0^5 = 6[5-5+\frac{5}{3}] = 10 \text{ cm}^3$$

52. $V = \int_{-r}^r A(x)dx = 2 \int_0^r A(x)dx = 2 \int_0^r \frac{1}{2}h(2\sqrt{r^2-x^2})dx = 2h \int_0^r \sqrt{r^2-x^2}\ dx$

$$= 2h\left[\frac{x}{2}\sqrt{r^2-x^2} + \frac{r^2}{2}\sin^{-1}\frac{x}{r}\right]_0^r \text{ [Formula 30]} = 2h\left[(0 + \frac{r^2}{2}\cdot\frac{\pi}{2}) - 0\right]$$

$$= \frac{1}{2}\pi r^2 h \quad \text{[See #49.]}$$

54. The cross-section of the base corresponding

to the coordinate y has length $2x = 2\sqrt{y}$.

The corresponding equilateral triangle has

area $A(y) = (2\sqrt{y})^2 \sqrt{3}/4 = y\sqrt{3}$.

Therefore, $V = \int_0^1 A(y)dy = \int_0^1 y\sqrt{3}\ dy = \sqrt{3}\left[\frac{y^2}{2}\right]_0^1 = \frac{\sqrt{3}}{2}$

56. Since the area of a semicircle of diameter y is $\frac{\pi y^2}{8}$, we have

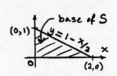

base of S

$(0,1)$ $y = 1 - \frac{x}{2}$ x

$(2,0)$

$$V = \int_0^2 A(x)dx = \int_0^2 (\frac{\pi y^2}{8})dx$$

$$= \frac{\pi}{8}\int_0^2 (1 - \frac{x}{2})^2 dx = \frac{\pi}{4}\int_0^2 (\frac{x}{2} - 1)^2 \frac{1}{2}dx$$

$$= \frac{\pi}{4}\left[\frac{1}{3}(\frac{x}{2} - 1)^3\right]_0^2 = \frac{\pi}{12}\left[0 - (-1)\right] = \frac{\pi}{12}$$

58. Each cross-section of the solid S in a plane $\perp$ x-axis is a square (since the edges of the cut lie on the cylinders, which are perpendicular). A quarter of this square and $\frac{1}{8}$ of S are shown.

The area of this quarter-square is $|PQ|^2 = r^2 - x^2$. Therefore $A(x) = 4(r^2 - x^2)$ and the volume of S is $V = \int_{-r}^{r} A(x)dx$

$$= 4\int_{-r}^{r}(r^2 - x^2)dx = 8\int_0^r (r^2 - x^2)dx = 8\left[r^2 x - \frac{1}{3}x^3\right]_0^r = 16r^3/3$$

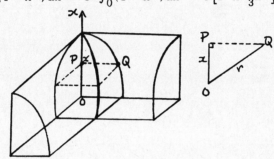

60. If the angle is $45°$, then the rectangular cross-section perpendicular to the y-axis at coordinate y has height y (since $|BC| = |AB| = y$ in Fig. 8.15), so $A(y) = 2y\sqrt{16 - y^2}$ and $V = \int_0^4 A(y)dy = \frac{128}{3}$. More generally, if the angle is θ, where

$0 \leq \theta < 90°$, then $|BC| = |AB|\tan\theta$, so $A(y) = (y\tan\theta)\,2\sqrt{16 - y^2}$

and $V = \int_0^4 A(y)dy = \frac{128}{3}\tan\theta$

62. $V = 2\int_0^{\sqrt{R^2 - r^2}} A(z)dz = 2\int_0^{\sqrt{R^2 - r^2}}\left[\pi(R^2 - z^2) - \pi r^2\right]dz$

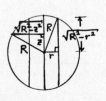

$$= 2\left[\pi R^2 z - \frac{1}{3}\pi z^3 - \pi r^2 z\right]_0^{\sqrt{R^2 - r^2}}$$

$$= 2\pi(R^2 - r^2)\sqrt{R^2 - r^2} - \frac{2}{3}\pi(R^2 - r^2)^{3/2}$$

$$= (4/3)\pi(R^2 - r^2)^{3/2}$$

254

(Note that this is the same as the volume of a sphere whose radius
is half the height of the solid obtained by drilling the hole of
radius r vertically through the center of the sphere of radius R.)

64.　(a) Volume $(S_1) = \int_0^h A(z)dz$ = volume (S_2) since the cross-sectional

area $A(z)$ at each height z is the same for both solids.

(b) Assuming that the cross-sections are circles, we compute

$V = \int_0^h A(z)dz = \int_0^h \pi r^2 dz = \pi r^2 h$. Thus the obliqueness of the

cylinder does not affect its volume.

66.　By Simpson's rule, $V = \int_0^{10} A(x)dx \approx \frac{1}{3}[A(0)+4A(1)+2A(2)+4A(3)+2A(4)$

$+4A(5)+2A(6)+4A(7)+2A(8)+4A(9)+A(10)] = 5.7\overline{6} \approx 5.8$ m

Section 8.2

CHAPTER 8

Exercises 8.2

2.　$V = \int_1^{10} 2\pi x \cdot \frac{1}{x}\, dx = 2\pi\big[x\big]_1^{10} = 18\pi$

4.　$V = \int_0^{\sqrt{\pi}} 2\pi x \sin(x^2)dx = \pi\big[-\cos(x^2)\big]_0^{\sqrt{\pi}} = \pi[1-(-1)] = 2\pi$

6.　The curves $y^2 = x$ and $x = 2y$ intersect at $(0,0)$ and $(4,2)$.

$V = \int_0^4 2\pi x(\sqrt{x} - \frac{x}{2})dx = 2\pi \int_0^4 x^{3/2}dx - \pi \int_0^4 x^2 dx$

$= 2\pi \frac{2}{5}x^{5/2}\Big]_0^4 - \pi \frac{x^3}{3}\Big]_0^4 = \frac{4\pi}{5}(32) - \frac{64\pi}{3} = \frac{64\pi}{15}$

8.　$V = \int_1^3 2\pi x(-x^2+4x-3)dx = 2\pi\big[-\frac{x^4}{4} + \frac{4x^3}{3} - \frac{3x^2}{2}\big]_1^3 = 2\pi\big[(-\frac{81}{4} + 36 - \frac{27}{2})$

$- (-\frac{1}{4} + \frac{4}{3} - \frac{3}{2})\big] = \frac{16\pi}{3}$

10.　$V = \int_0^3 2\pi x \frac{1}{1+x^2}\, dx = \pi \int_0^3 \frac{2x\, dx}{1+x^2} = \pi\big[\ln(1+x^2)\big]_0^3 = \pi \ln 10$

12.　$V = \int_2^3 2\pi x[\sqrt{x-2} - (x-2)]dx = \int_0^1 2\pi(u+2)(\sqrt{u}-u)du \quad [u = x-2]$

$= 2\pi \int_0^1 (u^{3/2}-u^2+2u^{1/2}-2u)du = 2\pi\big[\frac{2}{5}u^{5/2} - \frac{u^3}{3} + \frac{4}{3}u^{3/2} - u^2\big]_0^1$

$= 2\pi(\frac{2}{5} - \frac{1}{3} + \frac{4}{3} - 1) = \frac{4\pi}{5}$

255

14. $V = \int_0^1 2\pi x(e^x - e^{-x})dx = 2\pi\left[xe^x - e^x + xe^{-x} + e^{-x}\right]_0^1 = 2\pi\left[\frac{2}{e} - 0\right] = \frac{4\pi}{e}$

16. $V = \int_2^5 2\pi y \cdot y^2 dy = 2\pi \left.\frac{y^4}{4}\right]_2^5 = \frac{\pi}{2}(625-16) = \frac{609\pi}{2}$

18. $V = \int_1^\pi 2\pi y \cdot \ln y \, dy = 2\pi\left[\frac{y^2}{4}(2\ln y - 1)\right]_1^\pi$ (by parts)

$= 2\pi\left[\frac{\pi^2}{4}(2\ln\pi - 1) - \frac{1}{4}(0-1)\right] = \pi^3\ln\pi - \frac{\pi^3}{2} + \frac{\pi}{2}$

20. $V = \int_0^{\pi/4} 2\pi y \cos y \, dy = 2\pi[y \sin y + \cos y]_0^{\pi/4}$ (by parts)

$= 2\pi\left[\frac{\pi}{4}\frac{\sqrt{2}}{2} + \frac{\sqrt{2}}{2} - 1\right] = \frac{\pi^2\sqrt{2}}{4} + \pi\sqrt{2} - 2\pi$

22. $V = \int_0^1 2\pi y[(2-y)-y]dy = 4\pi \int_0^1 y(1-y)dy$

$= 4\pi\left[\frac{y^2}{2} - \frac{y^3}{3}\right]_0^1 = 4\pi\left(\frac{1}{6}\right) = \frac{2\pi}{3}$

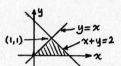

24. $V = \int_{-2}^{-1} 2\pi(-x) \cdot x^2 dx = 2\pi\left[-\frac{x^4}{4}\right]_{-2}^{-1} = 2\pi\left[\left(-\frac{1}{4}\right)-(-4)\right] = \frac{15\pi}{2}$

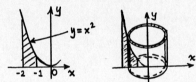

26. $V = \int_1^2 2\pi(4-x)x^2 dx = 2\pi\left[\frac{4x^3}{3} - \frac{x^4}{4}\right]_1^2 = 2\pi\left[\left(\frac{32}{3}-4\right)-\left(\frac{4}{3}-\frac{1}{4}\right)\right] = \frac{67\pi}{6}$

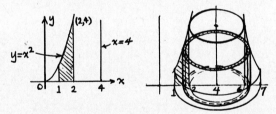

28. $V = \int_0^4 2\pi(2+x)[(8x-2x^2)-(4x-x^2)]dx = \int_0^4 2\pi(2+x)(4x-x^2)dx$

$= 2\pi \int_0^4 (8x+2x^2-x^3)dx = 2\pi\left[4x^2 + \frac{2}{3}x^3 - \frac{x^4}{4}\right]_0^4 = 2\pi\left(64+\frac{128}{3}-64\right) = \frac{256\pi}{3}$

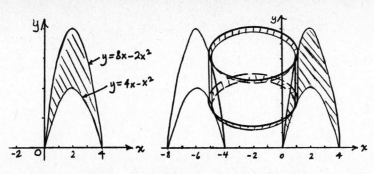

30. $V = \int_0^1 2\pi(3-y)(e-e^y)dy = 2\pi \int_0^1 (3e-ey-3e^y+ye^y)dy$

$= 2\pi\left[3ey-\frac{e}{2}y^2-3e^y+ye^y-e^y\right]_0^1 = 2\pi[(3e-\frac{e}{2}-3e+e-e)-(-3-1)] = \pi(8-e)$

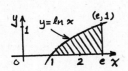

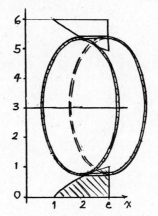

32. Use shells: $V = \int_1^2 2\pi x(-x^2+3x-2)dx = 2\pi \int_1^2 (-x^3+3x^2-2x)dx$

$= 2\pi\left[-\frac{x^4}{4}+x^3-x^2\right]_1^2 = 2\pi[(-4+8-4)-(-\frac{1}{4}+1-1)] = \frac{\pi}{2}$

34. $-x^2+7x-10 = x-2 \Leftrightarrow x^2-6x+8 = 0 \Leftrightarrow x = 2$ or $4 \Leftrightarrow (x,y) = (2,0)$ or

$(4,2)$. Use washers:

$V = \pi \int_2^4 [(-x^2+7x-10)^2-(x-2)^2]dx = \pi \int_2^4 (x^4-14x^3+68x^2-136x+96)dx$

$= \pi\left[\frac{x^5}{5}-\frac{7x^4}{2}+\frac{68x^3}{3}-68x^2+96x\right]_2^4$

$= \pi[(\frac{1024}{5}-896+\frac{4352}{3}-1088+384)-(\frac{32}{5}-56+\frac{544}{3}-272+192)] = \frac{56\pi}{15}$

36. Use shells: $V = \int_0^2 2\pi x^2\sqrt{1+x^3}\,dx = \frac{2\pi}{3}\cdot\frac{2}{3}(1+x^3)^{3/2}\Big]_0^2 = (\frac{4\pi}{9})(27-1)$

$= \frac{104\pi}{9}$

257

38. Using shells, we have $V = 2\pi \int_0^2 y \cdot 2\sqrt{1-(y-1)^2} \, dy$

    $= 4\pi \int_{-1}^1 (u+1)\sqrt{1-u^2} \, du \ [u = y-1] = 4\pi \int_{-1}^1 \sqrt{1-u^2} \, du$

    $- 4\pi \int_{-1}^1 u\sqrt{1-u^2} \, du$. The 1st definite integral is the area of a
    semicircle of radius 1, namely $\pi/2$. The second equals zero because
    its integrand is an odd function. Thus $V = 4\pi(\pi/2) - 4\pi \cdot 0 = 2\pi^2$.
    Note: We could have used disks (a particular case of Exercise
    8.1.49 with $R = r = 1$).

40. $V = \int_{R-r}^{R+r} 2\pi x \cdot 2\sqrt{r^2-(x-R)^2} \, dx$

    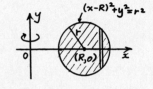

    $= \int_{-r}^r 4\pi(u+R)\sqrt{r^2-u^2} \, du \quad [u = x-R]$

    $= 4\pi R \int_{-r}^r \sqrt{r^2-u^2} \, du + 4\pi \int_{-r}^r u\sqrt{r^2-u^2} \, du$

    $= 4\pi R(\pi r^2/2) + 4\pi \cdot 0 = 2\pi R r^2$ by the same reasoning used in #38.

42. $V = \int_r^R 2\pi x \cdot 2\sqrt{R^2-x^2} \, dx = -2\pi \int_r^R \sqrt{R^2-x^2}(-2x)dx$

    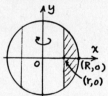

    $= -2\pi \frac{2}{3}(R^2-x^2)^{3/2} \Big]_r^R$

    $= -\frac{4}{3}\pi[0-(R^2-r^2)^{3/2}] = \frac{4}{3}\pi(R^2-r^2)^{3/2}$

44. (i) $\quad V = \int_a^b 2\pi(x-c)f(x)dx \qquad$ (ii) $\quad V = \int_a^b 2\pi(c-x)f(x)dx$

    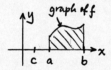 

Section 8.3

Exercises 8.3

2. $x^2 = 64y^3$, $x = 8y^{3/2}$, $dx/dy = 12y^{1/2}$, $1 + (dx/dy)^2 = 1+144y$

    $L = \int_1^4 \sqrt{1+144y} \, dy = \int_{145}^{577} u^{1/2} \frac{1}{144} \, du \quad [u = 1+144y \Rightarrow du = 144dy]$

    $= \frac{1}{144} \frac{2}{3} u^{3/2} \Big]_{145}^{577} = \frac{577^{3/2}-145^{3/2}}{216}$

4. $y = 1-x^{2/3}$, $\frac{dy}{dx} = -\frac{2}{3}x^{-1/3}$, $1 + (\frac{dy}{dx})^2 = 1 + \frac{4}{9}x^{-2/3}$

$L = \int_{-8}^{-1} \sqrt{1 + \frac{4}{9x^{2/3}}}\, dx = -\int_{-8}^{-1} \frac{\sqrt{9x^{2/3}+4}}{3x^{1/3}}\, dx$ [since $\sqrt{x^2} = -x$ for $x<0$]

$= \frac{1}{18} \int_{13}^{40} \sqrt{u}\, du$ [u = $9x^{2/3}+4 \Rightarrow du = 6x^{-1/3}dx$]

$= \frac{1}{27} u^{3/2} \Big]_{13}^{40} = \frac{1}{27}(80\sqrt{10}-13\sqrt{13})$ [Another method: Let $u = x^{1/3}$.]

6. $9y^2 = x(x-3)^2$, $3y = x^{1/2}(x-3)$, $y = \frac{1}{3}x^{3/2}-x^{1/2}$, $y' = \frac{1}{2}x^{1/2}-\frac{1}{2}x^{-1/2}$,

$(y')^2 = \frac{1}{4}x-\frac{1}{2}+\frac{1}{4}x^{-1}$, $1+(y')^2 = \frac{1}{4}x+\frac{1}{2}+\frac{1}{4}x^{-1}$, $\sqrt{1+(y')^2} = \frac{1}{2}x^{1/2}+\frac{1}{2}x^{-1/2}$.

$L = \int_0^4 (\frac{1}{2}x^{1/2}+\frac{1}{2}x^{-1/2})dx = \frac{1}{2}\left[\frac{2}{3}x^{3/2}+2x^{1/2}\right]_0^4 = \frac{1}{2}(\frac{16}{3}+4) = \frac{14}{3}$

8. $y = \frac{x^3}{6} + \frac{1}{2x}$, $\frac{dy}{dx} = \frac{x^2}{2} - \frac{x^{-2}}{2}$, $1+(\frac{dy}{dx})^2 = \frac{x^4}{4} + \frac{1}{2} + \frac{x^{-4}}{4}$,

$L = \int_1^2 (\frac{x^2}{2} + \frac{x^{-2}}{2})dx = \frac{1}{2}\left[\frac{x^3}{3} - \frac{1}{x}\right]_1^2 = \frac{1}{2}[(\frac{8}{3}-\frac{1}{2})-(\frac{1}{3}-1)] = \frac{17}{12}$

10. $y = \frac{x^2}{2} - \frac{\ln x}{4}$, $\frac{dy}{dx} = x - \frac{1}{4x}$, $1+(\frac{dy}{dx})^2 = x^2 + \frac{1}{2} + \frac{1}{16x^2}$,

$L = \int_2^4 (x + \frac{1}{4x})dx = \left[\frac{x^2}{2} + \frac{\ln x}{4}\right]_2^4 = (8 + \frac{2\ln 2}{4}) - (2 + \frac{\ln 2}{4}) = 6 + \frac{\ln 2}{4}$

12. $y = \ln(\sin x)$, $\frac{dy}{dx} = \cot x$, $1 + (\frac{dy}{dx})^2 = 1 + \cot^2 x = \csc^2 x$,

$L = \int_{\pi/6}^{\pi/3} \csc x\, dx = \ln(\csc x - \cot x)]_{\pi/6}^{\pi/3}$

$= \ln(2/\sqrt{3} - 1/\sqrt{3}) - \ln(2-\sqrt{3}) = \ln(1+2/\sqrt{3})$

14. $y = \ln\left[\frac{e^x+1}{e^x-1}\right] = \ln(e^x+1)-\ln(e^x-1)$, $y' = \frac{e^x}{e^x+1} - \frac{e^x}{e^x-1} = \frac{-2e^x}{e^{2x}-1} \Rightarrow$

$1+(y')^2 = 1 + \frac{4e^{2x}}{(e^{2x}-1)^2} = \frac{(e^{2x}+1)^2}{(e^{2x}-1)^2} \Rightarrow \sqrt{1+(y')^2} = \frac{e^{2x}+1}{e^{2x}-1} = \frac{e^x+e^{-x}}{e^x-e^{-x}} =$

$\frac{\cosh x}{\sinh x} \Rightarrow L = \int_a^b \frac{\cosh x}{\sinh x}\, dx = \ln \sinh x\Big]_a^b = \ln\left[\frac{\sinh b}{\sinh a}\right] = \ln\left[\frac{e^b-e^{-b}}{e^a-e^{-a}}\right]$

16. $y = \ln x$, $\frac{dy}{dx} = \frac{1}{x}$, $\sqrt{1+(\frac{dy}{dx})^2} = \sqrt{1+(\frac{1}{x})^2} = \frac{\sqrt{1+x^2}}{x} \Rightarrow L = \int_1^{\sqrt{3}} \frac{\sqrt{1+x^2}}{x}\, dx$

$= \left[\sqrt{1+x^2} - \ln\frac{1+\sqrt{1+x^2}}{x}\right]_1^{\sqrt{3}}$ [Formula 23 or as in Ex. 15]

$= 2 - \ln\frac{1+2}{\sqrt{3}} - \sqrt{2} + \ln(1+\sqrt{2}) = 2 - \sqrt{2} + \ln(\sqrt{2}+1) - \frac{1}{2}\ln 3$

18. $y^2 = 4x$, $x = \frac{1}{4}y^2$, $\frac{dy}{dx} = \frac{1}{2}y$, $1+(\frac{dy}{dx})^2 = 1 + \frac{y^2}{4}$, $L = \int_0^2 \sqrt{1+y^2/4}\ dy$

$= \int_0^1 \sqrt{1+u^2} \cdot 2du$ [$u = \frac{y}{2} \Rightarrow dy = 2du$] $= \left[u\sqrt{1+u^2} + \ln|u+\sqrt{1+u^2}|\right]_0^1$

[Formula 21 or let $u = \tan\theta$] $= \sqrt{2} + \ln(1+\sqrt{2})$

20. $y = x^4-x^2$, $y' = 4x^3-2x$, $1+(y')^2 = 1+[2x(2x^2-1)]^2 = 1+4x^2(2x^2-1)^2$.

$L = \int_{-1}^2 \sqrt{1+4x^2(2x^2-1)^2}\ dx = \int_{-1}^2 \sqrt{16x^6-16x^4+4x^2+1}\ dx$

22. $y = \tan x$, $1+(y')^2 = 1 + \sec^4 x$, $L = \int_0^{\pi/4} \sqrt{1 + \sec^4 x}\ dx$

24. $\frac{x^2}{a^2} + \frac{y^2}{b^2} = 1$, $y = \pm b\sqrt{1-x^2/a^2} = \pm\frac{b}{a}\sqrt{a^2-x^2}$. $y = \frac{b}{a}\sqrt{a^2-x^2} \Rightarrow \frac{dy}{dx} = \frac{-bx}{a\sqrt{a^2-x^2}}$

$\Rightarrow (\frac{dy}{dx})^2 = \frac{b^2x^2}{a^2(a^2-x^2)}$, so $L = 2\int_{-a}^a \left[1 + \frac{b^2x^2}{a^2(a^2-x^2)}\right]^{1/2} dx$

$= \frac{4}{a}\int_0^a \left[\frac{(b^2-a^2)x^2+a^4}{a^2-x^2}\right]^{1/2} dx$

26. (a) $y = \frac{x^3}{3} + \frac{1}{4x}$ is odd and $y' = x^2-\frac{1}{4x^2}$,

$y'' = 2x + \frac{1}{8x^3} \Rightarrow y' > 0$ for $x > 1/\sqrt{2}$,

$y'' > 0$ for $x > 0 \Rightarrow$ min when $x = 1/\sqrt{2}$,

CU on $(0,\infty)$, VA $x = 0$.

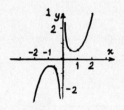

(b) $1+(\frac{dy}{dx})^2 = x^4 + \frac{1}{2} + \frac{1}{16x^4}$, $s(x) = \int_1^x \left[t^2+\frac{1}{4t^2}\right]dt = \left[\frac{t^3}{3} - \frac{1}{4t}\right]_1^x$

$= \frac{x^3}{3} - \frac{1}{4x} - (\frac{1}{3} - \frac{1}{4}) = \frac{x^3}{3} - \frac{1}{4x} - \frac{1}{12}$ for $x > 0$

28. $y = a \cosh(\frac{x}{a})$, $y' = \sinh(\frac{x}{a})$, $1+(y')^2 = \cosh^2(\frac{x}{a})$.

$L = \int_{-b}^b \cosh(\frac{x}{a})dx = a \sinh(\frac{x}{a})\Big]_{-b}^b = 2a \sinh(\frac{b}{a})$

30. (a)

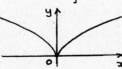

(b) $y = x^{2/3} \Rightarrow 1+(\frac{dy}{dx})^2 = 1+(\frac{2}{3}x^{-1/3})^2 = 1 + \frac{4}{9}x^{-2/3} \Rightarrow$

$L = \int_0^1 \sqrt{1+\frac{4}{9}x^{-2/3}}dx$ (improper). $x = y^{3/2} \Rightarrow 1+(\frac{dx}{dy})^2 = 1+(\frac{3}{2}y^{1/2})^2$

$= 1 + \frac{9}{4}y \Rightarrow L = \int_0^1 \sqrt{1 + \frac{9}{4}y}\ dy$. The second integral equals

$\frac{4}{9}\cdot\frac{2}{3}(1 + \frac{9}{4}y)^{3/2}\Big]_0^1 = \frac{8}{27}\left[\frac{13\sqrt{13}}{8} - 1\right] = (13\sqrt{13}-8)/27$.

The first integral can be evaluated as follows:

$$\int_0^1 \sqrt{1+\frac{4}{9}x^{-2/3}}\,dx = \int_0^1 \frac{\sqrt{9x^{2/3}+4}}{3x^{1/3}}\,dx = \lim_{t\to 0^+} \frac{1}{18}\frac{2}{3}(9x^{2/3}+4)\Big]_t^1 \quad \text{[as in Ex. 4]}$$

$$= (13\sqrt{13}-8)/27$$

(c) $L = \int_0^1 \sqrt{1+\frac{9}{4}y}\,dy + \int_0^8 \sqrt{1+\frac{9}{4}y}\,dy = \frac{13\sqrt{13}-8}{27} + \frac{8}{27}(1+\frac{9}{4}y)^{3/2}\Big]_0^8$

$$= \frac{13\sqrt{13}-8}{27} + \frac{8}{27}(19\sqrt{19}-1) = (13\sqrt{13}+152\sqrt{19}-16)/27$$

32. $y = x^4$, $1+(y')^2 = 1+(4x^3)^2 = 1+16x^6$, $L = \int_0^2 \sqrt{1+16x^6}\,dx$. Let $f(x)$

$= \sqrt{1+16x^6}$. Then $L = \frac{1/5}{3}[f(0)+4f(.2)+2f(.4)+4f(.6)+2f(.8)+4f(1)$

$+2f(1.2)+4f(1.4)+2f(1.6)+4f(1.8)+f(2)] \approx 16.65$

34. $y = \tan x$, $1+(y')^2 = 1 + \sec^4 x$, $L = \int_0^{\pi/4} \sqrt{1 + \sec^4 x}\,dx$. Let $g(x)$

$= \sqrt{1 + \sec^4 x}$. Then $L \approx \frac{\pi/40}{3}\Big[g(0)+4g(\frac{\pi}{40})+2g(\frac{2\pi}{40})+4g(\frac{3\pi}{40})+2g(\frac{4\pi}{40})$

$+4g(\frac{5\pi}{40})+2g(\frac{6\pi}{40})+4g(\frac{7\pi}{40})+2g(\frac{8\pi}{40})+4g(\frac{9\pi}{40})+g(\frac{\pi}{4})\Big] \approx 1.278$

Section 8.4

Exercises 8.4

2. The curve $y^2 = 4x+4$ is symmetric about the x-axis, which is the axis of rotation, so we need only consider the upper half of the curve, given by $y = \sqrt{4x+4} = 2\sqrt{x+1}$. $\frac{dy}{dx} = 1/\sqrt{x+1}$, $\sqrt{1+(\frac{dy}{dx})^2}$

$= \sqrt{1+\frac{1}{(x+1)}} \Rightarrow S = 2\pi\int_0^8 2\sqrt{x+1}\sqrt{1+\frac{1}{(x+1)}}\,dx = 4\pi\int_0^8 \sqrt{x+2}\,dx$

$= 4\pi\frac{2}{3}(x+2)^{3/2}\Big]_0^8 = \frac{8\pi}{3}(10\sqrt{10}-2\sqrt{2})$

[Another method: Use $S = \int_2^6 2\pi y\sqrt{1+(\frac{dx}{dy})^2}\,dy$, where $x = (\frac{y^2}{4})-1$.]

4. $y = x^3$, $y' = 3x^2 \Rightarrow S = \int_0^2 2\pi y\sqrt{1+(y')^2}\,dx = 2\pi\int_0^2 x^3\sqrt{1+9x^4}\,dx$

[Let $u = 1+9x^4$. Then $du = 36x^3 dx$.]

$= \frac{2\pi}{36}\int_1^{145}\sqrt{u}\,du = \frac{\pi}{18}\frac{2}{3}u^{3/2}\Big]_1^{145} = \frac{\pi}{27}(145\sqrt{145}-1)$

6. $y = \frac{x^2}{4} - \frac{\ln x}{2}$, $\frac{dy}{dx} = \frac{x}{2} - \frac{1}{2x}$, $1 + (\frac{dy}{dx})^2 = \frac{x^2}{4} + \frac{1}{2} + \frac{1}{4x^2}$ $\Rightarrow$

$S = 2\pi \int_1^4 (\frac{x^2}{4} - \frac{\ln x}{2})(\frac{x}{2} + \frac{1}{2x}) dx = \frac{\pi}{2} \int_1^4 (\frac{x^2}{2} - \ln x)(x + \frac{1}{x}) dx$

$= \frac{\pi}{2} \int_1^4 (\frac{x^3}{2} + \frac{x}{2} - x\ln x - \frac{\ln x}{x}) dx = \frac{\pi}{2} [\frac{x^4}{8} + \frac{x^2}{4} - \frac{x^2}{2}\ln x + \frac{x^2}{4} - \frac{1}{2}(\ln x)^2]_1^4$

$= \frac{\pi}{2} [(32 + 4 - 8\ln 4 + 4 - \frac{1}{2}(\ln 4)^2) - (\frac{1}{8} + \frac{1}{4} - 0 + \frac{1}{4} - 0)] = \pi[\frac{315}{16} - 8\ln 2 - (\ln 2)^2]$

8. $y = \cos x$, $\sqrt{1 + (\frac{dy}{dx})^2} = \sqrt{1 + \sin^2 x}$ $\Rightarrow$ $S = 2\pi \int_0^{\pi/3} \cos x \sqrt{1 + \sin^2 x} \, dx$

$= 2\pi \int_0^{\sqrt{3}/2} \sqrt{1 + u^2} \, du$ $[u = \sin x]$

$= 2\pi \int_0^\alpha \sec^3\theta \, d\theta$ $[u = \tan\theta, \, du = \sec^2\theta \, d\theta]$

$= \pi[\sec\theta \tan\theta + \ln|\sec\theta + \tan\theta|]_0^\alpha$

$\sqrt{7}$ $\sqrt{3}$ α 2 $\alpha = \tan^{-1}(\sqrt{3}/2)$

$= \pi[\frac{\sqrt{7}}{2} \frac{\sqrt{3}}{2} + \ln[\frac{\sqrt{7}}{2} + \frac{\sqrt{3}}{2}]] = \pi[\frac{\sqrt{21}}{4} + \ln[\frac{\sqrt{7} + \sqrt{3}}{2}]]$

10. $2y = 3x^{2/3}$, $y = \frac{3}{2}x^{2/3}$, $\frac{dy}{dx} = x^{-1/3}$, $1 + (\frac{dy}{dx})^2 = 1 + x^{-2/3}$

$S = 2\pi \int_1^8 \frac{3}{2}x^{2/3} \sqrt{1 + x^{-2/3}} \, dx = 3\pi \int_1^2 u^2 \sqrt{1 + 1/u^2} \, 3u^2 du$

$[u = x^{1/3} \Rightarrow x = u^3, \, dx = 3u^2 du]$ $= 9\pi \int_1^2 u^3 \sqrt{u^2 + 1} \, du$

$= 9\pi \int_{\pi/4}^{\tan^{-1}2} \tan^3\theta \sec^3\theta \, d\theta$ $[u = \tan\theta \Rightarrow du = \sec^2\theta \, d\theta]$

$= 9\pi \int_{\pi/4}^{\tan^{-1}2} \sec^2\theta(\sec^2\theta - 1)\sec\theta\tan\theta d\theta = 9\pi \int_{\sqrt{2}}^{\sqrt{5}} v^2(v^2 - 1) dv$ $[v = \sec\theta]$

$= 9\pi[\frac{v^5}{5} - \frac{v^3}{3}]_{\sqrt{2}}^{\sqrt{5}} = 9\pi[5\sqrt{5} - \frac{5\sqrt{5}}{3} - \frac{4\sqrt{2}}{5} + \frac{2\sqrt{2}}{3}] = \frac{3\pi}{5}(50\sqrt{5} - 2\sqrt{2})$

12. $x = \frac{1}{3}(y^2 + 2)^{3/2}$, $\frac{dx}{dy} = \frac{1}{2}(y^2 + 2)^{1/2}(2y) = y\sqrt{y^2 + 2}$, $1 + (\frac{dx}{dy})^2 = 1 + y^2(y^2 + 2)$

$= (y^2 + 1)^2 \Rightarrow S = 2\pi \int_1^2 y(y^2 + 1) dy = 2\pi[\frac{y^4}{4} + \frac{y^2}{2}]_1^2 = 2\pi(4 + 2 - \frac{1}{4} - \frac{1}{2}) = \frac{21\pi}{2}$

14. $x = 2\ln y$, $1 + (\frac{dx}{dy})^2 = 1 + (\frac{2}{y})^2 = 1 + \frac{4}{y^2} = \frac{y^2 + 4}{y^2}$ $\Rightarrow$ $S = 2\pi \int_1^{\sqrt{3}} y \frac{\sqrt{y^2 + 4}}{y} dy$

$= 2\pi \int_1^{\sqrt{3}} \sqrt{y^2 + 4} \, dy = 2\pi[\frac{y}{2}\sqrt{y^2 + 4} + 2\ln|y + \sqrt{y^2 + 4}|]_1^{\sqrt{3}}$ [Formula 21 or let

$y = 2\tan\theta]$ $= \pi[\sqrt{21} + 4\ln(\sqrt{3} + \sqrt{7}) - \sqrt{5} - 4\ln(1 + \sqrt{5})]$

16. $y = x^2$, $1 + (y')^2 = 1 + (2x)^2 = 1 + 4x^2$ $\Rightarrow$ $S = 2\pi \int_0^1 x^2 \sqrt{1 + 4x^2} \, dx$

$= 2\pi \int_0^2 \frac{u^2}{4} \sqrt{1 + u^2} \, \frac{1}{2}du$ $[u = 2x]$ $= \frac{\pi}{4} \int_0^2 u^2 \sqrt{1 + u^2} \, du$

$$= \frac{\pi}{4}\left[\frac{u}{8}(1+2u^2)\sqrt{1+u^2} - \frac{1}{8}\ln|u+\sqrt{1+u^2}|\right]_0^2 \quad [u = \tan\theta \text{ or Formula 22}]$$

$$= \frac{\pi}{4}\left[\frac{1}{4}(9)\sqrt{5} - \frac{1}{8}\ln(2+\sqrt{5}) - 0\right] = \pi[18\sqrt{5} - \ln(2+\sqrt{5})]/32$$

18. $x = \sqrt{2y-y^2}$, $\frac{dx}{dy} = (1-y)/\sqrt{2y-y^2}$, $1+(\frac{dx}{dy})^2 = 1 + \frac{1-2y+y^2}{2y-y^2} = \frac{1}{2y-y^2} \Rightarrow$

$$S = 2\pi\int_0^1 \sqrt{2y-y^2}(1/\sqrt{2y-y^2})dy = 2\pi\int_0^1 dy = 2\pi$$

20. $4x+3y = 19, y = -\frac{4}{3}x+\frac{19}{3}$, $\frac{dy}{dx} = -\frac{4}{3} \Rightarrow S = 2\pi\int_1^4 x\sqrt{1+\frac{16}{9}} \, dx = 2\pi\cdot\frac{5}{3}\int_1^4 x \, dx$

$$= \frac{10\pi}{3}\left[\frac{x^2}{2}\right]_1^4 = \frac{10\pi}{3}(8-\frac{1}{2}) = 25\pi. \quad [\text{NOTE: This area can also be found}$$

from formula (8.18): $A = 2\pi rl = 2\pi(5/2)(5) = 25\pi.$]

22. $y = 1-x^2$, $1+(\frac{dy}{dx})^2 = 1+4x^2 \Rightarrow S = 2\pi\int_0^1 x\sqrt{1+4x^2} \, dx = \frac{\pi}{4}\int_0^1 \sqrt{4x^2+1} \, 8x \, dx$

$$= \frac{\pi}{4}\frac{2}{3}(4x^2+1)^{3/2}\Big]_0^1 = \frac{\pi}{6}(5\sqrt{5}-1)$$

24. $x = a\cosh(\frac{y}{a})$, $1+(\frac{dx}{dy})^2 = 1 + \sinh^2(\frac{y}{a}) = \cosh^2(\frac{y}{a}) \Rightarrow$

$$S = 2\pi\int_{-a}^a a\cosh(\frac{y}{a})\cosh(\frac{y}{a})dy = 4\pi a\int_0^a \cosh^2(\frac{y}{a})dy$$

$$= 2\pi a\int_0^a[1 + \cosh(\frac{2y}{a})]dy = 2\pi a\left[y + \frac{a}{2}\sinh(\frac{2y}{a})\right]_0^a$$

$$= 2\pi a[a + \frac{a}{2}\sinh 2] = 2\pi a^2[1 + \frac{1}{2}\sinh 2] \text{ or } \pi a^2(e^2+4-e^{-2})/2$$

26. $S = 2\pi\int_0^{\pi/4}\tan x\sqrt{1+(\sec^2 x)^2}dx \approx 2\pi\cdot\frac{\pi/40}{3}\left[f(0)+4f(\frac{\pi}{40})+2f(\frac{\pi}{20})+4f(\frac{3\pi}{40})\right.$

$$\left.+2f(\frac{\pi}{10})+4f(\frac{\pi}{8})+2f(\frac{3\pi}{20})+4f(\frac{7\pi}{40})+2f(\frac{\pi}{5})+4f(\frac{9\pi}{40})+f(\frac{\pi}{4})\right] \approx 3.84$$

where $f(x) = \tan x \sqrt{1 + \sec^4 x}$

28. The loop lies between $x = 0$ and $x = 3a$ and is symmetric about the x-axis. We can assume without loss of generality that $a > 0$. (We must have $a \neq 0$; otherwise the curve consists of the parallel lines $x = 0$ and $x = 3a$, so there is no loop.) The upper half of the loop is given by $y = (1/3\sqrt{a})\sqrt{x}(3a-x) = \sqrt{a}x^{1/2} - x^{3/2}/3\sqrt{a}$, $0 \le x \le 3a$. The desired surface area is twice the area generated by the upper

half of the loop; i.e., $S = 2(2\pi)\int_0^{3a} x\sqrt{1+(\frac{dy}{dx})^2}dx$.

$\frac{dy}{dx} = \frac{\sqrt{a}}{2}x^{-1/2} - \frac{x^{1/2}}{2\sqrt{a}}$, so $1+(\frac{dy}{dx})^2 = \frac{a}{4x} + \frac{1}{2} + \frac{x}{4a}$. Therefore

$$S = 2(2\pi)\int_0^{3a} x(\frac{\sqrt{a}}{2}x^{-1/2} + \frac{x^{1/2}}{2\sqrt{a}})dx = 2\pi\int_0^{3a}(\sqrt{a}x^{1/2} + \frac{x^{3/2}}{\sqrt{a}})dx$$

$$= 2\pi\left[\frac{2\sqrt{a}}{3}x^{3/2} + \frac{2}{5\sqrt{a}}x^{5/2}\right]_0^{3a} = 2\pi\left[\frac{2\sqrt{a}}{3}3a\sqrt{3a} + \frac{2}{5\sqrt{a}}9a^2\sqrt{3a}\right] = \frac{56\sqrt{3}\pi a^2}{5}$$

30. $S = 2\pi\int_0^\infty y\sqrt{1+(\frac{dy}{dx})^2}\,dx = 2\pi\int_0^\infty e^{-x}\sqrt{1+e^{-2x}}\,dx = 2\pi\int_0^1\sqrt{1+u^2}\,du$

$[u = e^{-x}, du = -e^{-x}dx] = 2\pi\left[\frac{u}{2}\sqrt{1+u^2} + \frac{1}{2}\ln|u+\sqrt{1+u^2}|\right|_0^1$ [u = tan θ or

$u = \sinh t$ or Formula 21] $= 2\pi[\frac{1}{2}\sqrt{2} + \frac{1}{2}\ln(1+\sqrt{2})] = \pi[\sqrt{2} + \ln(1+\sqrt{2})]$

32. The upper half of the torus is generated by rotating the curve
$(x-R)^2+y^2 = r^2$, y>0, about the y-axis. $y\frac{dy}{dx} = -(x-R) \Rightarrow 1+(\frac{dy}{dx})^2$

$$= 1+\frac{(x-R)^2}{y^2} = \frac{y^2+(x-R)^2}{y^2} = \frac{r^2}{r^2-(x-R)^2}. \text{ Thus } S = 2\int_{R-r}^{R+r} 2\pi x\sqrt{1+(\frac{dy}{dx})^2}\,dx$$

$$= 4\pi\int_{R-r}^{R+r} \frac{rx}{\sqrt{r^2-(x-R)^2}}\,dx = 4\pi r\int_{-r}^{r} \frac{u+R}{\sqrt{r^2-u^2}}\,du \text{ [u = x-R]} = 4\pi r\int_{-r}^{r} \frac{u\,du}{\sqrt{r^2-u^2}}$$

$$+ 4\pi Rr\int_{-r}^{r} \frac{du}{\sqrt{r^2-u^2}} = 4\pi r\cdot 0 + 8\pi Rr\int_0^r \frac{du}{\sqrt{r^2-u^2}} \quad \text{[since the first}$$

integrand is an odd function and the 2nd is an even function]

$$= 8\pi Rr \sin^{-1}(\frac{u}{r})\Big]_0^r = 8\pi Rr\cdot\frac{\pi}{2} = 4\pi^2 Rr$$

34. Take the sphere $x^2+y^2+z^2 = \frac{d^2}{4}$ and let the

intersecting planes be y=c and y=c+h, where
$-\frac{d}{2}\le c\le\frac{d}{2}-h$. The sphere intersects the

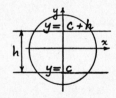

xy-plane in the circle $x^2+y^2 = \frac{d^2}{4}$. From

this equation, we get $x\frac{dx}{dy} + y = 0$, so

$\frac{dx}{dy} = -\frac{y}{x}$. The desired surface area is $S = 2\pi\int x\,ds$

$$= 2\pi\int_c^{c+h} x\sqrt{1+(dx/dy)^2}\,dy = 2\pi\int_c^{c+h} x\sqrt{1+y^2/x^2}\,dy = 2\pi\int_c^{c+h}\sqrt{x^2+y^2}\,dy$$

$$= 2\pi\int_c^{c+h} \frac{d}{2}\,dy = \pi d\int_c^{c+h} dy = \pi dh$$

36. The analogue of $f(x_i^*)$ in the derivation of (8.20) is now $c-f(x_i^*)$,

so $S = \lim_{\|P\|\to 0} \sum_{i=1}^n 2\pi[c-f(x_i^*)]\sqrt{1+[f'(x_i^*)]^2}\,\Delta x_i$

$$= \int_a^b 2\pi[c-f(x)]\sqrt{1+[f'(x)]^2}\,dx$$

38. Since $g(x) = f(x)+c$, we have $g'(x) = f'(x)$. Thus

$$S_g = \int_a^b 2\pi g(x)\sqrt{1+[g'(x)]^2}\, dx = \int_a^b 2\pi[f(x)+c]\sqrt{1+[f'(x)]^2}\, dx$$

$$= \int_a^b 2\pi f(x)\sqrt{1+[f'(x)]^2}\,dx + 2\pi c \int_a^b \sqrt{1+[f'(x)]^2}\,dx = S_f + 2\pi cL$$

Section 8.5

Exercises 8.5

2. $F = mg = (60)(9.8) = 588$ N; $W = Fd = 588 \cdot 2 = 1176$ J

4. $W = \int_1^2 \cos(\frac{\pi x}{3})dx = \frac{3}{\pi}\int_{\pi/3}^{2\pi/3} \cos u\, du$ $\quad [u = \frac{\pi x}{3},\ du = (\frac{\pi}{3})dx]$

$= \frac{3}{\pi}[\sin u]_{\pi/3}^{2\pi/3} = \frac{3}{\pi}(\frac{\sqrt{3}}{2} - \frac{\sqrt{3}}{2}) = 0$ J. **Interpretation:** From $x = 1$ to

$x = \frac{3}{2}$, the force does work equal to $\int_1^{3/2}\cos(\frac{\pi x}{3})dx = \frac{3}{\pi}(1-\frac{\sqrt{3}}{2})$ J in

accelerating the particle and increasing its kinetic energy. From
$x = 3/2$ to $x = 2$, the force opposes the motion of the particle,
decreasing its kinetic energy. This is negative work, equal in
magnitude but opposite in sign to the work done from $x = 1$ to
$x = 3/2$.

6. $25 = f(x) = kx = k(.1)$ (10 cm = .1 m), so $k = 250$ N/m. Thus
$f(x) = 250x$ and the work required is $W = \int_0^{.05} 250x\, dx = \left[125x^2\right]_0^{.05}$

$= 125(.0025) = .3125 \approx .31$ J.

8. If $12 = \int_0^1 kx\, dx = \frac{1}{2}kx^2\Big]_0^1 = \frac{k}{2}$, then $k = 24$ and the work required is
$\int_0^{3/4} 24x\, dx = 12x^2\Big]_0^{3/4} = 12 \cdot \frac{9}{16} = \frac{27}{4} = 6.75$ ft-lb.

10. Let L be the natural length of the spring in meters. Then
$6 = \int_{.10-L}^{.12-L} kx\, dx = \frac{1}{2}kx^2\Big]_{.10-L}^{.12-L} = \frac{1}{2}k[(.12-L)^2-(.10-L)^2]$ and

$10 = \int_{.12-L}^{.14-L} kx\, dx = \frac{1}{2}kx^2\Big]_{.12-L}^{.14-L} = \frac{1}{2}k[(.14-L)^2-(.12-L)^2]$. In other

words, $12 = k(.0044-.04L)$ and $20 = k(.0052-.04L)$. Subtracting the
first relation from the second gives $8 = .0008k$, so $k = 10,000$.
Now the second relation becomes $20 = 52-400L$, so $L = \frac{32}{400}$ m $= 8$ cm.

12. The cable weighs 1.5 lb/ft. Each part of the top 10 ft of cable is
lifted a distance equal to its distance from the top.

The remaining 30 ft of cable is lifted 10 ft. Thus $W = \int_0^{10} \frac{3}{2}x \, dx$
$+ \int_{10}^{40} \frac{3}{2} \cdot 10 \, dx = \frac{3}{4}x^2 \Big]_0^{10} + 15x \Big]_{10}^{40} = \frac{3}{4}(100) + 15(30) = 75 + 450 = 525$ ft-lb.

14. The work needed to lift the bucket itself is 4 lb·80 ft = 320 ft-lb
At time t (in seconds) the bucket is 2t ft above its original 80 ft
depth, but it now holds only 40-.2t lb of water. In terms of
distance, the bucket holds $40 - \frac{x}{10}$ lb of water when it is x ft above
its original 80 ft depth. Moving this amount of water a distance
Δx requires $(40 - \frac{x}{10})\Delta x$ ft-lb of work. Thus the work needed to lift
the water is $\int_0^{80}(40 - \frac{x}{10})dx = \left[40x - \frac{x^2}{20}\right]_0^{80} = 3200 - 320$ ft-lb. Adding in
the work of lifting the bucket gives a total of 3200 ft-lb of work.

16. A horizontal cylindrical slice of water Δx ft thick has a volume of
$\pi r^2 h = \pi \cdot 12^2 \cdot \Delta x$ ft^3 and weighs $(62.5 \text{ lb/ft}^3)(144\pi\Delta x \text{ ft}^3) = 9000\pi\Delta x$
lb. If the slice lies x ft below the edge of the pool ($1 \leq x \leq 5$),
then the work needed to pump it out is $9000\pi x\Delta x$. Thus
$W = \int_1^5 9000\pi x \, dx = 4500\pi x^2 \Big]_1^5 = 4500\pi(25 - 1) = 108,000\pi$ ft-lb.

18. For convenience, measure depth x from the middle of the tank, so
that $-1.5 \leq x \leq 1.5$ m. Lifting a slice of water of thickness Δx at
depth x requires a work contribution of $\Delta W \approx (9.8 \times 10^3)(2\sqrt{(1.5)^2 - x^2})$
$(6\Delta x)(2.5 + x)$, so $W \approx \int_{-1.5}^{1.5}(9.8 \times 10^3)12\sqrt{2.25 - x^2}(2.5 + x)dx$
$= (9.8 \times 10^3)\left[60\int_0^{3/2}\sqrt{(9/4) - x^2} \, dx + 12\int_{-3/2}^{3/2} x\sqrt{(9/4) - x^2} \, dx\right]$. The
second integral vanishes because its integrand is an odd function,
so $W \approx (9.8 \times 10^3)60\int_0^{3/2}\sqrt{(9/4) - x^2} \, dx$
$= (9.8 \times 10^3)60\left[\frac{x}{2}\sqrt{(9/4) - x^2} + \frac{9}{8}\sin^{-1}(\frac{2x}{3})\right]_0^{3/2}$ [Formula 30]
$= (9.8 \times 10^3)(60)(\frac{9}{8})(\frac{\pi}{2}) = 330750 \pi \approx 1.04 \times 10^6$ J

[Note: $\int_0^{3/2}\sqrt{(9/4) - x^2} \, dx$ can be computed instantly if we notice
that it represents the area of a quarter-circle of radius 3/2.]

20. Let x be depth in ft, so that $0 \leq x \leq 5$. Then
$\Delta W = (62.5)\pi(\sqrt{5^2 - x^2})^2\Delta x \cdot x$ ft-lb and $W \approx 62.5\pi\int_0^5 x(25 - x^2)dx$
$= 62.5\pi\left[\frac{25}{2}x^2 - \frac{x^4}{4}\right]_0^5 = 62.5\pi(\frac{625}{2} - \frac{625}{4}) = 62.5\pi(\frac{625}{4}) \approx 3.07 \times 10^4$ ft-lb

22. $W \approx (9.8 \times 920) \int_0^{3/2} 12\sqrt{(9/4)-x^2} (\frac{5}{2}+x)dx = 9016 \left[30\int_0^{3/2} \sqrt{(9/4)-x^2} \, dx + \right.$

$\left. 12\int_0^{3/2} x\sqrt{(9/4)-x^2} \, dx \right]$. Here $\int_0^{3/2} \sqrt{(9/4)-x^2} \, dx = \frac{1}{4}\pi(\frac{3}{2})^2 = \frac{9\pi}{16}$ and

$\int_0^{3/2} x\sqrt{(9/4)-x^2} \, dx = \int_0^{9/4} \frac{1}{2}u^{1/2}du \quad [u = \frac{9}{4} - x^2, \ du = -2x \ dx]$

$= \frac{1}{3}u^{3/2} \Big|_0^{9/4} = \frac{1}{3}(\frac{27}{8}) = \frac{9}{8}$, so $W \approx 9016[30 \cdot \frac{9\pi}{16} + 12 \cdot \frac{9}{8}]$

$= 9016(\frac{135\pi}{8} + \frac{27}{2}) \approx 6.00 \times 10^5$ J

24. $160 \ lb/in^2 = 160 \cdot 144 \ lb/ft^2$, $100 \ in^3 = \frac{100}{1728} \ ft^3$, and $800 \ in^3$

$= \frac{800}{1728} \ ft^3$. $k = PV^{1.4} = (160 \cdot 144)(\frac{100}{1728})^{1.4} = 23040(\frac{25}{432})^{1.4} \approx 426.5$.

Therefore $P \approx 426.5V^{-1.4}$ and $W = \int_{100/1728}^{800/1728} 426.5V^{-1.4}dV =$

$426.5 \left[\frac{V^{-.4}}{-.4}\right]_{25/432}^{25/54} = (426.5)(2.5)\left[(\frac{432}{25})^{.4}-(\frac{54}{25})^{.4}\right] \approx 1.88 \times 10^3 \ ft\text{-}lb.$

26. By #25, $W = GMm(\frac{1}{R} - \frac{1}{R+1,000,000})$ where

M = mass of earth in kg   R = radius of earth in m

m = mass of satellite in kg   (Note 1000 km = 1,000,000 m).

Thus $W = (6.67 \times 10^{-11})(5.98 \times 10^{24})(1000) \times (\frac{1}{6.37 \times 10^6} - \frac{1}{7.37 \times 10^6})$

$\approx 8.50 \times 10^9$ J

Exercises 8.6

2. (a) $P = \rho g d = 1030(9.8)(2.5) = 25235 \approx 2.52 \times 10^4$ Pa $= 25.2$ kPa

(b) $F = PA \approx (2.52 \times 10^4 \text{ N/m}^2)(50 \text{ m}^2) = 1.26 \times 10^6$ N

(c) $F = \int_0^{2.5} \rho g x \cdot 5 \, dx = (1030)(9.8)(5)\int_0^{2.5} x \, dx \approx 2.52 \times 10^4 \left. x^2 \right]_0^{2.5}$

$\approx 1.58 \times 10^5$ N

4. $F = \int_5^{10} \rho g(x-5) \cdot 2\sqrt{100-x^2} \, dx = \rho g \int_5^{10} 2x\sqrt{100-x^2} \, dx - 10\rho g \int_5^{10} \sqrt{100-x^2} \, dx$

$= -\rho g \cdot \frac{2}{3}(100-x^2)^{3/2} - 10\rho g(\frac{x}{2}\sqrt{100-x^2} + 50\sin^{-1}(\frac{x}{10}))\Big]_5^{10} = \frac{2}{3}\rho g(75)^{3/2}$

$- 10\rho g\left[50(\frac{\pi}{2}) - \frac{5}{2}\sqrt{75} - 50(\frac{\pi}{6})\right] = 250\rho g(\frac{3\sqrt{3}}{2} - \frac{2\pi}{3}) \approx 1.23 \times 10^6$ N

6. $F = \int_{-10}^0 \rho g(x+10)2\sqrt{100-x^2} \, dx = \rho g \int_{-10}^0 \sqrt{100-x^2} \, 2x \, dx$

$+ 20\rho g \int_{-10}^0 \sqrt{100-x^2} \, dx = \rho g \int_0^{100} u^{1/2}(-du) + 20\rho g \cdot \frac{1}{4}\pi(10)^2$

$= -\frac{2}{3}\rho g u^{3/2}\Big]_0^{100} + 500\rho g\pi = -\frac{2000}{3}\rho g + 500\rho g\pi = 1000\rho g(\frac{\pi}{2} - \frac{2}{3}) \approx 8.86 \times 10^6$ N

Alternative solution: $F = \int_0^{10} \rho g(10-x)2\sqrt{100-x^2} \, dx$

8. $F = \int_0^h \rho g x \cdot \frac{b}{h} x \, dx = \frac{\rho g b}{3h} x^3\Big]_0^h = \frac{\rho g b h^2}{3}$

$= 1000 g b h^2/3$ (metric units assumed)

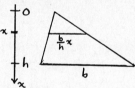

10. $F = \int_0^h \rho g(h-x)\frac{b}{h}x \, dx = \frac{\rho g b}{h}\int_0^h (hx-x^2)dx$

$= \frac{\rho g b}{h}\left[\frac{hx^2}{2} - \frac{x^3}{3}\right]\Big]_0^h = \frac{\rho g b}{h}\frac{h^3}{6} = \frac{\rho g b h^2}{6}$

$= \frac{1000 g b h^2}{6}$

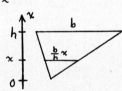

12. $F = \int_0^h \rho g x[a+\frac{x}{h}(b-a)]dx = \rho g a \int_0^h x \, dx$

$+ \frac{\rho g(b-a)}{h}\int_0^h x^2 dx = \rho g a\frac{h^2}{2} + \rho g\frac{b-a}{h}\frac{h^3}{3}$

$= \rho g h^2(\frac{a}{2}+\frac{b-a}{3}) = \rho g h^2\frac{a+2b}{6} \approx \frac{500}{3}g h^2(a+2b)$ N

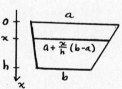

14. $F = \int_0^4 \rho g(4-x)(2x/\sqrt{3})dx = (8\rho g/\sqrt{3})\int_0^4 x \, dx - (2\rho g/\sqrt{3})\int_0^4 x^2 dx$

$= (8\rho g/\sqrt{3})\frac{x^2}{2}\Big]_0^4 - (2\rho g/\sqrt{3})\frac{x^3}{3}\Big]_0^4 = (2\rho g/\sqrt{3})(32-\frac{64}{3}) = \frac{64\rho g}{3\sqrt{3}} \approx 1.01 \times 10^5$ N

16. $F = \int_0^2 \rho g(10-x)2\sqrt{4-x^2}\, dx = 20\rho g \int_0^2 \sqrt{4-x^2}\, dx$

$\quad - \rho g \int_0^2 \sqrt{4-x^2}\, 2x\, dx = 20\rho g \frac{1}{4}\pi(2^2)$

$\quad - \rho g \int_0^4 u^{1/2} du \quad [u = 4-x^2,\ du = -2x\, dx]$

$\quad = 20\pi\rho g - \frac{2}{3}\rho g u^{3/2}\Big]_0^4 = 20\pi\rho g - \frac{16}{3}\rho g = \rho g(20\pi - \frac{16}{3}) \approx 5.63\times10^5\ N$

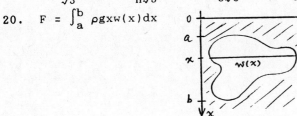

18. The height of the dam is $h = 15\sqrt{19}(\sqrt{3}/2)$,

so $F = \int_0^h \delta x(100 - \frac{50x}{h})\frac{2}{\sqrt{3}}\, dx$

$\quad = \frac{200\delta}{\sqrt{3}} \int_0^h x\, dx - \frac{100\delta}{h\sqrt{3}} \int_0^h x^2 dx$

$\quad = \frac{200\delta}{\sqrt{3}}\frac{h^2}{2} - \frac{100\delta}{h\sqrt{3}}\frac{h^3}{3} = \frac{200\delta h^2}{3\sqrt{3}} = \frac{200(62.5)}{3\sqrt{3}}\frac{12825}{4} \approx 7.71\times10^6\ lb$

20. $F = \int_a^b \rho g x w(x) dx$

Exercises 8.7

2. $M_x = 2\cdot1 + 3\cdot(-2) + 1\cdot4 = 0;\ M_y = 2\cdot5 + 3\cdot3 + 1\cdot(-2) = 17,$

$\quad m = 2+3+1 = 6,\ (\bar{x},\bar{y}) = (\frac{17}{6},0)$

4. $M_x = 3\cdot0 + 3\cdot8 + 8\cdot(-4) + 6\cdot(-5) = -38;\ M_y = 3\cdot0 + 3\cdot1 + 8\cdot3$

$\quad + 6\cdot(-6) = -9;\ m = 3+3+8+6 = 20,\ (\bar{x},\bar{y}) = (-\frac{9}{20},-\frac{19}{10})$

6. By symmetry, $\bar{x} = 0$ and $A = 2\int_0^1(1-x^2)dx = 2(x-\frac{x^3}{3})\Big]_0^1 = \frac{4}{3};$

$\quad \bar{y} = \frac{1}{A}\int_{-1}^1 \frac{1}{2}(1-x^2)^2 dx = \frac{1}{A}\int_0^1(1-x^2)^2 dx = \frac{3}{4}(x-\frac{2}{3}x^3+\frac{1}{5}x^5)\Big]_0^1 = \frac{3}{4}(1-\frac{2}{3}+\frac{1}{5}) = \frac{2}{5}.$

$\quad (\bar{x},\bar{y}) = (0,2/5)$

8. $A = \int_0^4 \sqrt{x}\ dx = \frac{2}{3}x^{3/2}\Big]_0^4 = \frac{2}{3}\cdot 8 = \frac{16}{3}$, $\bar{x} = \frac{1}{A}\int_0^4 x\sqrt{x}\ dx = \frac{3}{16}\frac{2}{5}x^{5/2}\Big]_0^4$

$= \frac{3}{16}\cdot\frac{2}{5}\cdot 32 = \frac{12}{5}$, $\bar{y} = \frac{1}{A}\int_0^4 \frac{1}{2}(\sqrt{x})^2 dx = \frac{3}{16}\frac{1}{2}\int_0^4 x\ dx = \frac{3}{32}\frac{x^2}{2}\Big]_0^4 = \frac{3}{32}\cdot 8 = \frac{3}{4}$

$(\bar{x},\bar{y}) = (12/5, 3/4)$

10. $A = \int_2^4 \frac{dx}{x-1} = \ln|x-1|\Big]_2^4 = \ln 3 - \ln 1 = \ln 3$, $\bar{x} = \frac{1}{A}\int_2^4 \frac{x}{x-1}\ dx$

$= \frac{1}{A}\int_2^4 (1+\frac{1}{x-1})dx = \frac{1}{A}(x+\ln|x-1|)\Big]_2^4 = \frac{1}{\ln 3}[(4+\ln 3)-(2+\ln 1)] = 1+2/\ln 3$,

$\bar{y} = \frac{1}{A}\int_2^4 \frac{1}{2}\frac{1}{(x-1)^2}\ dx = \frac{1}{2\ln 3}\Big[\frac{-1}{x-1}\Big]_2^4 = \frac{1}{2\ln 3}(-\frac{1}{3}+1) = \frac{1}{3\ln 3}$,

$(\bar{x},\bar{y}) = (1+\frac{2}{\ln 3}, \frac{1}{3\ln 3})$

12. $A = \int_0^{\pi/2}\sin x\ dx = -\cos x\Big]_0^{\pi/2} = 0-(-1) = 1$, $\bar{x} = \frac{1}{A}\int_0^{\pi/2} x \sin x\ dx$

$= \int_0^{\pi/2} x \sin x\ dx = -x\cos x + \sin x\Big]_0^{\pi/2} = 1$, $\bar{y} = \frac{1}{A}\int_0^{\pi/2} \frac{1}{2}\sin^2 x\ dx =$

$\frac{1}{4}\int_0^{\pi/2}(1 - \cos 2x)dx = \frac{1}{4}(x - \frac{1}{2}\sin 2x)\Big]_0^{\pi/2} = \frac{1}{4}\cdot\frac{\pi}{2} = \frac{\pi}{8}$, $(\bar{x},\bar{y}) = (1,\frac{\pi}{8})$

14. $A = \int_1^e \ln x\ dx = x \ln x - x\Big]_1^e = 0-(-1) = 1$, $\bar{x} = \frac{1}{A}\int_1^e x \ln x\ dx$

$= \frac{x^2}{2}\ln x - \frac{x^2}{4}\Big]_1^e = (\frac{e^2}{2}-\frac{e^2}{4})-(-\frac{1}{4}) = \frac{e^2+1}{4}$, $\bar{y} = \frac{1}{A}\int_1^e \frac{1}{2}(\ln x)^2 dx$

$= \frac{1}{2}\int_1^e (\ln x)^2 dx$. [To evaluate $\int(\ln x)^2 dx$, take $u = \ln x$ and $dv =$

$\ln x\ dx$, so that $du = \frac{1}{x}\ dx$ and $v = x \ln x - x$. Then $\int(\ln x)^2 dx =$

$x(\ln x)^2 - x(\ln x) - \int(x \ln x - x)\frac{1}{x}\ dx = x(\ln x)^2 - x(\ln x) -$

$\int(\ln x - 1)dx = x(\ln x)^2 - x \ln x - x \ln x + x + x + C$

$= x(\ln x)^2 - 2x \ln x + 2x + C.$] Thus $\bar{y} = \frac{1}{2}\Big[x(\ln x)^2 - 2x \ln x + 2x\Big]_1^e$

$= \frac{1}{2}[(e-2e+2e)-(0-0+2)] = \frac{e-2}{2}$. $(\bar{x},\bar{y}) = (\frac{e^2+1}{4},\frac{e-2}{2})$

16. By symmetry, $\bar{x} = 0$ and $A = 2\int_0^2[(8-x^2)-x^2]dx = 2\int_0^2(8-2x^2)dx$

$= 2(8x-\frac{2}{3}x^3)\Big]_0^2 = 2(16-\frac{16}{3}) = \frac{64}{3}$, $\bar{y} = \frac{1}{A}\int_{-2}^2 \frac{1}{2}[(8-x^2)^2-(x^2)^2]dx$

$= \frac{1}{A}\int_0^2(64-16x^2)dx = \frac{3}{64}\cdot 16 \cdot (4x-\frac{x^3}{3})\Big]_0^2 = \frac{3}{4}(8-\frac{8}{3}) = \frac{3}{4}\cdot\frac{16}{3} = 4$. (This result

could also have been predicted from symmetry considerations.)
$(\bar{x},\bar{y}) = (0,4)$

18. $A = \int_0^1 x\ dx + \int_1^2 \frac{1}{x}\ dx = \frac{x^2}{2}\Big]_0^1 + \ln x\Big]_1^2 = \frac{1}{2} + \ln 2$,

$\bar{x} = \frac{1}{A}\Big[\int_0^1 x^2 dx + \int_1^2 1\ dx\Big] = \frac{1}{A}\Big[\Big[\frac{x^3}{3}\Big]_0^1 + [x]_1^2\Big] = \frac{1}{A}(\frac{1}{3}+1) = \frac{2}{1+2\ln 2}\cdot\frac{4}{3}$

$= \frac{8}{3(1+2\ln 2)}$, $\bar{y} = \frac{1}{A}\Big[\int_0^1 \frac{1}{2}x^2 dx + \int_1^2 \frac{1}{2x^2}\ dx\Big] = \frac{1}{2A}\Big[\Big[\frac{x^3}{3}\Big]_0^1 + \Big[\frac{-1}{x}\Big]_1^2\Big]$

270

$$= \frac{1}{2A}(\frac{1}{3}+\frac{1}{2}) = \frac{5}{12A} = \frac{5}{6+12\ln2}. \quad (\bar{x},\bar{y}) = (\frac{8}{3(1+2\ln2)},\frac{5}{6(1+2\ln2)})$$

Remark The principle used in this problem is stated after Example 2: the moment of the union of two non-overlapping regions is the sum of the moments of the individual regions.

20. The equation $y^2 = x^3-x^4$ implies that $x^3-x^4 \geq 0$, so $0 \leq x \leq 1$. For each value of x in [0,1], there are two values of y satisfying $y^2 = x^3-x^4$, one positive and the other its negative. $y \neq 0$ for x in (0,1), but $y = 0$ when $x = 0$ or 1. Thus the curve forms a loop between (0,0) and (1,0). The loop is symmetric about the x-axis, so the centroid of the region inside the loop satisfies $\bar{y} = 0$. The area inside the loop is given by $A = 2\int_0^1 \sqrt{x^3-x^4} \, dx = 2\int_0^1 x\sqrt{x-x^2} \, dx$

$$= 2\left[\frac{1}{6}(2x^2-\frac{1}{2}x-\frac{3}{4})\sqrt{x-x^2} + \frac{1}{16}\cos^{-1}\left[\frac{1/2-x}{1/2}\right]\right]_0^1 \quad [\text{Formula 114 with } a = \frac{1}{2}]$$

$$= \left[\frac{8x^2-2x-3}{12}\sqrt{x-x^2} + \frac{1}{8}\cos^{-1}(1-2x)\right]_0^1 = [(\frac{1}{4}\cdot0+\frac{1}{8}\pi)-(\frac{-1}{4}\cdot0+\frac{1}{8}\cdot0)] = \frac{\pi}{8};$$

$$\bar{x} = \frac{1}{A}\int_0^1 x\cdot2\sqrt{x^3-x^4} \, dx = \frac{16}{\pi}\int_0^1 x^2\sqrt{x-x^2} \, dx \overset{(*)}{=} \frac{16}{\pi}\frac{5\pi}{128} = \frac{5}{8}; \quad (\bar{x},\bar{y}) = (\frac{5}{8},0).$$

Justification of (*): $\int_0^1 x^2\sqrt{x-x^2} \, dx = \int_0^1 x^2\sqrt{(1/2)^2-(x-1/2)^2} \, dx$

$$= \int_{-1/2}^{1/2}(u+a)^2\sqrt{a^2-u^2} \, du \quad [u = x-a, \ a = \frac{1}{2}]$$

$$= \int_{-\pi/2}^{\pi/2} a^2(\sin\theta+1)^2 a^2\cos^2\theta \, d\theta \quad [u = a\sin\theta, \ du = a\cos\theta \, d\theta]$$

$$= a^4\int_{-\pi/2}^{\pi/2}(\sin^2\theta\cos^2\theta + 2\cos^2\theta\sin\theta + \cos^2\theta) \, d\theta$$

$$= \frac{a^4}{4}\int_{-\pi/2}^{\pi/2}\sin^2 2\theta \, d\theta + 2a^4\int_{-\pi/2}^{\pi/2}\cos^2\theta\sin\theta \, d\theta + a^4\int_{-\pi/2}^{\pi/2}\cos^2\theta \, d\theta$$

$$= \frac{a^4}{2}\int_0^{\pi/2}\sin^2 2\theta \, d\theta + 2a^4\int_0^{\pi/2}\cos^2\theta \, d\theta \quad [\text{Theorem 5.33}]$$

$$= \frac{a^4}{4}\int_0^{\pi/2}(1-\cos4\theta) \, d\theta + a^4\int_0^{\pi/2}(1+\cos2\theta) \, d\theta$$

$$= \frac{a^4}{4}\left[\theta - \frac{1}{4}\sin4\theta\right]_0^{\pi/2} + a^4\left[\theta + \frac{1}{2}\sin2\theta\right]_0^{\pi/2} = \frac{a^4}{4}\cdot\frac{\pi}{2} + a^4\cdot\frac{\pi}{2} = \frac{5\pi}{8}a^4 = \frac{5\pi}{128}.$$

A similar (but shorter) calculation could have been used instead of Formula 114 to show that $\int_0^1 x\sqrt{x-x^2} \, dx = \frac{\pi}{16}$.

22. By symmetry about the line $y = x$, we expect $\bar{x} = \bar{y}$, but we'll calculate both anyway. $A = \frac{1}{4}\pi r^2$, so $m = \rho A = \frac{1}{2}\pi r^2$.

$$M_x = \rho\int_0^r \frac{1}{2}(\sqrt{r^2-x^2})^2 \, dx = \int_0^r(r^2-x^2) \, dx = r^2x - \frac{x^3}{3}\Big]_0^r = \frac{2r^3}{3};$$

$$M_y = \rho \int_0^r x\sqrt{r^2-x^2}\ dx = \int_0^r (r^2-x^2)^{1/2}\ 2x\ dx = \int_0^{r^2} u^{1/2} du \quad [u = r^2-x^2]$$

$$= \frac{2}{3}u^{3/2}\Big]_0^{r^2} = 2r^3/3; \quad \overline{x} = \frac{1}{m}M_y = \frac{2}{\pi r^2}\ \frac{2r^3}{3} = \frac{4r}{3\pi}; \quad \overline{y} = \frac{1}{m}M_x = \frac{4r}{3\pi}.$$

$$(\overline{x},\overline{y}) = (\frac{4r}{3\pi},\ \frac{4r}{3\pi})$$

24. By symmetry, $M_y = 0$ and $\overline{x} = 0$; $A = \frac{1}{2}\pi\cdot 1^2 + 4$, so $m = \rho A = 5(\frac{\pi}{2}+4) =$

$$\frac{5(\pi+8)}{2}; \quad M_x = \rho\cdot 2\int_0^1 \frac{1}{2}\Big[(\sqrt{1-x^2})^2 - (-2)^2\Big]dx = 5\int_0^1 (-x^2-3)dx$$

$$= -5(\frac{x^3}{3} + 3x)\Big]_0^1 = -5\cdot\frac{10}{3} = -\frac{50}{3}; \quad \overline{y} = \frac{1}{m}M_x = \frac{2}{5(\pi+8)}\cdot\frac{-50}{3} = \frac{-20}{3(\pi+8)}.$$

$$(\overline{x},\overline{y}) = (0,-20/3(\pi+8))$$

26. A sphere can be generated by rotating a semicircle about its
diameter. By Example 3, the center of mass travels a distance
$2\pi\overline{y} = 2\pi(4r/3\pi) = 8r/3$, so by the Theorem of Pappus, the volume of
the sphere is $V = Ad = \frac{\pi r^2}{2}\cdot\frac{8r}{3} = \frac{4}{3}\pi r^3$.

28. The quadrilateral is a parallelogram. By
symmetry, the centroid is its center $(7/2,2)$
(the midpoint of either diagonal). Its area
$A = bh = 6\cdot 4 = 24$. The Theorem of Pappus
implies that the volume of the solid is
$V = Ad = A\cdot 2\pi\overline{x} = 24\cdot 2\pi(7/2) = 168\pi.$

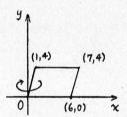

Section 8.8

Exercises 8.8

2. $\dfrac{dy}{dx} = \dfrac{x + \sin x}{3y^2} \Rightarrow \int 3y^2 dy = \int (x + \sin x)dx \Rightarrow y^3 = \dfrac{x^2}{2} - \cos x + C$

$\Rightarrow y = \sqrt[3]{(x^2/2) - \cos x + C}$

4. $y' = xy \Rightarrow \int\dfrac{dy}{y} = \int x\ dx\ (y\neq 0) \Rightarrow \ln|y| = \dfrac{x^2}{2} + C \Rightarrow |y| = e^C e^{x^2/2} \Rightarrow$

$y = Ke^{x^2/2}$, where $K = \pm e^C$ is a constant. (In our derivation, K was
nonzero, but we can restore the excluded case $y = 0$ by allowing K
to be zero.)

6. $e^{-y}y' + \cos x = 0 \Rightarrow e^{-y}\dfrac{dy}{dx} = -\cos x \Rightarrow \int e^{-y}dy = -\int \cos x\, dx \Rightarrow$

   $-e^{-y} = -\sin x - C \Rightarrow e^{-y} = \sin x + C$ [Note $e^{-y} > 0$] $\Rightarrow$

   $e^{-y} = |\sin x + C| \Rightarrow -y = \ln|\sin x + C| \Rightarrow y = -\ln|\sin x + C|$

8. $y' = \dfrac{\ln x}{xy+xy^3} = \dfrac{\ln x}{x(y+y^3)} \Rightarrow \int (y+y^3)dy = \int \dfrac{\ln x}{x}\, dx \Rightarrow \dfrac{y^2}{2} + \dfrac{y^4}{4} = \dfrac{1}{2}(\ln x)^2 + C_1$

   $\Rightarrow y^4 + 2y^2 = 2(\ln x)^2 + 2C_1 \Rightarrow (y^2+1)^2 = 2(\ln x)^2 + K$ [K = $2C_1 + 1$] $\Rightarrow$

   $y^2 + 1 = \sqrt{2(\ln x)^2 + K}$

10. $\dfrac{dx}{dt} = 1+t-x-tx = (1+t)(1-x) \Rightarrow \int \dfrac{dx}{1-x} = \int (1+t)dt$ (x≠1) $\Rightarrow$

    $-\ln|1-x| = \dfrac{1}{2}t^2 + t + C \Rightarrow |1-x| = e^{-(t^2/2+t+C)} \Rightarrow 1-x = \pm e^{-(t^2/2+t+C)}$

    $\Rightarrow x = 1 + Ae^{-(t^2/2+t)}$ (A = $\pm e^C$ or 0)

12. $xy' = \sqrt{1-y^2}$, x>0, y(1) = 0. $x\dfrac{dy}{dx} = \sqrt{1-y^2} \Rightarrow \displaystyle\int \dfrac{dy}{\sqrt{1-y^2}} = \int \dfrac{dx}{x} \Rightarrow \sin^{-1}y$

    $= \ln|x| + C = \ln x + C$ (since x>0). When x = 1, y = 0, so

    $\sin^{-1}0 = \ln 1 + C \Rightarrow C = 0$. Now $\sin^{-1}y = \ln x$, so y = sin(ln x).

14. $\dfrac{dy}{dx} = \dfrac{1+x}{xy}$, x>0, y(1) = -4. $\int y\, dy = \int \dfrac{1+x}{x}\, dx = \int (\dfrac{1}{x}+1)dx \Rightarrow$

    $y^2/2 = \ln|x| + x + C = \ln x + x + C$ (since x>0); y(1) = -4 $\Rightarrow (-4)^2/2$

    $= \ln 1 + 1 + C \Rightarrow 8 = 0+1+C \Rightarrow C = 7$, so $y^2 = 2 \ln x + 2x + 14$

16. $\dfrac{dy}{dx} = e^{x-y} = \dfrac{e^x}{e^y}$, y(0) = 1. $\int e^y dy = \int e^x dx \Rightarrow e^y = e^x + C$. y(0) = 1 $\Rightarrow$

    $e^1 = e^0 + C \Rightarrow C = e-1$, so $e^y = e^x + e - 1$ and $y = \ln(e^x + e - 1)$

18. $x\, dx + 2y\sqrt{x^2+1}\, dy = 0$, y(0) = 1. $\int 2y\, dy = -\displaystyle\int \dfrac{x\, dx}{\sqrt{x^2+1}} \Rightarrow$

    $y^2 = -\sqrt{x^2+1} + C$. y(0) = 1 $\Rightarrow 1 = -1+C \Rightarrow C = 2$, so $y^2 = 2 - \sqrt{x^2+1}$

20. $\dfrac{dy}{dt} = \dfrac{ty+3t}{t^2+1} = \dfrac{t(y+3)}{t^2+1}$, y(2) = 2. $\int \dfrac{dy}{y+3} = \int \dfrac{t\, dt}{t^2+1} \Rightarrow \ln|y+3| = \dfrac{1}{2}\ln(t^2+1) + C$

    $\Rightarrow y+3 = A\sqrt{t^2+1}$. y(2) = 2 $\Rightarrow 5 = A\sqrt{5} \Rightarrow A = \sqrt{5} \Rightarrow y = -3 + \sqrt{5t^2+5}$

22. Let y = g(x). Then $\dfrac{dy}{dx} = y(1+y)$ and y(0) = 1. $\int \dfrac{dy}{y(1+y)} = \int dx \Rightarrow$

    $\int (\dfrac{1}{y} - \dfrac{1}{1+y})dy = \int dx \Rightarrow \ln|y| - \ln|1+y| = x+C \Rightarrow |\dfrac{y}{1+y}| = e^C e^x \Rightarrow$

    $\dfrac{y}{1+y} = Ae^x$; y(0) = 1 $\Rightarrow \dfrac{1}{2} = A$ so $\dfrac{y}{1+y} = \dfrac{e^x}{2}$. Solve for y: $y = \dfrac{e^x}{2-e^x}$.

24. (a) If $y(t)$ is the amount of salt (in kg) after t minutes, then $y(0) = 0$ and the total amount of liquid in the tank remains constant at 1000 L.

$$\frac{dy}{dt} = \left[.05\frac{kg}{L}\right]\left[5\frac{L}{min}\right] + \left[.04\frac{kg}{L}\right]\left[10\frac{L}{min}\right] - \left[\frac{y(t)}{1000}\frac{kg}{L}\right]\left[15\frac{L}{min}\right] = .25 + .40 - .015y$$

$= .65 - .015y = \frac{130 - 3y}{200}\frac{kg}{min}$, so $\int\frac{dy}{130 - 3y} = \int\frac{dt}{200}$ and $-\frac{1}{3}\ln|130 - 3y| = \frac{t}{200}$

$+ C$; since $y(0) = 0$, we have $-\frac{1}{3}\ln 130 = C$, so $-\frac{1}{3}\ln|130 - 3y| =$

$\frac{t}{200} - \frac{1}{3}\ln 130$, $\ln|130 - 3y| = \frac{-3t}{200} + \ln 130 = \ln(130e^{-3t/200})$, and

$|130 - 3y| = 130e^{-3t/200}$. Since y is continuous, $y(0) = 0$, and the right-hand side is never zero, we deduce that $130 - 3y(t)$ is always positive. Thus $130 - 3y = 130e^{-3t/200}$ and $y = \frac{130}{3}(1 - e^{-3t/200})$ kg.

(b) After an hour, $y = \frac{130}{3}(1 - e^{-180/200}) = \frac{130}{3}(1 - e^{-.9}) \approx 25.7$ kg.

Note: As $t \to \infty$, $y(t) \to \frac{130}{3} = 43\frac{1}{3}$ kg.

26. (a) If $b = a$, then $\frac{dx}{dt} = k(a - x)^2$, so $\int\frac{dx}{(a - x)^2} = \int k\,dt$ and $\frac{1}{a - x} = kt + C$.

Taking $x(0) = 0$, we get $C = \frac{1}{a}$. Thus $a - x = \frac{1}{kt + 1/a}$ and $x = a - \frac{a}{akt + 1}$

$= \frac{a^2 kt}{akt + 1}\frac{moles}{L}$.

(b) Suppose $[C] = \frac{a}{2}$ after 20 seconds. If t is measured in seconds

then $x(20) = \frac{a}{2}$, so $\frac{a}{2} = \frac{20a^2 k}{20ak + 1}$ and $40a^2 k = 20a^2 k + a$. Thus $20a^2 k = a$

and $k = \frac{1}{20a}$, so $x = \frac{a^2 t/20a}{1 + at/20a} = \frac{at/20}{1 + t/20} = \frac{at}{t + 20}\frac{moles}{L}$.

28. Assuming that $\frac{dy}{dt} = ky(M - y)$ with $M = 100$ and $\frac{dy}{dt}(0) = .02y(0) =$

$.02(5) = .10$, we get $.10 = ky(0)(M - y(0)) = 5k(100 - 5) = 475k$, so $k =$

$\frac{.10}{475} = \frac{1}{4750}$. The solution to (8.51) is $y(t) = \dfrac{y_0 M}{y_0 + (M - y_0)e^{-kMt}}$

$= \dfrac{500}{5 + 95e^{-2t/95}}$ from which we compute $y(14) \approx 6.6$ billion, $y(114) \approx$

36.7 billion, and $y(514) \approx 100$ billion. According to this model, the population initially grows at the same rate as before, but then levels off at M (100 billion).

30. (a) $\frac{dy}{dt} = c\ln\left[\frac{M}{y}\right]y \Rightarrow \int\frac{dy}{y\ln(M/y)} = \int c\,dt$. Let $u = \ln(M/y) = \ln M - \ln y$.

Then $du = -dy/y$, so $-\int\frac{du}{u} = ct + K \Rightarrow -\ln|u| = ct + K \Rightarrow |u| = e^{-(ct+K)}$

$\Rightarrow \left|\ln\left[\frac{M}{y}\right]\right| = e^{-(ct+K)} \Rightarrow \ln\left[\frac{M}{y}\right] = e^{-(ct+K)}$ $\quad [\ln(\frac{M}{y}) \geq 0$ since $M \geq y]$

274

$\Rightarrow \dfrac{M}{y} = e^{e^{-(ct+K)}} \quad \Rightarrow \quad y(t) = Me^{-e^{-(ct+K)}}$. Taking $t = 0$, we get

$y_0 = Me^{-e^{-K}}$, so $e^{-K} = \ln(M/y_0)$ and $e^{-(ct+K)} = e^{-K}e^{-ct}$

$= \ln(M/y_0)e^{-ct}$. Thus $y(t) = Me^{-\ln(M/y_0)e^{-ct}}$, $c \neq 0$.

(b) $\lim\limits_{t\to\infty} y(t) = M$ since $\lim\limits_{t\to\infty} e^{-ct} = 0$.

(c) Let $b = \ln\left[\dfrac{M}{y_0}\right]$. Then $b>0$ since $M>y_0$, and $y(t) = Me^{-be^{-ct}}$. We

compute $y'(t) = Me^{-be^{-ct}}\dfrac{d}{dt}(-be^{-ct}) = Me^{-be^{-ct}}(bce^{-ct}) =$

$Mbce^{-ct-be^{-ct}}$; $y''(t) = Mbce^{-ct-be^{-ct}}\dfrac{d}{dt}(-ct-be^{-ct}) =$

$Mbce^{-ct-be^{-ct}}(-c+bce^{-ct})$. y' never vanishes, so there are no local

extrema. $y'' = 0 \Leftrightarrow -c+bce^{-ct} = 0 \Leftrightarrow be^{-ct} = 1 \Leftrightarrow e^{ct} = b \Leftrightarrow t =$

$(\ln b)/c$. If $b \leq 1$ (that is, if $M/y_0 \leq e$), then $-c+bce^{-ct} =$

$c(be^{-ct}-1)<0$, so the graph is concave down on $(0,\infty)$ with no

inflection points there. If $b>1$, then the graph is concave up on

$(0,(\ln b)/c)$, has an inflection point at $t = (\ln b)/c$, and is concave

down on $(\dfrac{\ln b}{c},\infty)$. Note that $t = \dfrac{\ln b}{c} \Rightarrow e^{-ct} = e^{-\ln b} = \dfrac{1}{b} \Rightarrow y =$

$Me^{-b(1/b)} = M/e$.

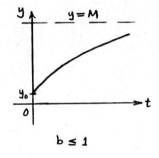

$b \leq 1$

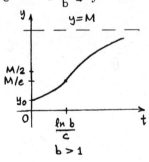

$b > 1$

32. Let b = number of hours before noon that it began to snow, t = time
measured in hours after noon, $x = x(t)$ = distance traveled by plow
at time t. Then dx/dt = speed of plow. Since the snow falls
steadily, the height at time t is $h(t) = k(t+b)$, where k is a
constant. We are given that the rate of removal is constant, say R
(in m^2/h). If the width of the path is w, then

R = height $\times$ width $\times$ speed = $h(t) \times w \times \dfrac{dx}{dt} = k(t+b)w\dfrac{dx}{dt}$

Thus $\frac{dx}{dt} = \frac{C}{t+b}$ where C $(= \frac{R}{kw})$ is a constant. This is a separable equation. $\int dx = C \int \frac{dt}{t+b}$ ⇒ $x = C \ln(t+b) + K$. Put $t = 0$:

$0 = C \ln b + K$ ⇒ $K = -C \ln b$, so $x(t) = C \ln(t+b) - C \ln b = C \ln(1+\frac{t}{b})$

Put $t = 1$: $6000 = C \ln(1+1/b)$; put $t = 2$: $9000 = C \ln(1+2/b)$.
Solve for b: $\frac{\ln(1+1/b)}{6000} = \frac{\ln(1+2/b)}{9000}$ ⇒ $3 \ln(1+\frac{1}{b}) = 2 \ln(1+\frac{2}{b})$ ⇒

$(1+\frac{1}{b})^3 = (1+\frac{2}{b})^2$ ⇒ $1+\frac{3}{b}+\frac{3}{b^2}+\frac{1}{b^3} = 1+\frac{4}{b}+\frac{4}{b^2}$ ⇒ $\frac{1}{b}+\frac{1}{b^2}-\frac{1}{b^3} = 0$ ⇒

$b^2+b-1 = 0$ ⇒ $b = (-1\pm\sqrt{5})/2$. But $b>0$, so $b = (-1+\sqrt{5})/2$. The snow began to fall $(\sqrt{5}-1)/2$ hours before noon, i.e., at about 11:23 AM.

Chapter 8 Review

Review Exercises for Chapter 8

2. $V = \int_0^1 \pi\left[(x^2)^2-(x^3)^2\right]dx = \pi \int_0^1 (x^4-x^6)dx = \pi\left[\frac{x^5}{5} - \frac{x^7}{7}\right]_0^1 = \pi(\frac{1}{5}-\frac{1}{7}) = \frac{2\pi}{35}$

4. $V = \int_0^8 \pi(y^{1/3})^2 dy = \pi\int_0^8 y^{2/3} dy = \pi \cdot \frac{3}{5}y^{5/3}\Big]_0^8 = \frac{96\pi}{5}$

6. $V = \int_{3\pi/2}^{5\pi/2} 2\pi x \cos x\, dx = 2\pi\left[x \sin x + \cos x\right]_{3\pi/2}^{5\pi/2}$

$= 2\pi\left[(\frac{5\pi}{2}\cdot 1+0)-(\frac{3\pi}{2}\cdot(-1)+0)\right] = 2\pi(4\pi) = 8\pi^2$

8. $V = \int_0^2 2\pi(8-x^3)(2-x)dx = 2\pi\int_0^2 (x^4-2x^3-8x+16)dx$

$= 2\pi\left[\frac{x^5}{5} - \frac{x^4}{2} - 4x^2 + 16x\right]_0^2 = 2\pi(\frac{32}{5} - 8 - 16 + 32) = \frac{144\pi}{5}$

10. $V = \int_{-1}^1 A(x)dx = 2\int_0^1 A(x)dx = 2\int_0^1[(2-x^2)-x^2]^2 dx = 2\int_0^1[2(1-x^2)]^2 dx$

$= 8\int_0^1(1-2x^2+x^4)dx = 8\left[x-\frac{2}{3}x^3+\frac{x^5}{5}\right]_0^1 = 8(1-\frac{2}{3}+\frac{1}{5}) = \frac{64}{15}$

12. $y = \sqrt{x-x^2}+\sin^{-1}\sqrt{x}$ is defined when $x-x^2 \geq 0$, that is, for x in $[0,1]$. (The function $\sin^{-1}\sqrt{x}$ is defined when $x \geq 0$ and $|\sqrt{x}| \leq 1$, but this adds no further restrictions on x.) $\frac{dy}{dx} = \frac{1-2x}{2\sqrt{x-x^2}} + \frac{1}{2\sqrt{x}\sqrt{1-x}} = \frac{2-2x}{2\sqrt{x-x^2}}$

$= \sqrt{(1-x)/x}$, so $1+(\frac{dy}{dx})^2 = 1+\frac{1-x}{x} = \frac{1}{x}$. Thus $L = \int_0^1 \sqrt{1+(\frac{dy}{dx})^2}\, dx$

$= \int_0^1 \sqrt{1/x}\, dx = \int_0^1 x^{-1/2}\, dx = 2x^{1/2}\Big]_0^1 = 2$.

14. $y = e^x$, $0 \leq x \leq 1$, $\sqrt{1+(\frac{dy}{dx})^2} = \sqrt{1+(e^x)^2}$, so $S = \int_0^1 2\pi e^x \sqrt{1+(e^x)^2}\ dx$

$= 2\pi \int_1^e \sqrt{1+u^2}\ du\ [u = e^x] = 2\pi \left[\frac{u}{2}\sqrt{1+u^2} + \frac{1}{2}\ln|u+\sqrt{1+u^2}| \right]_1^e$ [Formula 21]

$= 2\pi \left[\frac{e}{2}\sqrt{1+e^2} + \frac{1}{2}\ln(e+\sqrt{1+e^2}) - \frac{1}{2}\sqrt{2} - \frac{1}{2}\ln(1+\sqrt{2}) \right]$

$= \pi \left[e\sqrt{1+e^2} + \ln(e+\sqrt{1+e^2}) - \sqrt{2} - \ln(1+\sqrt{2}) \right]$

16. $y = \frac{1}{x^2}$, $1 \leq x \leq 2 \Rightarrow S = \int_1^2 2\pi y\sqrt{1+(\frac{dy}{dx})^2}\ dx = 2\pi \int_1^2 \frac{1}{x^2}\sqrt{1+(2/x^3)^2}\ dx$.

By Simpson's Rule with $n = 10$, $S \approx 2\pi \cdot \frac{1/10}{3}[g(1)+4g(1.1)+2g(1.2)$

$+4g(1.3)+2g(1.4)+4g(1.5)+2g(1.6)+4g(1.7)+2g(1.8)+4g(1.9)+g(2)]$

where $g(x) = \sqrt{1+(2/x^3)^2}/x^2$. Thus $S \approx \frac{2\pi}{30}[2.236+4(1.492)+2(1.062)$

$+4(.800)+2(.631)+4(.517)+2(.435)+4(.374)+2(.326)+4(.289)+.258]$

$\approx \frac{2\pi}{30}(21.285) \approx 4.46$.

18. Work to raise elevator alone = 1600 lb x 30 ft = 48,000 ft-lb.
    Work to raise bottom 170 ft of cable = 170 ft x 10 lb/ft x 30 ft
    $= 51,000$ ft-lb. Work to raise top 30 ft of cable = $\int_0^{30} 10x\ dx$

    $= 5x^2 \big]_0^{30} = 5 \cdot 900 = 4500$ ft-lb. Total work = 48,000 + 51,000 +

    4,500 = 103,500 ft-lb.

20. $F = \int_0^4 \delta(4-y)4\sqrt{y}\ dy$

    $= 4\delta\int_0^4 (4y^{1/2} - y^{3/2})dy$

    $= 4\delta(\frac{8}{3}y^{3/2} - \frac{2}{5}y^{5/2})\big]_0^4$

    $= 4\delta(\frac{64}{3} - \frac{64}{5}) = 256\delta(\frac{1}{3} - \frac{1}{5}) = \frac{512}{15}\delta$

    $\approx 2.13 \times 10^3$ lb

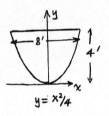

$y = x^2/4$

22. The region is symmetric about the line $x = 2$, so $\bar{x} = 2$.

    $A = \int_0^4 (4x-x^2)dx = 2x^2 - \frac{x^3}{3}\big]_0^4 = 32 - \frac{64}{3} = \frac{32}{3}$; $\bar{y} = \frac{1}{A}\int_0^4 \frac{1}{2}(4x-x^2)^2 dx$

    $= \frac{3}{64} \int_0^4 (16x^2-8x^3+x^4)dx = \frac{3}{64}(\frac{16}{3}x^3 - 2x^4 + \frac{x^5}{5})\big]_0^4$

    $= \frac{3}{64}\left[\frac{16}{3} \cdot 64 - 2 \cdot 256 + \frac{16 \cdot 64}{5} \right] = \frac{8}{5}$. $(\bar{x},\bar{y}) = (2,\frac{8}{5})$

24. (a) $A = \int_0^1 (2x-x^2-x^3)dx = x^2 - \frac{x^3}{3} - \frac{x^4}{4}\Big]_0^1 = 1 - \frac{1}{3} - \frac{1}{4} = \frac{5}{12}$

(b) $\bar{x} = \frac{1}{A}\int_0^1 x(2x-x^2-x^3)dx = \frac{12}{5}\int_0^1 (2x^2-x^3-x^4)dx = \frac{12}{5}(\frac{2}{3}x^3 - \frac{x^4}{4} - \frac{x^5}{5})\Big]_0^1$

$= \frac{12}{5}(\frac{2}{3}-\frac{1}{4}-\frac{1}{5}) = \frac{13}{25}$; $\bar{y} = \frac{1}{A}\int_0^1 \frac{1}{2}[(2x-x^2)^2-(x^3)^2]dx = \frac{6}{5}\int_0^1 (4x^2-4x^3+x^4-x^6)dx$

$= \frac{6}{5}(\frac{4}{3}x^3-x^4+\frac{x^5}{5}-\frac{x^7}{7})\Big]_0^1 = \frac{6}{5}(\frac{4}{3}-1+\frac{1}{5}-\frac{1}{7}) = \frac{82}{175}$; $(\bar{x},\bar{y}) = (\frac{13}{25},\frac{82}{175})$

(c) By the Theorem of Pappus, $V = A\cdot 2\pi\bar{y} = \frac{5}{12}\cdot 2\pi\cdot\frac{82}{175} = \frac{41\pi}{105}$

(d) By the Theorem of Pappus, $V = A\cdot 2\pi\bar{x} = \frac{5}{12}\cdot 2\pi\cdot\frac{13}{25} = \frac{13\pi}{30}$

26. $\frac{dy}{dx} = \frac{y^2+1}{xy}$, $x>0$ $\Rightarrow$ $\int \frac{y\,dy}{y^2+1} = \int \frac{dx}{x}$ $\Rightarrow$ $\frac{1}{2}\ln(y^2+1) = \ln x + C$ $\Rightarrow$

$\ln\sqrt{y^2+1} = \ln(e^C x)$ $\Rightarrow$ $\sqrt{y^2+1} = e^C x$ $\Rightarrow$ $y^2 = Kx^2-1$ $(K = e^{2C}>0)$

28. $2u\frac{du}{dt} = te^t$, $u(0) = 1$. $\int 2u\,du = \int te^t dt$ $\Rightarrow$ $u^2 = (t-1)e^t+C$, where

$1 = [u(0)]^2 = -e^0+C = C-1$, so $C = 2$ and $u^2 = (t-1)e^t+2$ $\Rightarrow$

$u(t) = \sqrt{(t-1)e^t+2}$ since $u(0) = 1>0$.

CHAPTER 9

Exercises 9.1

2. (a)

t	x	y
-3	-7	5
-2	-5	4
-1	-3	3
0	-1	2
1	1	1
2	3	0

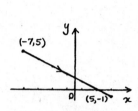

(b) $x = 2t-1$, $y = 2-t$, $-3 \leq t \leq 3$
$x = 2(2-y)-1 = 3-2y$, so
$x+2y = 3$, with $-7 \leq x \leq 5$

4. (a)

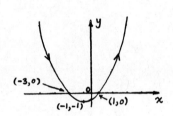

(b) $x = 2t-1$, $y = t^2-1$

$y = \left[\dfrac{x+1}{2}\right]^2 - 1$, so $y+1 = \dfrac{1}{4}(x+1)^2$

6. (a)

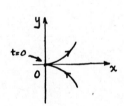

(b) $x = t^2$, $y = t^3$

$x = t^2 = (\sqrt[3]{y})^2 = y^{2/3}$, or

$y = \pm x^{3/2}$

8. (a)

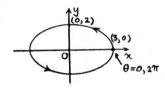

(b) $x = 3\cos\theta$, $y = 2\sin\theta$, $0 \leq \theta \leq 2\pi$

$(x/3)^2+(y/2)^2 = \cos^2\theta + \sin^2\theta = 1$,

or $\dfrac{x^2}{9} + \dfrac{y^2}{4} = 1$

10. (a)

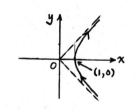

(b) $x = \sec\theta$, $y = \tan\theta$, $-\pi/2 < \theta < \pi/2$

$x^2-y^2 = \sec^2\theta - \tan^2\theta = 1$, $x \geq 1$,

or $x = \sqrt{y^2+1}$

12. (a)

(b) $x = e^t$, $y = e^{-t}$

$y = 1/x$, $x > 0$

14. (a)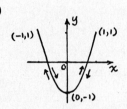

(b) $x = \cos t$, $y = \cos 2t$

$y = \cos 2t = 2\cos^2 t - 1 = 2x^2 - 1$,

so $y + 1 = 2x^2$, $-1 \leq x \leq 1$

16. (a)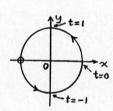

(b) $x = \dfrac{1-t^2}{1+t^2}$, $y = \dfrac{2t}{1+t^2}$

$x^2 + y^2 = 1$, $x \neq -1$

18. (a)

(b) $x = \dfrac{1-t}{1+t}$, $y = t^2$, $0 \leq t \leq 1$

$x = \dfrac{1-\sqrt{y}}{1+\sqrt{y}}$, $0 \leq y \leq 1$, or $y = \left[\dfrac{1-x}{1+x}\right]^2$, $0 \leq x \leq 1$

20. (a)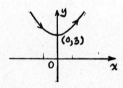

(b) $x = 4\sinh t$, $y = 3\cosh t$

$(y/3)^2 - (x/4)^2 = \cosh^2 t - \sinh^2 t =$

1 with $y \geq 3$, so $\dfrac{y^2}{9} - \dfrac{x^2}{16} = 1$, $y \geq 3$

22. $(x-2)^2 + (y-3)^2 = \cos^2 t + \sin^2 t = 1$, so the motion takes place on a unit circle centered at $(2,3)$ As t goes from 0 to 2π, the particle makes one complete counterclockwise rotation around the circle, starting and ending at $(3,3)$.

24. $x = \cos^2 t = y^2$, so the particle moves along the parabola $x = y^2$. As t goes from 0 to 4π, the particle moves from $(1,1)$ down to $(1,-1)$ (at $t=\pi$), back up to $(1,1)$ again (at $t=2\pi$), and then repeats this entire cycle between $t=2\pi$ and $t=4\pi$.

26. $y = \csc t = \dfrac{1}{\sin t} = 1/x$. The particle slides down the first

quadrant branch of the hyperbola $xy=1$ from $(1/2,2)$ to
$(\sin 1, \csc 1) \approx (0.84147, 1.1884)$ as t goes from $\pi/6$ to 1.

28. $x = t \cos t$, $y = t \sin t$. $x^2 + y^2 = t^2$, so (x,y) is $|t|$ units away
from the origin. For $t \neq 0$, $y/x = \tan t$, so t can be viewed as the
"angle of inclination" of the line segment from $(0,0)$ to (x,y).
Thus for $t > 0$ (x,y) moves in a spiral so that the angle t (in
radians) equals the distance from $(0,0)$ to (x,y). [In polar
coordinates (see Section 9.4), this is the
curve $r = \theta$.] Negative values of t yield a
mirror image spiral. Part of the graph is
shown at the right. The curve is
symmetric about the y-axis.

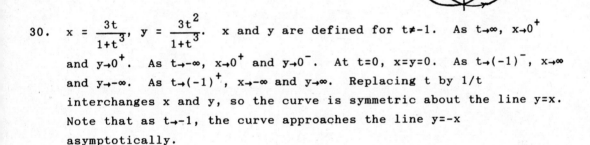

30. $x = \dfrac{3t}{1+t^3}$, $y = \dfrac{3t^2}{1+t^3}$. x and y are defined for $t \neq -1$. As $t \to \infty$, $x \to 0^+$
and $y \to 0^+$. As $t \to -\infty$, $x \to 0^+$ and $y \to 0^-$. At $t=0$, $x=y=0$. As $t \to (-1)^-$, $x \to \infty$
and $y \to -\infty$. As $t \to (-1)^+$, $x \to -\infty$ and $y \to \infty$. Replacing t by $1/t$
interchanges x and y, so the curve is symmetric about the line $y=x$.
Note that as $t \to -1$, the curve approaches the line $y=-x$
asymptotically.

t:	-100	-10	-5	-3	-2	-1.5	-1.1	-.9	-.7	-.5
x:	.0003	.03	.12	.35	.86	1.89	9.97	-9.96	-3.20	-1.71
y:	-.03	-.3	-.6	-1.04	-1.7	-2.84	-10.97	8.97	2.24	.86

t:	-.2	0	.5	1	2	3	5	10	100
x:	-.60	0	1.33	1.5	.67	.32	.12	.03	.0003
y:	.12	0	.67	1.5	1.33	.96	.60	.30	.03

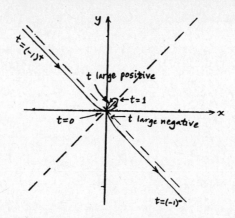

32. (a) If $\alpha=30°$ and $v_o=500$ m/s, then the equations become $x=250\sqrt{3}t$ and

$y=250t-4.9t^2$. $y=0$ when $t=0$ (when the gun is fired) and again when

$t = 250/4.9 \approx 51$ s. Then $x = (250\sqrt{3})(250/4.9) \approx 22092$ m.

(b) $y = -4.9\left[t^2-\frac{250}{4.9}t\right] = -4.9\left[t-\frac{125}{4.9}\right]^2 + \frac{125^2}{4.9} \leq \frac{125^2}{4.9}$ with equality

when $t = \frac{125}{4.9}$ s, so the maximum height attained is $\frac{125^2}{4.9} \approx 3189$ m.

(c) $t=\frac{x}{v_o\cos\alpha}$, so $y = (v_o\sin\alpha)\frac{x}{v_o\cos\alpha} - \frac{1}{2}g\left[\frac{x}{v_o\cos\alpha}\right]^2 =$

$(\tan\alpha)x - \left[\frac{g}{2v_o^2\cos^2\alpha}\right] \cdot x^2$, which is the equation of a parabola.

34.

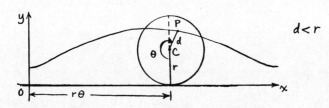 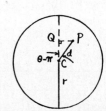

$d < r$

The diagrams above depict the case $\pi < \theta < 3\pi/2$, $d < r$. As in Exercise
33, C has coordinates $(r\theta,r)$. Now Q (in the right-hand diagram)
has coordinates $(r\theta,r+d\cdot\cos(\theta-\pi)) = (r\theta,r-d\cdot\cos\theta)$, so the typical
point P of the trochoid has coordinates $(r\theta+d\cdot\sin(\theta-\pi),r-d\cdot\cos\theta)$.
That is, P has coordinates (x,y), where

$$x = r\theta - d\sin\theta \quad \text{and} \quad y = r - d\cos\theta.$$

When $d=r$, these equations agree with those of the cycloid.

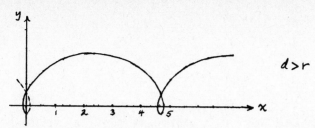

$d > r$

36. The center Q of the smaller circle has coordinates $((a+b)\cos\theta,(a+b)\sin\theta)$. Arc PS has length $a\theta$ (as in Exercise 35), so that $\angle PQS = \dfrac{a\theta}{b}$, $\angle PQR = \pi-\dfrac{a\theta}{b}$, and

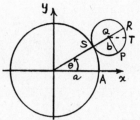

$\angle PQT = \pi-\dfrac{a\theta}{b}-\theta = \pi-\left[\dfrac{a+b}{b}\right]\theta$ since $\angle RQT = \theta$.

Thus the coordinates of P are

$x = (a+b)\cos\theta + b\cdot\cos(\pi-\dfrac{a+b}{b}\theta) = (a+b)\cos\theta - b\cdot\cos\left[\dfrac{a+b}{b}\theta\right]$, and

$y = (a+b)\sin\theta - b\cdot\sin(\pi-\dfrac{a+b}{b}\theta) = (a+b)\sin\theta - b\cdot\sin\left[\dfrac{a+b}{b}\theta\right]$.

If $b=a/4$, then $x = \dfrac{5a}{4}\cos\theta - \dfrac{a}{4}\cos 5\theta$, $y = \dfrac{5a}{4}\sin\theta - \dfrac{a}{4}\sin 5\theta$.

283

Exercises 9.2

2. $x=1-t^3$, $y=t^2-3t+1$; $t=1$. $\frac{dy}{dt}=2t-3$, $\frac{dx}{dt}=-3t^2$; $\frac{dy}{dx} = \frac{dy/dt}{dx/dt} = \frac{2t-3}{-3t^2}$. When

$t=1$, $\frac{dy}{dx}=(-1/-3)=1/3$ and $(x,y)=(0,-1)$, so the equation of the

tangent is $y+1=\frac{1}{3}(x-0)$, or $x-3y=3$.

4. $x=\ln t$, $y=te^t$; $t=1$. $\frac{dy}{dt}=(t+1)e^t$, $\frac{dx}{dt}=\frac{1}{t}$, $\frac{dy}{dx} = \frac{dy/dt}{dx/dt} = t(t+1)e^t$. When

$t=1$, $(x,y)=(0,e)$ and $\frac{dy}{dx}=2e$, so the equation of the tangent is

$y-e=2e(x-0)$ or $2ex-y+e=0$.

6. $x = t \sin t$, $y = t \cos t$; $t=\pi$. $\frac{dy}{dt} = \cos t - t \sin t$,

$\frac{dx}{dt} = \sin t + t \cos t$, and $\frac{dy}{dx} = \frac{dy/dt}{dx/dt} = \frac{\cos t - t \sin t}{\sin t + t \cos t}$. When $t=\pi$,

$(x,y) = (0,-\pi)$ and $\frac{dy}{dx} = -1/(-\pi) = 1/\pi$, so the equation of the

tangent is $y+\pi=\frac{1}{\pi}(x-0)$ or $x-\pi y=\pi^2$.

8. (a) $x=2t+3$, $y=t^2+2t$; $(5,3)$. $\frac{dy}{dt}=2t+2$, $\frac{dx}{dt}=2$, so $\frac{dy}{dx}=\frac{dy/dt}{dx/dt}=t+1$. At

$(5,3)$, $t=1$ and $\frac{dy}{dx}=2$, so the tangent is $y-3=2(x-5)$ or $2x-y=7$.

(b) $y=t^2+2t=\left[\frac{x-3}{2}\right]^2+2\left[\frac{x-3}{2}\right]=\frac{(x-3)^2}{4}+x-3$, so $\frac{dy}{dx}=\frac{x-3}{2}+1$. When $x=5$, $\frac{dy}{dx}=2$,

so the equation of the tangent is $2x-y=7$, as before.

10. (a) $x=t^3$, $y=t^2$; $(1,1)$. $\frac{dy}{dt}=2t$, $\frac{dx}{dt}=3t^2$, so $\frac{dy}{dx} = \frac{dy/dt}{dx/dt} = \frac{2t}{3t^2} = \frac{2}{3t}$

(for $t\neq0$). At $(1,1)$, we have $t=1$ and $\frac{dy}{dx}=2/3$, so the tangent is

$y-1=\frac{2}{3}(x-1)$ or $2x-3y+1=0$.

(b) $y=x^{2/3}$, so $\frac{dy}{dx}=(2/3)x^{-1/3}$. When $x=1$, this is $2/3$, so the

tangent is $2x-3y+1=0$, as before.

12. $x=t^3+t^2+1$, $y=1-t^2$. $\frac{dy}{dt}=-2t$, $\frac{dx}{dt}=3t^2+2t$, so $\frac{dy}{dx} = \frac{dy/dt}{dx/dt} =$

$\frac{-2t}{3t^2+2t} = \frac{-2}{3t+2}$. $\frac{d}{dt}\left[\frac{dy}{dx}\right] = \frac{6}{(3t+2)^2}$; $\frac{d^2y}{dx^2} = \frac{d(dy/dx)/dt}{dx/dt} = \frac{6}{t(3t+2)^3}$.

14. $x=t^4-t^2+t$, $y=\sqrt[3]{t}$. $\frac{dy}{dx} = \frac{dy/dt}{dx/dt} = \frac{(1/3)t^{-2/3}}{4t^3-2t+1} = \frac{1}{3t^{2/3}(4t^3-2t+1)}$;

$\frac{d}{dt}\left[\frac{dy}{dx}\right] = -\left[\frac{d}{dt}[3t^{2/3}(4t^3-2t+1)]\right]/[3t^{2/3}(4t^3-2t+1)]^2 =$

$\frac{-t^{-1/3}[3t(12t^2-2)+2(4t^3-2t+1)]}{9t^{4/3}(4t^3-2t+1)^2} = \frac{-44t^3+10t-2}{9t^{5/3}(4t^3-2t+1)^2}$;

$$\frac{d^2y}{dx^2} = \frac{d(dy/dx)/dt}{dx/dt} = \frac{-44t^3+10t-2}{9t^{5/3}(4t^3-2t+1)^3}.$$

16. $x = t + 2\cos t$, $y = \sin 2t$. $\dfrac{dy}{dx} = \dfrac{dy/dt}{dx/dt} = \dfrac{2\cos 2t}{1 - 2\sin t}$;

$$\frac{d}{dt}\left[\frac{dy}{dx}\right] = \frac{(1-2\sin t)(-4\sin 2t)-2\cos 2t(-2\cos t)}{(1 - 2\sin t)^2}$$

$$= \frac{4(\cos t - \sin 2t + \sin t \sin 2t)}{(1 - 2\sin t)^2};$$

$$\frac{d^2y}{dx^2} = \frac{d(dy/dx)/dt}{dx/dt} = \frac{4(\cos t - \sin 2t + \sin t \sin 2t)}{(1 - 2\sin t)^3}.$$

18. $x=1+t^2$, $y=t\ln t$. $\dfrac{dy}{dx} = \dfrac{dy/dt}{dx/dt} = \dfrac{1+\ln t}{2t}$; $\dfrac{d}{dt}\left[\dfrac{dy}{dx}\right] = \dfrac{2t(1/t)-(1+\ln t)2}{(2t)^2}$

$$= \frac{-\ln t}{2t^2}; \quad \frac{d^2y}{dx^2} = \frac{d(dy/dx)/dt}{dx/dt} = \frac{-\ln t}{4t^3}.$$

20. $x=t^3-3t^2$, $y=t^3-3t$. $\dfrac{dx}{dt}=3t^2-6t=3t(t-2)$; $\dfrac{dy}{dt}=3t^2-3=3(t-1)(t+1)$. $\dfrac{dy}{dt}=0$

$\Longleftrightarrow t=1$ or $-1 \Longleftrightarrow (x,y)=(-2,-2)$ or $(-4,2)$. $\dfrac{dx}{dt}=0 \Longleftrightarrow t=0$ or $2 \Longleftrightarrow$

$(x,y)=(0,0)$ or $(-4,2)$. So the tangent is
horizontal at $(-2,-2)$ and vertical at
$(0,0)$. At $(-4,2)$ the curve crosses itself
and there are two tangents, one horizontal
and one vertical.

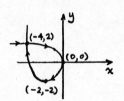

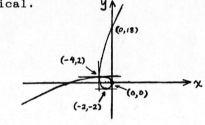

22. $x=\sin 2t=2\sin t\cos t$, $y=\sin t$.

$\dfrac{dx}{dt}=2\cos 2t=2(\cos^2 t-\sin^2 t)$, $\dfrac{dy}{dt}=\cos t$. $\dfrac{dy}{dt}=0$

$\Longleftrightarrow \cos t=0 \Longleftrightarrow (x,y)=(0,\pm1)$. $\dfrac{dx}{dt}=0 \Longleftrightarrow$

$|\cos t|=|\sin t|=\sqrt{2}/2 \Longleftrightarrow (x,y)=(\pm1,\sqrt{2}/2)$ or
$(\pm1,-\sqrt{2}/2)$. The tangent is horizontal at
$(0,\pm1)$ and vertical at $(\pm1,\pm\sqrt{2}/2)$ (all sign
combinations allowed).

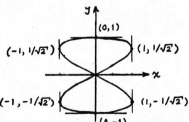

24. $x=a(\cos\theta-\cos^2\theta)$, $y=a(\sin\theta-\sin\theta\cos\theta)$.

$\dfrac{dx}{d\theta}=a(-\sin\theta+2\cos\theta\sin\theta)$,

$\dfrac{dy}{d\theta}=a(\cos\theta+\sin^2\theta-\cos^2\theta)=a(\cos\theta+1-2\cos^2\theta)$

$\dfrac{dy}{d\theta}=0 \iff 0 = 2\cos^2\theta-\cos\theta-1$

$= (2\cos\theta+1)(\cos\theta-1) \iff \cos\theta=-1/2$ or $1 \iff$

$(x,y)=(-3a/4,\pm3\sqrt{3}a/4)$ or $(0,0)$. $\dfrac{dx}{d\theta}=0 \iff$

$(2\cos\theta-1)\sin\theta=0 \iff \cos\theta=1/2$ or $\sin\theta=0 \iff (x,y)=(0,0)$ or

$(a/4,\pm\sqrt{3}a/4)$ or $(-2a,0)$. The curve has horizontal tangents at

$(-3a/4,\pm3\sqrt{3}a/4)$ and vertical tangents at $(-2a,0)$ and $(a/4,\pm\sqrt{3}a/4)$.

Since $\dfrac{dy}{dx} = \dfrac{dy/d\theta}{dx/d\theta} = \dfrac{(2\cos\theta+1)(1-\cos\theta)}{(2\cos\theta-1)\sin\theta}$, we see that

$\lim\limits_{\theta\to0} \dfrac{dy}{dx} = \lim\limits_{\theta\to0} \dfrac{2\cos\theta+1}{2\cos\theta-1}\cdot\lim\limits_{\theta\to0} \dfrac{1-\cos\theta}{\sin\theta} = 3\cdot0=0$ (using l'Hospital's rule).

Thus the curve has a horizontal tangent at $(0,0)$, a point where

both $\dfrac{dx}{d\theta}$ and $\dfrac{dy}{d\theta}$ are 0. (The curve is the cardioid $r=a(1-\cos\theta)$; see

Section 9.4.)

26. $x=1-2\cos^2 t=-\cos2t$, $y=(\tan t)(1-2\cos^2 t)=-(\tan t)\cos2t$. To find a

point where the curve crosses itself, we look for two values of t

that yield the same point (x,y). Call these values t_1 and t_2.

Then $\cos^2 t_1=\cos^2 t_2$ (from the equation for x) and either

$\tan t_1 = \tan t_2$ or $\cos^2 t_1=\cos^2 t_2=1/2$ (from the equation for y). We

can satisfy $\cos^2 t_1=\cos^2 t_2$ and $\tan t_1 = \tan t_2$ by choosing t_1

arbitrarily and taking $t_2=t_1+\pi$, so evidently the whole curve is

retraced every time t traverses an interval of length π. Thus we

can restrict our attention to the interval $(-\pi/2,\pi/2)$. If $t_2=-t_1$.

then $\cos^2 t_2=\cos^2 t_1$, but $\tan t_2 = -\tan t_1$. This suggests that we

try to satisfy the condition $\cos^2 t_1=\cos^2 t_2=1/2$. Taking $t_1=\pi/4$ and

$t_2=-\pi/4$ gives $(x,y)=(0,0)$ for both values of t.

$\frac{dx}{dt}$ = 2 sin 2t and $\frac{dy}{dt}$ = 2 sin 2t tan t - cos 2t sec^{2}t. When t=π/4, $\frac{dx}{dt}$=2 and $\frac{dy}{dt}$=2, so $\frac{dy}{dx}$=1. When t=-π/4, $\frac{dx}{dt}$=-2 and $\frac{dy}{dt}$=2, so $\frac{dy}{dx}$=-1. Thus the equations of the two tangents at (0,0) are y=x and y=-x.

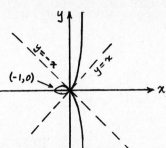

28. $\frac{dy}{d\theta}$=r·sinθ, $\frac{dx}{d\theta}$=r(1-cosθ), so $\frac{dy}{dx}$=$\frac{sin\theta}{1-cos\theta}$. At (0,0), θ=0, and

$\lim\limits_{\theta\to 0^+}\frac{dy}{dx}$ = $\lim\limits_{\theta\to 0^+}\frac{cos\theta}{sin\theta}$ = ∞ (using l'Hospital's rule), so the cycloid has

a vertical tangent at (0,0).

30. x = a cos^{3}θ, y = a sin^{3}θ.

(a) $\frac{dx}{d\theta}$=-3a·cos^{2}θ·sinθ, $\frac{dy}{d\theta}$=3a·sin^{2}θ·cosθ, so $\frac{dy}{dx}$=-$\frac{sin\theta}{cos\theta}$=-tanθ.

(b) The tangent is horizontal ⟺ $\frac{dy}{dx}$=0 ⟺ tanθ=0 ⟺ θ=nπ ⟺

(x,y)=(±a,0). The tangent is vertical ⟺ cosθ=0 ⟺ θ is an odd

multiple of π/2 ⟺ (x,y)=(0,±a).

(c) $\frac{dy}{dx}$=±1 ⟺ tanθ=±1 ⟺ θ is an odd multiple of π/4 ⟺

(x,y)=(±√2a/4,±√2a/4) (all sign choices allowed).

32. (a) x=3t^2+1, y=2t^3+1, $\frac{dx}{dt}$=6t, $\frac{dy}{dt}$=6t^2, so $\frac{dy}{dx}$=$\frac{6t^2}{6t}$=t (even where t=0).

So at the point corresponding to parameter value t, the equation of

the tangent line is y-(2t^3+1)=t[x-(3t^2+1)]. If this line is to

pass through (4,3), we must have 3-(2t^3+1)=t[4-(3t^2+1)] ⟺

2t^3-2=3t^3-3t ⟺ t^3-3t+2=0 ⟺ (t-1)^2(t+2)=0 ⟺ t=1 or -2. Hence the

desired equations are y-3=x-4, or y=x-1, tangent to the curve at

(4,3), and y-(-15)=-2(x-13), or y=-2x+11, tangent to the curve at

(13,-15).

34. t+1/t=2.5 ⟺ t=1/2 or 2, and for 1/2<t<2, we have t+1/t<2.5.

x=-3/2 when t= 1/2 and x=3/2 when t=2.

A = $\int_{-3/2}^{3/2}$ (2.5-y)dx = $\int_{1/2}^{2}$$\left[\frac{5}{2}-t-\frac{1}{t}\right]$$\left[1+\frac{1}{t^2}\right]$dt   [x = t-$\frac{1}{t}$ ⟹ dx=$\left[1+\frac{1}{t^2}\right]$dt]

= $\int_{1/2}^{2}$ (-t+5/2-2t^{-1}+(5/2)t^{-2}-t^{-3}) dt

= $\frac{-t^2}{2}$ + $\frac{5t}{2}$ - 2ln|t| - $\frac{5}{2t}$ + $\frac{1}{2t^2}$ $\Big]_{1/2}^{2}$

= (-2+5-2ln2-5/4+1/8) - (-1/8+5/4+2ln2-5+2) = 15/4 - 4ln2

36. By symmetry, $A = 4\int_0^a y\, dx = 4\int_{\pi/2}^0 a\sin^3\theta\cdot(-3a\cos^2\theta\sin\theta)\, d\theta$

$= 12a^2\int_0^{\pi/2}\sin^4\theta\cdot\cos^2\theta\, d\theta$. Now $\int\sin^4\theta\cdot\cos^2\theta\, d\theta = \int\sin^2\theta\cdot\dfrac{\sin^2 2\theta}{4}\, d\theta =$

$\dfrac{1}{8}\int(1-\cos 2\theta)\cdot\sin^2 2\theta\, d\theta = \dfrac{1}{8}\int\left[\dfrac{1-\cos 4\theta}{2} - \sin^2 2\theta\cdot\cos 2\theta\right]d\theta$

$= \dfrac{\theta}{16} - \dfrac{\sin 4\theta}{64} - \dfrac{\sin^3 2\theta}{48} + C$, so $\int_0^{\pi/2}\sin^4\theta\cdot\cos^2\theta\, d\theta$

$= \dfrac{\theta}{16} - \dfrac{\sin 4\theta}{64} - \dfrac{\sin^3 2\theta}{48}\Bigg]_0^{\pi/2} = \dfrac{\pi}{32}$. Thus $A = 12a^2(\pi/32) = 3\pi a^2/8$.

38. If f' is continuous and $f'(t)\neq 0$ for $a\leq t\leq b$, then either $f'(t)>0$ for all t in $[a,b]$ or $f'(t)<0$ for all t in $[a,b]$. Thus f is monotonic (strictly increasing or strictly decreasing) on $[a,b]$. It follows from Theorem 6.6 that f is invertible. Set $F = g\circ f^{-1}$, that is, define F by $F(x) = g(f^{-1}(x))$. Then $x = f(t) \Rightarrow f^{-1}(x) = t$, so $y = g(t) = g(f^{-1}(x)) = F(x)$.

Section 9.3

Exercises 9.3

2. $x=t^3$, $y=t^2$, $0\leq t\leq 4$. $\left[\dfrac{dx}{dt}\right]^2 + \left[\dfrac{dy}{dt}\right]^2 = (3t^2)^2 + (2t)^2 = 9t^4 + 4t^2$.

$L = \int_0^4\sqrt{(dx/dt)^2 + (dy/dt)^2}\, dt = \int_0^4\sqrt{9t^4 + 4t^2}\, dt = \int_0^4 t\sqrt{9t^2 + 4}\, dt$

$= \dfrac{1}{18}\int_4^{148} u^{1/2}du$ $[u=9t^2+4]$ $= \dfrac{1}{18}\cdot\dfrac{2}{3}\cdot u^{3/2}\Big]_4^{148} = \dfrac{1}{27}\left[148^{3/2} - 4^{3/2}\right]$

$= \dfrac{8}{27}\left[37^{3/2} - 1\right] = 8(37\sqrt{37} - 1)/27$

4. $x=3t-t^3$, $y=3t^2$, $0\leq t\leq 2$. $\left[\dfrac{dx}{dt}\right]^2 + \left[\dfrac{dy}{dt}\right]^2 = (3-3t^2)^2 + (6t)^2 = 9(1+2t^2+t^4)$

$= [3(1+t^2)]^2$. $L = \int_0^2 3(1+t^2)\, dt = 3t+t^3\Big]_0^2 = 14$

6. $x=a(\cos\theta+\theta\sin\theta)$, $y=a(\sin\theta-\theta\cos\theta)$, $0\leq\theta\leq\pi$.

$\left[\dfrac{dx}{d\theta}\right]^2 + \left[\dfrac{dy}{d\theta}\right]^2 = a^2[(-\sin\theta+\sin\theta+\theta\cos\theta)^2 + (\cos\theta-\cos\theta+\theta\sin\theta)^2]$

$= a^2\theta^2(\cos^2\theta+\sin^2\theta) = (a\theta)^2$. $L = \int_0^\pi a\theta\, d\theta = a\pi^2/2$

8. $x=t^2$, $y=1+4t$, $0\leq t\leq 2$. $\left[\dfrac{dx}{dt}\right]^2 + \left[\dfrac{dy}{dt}\right]^2 = (2t)^2 + 4^2 = 4(t^2+4)$.

$$L = \int_0^2 2\sqrt{t^2+4}\ dt = \int_0^{\pi/4} 2\cdot 2\sec\theta\cdot 2\sec^2\theta\ d\theta \quad [t=2\tan\theta,\ dt=2\sec^2\theta\ d\theta]$$

$$= 8\int_0^{\pi/4} \sec^3\theta\ d\theta = 4\Big[\sec\theta\cdot\tan\theta + \ln|\sec\theta+\tan\theta|\Big]_0^{\pi/4} \quad [\text{Formula 71}]$$

$$= 4\sqrt{2} + 4\ln(\sqrt{2}+1)$$

10. $x=e^t-t$, $y=4e^{t/2}$, $0\le t\le 1$. $\left[\dfrac{dx}{dt}\right]^2+\left[\dfrac{dy}{dt}\right]^2 = (e^t-1)^2+(2e^{t/2})^2 = e^{2t}+2e^t+1$

$$= (e^t+1)^2.\quad L = \int_0^1 (e^t+1)dt = e^t+t\Big]_0^1 = (e+1)-1 = e$$

12. $x=\cos^2 t$, $y=\cos t$, $0\le t\le 4\pi$.

$$\left[\dfrac{dx}{dt}\right]^2+\left[\dfrac{dy}{dt}\right]^2 = (-2\cos t\sin t)^2 + (-\sin t)^2 = \sin^2 t(4\cos^2 t+1).$$

$$\text{distance} = \int_0^{4\pi} |\sin t|\sqrt{4\cos^2 t+1}\ dt = 4\int_0^{\pi}\sin t\sqrt{4\cos^2 t+1}\ dt$$

$$= -4\int_1^{-1}\sqrt{4u^2+1}\ du \quad [u=\cos t,\ du=-\sin t\ dt] \quad = 4\int_{-1}^1\sqrt{4u^2+1}\ du$$

$$= 8\int_0^1\sqrt{4u^2+1}\ du = 8\int_0^{\tan^{-1}2}\sec\theta\cdot\tfrac{1}{2}\sec^2\theta\ d\theta = 4\int_0^{\tan^{-1}2}\sec^3\theta\ d\theta$$

$$= 2\sec\theta\tan\theta + 2\ln|\sec\theta+\tan\theta|\Big]_0^{\tan^{-1}2} = 4\sqrt{5} + 2\ln(\sqrt{5}+2)$$

$$L = \int_0^{\pi}|\sin t|\sqrt{4\cos^2 t+1}\ dt = \sqrt{5} + \tfrac{1}{2}\ln(\sqrt{5}+2)$$

14. $x = a\cos^3\theta$, $y = a\sin^3\theta$.

$$\left[\dfrac{dx}{d\theta}\right]^2+\left[\dfrac{dy}{d\theta}\right]^2 = (-3a\cos^2\theta\sin\theta)^2 + (3a\sin^2\theta\cos\theta)^2$$

$$= 9a^2\sin^2\theta\cos^2\theta.\quad L = 4\int_0^{\pi/2} 3a\sin\theta\cos\theta\ d\theta = 12a\dfrac{\sin^2\theta}{2}\Big]_0^{\pi/2} = 6a$$

16. As in #2, $S = \int_0^1 2\pi t^2\sqrt{9t^4+4t^2}\,dt = 2\pi\int_4^{13}\dfrac{u-4}{9}\cdot\sqrt{u}\cdot\dfrac{1}{18}du \quad [u=9t^2+4]$

$$= \dfrac{\pi}{81}\Big[\tfrac{2}{5}u^{5/2} - \tfrac{8}{3}u^{3/2}\Big]\Big]_4^{13} = 2\pi(247\sqrt{13}+64)/1215$$

18. As in #4, $S = \int_0^1 2\pi\cdot 3t^2\cdot 3(1+t^2)dt = 18\pi\int_0^1 (t^2+t^4)dt = 18\pi\Big[\tfrac{1}{3}t^3+\tfrac{1}{5}t^5\Big]_0^1$

$$= 48\pi/5$$

20. As in #14, $S = \int_0^{\pi/2} 2\pi\cdot a\sin^3\theta\cdot 3a\sin\theta\cos\theta\ d\theta$

$$= 6\pi a^2\int_0^{\pi/2}\sin^4\theta\cos\theta\ d\theta = (6\pi a^2/5)\sin^5\theta\Big]_0^{\pi/2} = 6\pi a^2/5$$

22. As in #10, $S = \int_0^1 2\pi(e^t-t)\sqrt{(e^t-1)^2+(2e^{t/2})^2}\,dt = \int_0^1 2\pi(e^t-t)(e^t+1)dt$

$$= 2\pi\Big[\tfrac{1}{2}e^{2t}+e^t-(t-1)e^t-\tfrac{1}{2}t^2\Big]_0^1 = \pi(e^2+2e-6)$$

24. By Formula 8.21, $S = \int_a^b 2\pi F(x)\sqrt{1+F'(x)^2}\,dx$. Now

$1+F'(x)^2 = 1 + \left[\dfrac{dy/dt}{dx/dt}\right]^2 = \dfrac{(dx/dt)^2+(dy/dt)^2}{(dx/dt)^2}$. Using the

Substitution Rule with $x = x(t) \;\Rightarrow\; dx = \dfrac{dx}{dt}\,dt$, we have

$S = \int_\alpha^\beta 2\pi y \sqrt{\dfrac{(dx/dt)^2+(dy/dt)^2}{(dx/dt)^2}} \dfrac{dx}{dt}\,dt = \int_\alpha^\beta 2\pi y\sqrt{(dx/dt)^2+(dy/dt)^2}\,dt$

Section 9.4

Section 9.4

2. $(3,0)$

$(3,2\pi),\ (-3,\pi)$

6. $(3,2)$

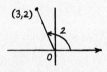

$(3,2+2\pi)\ (-3,2+\pi)$

10.

$x = 2\cos(2\pi/3) = -1$
$y = 2\sin(2\pi/3) = \sqrt{3}$

4. $(2,-\pi/7)$

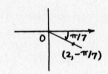

$(2,13\pi/7),\ (-2,6\pi/7)$

8. $(-2,3\pi/2)$

$(2,\pi/2),\ (-2,-\pi/2)$

12.

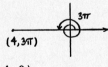

$(-4,0)$

290

14.

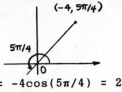

$x = -4\cos(5\pi/4) = 2\sqrt{2}$

$y = -4\sin(5\pi/4) = 2\sqrt{2}$

16.

$x = -2\cos(-5\pi/6) = \sqrt{3}$

$y = -2\sin(-5\pi/6) = 1$

18. $(x,y) = (-1,-\sqrt{3})$. $r = \sqrt{1+3} = 2$, $\tan\theta = y/x = \sqrt{3} \Rightarrow \theta = 4\pi/3$. $(2,4\pi/3)$

20. $(x,y) = (3,4)$

$r = \sqrt{9+16} = 5$

$\tan\theta = y/x = 4/3$

$\theta = \tan^{-1}(4/3)$

$(5,\tan^{-1}(4/3))$

22. $0 \le \theta \le \pi/3$

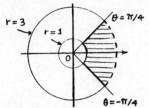

24. $1 \le r < 3$, $-\pi/4 \le \theta \le \pi/4$

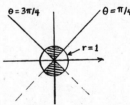

26. $-1 \le r \le 1$, $\pi/4 \le \theta \le 3\pi/4$

28. The points in Cartesian coordinates are $(r_1\cos\theta_1, r_1\sin\theta_1)$ and

$(r_2\cos\theta_2, r_2\sin\theta_2)$ respectively. So the square of the distance

between them is $(r_2\cos\theta_2 - r_1\cos\theta_1)^2 + (r_2\sin\theta_2 - r_1\sin\theta_1)^2$

$= r_1^2 - 2r_1 r_2\cos(\theta_1 - \theta_2) + r_2^2$, and the distance is

$\left[r_1^2 - 2r_1 r_2\cos(\theta_1 - \theta_2) + r_2^2\right]^{1/2}$.

30. $r = 2\sin\theta \Rightarrow r^2 = 2r\sin\theta \Rightarrow x^2 + y^2 = 2y$

32. $r = 5/(3-4\sin\theta) \Rightarrow 3r - 4r\sin\theta = 5 \Rightarrow 3r = 5 + 4r\sin\theta \Rightarrow$

$9r^2 = (5 + 4r\sin\theta)^2 \Rightarrow 9(x^2+y^2) = (5+4y)^2 \Rightarrow 9x^2 = 7y^2 + 40y + 25$

34. $r^2 = \theta \Rightarrow \tan(r^2) = \tan\theta \Rightarrow \tan(x^2+y^2) = y/x$

36. $y = x+1 \iff r\sin\theta = r\cos\theta + 1 \iff r(\sin\theta - \cos\theta) = 1$

38. $x^2 = 4y \iff r^2\cos^2\theta = 4r\sin\theta \iff r\cos^2\theta = 4\sin\theta \iff r = 4\tan\theta\sec\theta$

40. $x^2 - y^2 = 1 \iff r^2(\cos^2\theta - \sin^2\theta) = 1 \iff r^2\cos 2\theta = 1 \iff r^2 = \sec 2\theta$

42. r = -1

44. θ = -π/4

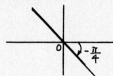

46. r = -4sinθ ⟺ r² = -4r sinθ
⟺ x²+y² = -4y ⟺
x²+(y+2)² = 4

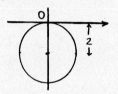

48. r = 2sinθ + 2cosθ ⟺
r² = 2r sinθ + 2r cosθ ⟺
x²+y² = 2y+2x ⟺
(x-1)²+(y-1)² = 2

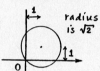

radius
is √2

50. r = 2(1-sinθ)

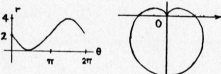

52. r = 1+cosθ

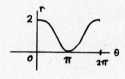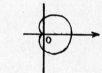

54. r = θ/2, -4π≤θ≤4π

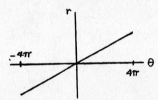

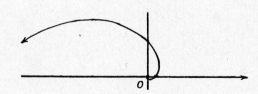

56. r = e^θ

58. r = 2+cosθ

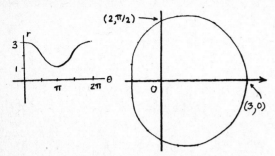

(2,π/2)

(3,0)

60. r = 3-4sinθ

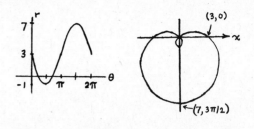

(3,0)

(7,3π/2)

62. r = sin2θ

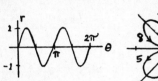
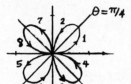

θ=π/4

64. r = 2cos3θ

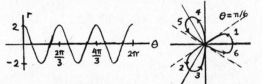

θ=π/6

66. r = sin4θ

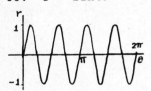
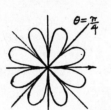

θ=π/4

68. r = -cos5θ

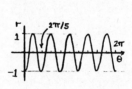
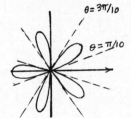

θ=3π/10

θ=π/10

70. r² = sin2θ

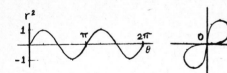

72. r = 2-cscθ

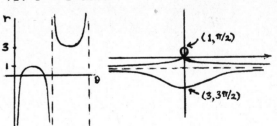

(1,π/2)

(3,3π/2)

74. $r^2\theta = 1 \Longleftrightarrow r = \pm 1/\sqrt{\theta}$ for θ > 0

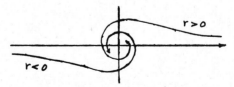
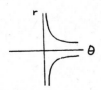

r>0

r<0

76. $\dfrac{dy}{dx} = \dfrac{(dr/d\theta)\sin\theta + r\cos\theta}{(dr/d\theta)\cos\theta - r\sin\theta} = \dfrac{(-\sin\theta+\cos\theta)\sin\theta+(\cos\theta+\sin\theta)\cos\theta}{(-\sin\theta+\cos\theta)\cos\theta-(\cos\theta+\sin\theta)\sin\theta} = -1$

when θ = π/4

78. $\dfrac{dy}{dx} = \dfrac{(dr/d\theta)\sin\theta + r\cos\theta}{(dr/d\theta)\cos\theta - r\sin\theta} = \dfrac{(1/\theta)\sin\theta + (\ln\theta)\cos\theta}{(1/\theta)\cos\theta - (\ln\theta)\sin\theta} = \dfrac{\sin e + e\cos e}{\cos e - e\sin e}$

when $\theta = e$

80. $\dfrac{dy}{dx} = \dfrac{(dr/d\theta)\sin\theta + r\cos\theta}{(dr/d\theta)\cos\theta - r\sin\theta} = \dfrac{-4\sin^2\theta + (2+4\cos\theta)\cos\theta}{-4\sin\theta\cos\theta - (2+4\cos\theta)\sin\theta}$

$= -\dfrac{2\cos2\theta + \cos\theta}{2\sin2\theta + \sin\theta} = -\dfrac{2(1/2) + \sqrt{3}/2}{2(\sqrt{3}/2) + 1/2} = -(4+3\sqrt{3})/11$ when $\theta = \pi/6$

82. $\dfrac{dy}{dx} = \dfrac{(dr/d\theta)\sin\theta + r\cos\theta}{(dr/d\theta)\cos\theta - r\sin\theta} = \dfrac{3\cos3\theta\sin\theta + \sin3\theta\cos\theta}{3\cos3\theta\cos\theta - \sin3\theta\sin\theta} = -\sqrt{3}$ when $\theta = \dfrac{\pi}{6}$

84. $y = r\sin\theta = \cos\theta\sin\theta + \sin^2\theta = \frac{1}{2}\sin2\theta + \sin^2\theta \Rightarrow \dfrac{dy}{d\theta} = \cos2\theta + \sin2\theta$

$= 0 \Rightarrow \tan2\theta = -1 \Rightarrow 2\theta = 3\pi/4$ or $7\pi/4 \Longleftrightarrow \theta = 3\pi/8$ or $7\pi/8 \Rightarrow$

horizontal tangents at $(\cos(3\pi/8)+\sin(3\pi/8),3\pi/8)$ and

$(\cos(7\pi/8)+\sin(7\pi/8),7\pi/8)$. $x = r\cos\theta = \cos^2\theta + \cos\theta\sin\theta \Rightarrow$

$\dfrac{dx}{d\theta} = -\sin2\theta + \cos2\theta = 0 \Rightarrow \tan2\theta = 1 \Rightarrow 2\theta = \pi/4$ or $5\pi/4 \Longleftrightarrow \theta = \pi/8$

or $5\pi/8 \Rightarrow$ vertical tangents at $(\cos(\pi/8)+\sin(\pi/8),\pi/8)$ and

$(\cos(5\pi/8)+\sin(5\pi/8),5\pi/8)$. [Note: These expressions can be

simplified using trigonometric identities. For example,

$\cos(\pi/8)+\sin(\pi/8) = (1/2)\sqrt{4+2\sqrt{2}}$.]

86. This is the lemniscate graphed in Exercise 70, which clearly has

both a horizontal and a vertical tangent at the origin.

$\dfrac{dr}{d\theta} = (1/r)\cos2\theta$ (by differentiating implicitly) so

$\dfrac{dy}{d\theta} = (1/r)\cos2\theta\sin\theta + r\cos\theta = (1/r)[\cos2\theta\sin\theta + r^2\cos\theta] =$

$(1/r)[\cos2\theta\sin\theta+\sin2\theta\cos\theta] = (1/r)\sin3\theta$. This is 0 when $\sin3\theta = 0$

$\Rightarrow \theta = \pi/3$ or $4\pi/3$ (restricting ourselves to θ's in the domain of

the lemniscate) so there are horizontal tangents at $(\sqrt[4]{3/4},\pi/3)$ and

$(\sqrt[4]{3/4},4\pi/3)$ (and $(0,0)$). Similarly, $\dfrac{dx}{d\theta} = (1/r)\cos3\theta = 0$ when

$\theta = \pi/6$ or $7\pi/6$, so there are vertical tangents at $(\sqrt[4]{3/4},\pi/6)$ and

$(\sqrt[4]{3/4},7\pi/6)$ (and $(0,0)$).

88. $\dfrac{dy}{d\theta} = e^\theta\sin\theta + e^\theta\cos\theta = e^\theta(\sin\theta+\cos\theta) = 0 \Rightarrow \sin\theta = -\cos\theta \Rightarrow \tan\theta = -1$

$\Rightarrow \theta = -\pi/4 + n\pi$ (n any integer) $\Rightarrow$ horizontal tangents at

$(e^{\pi(n-1/4)},\pi(n-1/4))$.

$\dfrac{dx}{d\theta} = e^\theta\cos\theta - e^\theta\sin\theta = e^\theta(\cos\theta-\sin\theta) = 0 \Rightarrow \sin\theta = \cos\theta \Rightarrow \tan\theta = 1 \Rightarrow$

$\theta = \pi/4 + n\pi$ (n any integer) $\Rightarrow$ vertical tangents at

$(e^{\pi(n+1/4)},\pi(n+1/4))$.

90. These curves are circles which intersect at the origin and at
    $(a/\sqrt{2}, \pi/4)$. At the origin, the first circle has a horizontal
    tangent and the second a vertical, so the tangents are
    perpendicular here. For the first circle,
    $\frac{dy}{d\theta}$ = a cosθ sinθ + a sin θ cos θ = a sin 2θ = a at θ=π/4 and
    $\frac{dx}{d\theta}$ = a cos$^2\theta$ - a sin$^2\theta$ = a cos 2θ = 0 at θ=π/4, so the tangent here
    is vertical. Similarly, for the second circle, $\frac{dy}{d\theta}$ = a cos 2θ = 0
    and $\frac{dx}{d\theta}$ = -a sin 2θ = -a at θ=π/4, so the tangent is horizontal, and
    again the tangents are perpendicular.

Section 9.5

Exercises 9.5

2. $A = \int_{-\pi/2}^{\pi/2} \frac{1}{2}e^{2\theta}d\theta = \frac{1}{4}e^{2\theta}\Big]_{-\pi/2}^{\pi/2} = (e^{\pi} - e^{-\pi})/4$

4. $A = \int_{\pi/4}^{3\pi/4} \frac{1}{2}(3\sin\theta)^2 d\theta = 2\int_{\pi/4}^{\pi/2}\frac{9}{4}(1-\cos2\theta)d\theta = \frac{9}{2}\Big[\theta - \frac{1}{2}\sin2\theta\Big]\Big]_{\pi/4}^{\pi/2}$

   $= 9(\pi+2)/8$

6. $A = \int_{\pi/6}^{5\pi/6}\frac{1}{2}\Big[\frac{1}{\theta}\Big]^2 d\theta = \frac{-1}{2\theta}\Big]_{\pi/6}^{5\pi/6} = 12/5\pi$

8. $A = 2\int_{0}^{\pi/12}\frac{1}{2}\cos^23\theta \ d\theta = \frac{1}{2}\int_{0}^{\pi/12}(1+\cos6\theta)d\theta = \frac{1}{2}\Big[\theta + \frac{1}{6}\sin6\theta\Big]_{0}^{\pi/12}$

   $= (\pi+2)/24$

10. $A = 2\int_{0}^{\pi/2}\frac{1}{2}(2\cos\theta)^2 d\theta = 4\int_{0}^{\pi/2}\cos^2\theta \ d\theta$

    $= 2\theta + \sin2\theta\Big]_{0}^{\pi/2} = \pi$

12. $A = 2\int_{0}^{\pi}\frac{1}{2}[4(1-\cos\theta)]^2 d\theta = 16\int_{0}^{\pi}(1-2\cos\theta+\cos^2\theta)d\theta$

    $= 8\int_{0}^{\pi}(3-4\cos\theta+\cos2\theta)d\theta = 4(6\theta-8\sin\theta+\sin2\theta)\Big]_{0}^{\pi} = 24\pi$

14. $A = 4\int_0^{\pi/4} \frac{1}{2}r^2 d\theta = 2\int_0^{\pi/4} \sin2\theta\ d\theta = -\cos2\theta\Big]_0^{\pi/4} = 1$

16. $A = 2\int_0^{\pi} \frac{1}{2}(3-\cos\theta)^2 d\theta = \int_0^{\pi}(9-6\cos\theta+\cos^2\theta)d\theta$

$= 9\pi - 0 + \int_0^{\pi}\cos^2\theta\ d\theta = 9\pi+\pi/2 = 19\pi/2$

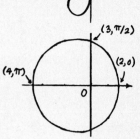

18. $A = 6\int_0^{\pi/6} \frac{1}{2}\sin^2 3\theta\ d\theta = \frac{3}{2}(\theta - \frac{1}{6}\sin6\theta)\Big]_0^{\pi/6} = \pi/4$

20. $A = 2\int_0^{\pi/4}\frac{1}{2}(3\sin2\theta)^2 d\theta = \frac{9}{2}\int_0^{\pi/4}(1-\cos4\theta)d\theta = \frac{9}{2}(\theta-\frac{1}{4}\sin4\theta)\Big]_0^{\pi/4} = 9\pi/8$

22. $A = 2\int_0^{\pi/8}\frac{1}{2}(2\cos4\theta)^2 d\theta = 2\int_0^{\pi/8}(1+\cos8\theta)d\theta = 2\Big[\theta + \frac{1}{8}\sin8\theta\Big]_0^{\pi/8} = \pi/4$

24.

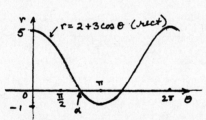 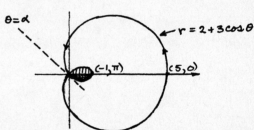

$2+3\cos\theta = 0 \Rightarrow \cos\theta = -2/3 \Rightarrow \theta = \cos^{-1}(-2/3)\ (=\alpha)$ or $2\pi-\cos^{-1}(-2/3)$

$\Rightarrow A = 2\int_\alpha^{\pi} \frac{1}{2}(2+3\cos\theta)^2 d\theta = \int_\alpha^{\pi}(4+12\cos\theta+9\cos^2\theta)d\theta$

$= \int_\alpha^{\pi}(\frac{17}{2}+12\cos\theta+\frac{9}{2}\cos2\theta)d\theta = \frac{17}{2}\theta+12\sin\theta+\frac{9}{4}\sin2\theta\Big]_\alpha^{\pi}$

$= \frac{17}{2}(\pi-\alpha) - 12\sin\alpha - \frac{9}{2}\sin\alpha\cos\alpha$

$= \frac{17}{2}(\pi-\cos^{-1}(-2/3)) - 12(\sqrt{5}/3) - \frac{9}{2}(\sqrt{5}/3)(-2/3) = \frac{17}{2}\cos^{-1}(2/3)-3\sqrt{5}$

26. $1-\sin\theta=1 \Rightarrow \sin\theta=0 \Rightarrow \theta=0$ or $\pi \Rightarrow$

$A = \int_{\pi}^{2\pi} \frac{1}{2}[(1-\sin\theta)^2-1]d\theta = \frac{1}{2}\int_{\pi}^{2\pi}(\sin^2\theta-2\sin\theta)d\theta$

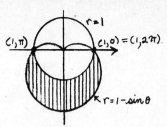

$= \frac{1}{4}\int_{\pi}^{2\pi}(1-\cos2\theta-4\sin\theta)d\theta = \frac{1}{4}(\theta-\frac{1}{2}\sin2\theta+4\cos\theta)\Big]_{\pi}^{2\pi}$

$= \pi/4 + 2$

28. $3\cos\theta = 2-\cos\theta \Rightarrow \cos\theta = 1/2 \Rightarrow \theta = \pm\pi/3 \Rightarrow$

$A = 2\int_{0}^{\pi/3} \frac{1}{2}[(3\cos\theta)^2-(2-\cos\theta)^2]d\theta$

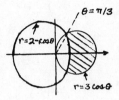

$= \int_{0}^{\pi/3}(8\cos^2\theta+4\cos\theta-4)d\theta = \int_{0}^{\pi/3}(4\cos2\theta+4\cos\theta)d\theta$

$= 2\sin2\theta + 4\sin\theta\Big]_{0}^{\pi/3} = 3\sqrt{3}$

30. $A=2\int_{\pi/3}^{\pi/2} \frac{1}{2}[(1+\cos\theta)^2-(3\cos\theta)^2]d\theta + 2\int_{\pi/2}^{\pi}\frac{1}{2}(1+\cos\theta)^2d\theta$

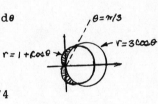

$= \int_{\pi/3}^{\pi}(1+\cos\theta)^2d\theta - \int_{\pi/3}^{\pi/2}9\cos^2\theta\,d\theta$

$= \theta+2\sin\theta+\frac{1}{2}(\theta+\frac{1}{2}\sin2\theta)\Big]_{\pi/3}^{\pi} - \frac{9}{2}(\theta+\frac{1}{2}\sin2\theta)\Big]_{\pi/3}^{\pi/2} = \pi/4$

32. $\sin\theta = \pm\sin2\theta = \pm2\sin\theta\cos\theta \Rightarrow \sin\theta(1\pm2\cos\theta) = 0$

From the figure we can see that the intersections occur where $\cos\theta = \pm1/2$, or $\theta = \pi/3$ and $2\pi/3$.

$A = 2\left\{\int_{0}^{\pi/3}\frac{1}{2}\sin^2\theta\,d\theta + \int_{\pi/3}^{\pi/2}\frac{1}{2}\sin^2 2\theta\,d\theta\right\}$

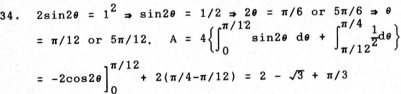

$= \frac{1}{2}(\theta-\frac{1}{2}\sin2\theta)\Big]_{0}^{\pi/3} + \frac{1}{2}(\theta-\frac{1}{4}\sin4\theta)\Big]_{\pi/3}^{\pi/2} = (4\pi-3\sqrt{3})/16$

34. $2\sin2\theta = 1^2 \Rightarrow \sin2\theta = 1/2 \Rightarrow 2\theta = \pi/6$ or $5\pi/6 \Rightarrow \theta$

$= \pi/12$ or $5\pi/12$. $\quad A = 4\left\{\int_{0}^{\pi/12}\sin2\theta\,d\theta + \int_{\pi/12}^{\pi/4}\frac{1}{2}d\theta\right\}$

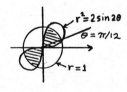

$= -2\cos2\theta\Big]_{0}^{\pi/12} + 2(\pi/4-\pi/12) = 2 - \sqrt{3} + \pi/3$

36. Let $\gamma = \tan^{-1}(b/a)$. Then $A = \int_{0}^{\gamma}\frac{1}{2}(a\sin\theta)^2d\theta +$

$\int_{\gamma}^{\pi/2}\frac{1}{2}(b\cos\theta)^2d\theta = \frac{1}{4}a^2\left[\theta-\frac{1}{2}\sin2\theta\right]_{0}^{\gamma} + \frac{1}{4}b^2\left[\theta+\frac{1}{2}\sin2\theta\right]_{\gamma}^{\pi/2}$

$$= \frac{\gamma}{4}(a^2-b^2)+\pi b^2/8-(a^2+b^2)(\sin\gamma\cos\gamma)/4$$

$$= \frac{a^2-b^2}{4}\tan^{-1}(b/a) + \pi b^2/8 - ab/4$$

38. Let $\alpha = \sin^{-1}(3/4)$.

$$A = 2\left\{\int_{-\alpha}^{\pi/2}\frac{1}{2}(3+4\sin\theta)^2 d\theta - \int_{-\pi/2}^{-\alpha}\frac{1}{2}(3+4\sin\theta)^2 d\theta\right\}$$

Now $\int(3+4\sin\theta)^2 d\theta = 9\theta - 24\cos\theta + 8\theta - 4\sin2\theta + C$

so $A = 34\alpha + 48\cos\alpha - 16\sin\alpha\cos\alpha$

$$= 34\sin^{-1}(3/4) + 9\sqrt{7}$$

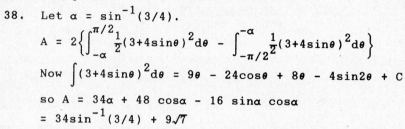

40. $2\cos2\theta = \pm2 \Rightarrow \cos2\theta = \pm1 \Rightarrow \theta = 0, \pi/2, \pi,$
    or $3\pi/2$ so the points are $(2,0)$, $(2,\pi/2)$,
    $(2,\pi)$, $(2,3\pi/2)$

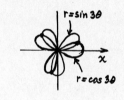

42. Clearly the pole lies on both curves.
    $\sin3\theta = \cos3\theta \Rightarrow \tan3\theta = 1 \Rightarrow 3\theta = \pi/4 + n\pi$
    (n any integer) $\Rightarrow \theta = \pi/12, 5\pi/12, 3\pi/4,$
    and the three remaining intersection points
    are $(1/\sqrt{2},\pi/12)$, $(-1/\sqrt{2},5\pi/12)$, $(1/\sqrt{2},3\pi/4)$
    (middle point is same as $(1/\sqrt{2},17\pi/12)$

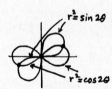

44. Clearly the pole is a point of
    intersection. $\sin2\theta = \cos2\theta \Rightarrow \tan2\theta = 1 \Rightarrow$
    $2\theta = \pi/4 + n\pi \Rightarrow \theta = \pi/8$ or $9\pi/8$ (since
    $\sin2\theta$ and $\cos2\theta$ must be positive in the
    equations). $(1/\sqrt[4]{2},\pi/8)$ and $(1/\sqrt[4]{2},9\pi/8)$

46. $L = \int_0^{3\pi}\sqrt{(e^{-\theta})^2+(-e^{-\theta})^2}\ d\theta = \sqrt{2}\int_0^{3\pi}e^{-\theta}d\theta = \sqrt{2}(1-e^{-3\pi})$

48. $L = \int_0^{2\pi}\sqrt{\theta^2+1}\ d\theta = \left[\frac{\theta}{2}\sqrt{\theta^2+1} + \frac{1}{2}\ln(\theta+\sqrt{\theta^2+1})\right]_0^{2\pi}$ [Formula 21]

$$= \pi\sqrt{4\pi^2+1} + \frac{1}{2}\ln(2\pi+\sqrt{4\pi^2+1})$$

50. $L = 2\int_0^\pi\sqrt{(1+\cos\theta)^2+(-\sin\theta)^2}\ d\theta = 2\sqrt{2}\int_0^\pi\sqrt{1+\cos\theta}\ d\theta$

$$= 2\sqrt{2}\int_0^\pi\sqrt{2\cos^2(\theta/2)}\ d\theta = 8\sin(\theta/2)\Big]_0^\pi = 8$$

52. $L = 2\int_0^\pi\sqrt{[\cos^2(\theta/2)]^2+[-\cos(\theta/2)\sin(\theta/2)]^2}\ d\theta = 2\int_0^\pi\cos(\theta/2)\ d\theta$

$$= 4\sin(\theta/2)\Big]_0^\pi = 4$$

Exercises 9.6

2. $x = -5y^2 \Rightarrow y^2 = -\frac{1}{5}x \Rightarrow 4p = -\frac{1}{5} \Rightarrow p = -1/20$

    $\Rightarrow$ vertex $(0,0)$, focus $(-1/20,0)$, directrix
    $x = 1/20$

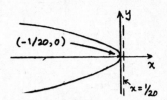

4. $x^2 = \frac{1}{2}y \Rightarrow 4p = \frac{1}{2} \Rightarrow p = 1/8 \Rightarrow$ vertex $(0,0)$,

    focus $(0,1/8)$, directrix $y = -1/8$

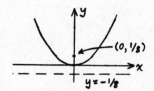

6. $x^2-6x+8y = 7 \Longleftrightarrow (x-3)^2 = -8y+16 = -8(y-2) \Rightarrow$

    $p = -2 \Rightarrow$ vertex $(3,2)$, focus $(3,0)$,
    directrix $y=4$

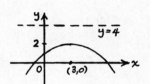

8. $x^2+12x-y+39 = 0 \Longleftrightarrow (x+6)^2 = y-3 \Rightarrow p = 1/4 \Rightarrow$

    vertex $(-6,3)$, focus $(-6,13/4)$, directrix
    $y = 11/4$

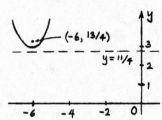

10. $x^2/4 + y^2/25 = 1 \Rightarrow a=5$, $b=2$, $c=\sqrt{25-4}=\sqrt{21} \Rightarrow$

    center $(0,0)$, vertices $(0,\pm 5)$, foci
    $(0,\pm\sqrt{21})$

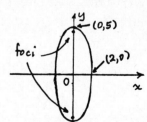

12. $x^2+4y^2 = 4 \Longleftrightarrow x^2/4 + y^2 = 1 \Rightarrow a=2$, $b=1$,

    $c=\sqrt{3} \Rightarrow$ center $(0,0)$, vertices $(\pm 2,0)$, foci
    $(\pm\sqrt{3},0)$

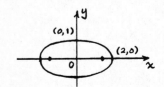

14. $\frac{y^2}{25} - \frac{x^2}{144} = 1 \Rightarrow a=5, b=12, c=13 \Rightarrow$ center

(0,0), vertices (0,±5), foci (0,±13),

asymptotes $y = \pm 5x/12$

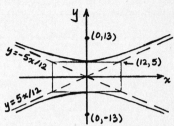

16. $x^2-y^2 = 1 \Rightarrow a=b=1, c=\sqrt{2} \Rightarrow$ center (0,0),

vertices (±1,0), foci (±$\sqrt{2}$,0), asymptotes

$y = \pm x$

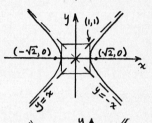

18. $16x^2+64x-9y^2-90y = 305 \Longleftrightarrow$

$\frac{(x+2)^2}{9} - \frac{(y+5)^2}{16} = 1 \Rightarrow a=3, b=4, c=5 \Rightarrow$

center (-2,-5), vertices (-5,-5) and

(1,-5), foci (-7,-5) and (3,-5), asymptotes

$y+5 = \pm(4/3)(x+2)$

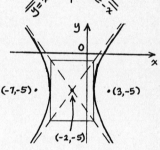

20. $x^2-6x+2y^2+4y = -7 \Longleftrightarrow \frac{(x-3)^2}{4} + \frac{(y+1)^2}{2} = 1 \Rightarrow$

$a=2, b=\sqrt{2}=c \Rightarrow$ center (3,-1), vertices

(1,-1,) and (5,-1), foci $(3\pm\sqrt{2},-1)$

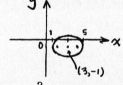

22. Vertex (0,0), parabola opens to the left $\Rightarrow p=-2 \Rightarrow y^2 = 4px = -8x$

24. Vertex (1,2), parabola opens down $\Rightarrow p=-3 \Rightarrow (x-1)^2=4p(y-2)=-12(y-2)$

$\Longleftrightarrow x^2-2x+12y-23 = 0$

26. Vertical axis $\Rightarrow (x-h)^2 = 4p(y-k)$. Substituting (-2,3) and (0,3)

gives $(-2-h)^2 = 4p(3-k)$ and $(-h)^2 = 4p(3-k) \Rightarrow (-2-h)^2=(-h)^2 \Rightarrow$

$4+4h+h^2=h^2 \Rightarrow h=-1 \Rightarrow 1 = 4p(3-k)$. Substituting (1,9) gives

$(1-(-1))^2 = 4p(9-k) \Rightarrow 4 = 4p(9-k)$. Solving for p from these

equations gives $p = 1/4(3-k) = 1/(9-k) \Rightarrow 4(3-k)=9-k \Rightarrow k=1 \Rightarrow p=1/8 \Rightarrow$

$(x+1)^2=\frac{1}{2}(y-1) \Rightarrow 2x^2+4x-y+3 = 0$

28. Center (0,0), c=4, a=5, major axis vertical $\Rightarrow b=3$ and $\frac{x^2}{9} + \frac{y^2}{25} = 1$

300

30. Center $(0,2)$, $c=1$, $a=3$, major axis horizontal $\Rightarrow b=2\sqrt{2}$ and
$x^2/9 + (y-2)^2/8 = 1$

32. Center $(0,0)$, $c=2$, major axis horizontal $\Rightarrow x^2/a^2 + y^2/b^2 = 1$ and
$b^2=a^2-c^2=a^2-4$. Since the ellipse passes through $(2,1)$, we have
$2a = |PF_1|+|PF_2| = \sqrt{17} + 1 \Rightarrow a^2=(9+\sqrt{17})/2$ and $b^2=(1+\sqrt{17})/2$, so the
ellipse is $2x^2/(9+\sqrt{17}) + 2y^2/(1+\sqrt{17}) = 1$.

34. Center $(0,0)$, horizontal axis, $c=6$, $a=4 \Rightarrow b=2\sqrt{5} \Rightarrow x^2/16 - y^2/20 = 1$

36. Center $(2,3)$, vertical axis, $c=5$, $a=3 \Rightarrow b=4 \Rightarrow \dfrac{(y-3)^2}{9} - \dfrac{(x-2)^2}{16} = 1$

38. Center $(4,2)$, horizontal axis, asymptotes $y-2 = \pm(x-4) \Rightarrow c=2$, $b/a=1$
$\Rightarrow a=b \Rightarrow c^2=4=a^2+b^2=2a^2 \Rightarrow a^2=2 \Rightarrow (x-4)^2/2 - (y-4)^2/2 = 1$

40. (a) Choose V to be the origin, with x-axis through V and F. Then F
is $(p,0)$, A is $(p,5)$, so substituting A into the equation $y^2=4px$
gives $25 = 4p^2$ so $p=5/2$ and $y^2=10x$.
(b) $x=11 \Rightarrow y=\sqrt{110} \Rightarrow |CD| = 2\sqrt{110}$

42. $|PF_1| - |PF_2| = \pm 2a \iff \sqrt{(x+c)^2+y^2} - \sqrt{(x-c)^2+y^2} = \pm 2a$

$\iff \sqrt{(x+c)^2+y^2} = \sqrt{(x-c)^2+y^2} \pm 2a$

$\iff (x+c)^2+y^2 = (x-c)^2+y^2+4a^2\pm 4a\sqrt{(x-c)^2+y^2}$

$\iff 4cx-4a^2 = \pm 4a\sqrt{(x-c)^2+y^2} \iff c^2x^2-2a^2cx+a^4 = a^2[x^2-2cx+c^2+y^2]$

$\iff (c^2-a^2)x^2-a^2y^2 = a^2(c^2-a^2) \iff b^2x^2 - a^2y^2 = a^2b^2$

[where $b^2=c^2-a^2$] $\iff x^2/a^2 - y^2/b^2 = 1$

44. $\lim\limits_{x\to\infty}\left[\dfrac{b}{a}\sqrt{x^2-a^2} - \dfrac{b}{a}x\right] = \dfrac{b}{a}\cdot\lim\limits_{x\to\infty}\dfrac{-a^2}{\sqrt{x^2-a^2} + x}$ [rationalizing] $= 0$

46. (a) $y^2=4px \Rightarrow 2yy'=4p \Rightarrow y'=2p/y$, so the tangent line is
$y-y_0 = (2p/y_0)(x-x_0) \Rightarrow y_0y-y_0^2 = 2p(x-x_0) \Rightarrow yy_0-4px_0 = 2px-2px_0$

$\Rightarrow yy_0 = 2p(x+x_0)$

(b) x-intercept is $-x_0$

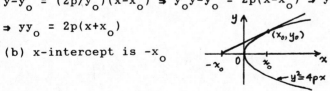

48. We can follow exactly the same sequence of steps as the derivation
of formula (9.22), except we use the points $(1,1)$ and $(-1,-1)$ in
the distance formula (first equation of that derivation) so
$\sqrt{(x-1)^2+(y-1)^2} + \sqrt{(x+1)^2+(y+1)^2} = 4$ will lead to $3x^2-2xy+3y^2 = 8$.

50. $x^2/a^2 + y^2/b^2 = 1 \Rightarrow 2x/a^2 + 2yy'/b^2 = 0 \Rightarrow y' = -b^2x/a^2y$ $(y \neq 0)$

Thus the slope of the tangent line at P is $-b^2x_1/a^2y_1$. The slope

of F_1P is $y_1/(x_1+c)$ and of F_2P is $y_1/(x_1-c)$. By Formula 1.16,

$$\tan\alpha = \frac{y_1/(x_1+c) + b^2x_1/a^2y_1}{1 - (b^2x_1y_1)/a^2y_1(x_1+c)} = \frac{a^2y_1^2 + b^2x_1(x_1+c)}{a^2y_1(x_1+c) - b^2x_1y_1}$$

$$= \frac{a^2b^2 + b^2cx_1}{c^2x_1y_1 + a^2cy_1} \quad [\text{using } b^2x_1^2+a^2y_1^2=a^2b^2 \text{ and } a^2-b^2=c^2]$$

$$= \frac{b^2(cx_1+a^2)}{cy_1(cx_1+a^2)} = b^2/cy_1$$

$$\tan\beta = \frac{-y_1/(x_1-c) - b^2x_1/a^2y_1}{1 - (b^2x_1y_1)/a^2y_1(x_1-c)} = \frac{-a^2y_1^2 - b^2x_1(x_1-c)}{a^2y_1(x_1-c) - b^2x_1y_1}$$

$$= \frac{-a^2b^2 + b^2cx_1}{c^2x_1y_1 - a^2cy_1} = \frac{b^2(cx_1-a^2)}{cy_1(cx_1-a^2)} = b^2/cy_1 \quad \text{So } \alpha=\beta.$$

Section 9.7

Exercises 9.7

2. $r = \dfrac{ed}{1 - e\cos\theta} = \dfrac{(4/3)3}{1 - (4/3)\cos\theta} = \dfrac{12}{3-4\cos\theta}$

4. $r = \dfrac{ed}{1 - e\sin\theta} = \dfrac{(1/2)4}{1 - (1/2)\sin\theta} = \dfrac{4}{2-\sin\theta}$

6. $r = 2\csc\theta \iff y = r\sin\theta = 2$, so

$r = \dfrac{ed}{1 + e\sin\theta} = \dfrac{(3/5)2}{1 + (3/5)\sin\theta} = \dfrac{6}{5+3\sin\theta}$

8. Directrix x=4 so $r = \dfrac{ed}{1 + e\cos\theta} = \dfrac{(2/5)4}{1 + (2/5)\cos\theta} = \dfrac{8}{5+2\cos\theta}$

10. $r = \dfrac{8/3}{1+\cos\theta} \Rightarrow e=1 \Rightarrow$ parabola; $ed=8/3 \Rightarrow d=8/3$

$\Rightarrow$ directrix x=8/3; vertex (4/3,0)

12. $r = \dfrac{10/3}{1 - (2/3)\sin\theta}$ e=2/3 ⇒ ellipse; ed=10/3

⇒ d=5 ⇒ directix y=-5; vertices (10,π/2)

and (2,3π/2); center (4,π/2)

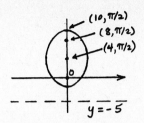

14. $r = \dfrac{5/2}{1 - (3/2)\sin\theta}$ ⇒ e=3/2 ⇒ hyperbola;

ed=5/2 ⇒ d=5/3 ⇒ directrix y = -5/3;

vertices (-5,π/2)=(5,3π/2) and (1,3π/2);

center (3,3π/2); foci (0,0) and (6,3π/2)

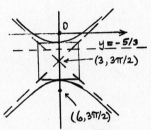

16. $r = \dfrac{6}{1+5\cos\theta}$ ⇒ e=5 ⇒ hyperbola; ed=6 ⇒ d=6/5

⇒ directrix x=6/5; vertices (1,0) and

(-3/2,π)=(3/2,0); center (5/4,0); foci

(0,0) and (5/2,0)

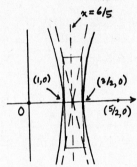

18. $r = \dfrac{8/3}{1 + (1/3)\cos\theta}$ ⇒ e=1/3 ⇒ ellipse; ed=8/3

⇒ d=8 ⇒ directrix x=8; vertices (2,0) and

(4,π); center (-1,0)

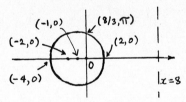

20. $r = \dfrac{1}{1-\sin\theta}$ ⇒ e=1 ⇒ parabola; ed=1 ⇒ d=1 ⇒

directrix y=-1; vertex (-1/2,π/2)

= (1/2,3π/2)

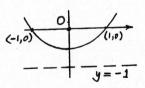

22. |PF| = e|Pℓ| ⇒ r = e[d - r sinθ] ⇒

r(1 + e sinθ) = ed ⇒ $r = \dfrac{ed}{1 + e\sin\theta}$

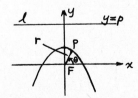

24. With directrix x=d, $r = \dfrac{ed}{1 + e\cos\theta}$. We are given e = 0.017 and

a = 3×10^8 = ed/(1-e^2), so ed = a(1-e^2) = 299,913,300, and

r ≈ 2.999×10^8/(1 + 0.017cosθ) ≈ 3×10^8/(1 + 0.017cosθ).

Section 9.8

Exercises 9.8

2. X = 4cos45° + 3sin45° = 7/$\sqrt{2}$, Y = -4sin45° + 3cos45° = -1/$\sqrt{2}$

4. Using the half-angle formulas (Equation 17 in Appendix B), we have
$\cos^2$15° = (1+cos30°)/2 = (1+$\sqrt{3}$/2)/2 = (2+$\sqrt{3}$)/4 ⇒

cos15° = (1/2)$\sqrt{2+\sqrt{3}}$ and similarly sin15° = (1/2)$\sqrt{2-\sqrt{3}}$. Thus

X = cos15°+sin15° = (1/2)($\sqrt{2+\sqrt{3}}$+$\sqrt{2-\sqrt{3}}$),

Y = -sin15°+cos15° = (1/2)($\sqrt{2+\sqrt{3}}$-$\sqrt{2-\sqrt{3}}$)

[Another method: Using the identity cosθ + sinθ = $\sqrt{2}$cos(θ-45°), we get the simpler expression X = cos15° + sin15° = $\sqrt{2}$cos(-30°) = $\sqrt{2}$($\sqrt{3}$/2) = $\sqrt{6}$/2. Similarly, Y = cos15° - sin15° = $\sqrt{2}$cos(15°+45°) = $\sqrt{2}$cos60° = $\sqrt{2}$/2.]

6. cot2θ = $\dfrac{A-C}{B}$ = 0 ⇒ θ = π/4 ⇒ [Equations

9.34] x = (X-Y)/$\sqrt{2}$, y = (X+Y)/$\sqrt{2}$
Substituting gives
$\dfrac{X^2-2XY+Y^2}{2} - \dfrac{X^2-Y^2}{2} + \dfrac{X^2+2XY+Y^2}{2}$ = 1 or

X^2/2 + Y^2/(2/3) = 1, which is an ellipse centered at (0,0), foci on the X-axis, a=$\sqrt{2}$, b=$\sqrt{6}$/3, and c=2$\sqrt{3}$/3.

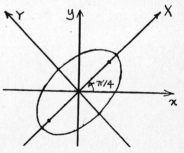

8. cot2θ = $\dfrac{0-1}{\sqrt{3}}$ = -1/$\sqrt{3}$ ⇒ θ = π/3 ⇒

x = X/2 - $\sqrt{3}$Y/2 and y = $\sqrt{3}$X/2 + Y/2
Substituting and simplifying gives
6X^2-2Y^2=4, or X^2/(2/3) - Y^2/2 = 1, a hyperbola with foci on the the X-axis, a=$\sqrt{6}$/3, b=$\sqrt{2}$, c=2$\sqrt{6}$/3, and center (0,0).

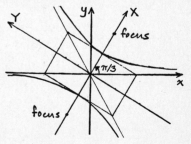

10. $\cot 2\theta = \dfrac{A-C}{B} = \dfrac{3-6}{-12\sqrt{5}} = 1/4\sqrt{5} \Rightarrow \cos 2\theta = 1/9 \Rightarrow$

$\cos\theta = \sqrt{\dfrac{1 + 1/9}{2}} = \sqrt{5}/3$ and $\sin\theta = 2/3 \Rightarrow$

$x = \dfrac{\sqrt{5}X-2Y}{3}$ and $y = \dfrac{2X+\sqrt{5}Y}{3}$ Substituting

into the given equation and simplifying we
get $-81X^2+162Y^2+81 = 0$ or $X^2-2Y^2=1$, a
hyperbola with foci on the X-axis, center
at $(0,0)$, $a=1$ $b=1/\sqrt{2}$, and $c=\sqrt{6}/2$.

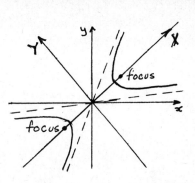

12. $\cot 2\theta = \dfrac{16-2}{-8\sqrt{2}} = -7/4\sqrt{2} \Rightarrow \cos 2\theta = -7/9 \Rightarrow$

$\cos\theta = 1/3$, $\sin\theta = 2\sqrt{2}/3 \Rightarrow x = \dfrac{X-2\sqrt{2}Y}{3}$ and

$y = \dfrac{2\sqrt{2}X+Y}{3}$ Substituting gives

$162Y^2-81X-108Y = 63 \Longleftrightarrow 18Y^2-9X-12Y = 7 \Longleftrightarrow$
$(Y-1/3)^2 = (1/2)(X+1)$, so this is a
parabola with vertex $(-1,1/3)$, directrix
$X = -9/8$, and focus $(-7/8,1/3)$.

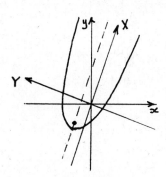

14. (a) $\cot 2\theta = 7/24 \Rightarrow$ [as in Example 3] $x = \dfrac{4X-3Y}{5}$ and $y = \dfrac{3X+4Y}{5} \Rightarrow$

[substituting and simplifying] $-25X^2+50Y^2-100X = 125 \Longleftrightarrow$
$2Y^2-(X+2)^2 = 1$ a hyperbola with center $(X,Y) = (-2,0)$ and foci on
the line $X = -2$.

(b) $a=1/\sqrt{2}$, $b=1 \Rightarrow c=\sqrt{6}/2 \Rightarrow$ XY-coordinates of foci are $(-2,\pm\sqrt{6}/2) \Rightarrow$
xy-coordinates are $x = -2\cdot4/5-(\pm\sqrt{6}/2)3/5$ and $y = -2\cdot3/5+(\pm\sqrt{6}/2)4/5$
giving $(-8/5-3\sqrt{6}/10, -6/5+2\sqrt{6}/5)$ and $(-8/5+3\sqrt{6}/10, -6/5-2\sqrt{6}/5)$

(c) XY-coordinates of vertices are $(-2,\pm1/\sqrt{2}) \Rightarrow$ xy-coordinates are
$x = -2\cdot4/5-(\pm1/\sqrt{2})3/5$ and $y = -2\cdot3/5+(\pm1/\sqrt{2})4/5$ giving
$(-8/5-3\sqrt{2}/10, -6/5+2\sqrt{2}/5)$ and $(-8/5+3\sqrt{2}/10, -6/5-2\sqrt{2}/5)$

(d) The asymptotes are $Y = \pm(a/b)(X+2) = \pm(1/\sqrt{2})(X+2)$ so by (9.35)
the equations in xy-coordinates are
$-x(3/5)+y(4/5) = \pm(1/\sqrt{2})[x(4/5)+y(3/5)+2] \Longleftrightarrow$
$(\pm2\sqrt{2}+3)x + (\pm3\sqrt{2}/2-4)y \pm 5\sqrt{2} = 0$.

(e) $e = c/a = \dfrac{\sqrt{6}/2}{1/\sqrt{2}} = \sqrt{3}$

16. From the solution to Exercise 15, we see that $(B')^2 - 4A'C'$
    $= (C-A)^2\sin^2 2\theta + 2B(C-A)\sin 2\theta\cos 2\theta + B^2\cos^2 2\theta$
    $-4(A\cos^2\theta + B\sin\theta\cos\theta + C\sin^2\theta) \times (A\sin^2\theta - B\sin\theta\cos\theta + C\cos^2\theta).$
    Multiplying this out and using the identities $\cos^2\theta - \sin^2\theta = \cos 2\theta$
    and $2\sin\theta\cos\theta = \sin 2\theta$, it simplifies to
    $B^2(\cos^2 2\theta + \sin^2 2\theta) - 2AC(4\sin^2\theta\cos^2\theta) - 4AC(\cos^4\theta + \sin^4\theta)$
    $= B^2 - 4AC(\cos^2\theta + \sin^2\theta)^2 = B^2 - 4AC$

18. In #9, $B^2-4AC = -22,500 < 0$, so an ellipse.
    In #10, $B^2-4AC = 648 > 0$, so a hyperbola.
    In #11, $B^2-4AC = 12 > 0$, so a hyperbola.
    In #12, $B^2-4AC = 0$, so a parabola.

Chapter 9 Review

Review Exercises for Chapter 9

2. $x=t^2+1$, $y=t^2-1$ $\Rightarrow$
   $y = x-2$, $x \geq 1$

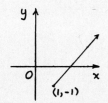

4. $x=1+\cos t$, $y=1+\sin^2 t$ $\Rightarrow$
   $(x-1)^2+(y-1) = 1$ $\Longleftrightarrow$
   $(x-1)^2 = -(y-2)$, $0 \leq x \leq 2$

6. $r = 3 - \sin\theta$

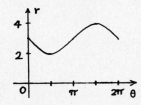

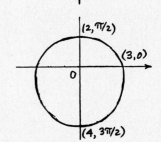

8. $r = \tan\theta \Rightarrow r\cos\theta = \sin\theta \Rightarrow x = \sin\theta$ so $|x| \leq 1$ The curve is also
    symmetric about the axes.

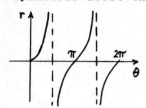
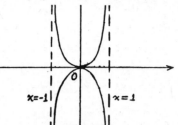

10. $r = 2\cos(\theta/2)$ The curve is symmetric about the pole and both the
     horizontal and vertical axes.

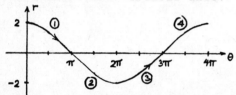
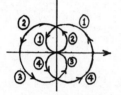

12. $r = \dfrac{5}{1-3\sin\theta}$ $e=3 \Rightarrow$ hyperbola; $p=5/3 \Rightarrow$
     directrix $y=-5/3$; vertices $(-5/2,\pi/2) =$
     $(5/2,3\pi/2)$ and $(5/4,3\pi/2) \Rightarrow$ center
     $(15/8,3\pi/2)$, $a=5/8$, $c=15/8 \Rightarrow b=5/2\sqrt{2}$ and
     foci $(0,0)$ and $(15/4,3\pi/2)$

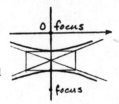

14. $x+y^2=0 \Longleftrightarrow r\cos\theta + r^2\sin^2\theta = 0 \Longleftrightarrow r = -\cos\theta/\sin^2\theta$ or $r=0 \Longleftrightarrow$
     $r = -\cot\theta\csc\theta$ (since $r=0$ when $\theta=\pi/2$)

16. $x=te^t$, $y=1+\sqrt{1+t}$. $\dfrac{dy}{dx} = \dfrac{dy/dt}{dx/dt} = \dfrac{1/2\sqrt{1+t}}{(1+t)e^t} = 1/2$ when $t=0$

18. $\dfrac{dy}{dx} = \dfrac{(dr/d\theta)\sin\theta + r\cos\theta}{(dr/d\theta)\cos\theta - r\sin\theta} = \dfrac{-2\cos\theta\sin\theta + (3-2\sin\theta)\cos\theta}{-2\cos^2\theta - (3-2\sin\theta)\sin\theta}$
     $= \dfrac{3\cos\theta-2\sin2\theta}{-3\sin\theta-2\cos2\theta} = 0$ when $\theta = \pi/2$

20. $x=t^6+t^3$, $y=t^4+t^2$. $\dfrac{dy}{dx} = \dfrac{dy/dt}{dx/dt} = \dfrac{4t^3+2t}{6t^5+3t^2} = \dfrac{4t^2+2}{6t^4+3t}$

     $\dfrac{d}{dt}\left[\dfrac{dy}{dx}\right] = \dfrac{(6t^4+3t)(8t)-(4t^2+2)(24t^3+3)}{(6t^4+3t)^2} = \dfrac{-48t^5-48t^3+12t^2-6}{(6t^4+3t)^2} \Rightarrow$

     $\dfrac{d^2y}{dx^2} = \dfrac{\frac{d}{dt}\left[\frac{dy}{dx}\right]}{dx/dt} = \dfrac{-48t^5-48t^3+12t^2-6}{(6t^4+3t)^2(6t^5+3t^2)} = \dfrac{-16t^5-16t^3+4t^2-2}{9t^4(2t^3+1)^3}$

22. From #21, $x = 2a \cos t - a \cos 2t$, $y = 2a \sin t - a \sin 2t$ $\Rightarrow$

$$A = 2\int_{\pi}^{0} (2a \sin t - a \sin 2t)(-2a \sin t + 2a \sin 2t)dt$$

$$= 4a^2 \int_{0}^{\pi} (2 \sin^2 t + \sin^2 2t - 3 \sin t \sin 2t)dt$$

$$= 4a^2 \int_{0}^{\pi} [(1 - \cos 2t) + \tfrac{1}{2}(1 - \cos 4t) - 6 \sin^2 t \cos t]dt$$

$$= 4a^2 \left[t - \tfrac{1}{2}\sin 2t + \tfrac{1}{2}t - \tfrac{1}{8}\sin 4t - 2 \sin^3 t\right]_{0}^{\pi} = 4a^2(3\pi/2) = 6\pi a^2$$

24. $r = 1-3\sin\theta$ The inner loop is traced out as θ goes from

$\alpha = \sin^{-1}(1/3)$ to $\pi-\alpha$, so $A = \int_{\alpha}^{\pi-\alpha} \tfrac{1}{2}r^2 d\theta = \int_{\alpha}^{\pi/2} (1-3\sin\theta)^2 d\theta$

$$= \int_{\alpha}^{\pi/2} [1-6\sin\theta+9(1-\cos 2\theta)/2]d\theta = 11\theta/2 + 6\cos\theta - (9\sin 2\theta)/4 \Big]_{\alpha}^{\pi/2}$$

$$= 11\pi/4 - (11/2)\sin^{-1}(1/3) - 3\sqrt{2}.$$

26. The two curves clearly both contain the pole. For other points of intersection $\cot\theta = 2\cos(\theta+2n\pi)$ or $-2\cos(\theta+\pi+2n\pi)$, both of which reduce to $\cot\theta = 2\cos\theta \Leftrightarrow \cos\theta = 2\sin\theta\cos\theta \Leftrightarrow \cos\theta(1-2\sin\theta) = 0 \Rightarrow$ $\cos\theta=0$ or $\sin\theta=1/2 \Rightarrow \theta = \pi/6, \pi/2, 5\pi/6, 3\pi/2 \Rightarrow$ intersection points are $(0,\pi/2)$, $(\sqrt{3},\pi/6)$, and $(\sqrt{3},11\pi/6)$.

28. $A = 2\int_{-\pi/2}^{\pi/6} \tfrac{1}{2}[(2+\cos 2\theta)^2-(2+\sin\theta)^2]d\theta$

$$= \int_{-\pi/2}^{\pi/6} [4\cos 2\theta+\cos^2 2\theta-4\sin\theta-\sin^2\theta]$$

$$= 2\sin 2\theta + \theta/2 + (\sin 4\theta)/8 + 4\cos\theta$$

$$- \theta/2 + (\sin 2\theta)/4 \Big]_{-\pi/2}^{\pi/6} = 51\sqrt{3}/16$$

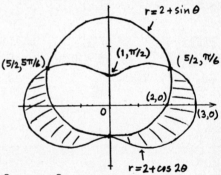

30. $(dx/dt)^2+(dy/dt)^2 = \left[-\sin t + \dfrac{(1/2)\sec^2(t/2)}{\tan(t/2)}\right]^2 + \cos^2 t$

$$= \left[-\sin t + \dfrac{1}{2\sin(t/2)\cos(t/2)}\right]^2 + \cos^2 t = \left[-\sin t + \dfrac{1}{\sin t}\right]^2 + \cos^2 t$$

$$= \csc^2 t - 1 = \cot^2 t \Rightarrow L = \int_{\pi/2}^{3\pi/4} |\cot t|dt = \int_{\pi/2}^{3\pi/4} -\cot t \; dt$$

$$= -\ln|\sin t|\Big]_{\pi/2}^{3\pi/4} = \ln\sqrt{2}$$

32. $L = \int_{0}^{\pi} \sqrt{r^2+(dr/d\theta)^2} d\theta = \int_{0}^{\pi} \sqrt{\sin^6(\theta/3) + \sin^4(\theta/3)\cos^2(\theta/3)} \; d\theta$

$$= \int_0^\pi \sin^2(\theta/3)\,d\theta = \tfrac{1}{2}\left(\theta - \tfrac{3}{2}\sin(2\theta/3)\right)\Big]_0^\pi = \pi/2 - 3\sqrt{3}/8$$

34. From the computations of Exercise 30, we find that

$$S = \int_{\pi/2}^{3\pi/4} 2\pi \sin t\,|\cot t|\,dt = 2\pi\int_{\pi/2}^{3\pi/4} -\cos t\,dt = \pi(2-\sqrt{2})$$

36. $x^2/4 - y^2/16 = 1$ is a hyperbola with center
     $(0,0)$, vertices $(\pm 2,0)$, $a=2$, $b=4$,
     $c=\sqrt{16+4}=2\sqrt{5}$, foci $(\pm 2\sqrt{5},0)$, and asymptotes
     $y = \pm 2x$.

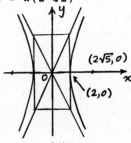

38. $25(x+1)^2 + 4(y-2)^2 = 100 \iff$
     $$\frac{(x+1)^2}{4} + \frac{(y-2)^2}{25} = 1 \text{ is an ellipse centered}$$
     at $(-1,2)$ with foci on the line $x = -1$,
     vertices $(-1,7)$ and $(-1,-3)$; $a=5$, $b=2 \Rightarrow$
     $c=\sqrt{21} \Rightarrow$ foci $(-1,2\pm\sqrt{21})$

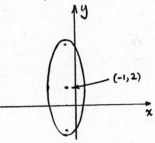

40. Center is $(0,0)$, and $c=5$, $a=2 \Rightarrow b=\sqrt{21}$; foci on y-axis $\Rightarrow$ equation of
     hyperbola is $y^2/4 - x^2/21 = 1$

42. Center is $(3,0)$ and $a = 8/2 = 4$, $c = 2 \Rightarrow b = \sqrt{4^2-2^2} = 2\sqrt{3} \Rightarrow$
     equation of ellipse is $\dfrac{(x-3)^2}{12} + \dfrac{y^2}{16} = 1$

44. (a) $\cot 2\theta = \dfrac{7-13}{-6\sqrt{3}} = 1/\sqrt{3} \Rightarrow \theta = \pi/6 \Rightarrow$ [Equations 9.34] $x = \dfrac{\sqrt{3}X-Y}{2}$ and

     $y = \dfrac{X+\sqrt{3}Y}{2}$ Substituting and simplifying gives $X^2+4Y^2-2X = 0 \iff$

     $(X-1)^2 + Y^2/(1/4) = 1$, an ellipse centered at $(1,0)$.
     (b) $a=1$, $b=1/2 \Rightarrow c=\sqrt{3}/2 \Rightarrow$ foci $(1\pm\sqrt{3}/2,0)$ in XY-coordinates $\Rightarrow$
     [Equations 9.34] xy-coordinates of foci are $x = (1\pm\sqrt{3}/2)(\sqrt{3}/2)$
     $= (2\sqrt{3}\pm3)/4$, $y = (1\pm\sqrt{3}/2)(1/2) = (2\pm\sqrt{3})/4$.
     (c) XY-coordinates of vertices are $(0,0)$ and $(2,0)$, so
     xy-coordinates are $(0,0)$ and $(\sqrt{3},1)$
     (d) $e = c/a = \sqrt{3}/2$

46. The asymptotes have slopes $\pm b/a = \pm\sqrt{e^2-1}$ [Equations 9.30], so the
     angles they make with the polar axis are $\pm\tan^{-1}\left[\sqrt{e^2-1}\right] =$
     $\cos^{-1}(\pm 1/e)$.

CHAPTER TEN

Exercises 10.1

2. $a_n = \frac{4n-3}{3n+4}$ $\left\{\frac{1}{7}, \frac{1}{2}, \frac{9}{13}, \frac{13}{16}, \frac{17}{19}, \dots\right\}$

4. $a_n = \left[-\frac{2}{3}\right]^n$ $\left\{-\frac{2}{3}, \frac{4}{9}, -\frac{8}{27}, \frac{16}{81}, -\frac{32}{243}, \right\}$

6. $a_n = \frac{(-7)^{n+1}}{n!}$ $\left\{49, -\frac{343}{2}, \frac{2401}{6}, -\frac{16807}{24}, \frac{117649}{120}, \dots\right\}$

8. $a_n = \cos n\pi$ $\{-1, 1, -1, 1, -1, \dots\}$

10. $a_1 = 0$, $a_2 = 1$, $a_n = a_{n-1} - a_{n-2}$ $\{0, 1, 1, 0, -1, \dots\}$

12. $a_n = \frac{1}{2n}$ $\qquad\qquad$ 14. $a_n = \frac{n+2}{(n+3)^2}$

16. $a_n = (-1)^{n+1}\left[\frac{3}{2}\right]^n$ $\qquad$ 18. $a_n = 1 - (-1)^n$

20. $\{4\sqrt{n}\}$ clearly diverges since $\sqrt{n} \to \infty$ as $n \to \infty$.

22. $\lim\limits_{n\to\infty} \frac{4n-3}{3n+4} = \lim\limits_{n\to\infty} \frac{4 - 3/n}{3 + 4/n} = \frac{4}{3}$. Convergent.

24. $\lim\limits_{n\to\infty} \frac{n^{1/3}+n^{1/4}}{n^{1/2}+n^{1/5}} = \lim\limits_{n\to\infty} \frac{\frac{1}{n^{1/6}} + \frac{1}{n^{1/4}}}{1 + \frac{1}{n^{3/10}}} = \frac{0}{1} = 0$ so the sequence converges.

26. $|a_n| = \dfrac{n}{1/n^3 + 1/n + 1} \to \infty$ as $n \to \infty$, so $\{a_n\}$ diverges.

28. $\left\{\left[-\frac{2}{\pi}\right]^n\right\}$ converges to 0 by 10.8, and hence $\left\{2+\left[-\frac{2}{\pi}\right]^n\right\}$ converges to $2 + 0 = 2$.

30. $\{a_n\} = \{1, 0, -1, 0, 1, 0, -1, \dots\}$. This sequence oscillates among 1, 0, and -1 and so the sequence diverges.

32. $\lim\limits_{n\to\infty} \frac{2n}{2n+1} = \lim\limits_{n\to\infty} \frac{2}{2+1/n} = 1$, so $\lim\limits_{n\to\infty} \arctan\left[\frac{2n}{2n+1}\right] = \arctan 1 = \frac{\pi}{4}$. Convergent.

34. $0 \le \dfrac{|\sin n|}{\sqrt{n}} \le \dfrac{1}{\sqrt{n}} \to 0$ as $n \to \infty$, so by the Squeeze Theorem and Theorem 10.6, $\left\{\dfrac{\sin n}{\sqrt{n}}\right\}$ converges to 0.

36. $\lim\limits_{n\to\infty} \frac{n!}{(n+2)!} = \lim\limits_{n\to\infty} \frac{1\cdot2\cdot3\cdots n}{1\cdot2\cdot3\cdots n(n+1)(n+2)} = \lim\limits_{n\to\infty} \frac{1}{(n+2)(n+1)} = 0$ Convergent.

38. $\lim\limits_{n\to\infty} \sin\left[\frac{1}{n}\right] = \sin 0 = 0$ since $\frac{1}{n} \to 0$ as $n\to\infty$, so by Theorem 10.6,

$\left\{(-1)^n \sin\left[\frac{1}{n}\right]\right\}$ converges to 0.

40. $\lim\limits_{x\to\infty} \frac{\ln(2+e^x)}{3x} \overset{H}{=} \lim\limits_{x\to\infty} \frac{e^x/(2+e^x)}{3} = \lim\limits_{x\to\infty} \frac{1}{6e^{-x} + 3} = \frac{1}{3}$, so by Theorem

10.2, $\lim\limits_{n\to\infty} \frac{\ln(2+e^n)}{3n} = \frac{1}{3}$. Convergent.

42. $a_n = \ln(n+1) - \ln(n) = \ln\left[\frac{n+1}{n}\right] = \ln\left[1+\frac{1}{n}\right] \to \ln(1) = 0$ as $n\to\infty$

Convergent.

44. $y = (1+3x)^{1/x} \Rightarrow \ln(y) = \frac{1}{x}\ln(1+3x) \Rightarrow \lim\limits_{x\to\infty} \ln y = \lim\limits_{x\to\infty} \frac{\ln(1+3x)}{x} \overset{H}{=}$

$\lim\limits_{x\to\infty} \frac{3/(1+3x)}{1} = 0 \Rightarrow \lim\limits_{x\to\infty} y = e^0 = 1$, so by Theorem 10.2,

$\left\{(1+3n)^{1/n}\right\}$ converges to 1.

46. $0 \le |a_n| = \frac{n|\cos n|}{n^2+1} \le \frac{n}{n^2+1} = \frac{1}{n + 1/n} \to 0$ as $n\to\infty$, so by the Squeeze

Theorem and Theorem 10.6, $\{a_n\}$ converges to 0.

48. $a_n = (\sqrt{n+1} - \sqrt{n})\sqrt{n+\frac{1}{2}} = (\sqrt{n+1} - \sqrt{n})\left[\frac{\sqrt{n+1} + \sqrt{n}}{\sqrt{n+1} + \sqrt{n}}\right]\sqrt{n+\frac{1}{2}} = \frac{\sqrt{n+1/2}}{\sqrt{n+1} + \sqrt{n}}$

$= \frac{\sqrt{1 + 1/2n}}{\sqrt{1 + 1/n} + 1} \to \frac{1}{2}$ as $n\to\infty$. Convergent.

50. $0 < |a_n| = \frac{3^n}{n!} = \frac{3}{1}\cdot\frac{3}{2}\cdot\frac{3}{3}\cdots\frac{3}{(n-1)}\cdot\frac{3}{n} \le 3\cdot\frac{3}{2}\cdot\frac{3}{n} = \frac{27}{2n} \to 0$ as $n\to\infty$, so by the

Squeeze Theorem and Theorem 10.6, $\{a_n\}$ converges to 0.

52. Let $y = (3^x+5^x)^{1/x}$. Then $\lim\limits_{x\to\infty} \ln y = \lim\limits_{x\to\infty} \frac{\ln(3^x+5^x)}{x} =$

$\lim\limits_{x\to\infty} \frac{3^x\ln3 + 5^x\ln5}{3^x + 5^x} = \lim\limits_{x\to\infty} \frac{(3/5)^x\ln3 + \ln5}{(3/5)^x + 1} = \ln5$, so $\lim\limits_{x\to\infty} y = e^{\ln5} = 5$,

and so $\left\{\sqrt[n]{3^n+5^n}\right\}$ converges to 5.

54. $a_n = \frac{1\cdot3\cdot5\cdots(2n-1)}{n!}$ We first prove by induction that $a_n \ge \left[\frac{3}{2}\right]^{n-1}$

for all n. This is clearly true for n=1, so let P(n) be the

statement that the above is true for n. We must show it is then

true for n+1. $a_{n+1} = a_n\cdot\frac{2n+1}{n+1} \ge \left[\frac{3}{2}\right]^{n-1}\cdot\frac{2n+1}{n+1}$ [induction hypothesis]

311

But $\frac{2n+1}{n+1} \geq \frac{3}{2}$ [since $2(2n+1) \geq 3(n+1) \Leftrightarrow 4n+2 \geq 3n+3 \Leftrightarrow n \geq 1$], and so we get that $a_{n+1} \geq \left[\frac{3}{2}\right]^{n-1} \cdot \frac{3}{2} = \left[\frac{3}{2}\right]^{n}$ which is P(n+1). Thus we have proved our first assertion, so since $\left\{(3/2)^{n-1}\right\}$ diverges (10.8), so does the given sequence $\{a_n\}$.

56. If $L = \lim\limits_{n\to\infty} a_n$ then $\lim\limits_{n\to\infty} a_{n+1} = L$ also, so L must satisfy $L = 1/(1+L)$ $\Rightarrow L^2 + L - 1 = 0 \Rightarrow L = \frac{-1+\sqrt{5}}{2}$ (since L has to be non-negative if it exists).

58. $\{1/5^n\}$ is decreasing, since $a_{n+1} \leq a_n \Leftrightarrow 1/5^{n+1} \leq 1/5^n \Leftrightarrow 5^{n+1} \geq 5^n$ $\Leftrightarrow 5 \geq 1$, which is obviously true.

60. $\left\{\frac{3n+4}{2n+5}\right\}$ is increasing since $a_{n+1} \geq a_n \Leftrightarrow \frac{3(n+1)+4}{2(n+1)+5} \geq \frac{3n+4}{2n+5} \Leftrightarrow$ $(3n+7)(2n+5) \geq (3n+4)(2n+7) \Leftrightarrow 6n^2+29n+35 \geq 6n^2+29n+28 \Leftrightarrow 35 \geq 28$.

62. $\left\{3 + \frac{(-1)^n}{n}\right\} = \left\{2, \frac{7}{2}, \frac{8}{3}, \ldots\right\}$ is not monotonic since $2 < \frac{7}{2} > \frac{8}{3}$.

64. Let $f(x) = \frac{\sqrt{x+1}}{5x+3}$. Then $f'(x) = \dfrac{(5x+3)\dfrac{1}{2\sqrt{x+1}} - 5\sqrt{x+1}}{(5x+3)^2} = \dfrac{-(5x+7)}{2(5x+3)^2\sqrt{x+1}}$, which is clearly negative for all $x \geq 1$. So $f(x)$ is decreasing for $x \geq 1$ and $\left\{\frac{\sqrt{n+1}}{5n+3}\right\}$ is a decreasing sequence.

66. (a) Let P(n) be the statement that $a_{n+1} \geq a_n$ and $a_n \leq 3$. P(1) is obviously true. We will assume P(n) is true and then show that as a consequence P(n+1) must also be true.
$a_{n+2} \geq a_{n+1} \Leftrightarrow \sqrt{2+a_{n+1}} \geq \sqrt{2+a_n} \Leftrightarrow 2+a_{n+1} \geq 2+a_n \Leftrightarrow a_{n+1} \geq a_n$ which is the induction hypothesis. $a_{n+1} \leq 3 \Leftrightarrow \sqrt{2+a_n} \leq 3 \Leftrightarrow 2+a_n \leq 9 \Leftrightarrow$ $a_n \leq 7$, which is certainly true because we are assuming $a_n \leq 3$. So P(n) is true for all n, and so $a_1 \leq a_n \leq 3$ (the sequence is bounded), and hence by Theorem 10.11 $\lim\limits_{n\to\infty} a_n$ exists.

(b) If $L = \lim\limits_{n\to\infty} a_n$ then $\lim\limits_{n\to\infty} a_{n+1} = L$ also, so $L = \sqrt{2+L} \Rightarrow$ $L^2 - L - 2 = (L+1)(L-2) = 0$, so $L=2$ (since it can't be negative).

312

68. (a) If f is continuous, then $f(L) = f(\lim_{n\to\infty} a_n) = \lim_{n\to\infty} f(a_n)$

$= \lim_{n\to\infty} a_{n+1} = L$.

(b) By repeatedly pressing the cosine key on the calculator until the displayed value stabilizes, we see that $L \approx 0.73909$.

70. Let $\epsilon > 0$. Let N be any positive integer larger than $\ln(\epsilon)/\ln(|r|)$. If $n > N$ then $n > \ln(\epsilon)/\ln(|r|) \Rightarrow n \ln(|r|) < \ln(\epsilon)$ [since $|r| < 1$ so $\ln(|r|) < 0$] $\Rightarrow \ln(|r|^n) < \ln(\epsilon) \Rightarrow |r|^n < \epsilon \Rightarrow |r^n - 0| < \epsilon$, and so by Definition 10.1, $\lim_{n\to\infty} r^n = 0$.

72. (a) $\dfrac{b^{n+1} - a^{n+1}}{b-a} = b^n + b^{n-1}a + b^{n-2}a^2 + b^{n-3}a^3 + \ldots + ba^{n-1} + a^n$

$< b^n + b^{n-1}b + b^{n-2}b^2 + b^{n-3}b^3 + \ldots + bb^{n-1} + b^n$

$= (n+1)b^n$

(b) Since $b-a > 0$, we have $b^{n+1} - a^{n+1} < (n+1)b^n(b-a) \Rightarrow$
$b^{n+1} - (n+1)b^n(b-a) < a^{n+1} \Rightarrow b^n[(n+1)a - nb] < a^{n+1}$.

(c) With this substitution, $(n+1)a - nb = 1$, and so

$b^n = \left[1 + \dfrac{1}{n}\right]^n < a^{n+1} = \left[1 + \dfrac{1}{n+1}\right]^{n+1}$.

(d) With this substitution, we get $(1 + 1/2n)^n[1/2] < 1 \Rightarrow$
$(1 + 1/2n)^n < 2 \Rightarrow (1 + 1/2n)^{2n} < 4$.

(e) $a_n < a_{2n}$ since $\{a_n\}$ is increasing, so $a_n < a_{2n} < 4$.

(f) Since $\{a_n\}$ is increasing and bounded above by 4, $a_1 \leq a_n \leq 4$
and so $\{a_n\}$ is bounded and monotone, and hence has a limit by Theorem 10.11.

Section 10.2

Exercises 10.2

2. $a = 1$, $|r| = \left|-\dfrac{1}{2}\right| < 1$ so the series converges with sum
$\dfrac{1}{1 - (-1/2)} = \dfrac{2}{3}$.

4. $a = \dfrac{1}{2^6}$, $|r| = \dfrac{1}{4} < 1$ so the series converges with sum $\dfrac{1/2^6}{1 - 1/4} = \dfrac{1}{48}$.

6. $a = -\frac{81}{100}$, $|r| = \left|-\frac{10}{9}\right| > 1$ so the series diverges.

8. $a = 1$, $|r| = \left|-\frac{3}{\pi}\right| < 1$ so the series converges to $\frac{1}{1 - (-3/\pi)} = \frac{\pi}{\pi+3}$.

10. $\sum_{n=1}^{\infty} \left[\frac{1}{e^2}\right]^n$ $a = \frac{1}{e^2} = |r| < 1$ so the series converges to

    $\frac{1/e^2}{1 - 1/e^2} = \frac{1}{e^2 - 1}$.

12. $\sum_{n=0}^{\infty} 4\left[\frac{4}{5}\right]^n$ $a = 4$, $|r| = \frac{4}{5} < 1$ so the series converges to $\frac{4}{1 - 4/5} = 20$.

14. $\sum_{n=1}^{\infty} 3\left[\frac{\sqrt{5}}{3}\right]^n$ $a = \sqrt{5}$, $|r| = \frac{\sqrt{5}}{3} < 1$ so the series converges to

    $\frac{\sqrt{5}}{1 - \sqrt{5}/3} = \frac{3\sqrt{5}}{3 - \sqrt{5}}$.

16. $\sum_{n=1}^{\infty} (-1)^{n-1} \frac{3^{2n}}{2^{3n+1}} = \sum_{n=1}^{\infty} -\frac{1}{2}\left[-\frac{9}{8}\right]^n$, $|r| = \frac{9}{8} > 1$ so the series diverges.

18. $s_n = \sum_{i=4}^{n} \frac{3}{i(i-1)} = \sum_{i=4}^{n} \left[-\frac{3}{i} + \frac{3}{i-1}\right]$ [partial fractions]

    $= \left[-\frac{3}{4} + 1\right] + \left[-\frac{3}{5} + \frac{3}{4}\right] + \left[-\frac{1}{2} + \frac{3}{5}\right] + \ldots + \left[-\frac{3}{n} + \frac{3}{n-1}\right]$ $\left[\begin{array}{c}\text{telescoping} \\ \text{series}\end{array}\right]$

    $= 1 - \frac{3}{n}$ so $\sum_{n=4}^{\infty} \frac{3}{n(n-1)} = \lim_{n\to\infty} s_n = 1$

20. $\lim_{n\to\infty} \frac{n^2}{3(n+1)(n+2)} = \lim_{n\to\infty} \frac{1}{3(1+1/n)(1+2/n)} = \frac{1}{3} \neq 0$ so the series

    diverges by the Test for Divergence.

22. $\sum_{n=1}^{\infty} \left[\frac{1}{2^{n-1}} + \frac{2}{3^{n-1}}\right] = \sum_{n=1}^{\infty} \frac{1}{2^{n-1}} + 2\sum_{n=1}^{\infty} \frac{1}{3^{n-1}} = \frac{1}{1-1/2} + 2\left[\frac{1}{1-1/3}\right] = 5$

24. $\lim_{n\to\infty} a_n = \lim_{n\to\infty} \left[\frac{1}{n} + 2^n\right]$ does not exist, so the series diverges by the

    Test for Divergence.

26. $s_n = \sum_{i=1}^{n} \frac{1}{4i^2-1} = \sum_{i=1}^{n} \left[\frac{1/2}{2i-1} - \frac{1/2}{2i+1}\right]$ [partial fractions]

    $= \left[\frac{1}{2}\cdot 1 - \frac{1}{2}\cdot\frac{1}{3}\right] + \left[\frac{1}{2}\cdot\frac{1}{3} - \frac{1}{2}\cdot\frac{1}{5}\right] + \left[\frac{1}{2}\cdot\frac{1}{5} - \frac{1}{2}\cdot\frac{1}{7}\right] + \ldots + \left[\frac{1}{2}\cdot\frac{1}{2n-1} - \frac{1}{2}\cdot\frac{1}{2n+1}\right]$

    $= \frac{1}{2} - \frac{1}{4n+2}$ so $\sum_{n=1}^{\infty} \frac{1}{4n^2-1} = \lim_{n\to\infty} s_n = \frac{1}{2}$

28. $\lim\limits_{n\to\infty} a_n = \lim\limits_{n\to\infty} \ln\left[\dfrac{n}{2n+5}\right] = \ln\dfrac{1}{2} \neq 0$ so the series diverges by the Test

for Divergence.

30. $s_n = \displaystyle\sum_{i=1}^{n} \dfrac{2i+1}{i^2(i+1)^2} = \sum_{i=1}^{n}\left[\dfrac{1}{i^2} - \dfrac{1}{(i+1)^2}\right]$ [partial fractions]

$= \left[1 - \dfrac{1}{4}\right] + \left[\dfrac{1}{4} - \dfrac{1}{9}\right] + \cdots + \left[\dfrac{1}{n^2} - \dfrac{1}{(n+1)^2}\right] = 1 - \dfrac{1}{(n+1)^2}$

$\displaystyle\sum_{n=1}^{\infty} \dfrac{2n+1}{n^2(n+1)^2} = \lim\limits_{n\to\infty} s_n = 1$

32. $\lim\limits_{n\to\infty} \dfrac{1}{5 + 2^{-n}} = \dfrac{1}{5} \neq 0$ so series diverges by the Test for Divergence.

34. $s_n = \displaystyle\sum_{i=1}^{n} \dfrac{1}{i(i+1)(i+2)} = \sum_{i=1}^{n}\left[\dfrac{1/2}{i} - \dfrac{1}{i+1} + \dfrac{1/2}{i+2}\right] = \sum_{i=1}^{n}\left[\dfrac{1/2}{i} - \dfrac{1/2}{i+1}\right] +$

$\displaystyle\sum_{i=1}^{n}\left[-\dfrac{1/2}{i+1} + \dfrac{1/2}{i+2}\right]$ both of which are clearly telescoping sums, so

$s_n = \left[\dfrac{1}{2} - \dfrac{1}{2(n+1)}\right] + \left[-\dfrac{1}{4} + \dfrac{1}{2(n+2)}\right] = \dfrac{1}{4} - \dfrac{1}{2(n+1)} + \dfrac{1}{2(n+2)}$

$\displaystyle\sum_{n=1}^{\infty} \dfrac{1}{i(i+1)(i+2)} = \lim\limits_{n\to\infty} s_n = \dfrac{1}{4}$

36. $0.\overline{15} = 0.15 + 0.0015 + 0.000015 + \cdots = \dfrac{.15}{1-.01} = \dfrac{15}{99} = \dfrac{5}{33}$

38. $1.1\overline{23} = 1.1 + .023 + .00023 + .0000023 + \cdots = 1.1 + \dfrac{.023}{1-.01}$

$= \dfrac{11}{10} + \dfrac{23}{990} = \dfrac{1112}{990} = \dfrac{556}{495}$

40. $4.\overline{1570} = 4 + .1570 + .00001570 + \cdots = 4 + \dfrac{.1570}{1-.0001} = \dfrac{41566}{9999}$

42. $\displaystyle\sum_{n=0}^{\infty} (3x)^n$ is geometric with $r = 3x$, so converges when $|3x| < 1 \Longleftrightarrow$

$-\dfrac{1}{3} < x < \dfrac{1}{3}$ to a sum of $\dfrac{1}{1-3x}$.

44. $\displaystyle\sum_{n=0}^{\infty} \left[\dfrac{1}{x}\right]^n$ is geometric with $r = \dfrac{1}{x}$ so converges when $\left|\dfrac{1}{x}\right| < 1 \Longleftrightarrow$

$|x| > 1 \Longleftrightarrow x > 1$ or $x < -1$, and the sum is $\dfrac{1}{1 - 1/x} = \dfrac{x}{x-1}$.

46. $\displaystyle\sum_{n=0}^{\infty} \tan^n x$ is geometric and converges when $|\tan x| < 1 \Longleftrightarrow$

$-1 < \tan x < 1 \Longleftrightarrow n\pi-\dfrac{\pi}{4} < x < n\pi+\dfrac{\pi}{4}$ (n any integer).

On these intervals the sum is $\dfrac{1}{1 - \tan x}$.

48. $|CD| = b \sin \theta$ $\qquad\qquad$ $|DE| = |CD| \sin \theta = b \sin^2\theta$

$|EF| = |DE| \sin \theta = b \sin^3\theta$ $\quad$ $|FG| = |EF| \sin \theta = b \sin^4\theta.....$

$|CD| + |DE| + |EF| + |FG| + \ldots = b \displaystyle\sum_{n=1}^{\infty} \sin^n\theta = b\left[\dfrac{\sin\theta}{1 - \sin\theta}\right]$ since

this is a geometric series with $r = \sin\theta$ and $|\sin\theta| < 1$ since $0 < \theta < \dfrac{\pi}{2}$.

50. If $\displaystyle\sum_{n=1}^{\infty} a_n$ is convergent then $\displaystyle\lim_{n\to\infty} a_n = 0$ by Theorem 10.17, so

$\displaystyle\lim_{n\to\infty} \dfrac{1}{a_n} \neq 0$, and so $\displaystyle\sum_{n=1}^{\infty} \dfrac{1}{a_n}$ is divergent by Theorem 10.18.

52. If $\displaystyle\sum ca_n$ were convergent, then $\displaystyle\sum \dfrac{1}{c}(ca_n) = \sum a_n$ would be also, by

Theorem 10.19. But this is a contradiction, so $\displaystyle\sum ca_n$ must diverge.

54. No. For example, take $\displaystyle\sum_{n=1}^{\infty} a_n = \sum_{n=1}^{\infty} n$ and $\displaystyle\sum_{n=1}^{\infty} b_n = \sum_{n=1}^{\infty} -n$, which both

diverge, yet $\displaystyle\sum_{n=1}^{\infty} (a_n + b_n) = \sum_{n=1}^{\infty} 0$ converges with sum 0.

Section 10.3

Exercises 10.3

2. $\displaystyle\sum_{n=1}^{\infty} \left[\dfrac{2}{n\sqrt{n}} + \dfrac{3}{n^3}\right] = 2\sum_{n=1}^{\infty} \dfrac{1}{n^{3/2}} + 3\sum_{n=1}^{\infty} \dfrac{1}{n^3}$, both of which are convergent

p-series ($3/2 > 1$ and $3 > 1$), so $\displaystyle\sum_{n=1}^{\infty} \left[\dfrac{2}{n\sqrt{n}} + \dfrac{3}{n^3}\right]$ converges by 10.19.

4. $\displaystyle\sum_{n=1}^{\infty} n^{-0.99} = \sum_{n=1}^{\infty} \dfrac{1}{n^{0.99}}$ diverges since $p = 0.99 < 1$.

6. $f(x) = \frac{1}{2x+3}$ is positive, continuous, and decreasing on $[1,\infty)$, so

applying the Integral Test, $\int_1^\infty \frac{dx}{2x+3} = \lim_{t\to\infty} \frac{1}{2}\ln(2x+3)\Big]_1^t = \infty \Rightarrow$

$\sum_{n=1}^\infty \frac{1}{2n+3}$ is divergent.

8. $f(x) = \frac{1}{x^2-1}$ is positive, continuous, and decreasing on $[2,\infty)$, so

applying the Integral Test, $\int_2^\infty \frac{dx}{x^2-1} = \int_2^\infty \left[\frac{-1/2}{x+1} + \frac{1/2}{x-1}\right]dx$

$= \lim_{t\to\infty} \ln\left[\frac{x-1}{x+1}\right]^{1/2}\Big]_2^t = \ln\sqrt{3} \Rightarrow \sum_{n=2}^\infty \frac{1}{n^2-1}$ converges.

10. $f(x) = \frac{x}{2^x}$ is positive and continuous on $[1,\infty)$, and since $f'(x) =$

$\frac{1 - x \ln 2}{2^x} < 0$ when $x > \frac{1}{\ln 2} \approx 1.44$, f is eventually decreasing, so

we can apply the Integral Test. $\int_1^\infty \frac{x}{2^x}\, dx =$

$\lim_{t\to\infty} -\frac{1}{\ln 2}\left[\frac{x}{2^x} + \frac{1}{2^x \ln 2}\right]_1^t = \frac{1}{2 \ln 2} + \frac{1}{2(\ln 2)^2}$ (since $\lim_{t\to\infty} \frac{t}{2^t} = 0$ by

l'Hospital's Rule), and so $\sum_{n=1}^\infty \frac{n}{2^n}$ converges.

12. $f(x) = \frac{1}{2x^2-x-1} = \frac{1}{(2x+1)(x-1)}$ is continuous and positive on $[2,\infty)$,

and since $f'(x) = \frac{1 - 4x}{(2x^2-x-1)^2} < 0$ on $[2,\infty)$ the function is

decreasing on $[2,\infty)$, so we can apply the Integral Test.

$\int_2^\infty \frac{dx}{(2x+1)(x-1)} = \int_2^\infty \left[\frac{-2/3}{2x+1} + \frac{1/3}{x-1}\right]dx = \lim_{t\to\infty}\left[\frac{1}{3}\ln(x-1) - \frac{1}{3}\ln(2x+1)\right]_2^t$

$= \lim_{t\to\infty} \frac{1}{3}\left[\ln\left[\frac{t-1}{2t+1}\right] - \ln\frac{1}{5}\right] = \frac{\ln 5 - \ln 2}{3} < \infty$ so the series converges.

14. $f(x) = \frac{1}{4x^2+1}$ is continuous, positive and decreasing on $[1,\infty)$, so

applying the Integral Test, $\int_1^\infty \frac{dx}{4x^2+1} = \lim_{t\to\infty} \frac{\arctan 2x}{2}\Big]_1^t$

$= \frac{\pi}{4} - \frac{\arctan 2}{2} < \infty \Rightarrow$ the series converges.

16. $f(x) = \dfrac{1}{x(\ln x)^2}$ is clearly continuous, positive and decreasing on

    $[2,\infty)$, so applying the Integral Test, $\displaystyle\int_2^\infty \dfrac{dx}{x(\ln x)^2} = \lim_{t\to\infty} \dfrac{-1}{\ln x}\bigg]_2^t$

    $= \dfrac{1}{\ln 2} < \infty \Rightarrow$ the series converges.

18. $f(x) = \left[\dfrac{\ln x}{x}\right]^2$ is continuous and positive for $x>1$, and since $f'(x)$

    $= \dfrac{2 \ln x (1 - \ln x)}{x^3} < 0$ for $x>e$, we can apply the Integral Test.

    $\displaystyle\int_1^\infty \left[\dfrac{\ln x}{x}\right]^2 dx = \lim_{t\to\infty} \left[-\dfrac{\ln^2 x + 2 \ln x + 2}{x}\right]_1^t = 2$ (use integration by

    parts and l'Hospital's Rule), and so the series converges.

20. $f(x) = \dfrac{1}{x \ln x \ln(\ln x)}$ is positive and continuous on $[3,\infty)$, and is

    decreasing since x, ln x, and ln(ln x) are all increasing; so we

    can apply the Integral test. $\displaystyle\int_3^\infty \dfrac{dx}{x \ln x \ln(\ln x)}$

    $= \lim_{t\to\infty} \ln(\ln(\ln x))\bigg]_3^t$ which diverges, and hence $\displaystyle\sum_{n=3}^\infty \dfrac{1}{n \ln n \ln(\ln n)}$

    diverges also.

22. $f(x) = \text{sech}^2 x$ is continuous, positive, and decreasing on $[1,\infty)$, so

    we can apply the Integral Test. $\displaystyle\int_1^\infty \text{sech}^2 x \, dx = \lim_{t\to\infty} \tanh x\bigg]_1^t$

    $= 1 - \tanh 1 < \infty$ and so $\displaystyle\sum_{n=1}^\infty \text{sech}^2 n$ converges.

24. As in Exercise 20 we can apply the Integral Test.

    $\displaystyle\int_3^\infty \dfrac{dx}{x \ln x (\ln(\ln x))^p} = \lim_{t\to\infty} \dfrac{(\ln(\ln x))^{-p+1}}{-p+1}\bigg]_3^t$ (for $p\neq 1$; if p=1 see

    Exercise 20) and $\lim_{t\to\infty} \dfrac{(\ln(\ln t))^{-p+1}}{-p+1}$ exists only if $-p+1 < 0 \Leftrightarrow$

    $p > 1$, so the series converges for $p > 1$.

26. If $p \leq 0$, $\lim_{n\to\infty} \dfrac{\ln n}{n^p} = \infty$ and the series diverges, so assume $p>0$. $f(x)$

    $= (\ln x)/x^p$ is positive and continuous and $f'(x)>0$ for $x>e^{1/p}$, so f

    is eventually decreasing and we can use the Integral Test.

Integration by parts gives $\displaystyle\int_1^\infty \frac{\ln x}{x^p}dx = \lim_{t\to\infty} \left.\frac{x^{1-p}[(1-p)\ln x - 1]}{(1-p)^2}\right]_1^t$

[for $p\neq 1$] $= \dfrac{1}{(1-p)^2}\left[\lim_{t\to\infty} t^{1-p}[(1-p)\ln t - 1] + 1\right]$ which exists

whenever $1-p < 0 \iff p > 1$. Since we have already done the case $p=1$

in Exercise 23 (set $p = -1$ in that problem), $\displaystyle\sum_{n=1}^\infty \frac{\ln n}{n^p}$ converges $\iff$

$p > 1$.

28. (a) From 10.21 with $f(x) = \frac{1}{x}$, $\frac{1}{2}+\frac{1}{3}+\frac{1}{4}+\ldots+\frac{1}{n} \leq \displaystyle\int_1^n \frac{1}{x}\,dx = \ln n$, so

$s_n = 1+\frac{1}{2}+\frac{1}{3}+\frac{1}{4}+\ldots+\frac{1}{n} \leq 1 + \ln n$.

(b) By part (a), $s_{10^6} \leq 1 + \ln 10^6 \approx 14.82 < 15$ and

$s_{10^9} \leq 1 + \ln 10^9 \approx 21.72 < 22$.

Section 10.4

Exercises 10.4

2. $\dfrac{3}{4^n+5} < \dfrac{3}{4^n}$ and $\displaystyle\sum_{n=1}^\infty \frac{3}{4^n}$ converges (geometric with $|r|=\frac{1}{4}<1$) so by the

Comparison Test $\displaystyle\sum_{n=1}^\infty \frac{3}{4^n+5}$ converges also.

4. $\dfrac{1}{\sqrt{n}-1} > \dfrac{1}{\sqrt{n}}$ and $\displaystyle\sum_{n=2}^\infty \frac{1}{\sqrt{n}}$ diverges (p-series with $p=\frac{1}{2}<1$) so $\displaystyle\sum_{n=2}^\infty \frac{1}{\sqrt{n}-1}$

diverges by the Comparison Test.

6. $\dfrac{\sin^2 n}{n\sqrt{n}} \leq \dfrac{1}{n\sqrt{n}} = \dfrac{1}{n^{3/2}}$ and $\displaystyle\sum_{n=1}^\infty \frac{1}{n^{3/2}}$ converges ($p=\frac{3}{2}>1$) so $\displaystyle\sum_{n=1}^\infty \frac{\sin^2 n}{n\sqrt{n}}$

converges by the Comparison Test.

8. $n^n \geq n^2$ for $n\geq 1$, so $\dfrac{1}{n^n} \leq \dfrac{1}{n^2}$ and since $\displaystyle\sum_{n=1}^\infty \frac{1}{n^2}$ converges ($p=2>1$), so

does $\displaystyle\sum_{n=1}^\infty \frac{1}{n^n}$ by the Comparison Test.

10. $\dfrac{1}{\sqrt{n(n+1)(n+2)}} < \dfrac{1}{\sqrt{n \cdot n \cdot n}} = \dfrac{1}{n^{3/2}}$ and since $\displaystyle\sum_{n=1}^{\infty} \dfrac{1}{n^{3/2}}$ converges $(p=\frac{3}{2}>1)$,

so does $\displaystyle\sum_{n=1}^{\infty} \dfrac{1}{\sqrt{n(n+1)(n+2)}}$ by the Comparison Test.

12. Use the Limit Comparison Test with $a_n = \dfrac{1}{\sqrt[3]{n(n+1)(n+2)}}$ and $b_n = \dfrac{1}{n}$.

$\displaystyle\lim_{n\to\infty} \dfrac{a_n}{b_n} = \lim_{n\to\infty} \dfrac{n}{\sqrt[3]{n(n+1)(n+2)}} = \lim_{n\to\infty} \dfrac{1}{\sqrt[3]{1(1 + 1/n)(1 + 2/n)}} = 1>0$, so

since $\displaystyle\sum_{n=1}^{\infty} \dfrac{1}{n}$ diverges, so does $\displaystyle\sum_{n=1}^{\infty} \dfrac{1}{\sqrt[3]{n(n+1)(n+2)}}$.

14. $\dfrac{n}{(n+1)2^n} < \dfrac{1}{2^n}$ and $\displaystyle\sum_{n=1}^{\infty} \dfrac{1}{2^n}$ is a convergent geometric series $(|r|=\frac{1}{2}<1)$,

so $\displaystyle\sum_{n=1}^{\infty} \dfrac{n}{(n+1)2^n}$ converges by the Comparison Test.

16. $\dfrac{5n}{2n^2-5} > \dfrac{5n}{2n^2} = \dfrac{5}{2}\left[\dfrac{1}{n}\right]$ and since $\dfrac{5}{2}\displaystyle\sum_{n=1}^{\infty} \dfrac{1}{n}$ diverges so does $\displaystyle\sum_{n=1}^{\infty} \dfrac{5n}{2n^2-5}$ by the

Comparison Test.

18. $\dfrac{n}{(n+1)(n+2)(n+3)} < \dfrac{n}{n^3} = \dfrac{1}{n^2}$ and $\displaystyle\sum_{n=1}^{\infty} \dfrac{1}{n^2}$ converges $(p=2>1)$, so

$\displaystyle\sum_{n=1}^{\infty} \dfrac{n}{(n+1)(n+2)(n+3)}$ converges also by the Comparison Test.

20. $\dfrac{\arctan n}{n^4} < \dfrac{\pi/2}{n^4}$ and $\dfrac{\pi}{2}\displaystyle\sum_{n=1}^{\infty} \dfrac{1}{n^4}$ converges $(p=4>1)$ so $\displaystyle\sum_{n=1}^{\infty} \dfrac{\arctan n}{n^4}$

converges by the Comparison Test.

22. Use the Limit Comparison Test with $a_n = \dfrac{1+2^n}{1+3^n}$ and $b_n = \dfrac{2^n}{3^n}$. $\displaystyle\lim_{n\to\infty} \dfrac{a_n}{b_n}$

$= \displaystyle\lim_{n\to\infty} \dfrac{(1/2)^n + 1}{(1/3)^n + 1} = 1>0$, so since $\displaystyle\sum_{n=1}^{\infty} b_n$ converges (geometric series

with $|r|=\frac{2}{3}<1$), $\displaystyle\sum_{n=1}^{\infty} \dfrac{1+2^n}{1+3^n}$ converges also.

24. Use the Limit Comparison Test with $a_n = \dfrac{1}{n^2-4}$ and $b_n = \dfrac{1}{n^2}$. $\displaystyle\lim_{n\to\infty} \dfrac{a_n}{b_n}$

$= \displaystyle\lim_{n\to\infty} \dfrac{n^2}{n^2-4} = 1>0$, and $\displaystyle\sum_{n=1}^{\infty} b_n$ converges $(p=2>1)$ so $\displaystyle\sum_{n=1}^{\infty} \dfrac{1}{n^2-4}$ converges.

26. Use the Limit Comparison Test with $a_n = \dfrac{3n^3-2n^2}{n^4+n^2+1}$ and $b_n = \dfrac{1}{n}$. $\displaystyle\lim_{n\to\infty} \dfrac{a_n}{b_n}$

$= \displaystyle\lim_{n\to\infty} \dfrac{3n^4-2n^3}{n^4+n^2+1} = 3>0$, so since $\displaystyle\sum_{n=1}^{\infty} b_n$ diverges, so does $\displaystyle\sum_{n=1}^{\infty}\dfrac{3n^3-2n^2}{n^4+n^2+1}$.

28. Use the Limit Comparison Test with $a_n = \dfrac{n^2-3n}{\sqrt[3]{n^{10}-4n^2}}$ and $b_n = \dfrac{1}{n^{4/3}}$.

$\displaystyle\lim_{n\to\infty}\dfrac{a_n}{b_n} = \lim_{n\to\infty}\dfrac{n^{10/3}-3n^{7/3}}{\sqrt[3]{n^{10}-4n^2}} = \lim_{n\to\infty}\dfrac{1-3/n}{\sqrt[3]{1-4n^{-8}}} = 1>0$, so since $\displaystyle\sum_{n=1}^{\infty} b_n$

converges $(p=\frac{4}{3}>1)$, so does $\displaystyle\sum_{n=1}^{\infty}\dfrac{n^2-3n}{\sqrt[3]{n^{10}-4n^2}}$.

30. Use the Limit Comparison Test with $a_n = \dfrac{2n^2+7n}{3^n(n^2+5n-1)}$ and $b_n = \dfrac{1}{3^n}$.

$\displaystyle\lim_{n\to\infty}\dfrac{a_n}{b_n} = \lim_{n\to\infty}\dfrac{2n^2+7n}{n^2+5n-1} = 2>0$, and since $\displaystyle\sum_{n=1}^{\infty} b_n$ is a convergent

geometric series, $\displaystyle\sum_{n=1}^{\infty}\dfrac{2n^2+7n}{3^n(n^2+5n-1)}$ converges also.

32. Use the Limit Comparison Test with $a_n = \dfrac{1}{\ln n}$ and $b_n = \dfrac{1}{n}$. $\displaystyle\lim_{n\to\infty}\dfrac{a_n}{b_n}$

$= \displaystyle\lim_{n\to\infty}\dfrac{n}{\ln n} = \lim_{n\to\infty}\dfrac{1}{1/n} = \infty$, so since $\displaystyle\sum_{n=2}^{\infty}\dfrac{1}{n}$ diverges, $\displaystyle\sum_{n=2}^{\infty}\dfrac{1}{\ln n}$ diverges.

34. $2^n n! = (2n)(2(n-1))(2(n-2))\cdots 2 \le (2n)! \Rightarrow \dfrac{1}{2^n} \ge \dfrac{n!}{2^n n!} \ge \dfrac{n!}{(2n)!}$ and

since $\displaystyle\sum_{n=1}^{\infty}\dfrac{1}{2^n}$ converges (geometric, $|r|=\frac{1}{2}<1$), so does $\displaystyle\sum_{n=1}^{\infty}\dfrac{n!}{(2n)!}$ by the

Comparison Test. [Another method: $\dfrac{n!}{(2n)!} = \dfrac{1\cdot 2\cdots n}{1\cdot 2\cdots n(n+1)(n+2)\cdots(2n)}$

$\le \dfrac{1}{(n+1)(n+2)} \le \dfrac{1}{n^2}$ for $n\ge 2$, so use the Comparison Test with $b_n = \dfrac{1}{n^2}$]

36. $\dfrac{n!}{n^n} = \dfrac{1\cdot 2\cdot 3\cdots (n-1)n}{n\cdot n\cdot n\cdots\cdots n\cdot n} \le \dfrac{1}{n}\cdot\dfrac{2}{n}\cdot 1\cdot 1\cdots 1$ for $n\ge 2$, so since $\displaystyle\sum_{n=1}^{\infty}\dfrac{2}{n^2}$ converges

$(p=2>1)$, $\displaystyle\sum_{n=1}^{\infty}\dfrac{n!}{n^n}$ converges also by the Comparison Test.

38. Use the Limit Comparison Test with $a_n = \dfrac{1}{n^{1+1/n}}$ and $b_n = \dfrac{1}{n}$. $\displaystyle\lim_{n\to\infty} \dfrac{a_n}{b_n}$

$= \displaystyle\lim_{n\to\infty} \dfrac{n}{n^{1+1/n}} = \lim_{n\to\infty} \dfrac{1}{n^{1/n}} = 1$ (since $\displaystyle\lim_{x\to\infty} x^{1/x} = 1$ by l'Hospital's

Rule), so $\displaystyle\sum_{n=1}^{\infty} \dfrac{1}{n}$ diverges $\Rightarrow$ $\displaystyle\sum_{n=1}^{\infty} \dfrac{1}{n^{1+1/n}}$ diverges.

40. Clearly if $p<0$ the series diverges since then $\displaystyle\lim_{n\to\infty} \dfrac{1}{n^p \ln n} = \infty$. If

$0 \leq p \leq 1$, then $n^p \ln n \leq n \ln n \Rightarrow \dfrac{1}{n^p \ln n} \geq \dfrac{1}{n \ln n}$ and $\displaystyle\sum_{n=2}^{\infty} \dfrac{1}{n \ln n}$

diverges (Exercise 13, Section 10.3), so $\displaystyle\sum_{n=2}^{\infty} \dfrac{1}{n^p \ln n}$ diverges. If

$p>1$, use the Limit Comparison Test with $a_n = \dfrac{1}{n^p \ln n}$ and $b_n = \dfrac{1}{n^p}$.

$\displaystyle\sum_{n=2}^{\infty} b_n$ converges, and $\displaystyle\lim_{n\to\infty} \dfrac{a_n}{b_n} = \lim_{n\to\infty} \dfrac{1}{\ln n} = 0$, so $\displaystyle\sum_{n=2}^{\infty} \dfrac{1}{n^p \ln n}$ also

converges. [Or use the Comparison Test since $n^p \ln n > n^p$ for $n>e$.]
In summary, the series converges if and only if $p>1$.

42. Since $\displaystyle\lim_{n\to\infty} \dfrac{a_n}{b_n} = 0$, there is a number $N>0$ such that $\left| \dfrac{a_n}{b_n} - 0 \right| < 1$ for

all $n > N$, and so $a_n < b_n$ since a_n and b_n are positive. Thus since

$\displaystyle\sum b_n$ converges, so does $\displaystyle\sum a_n$ by the Comparison Test.

44. Let $a_n = \dfrac{1}{n^2}$ and $b_n = \dfrac{1}{n}$. Then $\displaystyle\lim_{n\to\infty} \dfrac{a_n}{b_n} = \lim_{n\to\infty} \dfrac{1}{n} = 0$, but $\displaystyle\sum b_n$ diverges

while $\displaystyle\sum a_n$ converges.

Exercises 10.5

2. $-5 + \sum_{n=0}^{\infty} (-1)^{n-1} \frac{5}{3n+2}$ $a_n = \frac{5}{3n+2}$ is decreasing and positive for all

n, and $\lim_{n \to \infty} \frac{5}{3n+2} = 0$ so the series converges by the Alternating

Series Test.

4. $\sum_{n=2}^{\infty} (-1)^n \frac{1}{\ln n}$ $a_n = \frac{1}{\ln n}$ is positive and decreasing, and $\lim_{n \to \infty} \frac{1}{\ln n}$

$= 0$, so $\sum_{n=2}^{\infty} (-1)^n \frac{1}{\ln n}$ converges by the Alternating Series Test.

6. $\sum_{n=1}^{\infty} \frac{(-1)^n}{\sqrt{n+3}}$ $a_n = \frac{1}{\sqrt{n+3}}$ is positive and decreasing, and $\lim_{n \to \infty} \frac{1}{\sqrt{n+3}} = 0$,

so the series converges by the Alternating Series Test.

8. $\sum_{n=2}^{\infty} \frac{(-1)^{n-1}}{n \ln n}$ $a_n = \frac{1}{n \ln n}$ is positive and decreasing for $n \geq 2$, and

$\lim_{n \to \infty} \frac{1}{n \ln n} = 0$ so the series converges by the Alternating Series

Test.

10. $\sum_{n=1}^{\infty} (-1)^n \frac{n^2}{n^2+1}$ $\lim_{n \to \infty} \frac{n^2}{n^2+1} = 1$, so $\lim_{n \to \infty} (-1)^n \frac{n^2}{n^2+1}$ does not exist.

Thus the series diverges by the Divergence Test.

12. $\sum_{n=1}^{\infty} (-1)^{n+1} \frac{n}{2^n}$ $a_n = \frac{n}{2^n} > 0$ and $a_n \geq a_{n+1} \Leftrightarrow \frac{n}{2^n} \geq \frac{n+1}{2^{n+1}} \Leftrightarrow 2n \geq n+1 \Leftrightarrow$

$n \geq 1$ which is certainly true. $\lim_{n \to \infty} \frac{n}{2^n} = 0$ by l'Hospital's Rule, so

the series converges by the Alternating Series Test.

14. $\sum_{n=1}^{\infty} (-1)^{n-1} \left[\frac{\ln n}{n}\right] = 0 + \sum_{n=2}^{\infty} (-1)^{n-1} \left[\frac{\ln n}{n}\right]$ $a_n = \frac{\ln n}{n} > 0$ for $n \geq 2$,

and if $f(x) = \frac{\ln x}{x}$ then $f'(x) = \frac{1 - \ln x}{x^2} < 0$ if $x > e$, so $\{a_n\}$ is

eventually decreasing. $\lim_{n \to \infty} \frac{\ln n}{n} = \lim_{n \to \infty} \frac{1/n}{1} = 0$ so the series

converges by the Alternating Series Test.

16. $\sum_{n=1}^{\infty} (-1)^{n-1} \frac{(n+9)(n+10)}{n(n+1)}$ $\lim_{n\to\infty} \frac{(n+9)(n+10)}{n(n+1)} = 1$ so

$\lim_{n\to\infty} (-1)^{n-1} \frac{(n+9)(n+10)}{n(n+1)}$ does not exist and the series diverges

(Divergence Test).

18. $\sin\left[\frac{n\pi}{2}\right] = 0$ if n is even and $(-1)^k$ if n=2k+1, so series is

$\sum_{n=0}^{\infty} \frac{(-1)^n}{(2n+1)!}$. $a_n = \frac{1}{(2n+1)!} > 0$, $\{a_n\}$ is decreasing, and $\lim_{n\to\infty} \frac{1}{(2n+1)!}$

$= 0$ so the series converges by the Alternating Series Test.

20. $\sum_{n=1}^{\infty} (-1)^n \cos\left[\frac{\pi}{n}\right]$ $\lim_{n\to\infty} \cos\left[\frac{\pi}{n}\right] = \cos(0) = 1$, so $\lim_{n\to\infty} (-1)^n \cos\left[\frac{\pi}{n}\right]$ does

not exist and the series diverges (Divergence Test).

22. $\sum_{n=1}^{\infty} (-1)^n \frac{1}{\lceil n-10\pi \rceil}$ $a_n = \frac{1}{\lceil n-10\pi \rceil} > 0$ for all n, and $a_{n+1} < a_n$ for

$n > 10\pi$, so $\{a_n\}$ is eventually decreasing. $\lim_{n\to\infty} \frac{1}{\lceil n-10\pi \rceil} = 0$, so the

series converges by the Alternating Series Test.

24. If p>0 $\frac{1}{(n+1)^p} \le \frac{1}{n^p}$ and $\lim_{n\to\infty} \frac{1}{n^p} = 0$, so the series converges by the

Alternating Series Test. If p≤0, $\lim_{n\to\infty} \frac{(-1)^{n-1}}{n^p}$ does not exist, so

the series diverges by the Test for Divergence. Thus $\sum_{n=1}^{\infty} \frac{(-1)^{n-1}}{n^p}$

converges $\Longleftrightarrow$ p>0.

26. Let $f(x) = \frac{(\ln x)^p}{x}$. Then $f'(x) = \frac{(\ln x)^{p-1}[p - \ln x]}{x^2} < 0$ if $x > e^p$

so f is eventually decreasing for every p. Clearly $\lim_{n\to\infty} \frac{(\ln n)^p}{n} = 0$

if p≤0, and if p>0 we can apply l'Hospital's Rule ⟦p+1⟧ times to

get a limit of 0 as well. So the series converges for all p (by

the Alternating Series Test).

28. $a_6 = \frac{1}{6^4} \approx 0.00077 < 0.001$, so by Theorem 10.28,

$\sum_{n=1}^{\infty} \frac{(-1)^{n+1}}{n^4} \approx s_5 = 1 - \frac{1}{16} + \frac{1}{81} - \frac{1}{256} + \frac{1}{625} \approx 0.948$

30. $a_6 = \dfrac{6}{4^6} \approx 0.0015 < 0.002 \Rightarrow$

$\displaystyle\sum_{n=0}^{\infty} \dfrac{(-1)^n n}{4^n} \approx s_5 = 0 - \dfrac{1}{4} + \dfrac{1}{8} - \dfrac{3}{64} + \dfrac{1}{64} - \dfrac{5}{1024} \approx -0.161$

32. $a_4 = \dfrac{1}{(2 \cdot 4)!} = \dfrac{1}{40320} \approx 0.000025$ and $s_3 = 1 - \dfrac{1}{2} + \dfrac{1}{24} - \dfrac{1}{720} \approx 0.54028,$

so, correct to 4 decimal places, $\displaystyle\sum_{n=0}^{\infty} \dfrac{(-1)^n}{(2n)!} \approx 0.5403.$

34. $a_8 = \dfrac{1}{8^6} < 0.0000038$ and $s_7 = 1 - \dfrac{1}{64} + \dfrac{1}{729} - \dfrac{1}{4096} + \dfrac{1}{15625} - \dfrac{1}{46656} +$

$\dfrac{1}{117649} \approx 0.9855537,$ so correct to 5 decimal places,

$\displaystyle\sum_{n=1}^{\infty} \dfrac{(-1)^{n-1}}{n^6} \approx 0.98555.$

Section 10.6

Exercises 10.6

2. $\displaystyle\sum_{n=1}^{\infty} \dfrac{(-1)^n}{n^{1/2}}$ converges by the Alternating Series Test, but $\displaystyle\sum_{n=1}^{\infty} \dfrac{1}{n^{1/2}}$ is

a divergent p-series ($p=\frac{1}{2}<1$), so $\displaystyle\sum_{n=1}^{\infty} \dfrac{(-1)^n}{n^{1/2}}$ converges conditionally.

4. $\displaystyle\lim_{n\to\infty} \left| \dfrac{a_{n+1}}{a_n} \right| = \lim_{n\to\infty} \left| \dfrac{(-3)^{n+1}/(n+1)!}{(-3)^n/n!} \right| = 3 \lim_{n\to\infty} \dfrac{1}{n+1} = 0 < 1$ so the series

is absolutely convergent by the Ratio Test.

6. $\dfrac{1}{n^2+1} < \dfrac{1}{n^2}$ and $\displaystyle\sum_{n=1}^{\infty} \dfrac{1}{n^2}$ converges ($p=2>1$), so $\displaystyle\sum_{n=1}^{\infty} \dfrac{1}{n^2+1}$ converges

absolutely by the Comparison Test.

8. $\displaystyle\lim_{n\to\infty} \left| \dfrac{a_{n+1}}{a_n} \right| = \lim_{n\to\infty} \left| \dfrac{(n+1)!/e^{n+1}}{n!/e^n} \right| = \dfrac{1}{e} \lim_{n\to\infty} (n+1) = \infty$ so the series

diverges by the Ratio Test.

10. Let $a_n = \frac{\sqrt{n}}{n+1}$ and $b_n = \frac{1}{\sqrt{n}}$. Then $\lim\limits_{n\to\infty} \frac{a_n}{b_n} = \lim\limits_{n\to\infty} \frac{n}{n+1} = 1$, so since

$\sum\limits_{n=1}^{\infty} b_n$ diverges ($p=\frac{1}{2}<1$), so does $\sum\limits_{n=1}^{\infty} a_n$ by the Limit Comparison Test.

But $\lim\limits_{n\to\infty} \frac{\sqrt{n}}{n+1} = \lim\limits_{n\to\infty} \frac{1}{\sqrt{n} + 1/\sqrt{n}} = 0$, so $\sum\limits_{n=1}^{\infty} (-1)^{n-1} \frac{\sqrt{n}}{n+1}$ converges by the

Alternating Series Test, and so is conditionally convergent.

12. $\lim\limits_{n\to\infty} (-1)^n \frac{2^n}{n^2+1}$ does not exist, so $\sum\limits_{n=1}^{\infty} (-1)^n \frac{2^n}{n^2+1}$ diverges by the Test

for Divergence.

14. $\frac{\arctan n}{n^3} < \frac{\pi/2}{n^3}$ and $\sum\limits_{n=1}^{\infty} \frac{\pi/2}{n^3}$ converges ($p=3>1$), so $\sum\limits_{n=1}^{\infty} (-1)^n \frac{\arctan n}{n^3}$

converges absolutely by the Comparison Test.

16. $\lim\limits_{n\to\infty} \left| \frac{a_{n+1}}{a_n} \right| = \lim\limits_{n\to\infty} \left| \frac{5^n/(n+2)^2 4^{n+3}}{5^{n-1}/(n+1)^2 4^{n+2}} \right| = \frac{5}{4} \lim\limits_{n\to\infty} \left[\frac{n+1}{n+2} \right]^2 = \frac{5}{4} > 1$ so the

series diverges by the Ratio Test.

18. $\lim\limits_{n\to\infty} \left| \frac{a_{n+1}}{a_n} \right| = \lim\limits_{n\to\infty} \left| \frac{\frac{8-(n+1)^3}{(n+1)!}}{\frac{8-n^3}{n!}} \right| = \lim\limits_{n\to\infty} \frac{1}{n+1} \left| \frac{8-(n+1)^3}{8-n^3} \right| = 0 < 1$, so the

series converges absolutely by the Ratio Test.

20. $|\cos(n\pi/6)| \leq 1$, so since $\sum\limits_{n=1}^{\infty} \frac{1}{n\sqrt{n}}$ converges ($p=\frac{3}{2}>1$), the given

series converges absolutely by the Comparison Test.

22. $\lim\limits_{n\to\infty} \left| \frac{a_{n+1}}{a_n} \right| = \lim\limits_{n\to\infty} \frac{(n+1)!/(n+1)^{n+1}}{n!/n^n} = \lim\limits_{n\to\infty} \frac{n^n}{(n+1)^n} = \lim\limits_{n\to\infty} \frac{1}{\left[1+\frac{1}{n}\right]^n} = \frac{1}{e} < 1$,

so the series converges absolutely by the Ratio Test.

24. $\lim\limits_{n\to\infty} \sqrt[n]{|a_n|} = \lim\limits_{n\to\infty} \frac{1}{\ln n} = 0 < 1$ so the series converges absolutely by

the Root Test.

26. Since $\left\{ \frac{1}{n \ln n} \right\}$ is decreasing and $\lim\limits_{n\to\infty} \frac{1}{n \ln n} = 0$, the series

converges by the Alternating Series Test, but since $\sum\limits_{n=2}^{\infty} \frac{1}{n \ln n}$

diverges by the Integral Test (Exercise 13, Section 10.3), the

given series only converges conditionally.

28. $\lim_{n\to\infty} \left| \dfrac{a_{n+1}}{a_n} \right| = \lim_{n\to\infty} \left| \dfrac{\frac{(-2)^{n+1}(n+1)^2}{(n+3)!}}{\frac{(-2)^n n^2}{(n+2)!}} \right| = \lim_{n\to\infty} \dfrac{2(n+1)^2}{n^2(n+3)} = 0 < 1$, so the

series converges absolutely by the Ratio Test.

30. $\lim_{n\to\infty} \left| \dfrac{a_{n+1}}{a_n} \right| = \lim_{n\to\infty} \left| \dfrac{\frac{1\cdot 4\cdot 7\cdots(3n+1)}{3\cdot 5\cdot 7\cdots(2n+3)}}{\frac{1\cdot 4\cdot 7\cdots(3n-2)}{3\cdot 5\cdot 7\cdots(2n+1)}} \right| = \lim_{n\to\infty} \dfrac{3n+1}{2n+3} = \dfrac{3}{2} > 1$ so the

series diverges by the Ratio Test.

32. $\lim_{n\to\infty} \left| \dfrac{a_{n+1}}{a_n} \right| = \lim_{n\to\infty} \left| \dfrac{\frac{2^{n+1}(n+1)!}{5\cdot 8\cdot 11\cdots(3n+5)}}{\frac{2^n n!}{5\cdot 8\cdot 11\cdots(3n+2)}} \right| = \lim_{n\to\infty} \dfrac{2(n+1)}{3n+5} = \dfrac{2}{3} < 1$ so the

series converges absolutely by the Ratio Test.

34. $\lim_{n\to\infty} \left| \dfrac{a_{n+1}}{a_n} \right| = \lim_{n\to\infty} \dfrac{((n+1)!)^2/(2(n+1))!}{(n!)^2/(2n)!} = \lim_{n\to\infty} \dfrac{(n+1)^2}{(2n+2)(2n+1)} = \dfrac{1}{4} < 1$ so

the series converges absolutely by the Ratio Test.

36. $\lim_{n\to\infty} \sqrt[n]{|a_n|} = \lim_{n\to\infty} \dfrac{1}{\arctan n} = \dfrac{1}{\pi/2} = \dfrac{2}{\pi} < 1$ so the series converges

absolutely by the Root Test.

38. By the Triangle Inequality [(1.5) and Exercise 5.1.44] we have

$\left| \displaystyle\sum_{i=1}^{n} a_i \right| \le \displaystyle\sum_{i=1}^{n} |a_i| \;\Rightarrow\; -\displaystyle\sum_{i=1}^{n} |a_i| \le \displaystyle\sum_{i=1}^{n} a_i \le \displaystyle\sum_{i=1}^{n} |a_i| \;\Rightarrow$

$-\lim_{n\to\infty}\displaystyle\sum_{i=1}^{n} |a_i| \le \lim_{n\to\infty}\displaystyle\sum_{i=1}^{n} a_i \le \lim_{n\to\infty}\displaystyle\sum_{i=1}^{n} |a_i| \;\Rightarrow\; -\displaystyle\sum_{n=1}^{\infty} |a_n| \le \displaystyle\sum_{n=1}^{\infty} a_n \le \displaystyle\sum_{n=1}^{\infty} |a_n|$

$\Rightarrow\; \left| \displaystyle\sum_{i=1}^{n} a_i \right| \le \displaystyle\sum_{n=1}^{\infty} |a_n|$

40. (a) Since $\sum a_n$ is absolutely convergent, and since $|a_n^+| \le |a_n|$ and

$|a_n^-| \le |a_n|$ (because a_n^+ and a_n^- each equal either a_n or 0), we

conclude by the Comparison Test that both $\sum a_n^+$ and $\sum a_n^-$ must be

absolutely convergent. [Or use Theorem 10.19.]

(b) We will show by contradiction that both $\sum a_n^+$ and $\sum a_n^-$ must

diverge. For suppose that $\sum a_n^+$ converged. Then so would

327

$\sum(a_n^+ - \frac{1}{2}a_n)$ by Theorem 10.19. But $\sum(a_n^+ - \frac{1}{2}a_n) = \sum\left[\frac{a_n + |a_n|}{2} - \frac{a_n}{2}\right]$

$= \frac{1}{2}\sum|a_n|$ which diverges because $\sum a_n$ is only conditionally

convergent. Hence $\sum a_n^+$ can't converge. Similarly, neither can

$\sum a_n^-$.

Section 10.7

Exercises 10.7

2. $\lim\limits_{n\to\infty} \cos n$ does not exist, so the series diverges by the Test for

   Divergence.

4. $\lim\limits_{i\to\infty}\left|\frac{a_{i+1}}{a_i}\right| = \lim\limits_{i\to\infty}\frac{(i+1)^4/4^{i+1}}{i^4/4^i} = \frac{1}{4}\lim\limits_{i\to\infty}\left[\frac{i+1}{i}\right]^4 = \frac{1}{4} < 1$ so the series

   converges by the Ratio Test.

6. Let $f(x) = x^2 e^{-x^3}$. Then f is continuous and positive on $[1,\infty)$, and

   $f'(x) = \frac{x(2-3x^3)}{e^{x^3}} < 0$ for $x \geq 1$, so f is decreasing on $[1,\infty)$ as well,

   and we can apply the Integral Test. $\int_1^\infty x^2 e^{-x^3} dx = \lim\limits_{t\to\infty} -\frac{1}{3}e^{-x^3}\Big]_1^t = \frac{1}{3e}$,

   so the series converges.

8. $\lim\limits_{n\to\infty}\left|\frac{a_{n+1}}{a_n}\right| = \lim\limits_{n\to\infty}\frac{10^{n+1}/(n+1)!}{10^n/n!} = \lim\limits_{n\to\infty}\frac{10}{n+1} = 0 < 1$, so the series

   converges by the Ratio Test.

10. $\lim\limits_{m\to\infty}\frac{2m}{8m-5} = \frac{1}{4} \neq 0$ so the series diverges by the Test for Divergence.

12. $\lim\limits_{n\to\infty}\sqrt[n]{|a_n|} = \lim\limits_{n\to\infty}\frac{n^2+1}{2n^2+1} = \frac{1}{2} < 1$, so the series converges (Root Test).

14. Let $f(x) = \frac{\sqrt{x}}{e^{\sqrt{x}}}$. Then $f(x)$ is continuous and positive, and $f'(x)$

    $= \frac{1-\sqrt{x}}{2\sqrt{x}e^{\sqrt{x}}} < 0$ on $[1,\infty)$, so $f(x)$ is decreasing and we can use the

328

Integral Test. $\int_1^\infty \frac{\sqrt{x}}{e^{\sqrt{x}}} \, dx = \lim_{t\to\infty} \frac{-2x-4\sqrt{x}-4}{e^{\sqrt{x}}}\Bigg]_1^t = 0 - \left[-\frac{10}{e}\right] = \frac{10}{e}$ [using

integration by parts and l'Hospital's Rule], so the series

converges.

16. Let $a_n = \frac{3}{4n-5}$ and $b_n = \frac{1}{n}$. Then $\lim\limits_{n\to\infty} \frac{a_n}{b_n} = \frac{3}{4}$, so since $\sum\limits_{n=1}^\infty b_n$ diverges

(harmonic series), so does $\sum\limits_{n=1}^\infty \frac{3}{4n-5}$ by the Limit Comparison Test.

18. $\lim\limits_{k\to\infty} \left|\frac{a_{k+1}}{a_k}\right| = \lim\limits_{k\to\infty} \frac{(k+6)/5^{k+1}}{(k+5)/5^k} = \frac{1}{5}\lim\limits_{k\to\infty} \frac{k+6}{k+5} = \frac{1}{5} < 1$, so the series

converges by the Ratio Test.

20. $\lim\limits_{n\to\infty} \frac{n}{(n+1)(n+2)} = \lim\limits_{n\to\infty} \frac{1}{n + 3 + 2/n} = 0$, so since $\{a_n\}$ is a positive

decreasing sequence, $\sum\limits_{n=1}^\infty \frac{(-1)^n n}{(n+1)(n+2)}$ converges by the Alternating

Series Test.

22. Let $a_n = \frac{n^2}{\sqrt{n^5+n^2+2}}$ and $b_n = \frac{1}{\sqrt{n}}$. Then $\lim\limits_{n\to\infty} \frac{a_n}{b_n} = \lim\limits_{n\to\infty} \frac{1}{\sqrt{1+n^{-3}+2n^{-5}}} = 1$,

so since $\sum\limits_{n=1}^\infty b_n$ diverges (p-series with $p=\frac{1}{2}<1$), so does $\sum\limits_{n=1}^\infty \frac{n^2}{\sqrt{n^5+n^2+2}}$

by the Limit Comparison Test.

24. $\frac{|\cos(n/2)|}{n^2+4n} < \frac{1}{n^2}$ and since $\sum\limits_{n=1}^\infty \frac{1}{n^2}$ converges (p=2>1), $\sum\limits_{n=1}^\infty \frac{\cos(n/2)}{n^2+4n}$

converges absolutely by the Comparison Test.

26. Let $a_n = \frac{\tan(1/n)}{n}$ and $b_n = \frac{1}{n^2}$. Then $\lim\limits_{n\to\infty} \frac{a_n}{b_n} = \lim\limits_{n\to\infty} n\cdot\tan(1/n) =$

$\lim\limits_{n\to\infty} \frac{\tan(1/n)}{1/n} = \lim\limits_{n\to\infty} \frac{(-1/n^2)\sec^2(1/n)}{-1/n^2}$ [l'Hospital's Rule]

$= \sec^2(0) = 1>0$, so since $\sum\limits_{n=1}^\infty b_n$ converges (p=2>1), $\sum\limits_{n=1}^\infty \frac{\tan(1/n)}{n}$

converges also by the Limit Comparison Test.

28. Let $a_n = \dfrac{\sqrt[3]{n}+1}{n(\sqrt{n}+1)}$ and $b_n = n^{-7/6}$. Then $\lim\limits_{n\to\infty} \dfrac{a_n}{b_n} = \lim\limits_{n\to\infty} \dfrac{1 + n^{-1/3}}{1 + n^{-1/2}} = 1$,

so since $\sum\limits_{n=1}^{\infty} b_n$ converges ($p = 7/6 > 1$), $\sum\limits_{n=1}^{\infty} \dfrac{\sqrt[3]{n}+1}{n(\sqrt{n}+1)}$ converges by the

Limit Comparison Test.

30. $\lim\limits_{n\to\infty} \dfrac{2^{3n-1}}{n^2 + 1} = \infty$ [use l'Hospital's Rule twice] so the series diverges

by the Test for Divergence. [Or use the Ratio Test.]

32. Since $\left\{\dfrac{1}{n}\right\}$ is a decreasing sequence, $e^{1/n} \leq e^{1/1} = e$ for all $n \geq 1$,

and $\sum\limits_{n=1}^{\infty} \dfrac{e}{n^2}$ converges ($p=2>1$), so $\sum\limits_{n=1}^{\infty} \dfrac{e^{1/n}}{n^2}$ converges by the

Comparison Test. [Or use the Integral Test.]

34. Let $f(x) = \dfrac{\sqrt{x}}{x+5}$. Then $f(x)$ is continuous and positive on $[1,\infty)$, and

since $f'(x) = \dfrac{5-x}{2\sqrt{x}(x+5)^2} < 0$ for $x>5$, $f(x)$ is eventually decreasing,

so we can use the Alternating Series Test. $\lim\limits_{n\to\infty} \dfrac{\sqrt{n}}{n+5} =$

$\lim\limits_{n\to\infty} \dfrac{1}{n^{1/2}+5n^{-1/2}} = 0$, so the series converges.

36. $\lim\limits_{n\to\infty} \sqrt[n]{|a_n|} = \lim\limits_{n\to\infty} \dfrac{2n}{n^2} = \lim\limits_{n\to\infty} \dfrac{2}{n} = 0$ so the series converges by the Root

Test.

38. Note that $(\ln n)^{\ln n} = (e^{\ln \ln n})^{\ln n} = (e^{\ln n})^{\ln \ln n} = n^{\ln \ln n}$

and $\ln \ln n \to \infty$ as $n\to\infty$, so $\ln \ln n > 2$ for sufficiently large n.

For these n we have $(\ln n)^{\ln n} > n^2$, so $\dfrac{1}{(\ln n)^{\ln n}} < \dfrac{1}{n^2}$

Since $\sum \dfrac{1}{n^2}$ converges ($p=2>1$), so does $\sum\limits_{n=2}^{\infty} \dfrac{1}{(\ln n)^{\ln n}}$ by the

Comparison Test.

40. $\sqrt[n]{2}-1 = \dfrac{1}{2^{\frac{n-1}{n}} + 2^{\frac{n-2}{n}} + 2^{\frac{n-3}{n}} + \ldots + 2^{\frac{1}{n}}+1}$ [rationalize the numerator] $\geq \dfrac{1}{2n}$,

and since $\sum\limits_{n=1}^{\infty} \dfrac{1}{2n} = \dfrac{1}{2} \sum\limits_{n=1}^{\infty} \dfrac{1}{n}$ diverges (harmonic series), so does

$\sum\limits_{n=1}^{\infty} (\sqrt[n]{2}-1)$ by the Comparison Test. [Or use the Limit Comparison

Test with $a_n = \sqrt[n]{2}-1$ and $b_n = \frac{1}{n}$: $\lim\limits_{n\to\infty} \frac{a_n}{b_n} = \lim\limits_{n\to\infty} \frac{2^{1/n}-1}{1/n} = \ln 2 > 0.$]

Section 10.8

Exercises 10.8

R denotes the radius of convergence, and I the interval of convergence.

2. If $u_n = \frac{(-1)^n x^n}{\sqrt[3]{n}}$, then $\lim\limits_{n\to\infty} \left|\frac{u_{n+1}}{u_n}\right| = |x| \lim\limits_{n\to\infty} \left[\frac{n}{n+1}\right]^{1/3} = |x| < 1$ for

convergence (by the Ratio Test), and R=1. When x=1,

$\sum\limits_{n=1}^{\infty} u_n = \sum\limits_{n=1}^{\infty} \frac{(-1)^n}{\sqrt[3]{n}}$ which is a convergent alternating series, but when

x=-1, $\sum\limits_{n=1}^{\infty} u_n = \sum\limits_{n=1}^{\infty} \frac{1}{n^{1/3}}$ which is a divergent p-series ($p=\frac{1}{3}<1$), so

I=(-1,1].

4. If $u_n = \frac{x^n}{n^2}$ then $\lim\limits_{n\to\infty} \left|\frac{u_{n+1}}{u_n}\right| = |x| \lim\limits_{n\to\infty} \left[\frac{n}{n+1}\right]^2 = |x| < 1$ for

convergence (by the Ratio Test), so R=1. If x = ±1,

$\sum\limits_{n=1}^{\infty} |u_n| = \sum\limits_{n=1}^{\infty} \frac{1}{n^2}$ which converges (p=2>1), so I=[-1,1].

6. Here the Root Test is easier. If $u_n = n^n x^n$ then

$\lim\limits_{n\to\infty} \sqrt[n]{|u_n|} = \lim\limits_{n\to\infty} n|x| = \infty$ if $x\neq0$ so R=0 and I={0}.

8. If $u_n = n5^n x^n$ then $\lim\limits_{n\to\infty} \left|\frac{u_{n+1}}{u_n}\right| = 5|x| \lim\limits_{n\to\infty} \frac{n+1}{n} = 5|x| < 1$ for

convergence (by the Ratio Test), so $R=\frac{1}{5}$. If $x = \pm\frac{1}{5}$, $|u_n| = n\to\infty$ as

$n\to\infty$, so $\sum\limits_{n=1}^{\infty} u_n$ diverges (Test for Divergence) and I = (-1/5,1/5).

10. If $u_n = \dfrac{n^2 x^n}{10^n}$ then $\lim\limits_{n\to\infty} \left|\dfrac{u_{n+1}}{u_n}\right| = \dfrac{|x|}{10} \lim\limits_{n\to\infty} \left(\dfrac{n+1}{n}\right)^2 = \dfrac{|x|}{10} < 1$ for

    convergence (by the Ratio Test), so R=10. If $x = \pm 10$, $|u_n| = n^2 \to\infty$

    as $n\to\infty$, so $\sum\limits_{n=0}^{\infty} u_n$ diverges (Test for Divergence) and I = (-10,10).

12. If $u_n = \dfrac{(-1)^n x^{2n-1}}{(2n-1)!}$ then $\lim\limits_{n\to\infty} \left|\dfrac{u_{n+1}}{u_n}\right| = \lim\limits_{n\to\infty} \dfrac{|x|^2}{(2n+1)2n} = 0 < 1$ for all

    x. By the Ratio Test the series converges for all x, so R=∞ and
    I = (-∞,∞).

14. If $u_n = \dfrac{(x-4)^n}{n5^n}$ then $\lim\limits_{n\to\infty} \left|\dfrac{u_{n+1}}{u_n}\right| = \dfrac{|x-4|}{5} \lim\limits_{n\to\infty} \dfrac{n}{n+1} = \dfrac{|x-4|}{5} < 1$ for

    convergence, or -1 < x < 9 and R=5. When x=9, $\sum\limits_{n=1}^{\infty} u_n = \sum\limits_{n=1}^{\infty} \dfrac{1}{n}$ which

    diverges, and when x = -1, $\sum\limits_{n=1}^{\infty} u_n = \sum\limits_{n=1}^{\infty} \dfrac{(-1)^n}{n}$ which converges by the

    Alternating Series Test, so I = [-1,9).

16. If $u_n = \dfrac{(-3)^n (x-1)^n}{\sqrt{n+1}}$ then $\lim\limits_{n\to\infty} \left|\dfrac{u_{n+1}}{u_n}\right| = 3|x-1| \cdot \lim\limits_{n\to\infty} \left(\dfrac{n+1}{n+2}\right)^{1/2} = 3|x-1|$

    < 1 for convergence, or $\dfrac{2}{3} < x < \dfrac{4}{3}$ and $R=\dfrac{1}{3}$. When $x = \dfrac{4}{3}$, $\sum\limits_{n=0}^{\infty} u_n =$

    $\sum\limits_{n=0}^{\infty} \dfrac{(-1)^n}{\sqrt{n+1}}$ which is a convergent alternating series, and when $x = \dfrac{2}{3}$,

    $\sum\limits_{n=0}^{\infty} u_n = \sum\limits_{n=0}^{\infty} \dfrac{1}{\sqrt{n+1}}$ which is a divergent p-series $(p=\dfrac{1}{2}<1)$, so

    I = (2/3,4/3].

18. If $u_n = \dfrac{(x+1)^n}{n(n+1)}$ then $\lim\limits_{n\to\infty} \left|\dfrac{u_{n+1}}{u_n}\right| = |x+1| \cdot \lim\limits_{n\to\infty} \dfrac{n}{n+2} = |x+1| < 1$ for

    convergence, or -2 < x < 0 and R=1. If x = -2 or 0, then $|u_n|$

    $= \dfrac{1}{n^2+n} < \dfrac{1}{n^2}$ so $\sum\limits_{n=1}^{\infty} |u_n|$ converges since $\sum\limits_{n=1}^{\infty} \dfrac{1}{n^2}$ does, and I=[-2,0].

20. If $u_n = \dfrac{n!(x-\pi)^n}{10^n}$ then $\lim\limits_{n\to\infty} \left|\dfrac{u_{n+1}}{u_n}\right| = \dfrac{|x-\pi|}{10} \cdot \lim\limits_{n\to\infty}(n+1) = \infty$ if $x\neq\pi$, so R=0

    and I = {π}.

22. If $u_n = \dfrac{nx^n}{1 \cdot 3 \cdot 5 \cdots (2n-1)}$ then $\lim\limits_{n \to \infty} \left| \dfrac{u_{n+1}}{u_n} \right| = |x| \lim\limits_{n \to \infty} \dfrac{n+1}{n(2n+1)} = 0$ for

all x. So the series converges for all x $\Rightarrow$ R = ∞ and I = $(-\infty, \infty)$.

24. If $u_n = \dfrac{(-1)^n (2x+3)^n}{n \ln n}$ then $\lim\limits_{n \to \infty} \left| \dfrac{u_{n+1}}{u_n} \right| = |2x+3| \lim\limits_{n \to \infty} \dfrac{n \ln n}{(n+1) \ln (n+1)} =$

$|2x+3| < 1$ for convergence, so $-2 < x < -1$ and $R = \frac{1}{2}$. When x = -2,

$\displaystyle\sum_{n=2}^{\infty} u_n = \sum_{n=2}^{\infty} \dfrac{1}{n \ln n}$ which diverges (Integral Test), and when x = -1,

$\displaystyle\sum_{n=2}^{\infty} u_n = \sum_{n=2}^{\infty} \dfrac{(-1)^n}{n \ln n}$ which converges (Alternating Series Test), so

I = $(-2, -1]$.

26. If $u_n = \dfrac{x^n}{(\ln n)^n}$ then $\lim\limits_{n \to \infty} \sqrt[n]{|u_n|} = \lim\limits_{n \to \infty} \dfrac{|x|}{\ln n} = 0 < 1$ for all x, so $R = \infty$

and I = $(-\infty, \infty)$ by the Root Test.

28. If $u_n = \dfrac{2 \cdot 4 \cdot 6 \cdots (2n) x^n}{1 \cdot 3 \cdot 5 \cdots (2n-1)}$ then $\lim\limits_{n \to \infty} \left| \dfrac{u_{n+1}}{u_n} \right| = \lim\limits_{n \to \infty} |x| \left[\dfrac{2n+2}{2n+1} \right] = |x| < 1$

for convergence, so R = 1. If x = ±1, $|u_n| = \dfrac{2 \cdot 4 \cdot 6 \cdots (2n)}{1 \cdot 3 \cdot 5 \cdots (2n-1)} > 1$ for

all n (since each integer in the numerator is larger than the

corresponding one in the denominator), so $\displaystyle\sum_{n=1}^{\infty} u_n$ diverges in both

cases by the Test for Divergence, and I = $(-1, 1)$.

30. $A(x) = 1 + \displaystyle\sum_{n=1}^{\infty} u_n$ where $u_n = \dfrac{x^{3n}}{2 \cdot 3 \cdot 5 \cdot 6 \cdots (3n-1)(3n)}$, so $\lim\limits_{n \to \infty} \left| \dfrac{u_{n+1}}{u_n} \right| =$

$|x|^3 \lim\limits_{n \to \infty} \dfrac{1}{(3n+2)(3n+3)} = 0$ for all x, so the domain is R.

32. Since $\displaystyle\sum a_n x^n$ converges whenever $|x| < R$, $\displaystyle\sum a_n x^{2n} = \sum a_n (x^2)^n$

converges whenever $|x^2| < R \Leftrightarrow |x| < \sqrt{R}$, so the second series has

radius of convergence $\sqrt{R}$.

Exercises 10.9

2. $f(x) = \sin 2x$ $f(0) = 0$

    $f'(x) = 2 \cos 2x$ $f'(0) = 2$

    $f''(x) = -2^2 \sin 2x$ $f''(0) = 0$

    $f^{(3)}(x) = -2^3 \cos 2x$ $f^{(3)}(0) = -2^3$

    $f^{(4)}(x) = 2^4 \sin 2x$ $f^{(4)}(0) = 0$

    $f^{(n)}(0) = 0$ if n is even and $f^{(2n+1)}(0) = (-1)^n 2^{2n+1}$, so

$$\sin 2x = \sum_{n=0}^{\infty} \frac{f^{(n)}(0)}{n!} x^n = \sum_{n=0}^{\infty} \frac{f^{(2n+1)}(0)}{(2n+1)!} x^{2n+1} = \sum_{n=0}^{\infty} \frac{(-1)^n 2^{2n+1} x^{2n+1}}{(2n+1)!}.$$

$$\lim_{n\to\infty} \left| \frac{u_{n+1}}{u_n} \right| = \lim_{n\to\infty} \frac{2^2 |x|^2}{(2n+3)(2n+2)} = 0 \text{ for all x, so } R=\infty \text{ (Ratio Test).}$$

4. $f(x) = \cos x$ $f(-\frac{\pi}{4}) = \frac{\sqrt{2}}{2}$

    $f'(x) = -\sin x$ $f'(-\frac{\pi}{4}) = \frac{\sqrt{2}}{2}$

    $f''(x) = -\cos x$ $f''(-\frac{\pi}{4}) = -\frac{\sqrt{2}}{2}$

    $f^{(3)}(x) = \sin x$ $f^{(3)}(-\frac{\pi}{4}) = -\frac{\sqrt{2}}{2}$

    $f^{(4)}(x) = \cos x$ $f^{(4)}(-\frac{\pi}{4}) = \frac{\sqrt{2}}{2}$

$$f^{(n)}(-\frac{\pi}{4}) = \frac{(-1)^{\frac{n(n-1)}{2}} \sqrt{2}}{2} \text{ so } \cos x = \sum_{n=0}^{\infty} \frac{f^{(n)}(-\pi/4)}{n!} \left[x+\frac{\pi}{4}\right]^n$$

$$= \sum_{n=0}^{\infty} \frac{(-1)^{\frac{n(n-1)}{2}} \sqrt{2}}{2 \cdot n!} \left[x+\frac{\pi}{4}\right]^n, \text{ with } R=\infty \text{ by the Ratio Test.}$$

6. $f(x) = x/(1-x)$ $f(0) = 0$

    $f'(x) = (1-x)^{-2}$ $f'(0) = 1$

    $f''(x) = 2(1-x)^{-3}$ $f''(0) = 2$

    $f^{(3)}(x) = 3 \cdot 2(1-x)^{-4}$ $f^{(3)}(0) = 3 \cdot 2$

    $f^{(4)}(x) = 4 \cdot 3 \cdot 2(1-x)^{-5}$ $f^{(4)}(0) = 4 \cdot 3 \cdot 2$

    $f^{(n)}(0) = n!$ except when n=0 so $\frac{x}{1-x} = \sum_{n=1}^{\infty} \frac{n!}{n!} x^n = \sum_{n=1}^{\infty} x^n.$

$$\lim_{n\to\infty} \left| \frac{u_{n+1}}{u_n} \right| = |x| < 1 \text{ for convergence so } R=1.$$

8. $f(x) = x^{1/2}$ $f(4) = 2$

$f'(x) = \frac{1}{2}x^{-1/2}$ $f'(4) = 2^{-2}$

$f''(x) = -\frac{1}{4}x^{-3/2}$ $f''(4) = -2^{-5}$

$f^{(3)}(x) = \frac{3}{8}x^{-5/2}$ $f^{(3)}(4) = 3 \cdot 2^{-8}$

$f^{(4)}(x) = -\frac{15}{16}x^{-7/2}$ $f^{(4)}(4) = -15 \cdot 2^{-11}$

$f^{(n)}(4) = \frac{(-1)^{n-1} 1 \cdot 3 \cdot 5 \cdots (2n-3)}{2^{3n-1}}$ for $n \geq 2$, so

$\sqrt{x} = 2 + \frac{x-4}{4} + \sum_{n=2}^{\infty} \frac{(-1)^{n-1} 1 \cdot 3 \cdot 5 \cdots (2n-3)}{2^{3n-1} \, n!} (x-4)^n$. $\lim_{n \to \infty} \left| \frac{u_{n+1}}{u_n} \right| =$

$\frac{|x-4|}{8} \lim_{n \to \infty} \left[\frac{2n-1}{n+1} \right] = \frac{|x-4|}{4} < 1$ for convergence so $|x-4| < 4 \Rightarrow R = 4$.

10. $f(x) = \ln x$ $f(2) = \ln 2$

$f'(x) = x^{-1}$ $f'(2) = \frac{1}{2}$

$f''(x) = -x^{-2}$ $f''(2) = -\frac{1}{4}$

$f^{(3)}(x) = 2x^{-3}$ $f^{(3)}(2) = \frac{2}{8}$

$f^{(4)}(x) = -3 \cdot 2x^{-4}$ $f^{(4)}(2) = -\frac{3 \cdot 2}{16}$

$f^{(n)}(2) = \frac{(-1)^{n-1}(n-1)!}{2^n}$ for $n \geq 1$, so $\ln x = \ln 2 + \sum_{n=1}^{\infty} \frac{(-1)^{n-1}(x-2)^n}{n \cdot 2^n}$.

$\lim_{n \to \infty} \left| \frac{u_{n+1}}{u_n} \right| = \frac{|x-2|}{2} \lim_{n \to \infty} \frac{n}{n+1} = \frac{|x-2|}{2} < 1$ for convergence $\iff |x-2| < 2$

So $R=2$.

12. $f(x) = \cosh x$ $f(0) = 1$

$f'(x) = \sinh x$ $f'(0) = 0$

$f''(x) = \cosh x$ $f''(0) = 1$

$f^{(3)}(x) = \sinh x$ $f^{(3)}(0) = 0$

$f^{(n)}(0) = \begin{cases} 1 & \text{if } n \text{ is even} \\ 0 & \text{if } n \text{ is odd} \end{cases}$ so $\cosh x = \sum_{n=0}^{\infty} \frac{x^{2n}}{(2n)!}$ with $R=\infty$ by the

Ratio Test.

14. $\frac{1}{1+x} = \sum_{n=0}^{\infty} (-1)^n x^n$ (geometric series, $R=1$), so $\ln(1+x) = \int_0^x \frac{dt}{1+t}$

$= \int_0^x \left[\sum_{n=0}^{\infty} (-1)^n t^n \right] dt = \sum_{n=0}^{\infty} (-1)^n \frac{x^{n+1}}{n+1} = \sum_{n=1}^{\infty} \frac{(-1)^{n-1} x^n}{n}$ with $R=1$.

16. $\dfrac{x}{1-x} = x\left[\dfrac{1}{1-x}\right] = x\displaystyle\sum_{n=0}^{\infty} x^n = \sum_{n=0}^{\infty} x^{n+1} = \sum_{n=1}^{\infty} x^n$ with $R=1$.

18. $\tan^{-1}2x = 2\displaystyle\int_0^x \dfrac{dt}{1+4t^2} = 2\int_0^x \sum_{n=0}^{\infty}(-1)^n(4t^2)^n dt = 2\int_0^x \sum_{n=0}^{\infty}(-1)^n 4^n t^{2n} dt =$

   $2\displaystyle\sum_{n=0}^{\infty}\dfrac{(-1)^n 4^n x^{2n+1}}{2n+1} = \sum_{n=0}^{\infty}\dfrac{(-1)^n 2^{2n+1} x^{2n+1}}{2n+1}$ for $|4x^2|<1$ so $|x|<\dfrac{1}{2}$ and $R=\dfrac{1}{2}$.

20. $\dfrac{1}{x^4+16} = \dfrac{1}{16}\left[\dfrac{1}{1+(x/2)^4}\right] = \dfrac{1}{16}\displaystyle\sum_{n=0}^{\infty}(-1)^n\left[\dfrac{x}{2}\right]^{4n} = \sum_{n=0}^{\infty}\dfrac{(-1)^n x^{4n}}{2^{4n+4}}$ for $\left|\dfrac{x}{2}\right|<1 \iff$

   $|x|<2$ so $R=2$.

22. $\dfrac{1+x^2}{1-x^2} = 1 + \dfrac{2x^2}{1-x^2} = 1 + 2x^2\displaystyle\sum_{n=0}^{\infty}(x^2)^n = 1+\sum_{n=0}^{\infty}2x^{2n+2} = 1+\sum_{n=1}^{\infty}2x^{2n}$, $R=1$.

24. $\dfrac{2}{3x+4} = \dfrac{1}{2}\left[\dfrac{1}{1+3x/4}\right] = \dfrac{1}{2}\displaystyle\sum_{n=0}^{\infty}(-1)^n\left[\dfrac{3x}{4}\right]^n = \sum_{n=0}^{\infty}\dfrac{(-1)^n 3^n x^n}{2^{2n+1}}$, $\left|\dfrac{3x}{4}\right|<1$ so $R=\dfrac{4}{3}$.

26. $\sin 2x = \displaystyle\sum_{n=0}^{\infty}\dfrac{(-1)^n(2x)^{2n+1}}{(2n+1)!} = \sum_{n=0}^{\infty}\dfrac{(-1)^n 2^{2n+1} x^{2n+1}}{(2n+1)!}$, $R=\infty$.

28. $\cos(x^3) = \displaystyle\sum_{n=0}^{\infty}\dfrac{(-1)^n(x^3)^{2n}}{(2n)!} = \sum_{n=0}^{\infty}\dfrac{(-1)^n x^{6n}}{(2n)!}$, $R=\infty$.

30. $xe^{-x} = x\displaystyle\sum_{n=0}^{\infty}\dfrac{(-x)^n}{n!} = \sum_{n=0}^{\infty}\dfrac{(-1)^n x^{n+1}}{n!} = \sum_{n=1}^{\infty}\dfrac{(-1)^{n-1} x^n}{(n-1)!}$, $R=\infty$.

32. $\cos^2 x = \dfrac{1}{2}(1 + \cos2x) = \dfrac{1}{2}\left[1 + \displaystyle\sum_{n=0}^{\infty}\dfrac{(-1)^n(2x)^{2n}}{(2n)!}\right]$

   $= \dfrac{1}{2}\left[1 + 1 + \displaystyle\sum_{n=1}^{\infty}\dfrac{(-1)^n 2^{2n} x^{2n}}{(2n)!}\right] = 1 + \sum_{n=1}^{\infty}\dfrac{(-1)^n 2^{2n-1} x^{2n}}{(2n)!}$, $R=\infty$.

   [Another method: Use $\cos^2 x = 1-\sin^2 x$ and Exercise 31.]

34. $\dfrac{1 - \cos x}{x^2} = x^{-2}\left[1 - \displaystyle\sum_{n=0}^{\infty}\dfrac{(-1)^n x^{2n}}{(2n)!}\right] = x^{-2}\left[-\sum_{n=1}^{\infty}\dfrac{(-1)^n x^{2n}}{(2n)!}\right] =$

   $\displaystyle\sum_{n=1}^{\infty}\dfrac{(-1)^{n+1} x^{2n-2}}{(2n)!} = \sum_{n=0}^{\infty}\dfrac{(-1)^n x^{2n}}{(2n+2)!}$, since series $= \dfrac{1}{2}$ when $x=0$, $R=\infty$.

36. $f(x) = (1+2x)^{-1/2}$ $\qquad\qquad\qquad$ $f(0) = 1$

   $f'(x) = -\dfrac{1}{2}(1+2x)^{-3/2}(2)$ $\qquad\quad$ $f'(0) = -1$

   $f''(x) = \dfrac{3}{2}(1+2x)^{-5/2}(2)$ $\qquad\quad$ $f''(0) = 3$

   $f'''(x) = -3\cdot\dfrac{5}{2}(1+2x)^{-7/2}(2)$ $\qquad$ $f'''(0) = -3\cdot 5$

$f^{(n)}(0) = (-1)^n 1 \cdot 3 \cdot 5 \cdot 7 \cdots (2n-1)$, so

$$(1+2x)^{-1/2} = \sum_{n=0}^{\infty} \frac{f^{(n)}(0)}{n!} x^n = \sum_{n=0}^{\infty} \frac{(-1)^n 1 \cdot 3 \cdot 5 \cdots (2n-1)}{n!} x^n$$

$$\lim_{n \to \infty} \left| \frac{u_{n+1}}{u_n} \right| = \lim_{n \to \infty} \frac{2n+1}{n+1} |x| = 2|x| < 1 \text{ for convergence, so } R = 2.$$

[Another method: Use Exercise 35 and differentiate.]

38. $f(x) = (1+x)^{2/3}$ $\qquad\qquad$ $f(0) = 1$

$f'(x) = \frac{2}{3}(1+x)^{-1/3}$ $\qquad\qquad$ $f'(0) = \frac{2}{3}$

$f''(x) = -\frac{2}{3} \cdot \frac{1}{3}(1+x)^{-4/3}$ $\qquad\qquad$ $f''(0) = -2/3^2$

$f'''(x) = 2(4/3^3)(1+x)^{-7/3}$ $\qquad\qquad$ $f'''(0) = 2(4/3^3)$

$f^{(4)}(x) = -2 \cdot \frac{1 \cdot 4 \cdot 7}{3^4}(1+x)^{-10/3}$ $\qquad$ $f^{(4)}(0) = -2 \cdot \frac{1 \cdot 4 \cdot 7}{3^4}$

$f^{(n)}(0) = (-1)^{n-1} \cdot 2 \cdot \frac{1 \cdot 4 \cdot 7 \cdot 10 \cdots (3n-5)}{3^n}$, so

$$(1+x)^{2/3} = 1 + \frac{2}{3}x + 2 \sum_{n=2}^{\infty} \frac{(-1)^{n-1} 1 \cdot 4 \cdot 7 \cdots (3n-5) x^n}{3^n n!}$$

The Ratio Test gives R=1. [Or use Exercise 37 and integrate.]

40. $2^x = (e^{\ln 2})^x = e^{x \ln 2} = \sum_{n=0}^{\infty} \frac{(x \ln 2)^n}{n!} = \sum_{n=0}^{\infty} \frac{(\ln^n 2)x^n}{n!}$, $R=\infty$.

42. $\log_{10}(x+1) = \frac{\ln(x+1)}{\ln 10} = \sum_{n=1}^{\infty} \frac{(-1)^{n-1} x^n}{n(\ln 10)}$ [from Exercise 14], with R=1.

44. $\sin x = \sum_{n=0}^{\infty} \frac{(-1)^n x^{2n+1}}{(2n+1)!}$ so $\sin\left[\frac{\pi}{60}\right] = \frac{\pi}{60} - \frac{\left[\frac{\pi}{60}\right]^3}{3!} + \frac{\left[\frac{\pi}{60}\right]^5}{5!} - \cdots =$

$\frac{\pi}{60} - \frac{\pi^3}{1296000} + \frac{\pi^5}{93312000000} - \cdots$ But $\frac{\pi^5}{93312000000} < 0.00000001$, so

by Theorem 10.28 $\sin\left[\frac{\pi}{60}\right] \approx \frac{\pi}{60} - \frac{\pi^3}{1296000} \approx 0.05234.$

46. $\frac{\sin x}{x} = \frac{1}{x} \sum_{n=0}^{\infty} \frac{(-1)^n x^{2n+1}}{(2n+1)!} = \sum_{n=0}^{\infty} \frac{(-1)^n x^{2n}}{(2n+1)!}$ so $\int \frac{\sin x}{x} dx = \int \sum_{n=0}^{\infty} \frac{(-1)^n x^{2n}}{(2n+1)!} dx$

$= C + \sum_{n=0}^{\infty} \frac{(-1)^n x^{2n+1}}{(2n+1)(2n+1)!}$, with $R=\infty$.

48. $\int e^{x^3} dx = \int \sum_{n=0}^{\infty} \frac{x^{3n}}{n!} dx = C + \sum_{n=0}^{\infty} \frac{x^{3n+1}}{(3n+1)n!}$, with $R=\infty$.

50. $\dfrac{1}{1+x^5} = \sum\limits_{n=0}^{\infty} (-x^5)^n = \sum\limits_{n=0}^{\infty} (-1)^n x^{5n} \Rightarrow \dfrac{x}{1+x^5} = \sum\limits_{n=0}^{\infty} (-1)^n x^{5n+1} \Rightarrow \displaystyle\int \dfrac{x}{1+x^5}dx$

$= C + \sum\limits_{n=0}^{\infty} \dfrac{(-1)^n x^{5n+2}}{5n+2}$, with $R=1$.

52. $\cos(x^2) = \sum\limits_{n=0}^{\infty} \dfrac{(-1)^n (x^2)^{2n}}{(2n)!}$ so $\displaystyle\int_0^{0.5} \cos(x^2)dx = \int_0^{0.5} \sum\limits_{n=0}^{\infty} \dfrac{(-1)^n x^{4n}}{(2n)!}dx =$

$\sum\limits_{n=0}^{\infty} \dfrac{(-1)^n x^{4n+1}}{(4n+1)(2n)!} \Big]_0^{0.5} = 0.5 - \dfrac{(0.5)^5}{5 \cdot 2!} + \dfrac{(0.5)^9}{9 \cdot 4!} - \ldots$, but $\dfrac{(0.5)^9}{9 \cdot 4!} \approx$

0.000009, so $\displaystyle\int_0^{0.5} \cos(x^2)dx \approx 0.5 - \dfrac{(0.5)^5}{5 \cdot 2!} \approx 0.497$.

54. $f(x) = (1+x)^{-1/2}$ $\qquad\qquad f(0) = 1$

$f'(x) = -\dfrac{1}{2}(1+x)^{-3/2}$ $\qquad f'(0) = -\dfrac{1}{2}$

$f''(x) = \dfrac{3}{4}(1+x)^{-5/2}$ $\qquad f''(0) = \dfrac{3}{4}$

$f^{(3)}(x) = -\dfrac{15}{8}(1+x)^{-7/2}$ $\qquad f^{(3)}(0) = -\dfrac{15}{8}$

$\dfrac{1}{\sqrt{1+x}} = 1 - \dfrac{x}{2} + \dfrac{3}{4}\Big[\dfrac{x^2}{2!}\Big] - \dfrac{15}{8}\Big[\dfrac{x^3}{3!}\Big] + \ldots \Rightarrow \dfrac{1}{\sqrt{1+x^3}} = 1 - \dfrac{1}{2}x^3 + \dfrac{3}{8}x^6 - \dfrac{5}{16}x^9 \ldots$

$\Rightarrow \displaystyle\int_0^{0.1} \dfrac{dx}{\sqrt{1+x^3}} = x - \dfrac{x^4}{8} + \dfrac{3x^7}{56} - \dfrac{x^{10}}{32} \ldots \Big]_0^{0.1} \approx (0.1) - \dfrac{(0.1)^4}{8}$ since

$\dfrac{3(0.1)^7}{56} \approx 0.0000000054 < 10^{-8}$ so $\displaystyle\int_0^{0.1} \dfrac{dx}{\sqrt{1+x^3}} \approx 0.09998750$.

56. $\displaystyle\int_0^1 \cos(x^3)dx = \int_0^1 [1 - \dfrac{x^6}{2!} + \dfrac{x^{12}}{4!} - \dfrac{x^{18}}{6!} + \dfrac{x^{24}}{8!} - \ldots]dx =$

$\Big[x - \dfrac{x^7}{7 \cdot 2!} + \dfrac{x^{13}}{13 \cdot 4!} - \dfrac{x^{19}}{19 \cdot 6!} + \dfrac{x^{24}}{24 \cdot 8!} - \ldots\Big]_0^1 \approx 1 - \dfrac{1}{14} + \dfrac{1}{312} - \dfrac{1}{13680}$

since $\dfrac{1}{24 \cdot 8!} \approx 0.000001$, so $\displaystyle\int_0^1 \cos(x^3)dx \approx 0.9317$.

58. (a) $J_1(x) = \sum\limits_{n=0}^{\infty} \dfrac{(-1)^n x^{2n+1}}{n!(n+1)!2^{2n+1}}$ $\qquad J_1'(x) = \sum\limits_{n=0}^{\infty} \dfrac{(-1)^n (2n+1)x^{2n}}{n!(n+1)!2^{2n+1}}$

$J_1''(x) = \sum\limits_{n=1}^{\infty} \dfrac{(-1)^n (2n+1)(2n)x^{2n-1}}{n!(n+1)!2^{2n+1}}$

$x^2 J_1''(x) + x J_1'(x) + (x^2-1)J_1(x)$

$$= \sum_{n=1}^{\infty} \frac{(-1)^n (2n+1)(2n)x^{2n+1}}{n!(n+1)!2^{2n+1}} + \sum_{n=0}^{\infty} \frac{(-1)^n (2n+1)x^{2n+1}}{n!(n+1)!2^{2n+1}} + \sum_{n=0}^{\infty} \frac{(-1)^n x^{2n+3}}{n!(n+1)!2^{2n+1}}$$

$$- \sum_{n=0}^{\infty} \frac{(-1)^n x^{2n+1}}{n!(n+1)!2^{2n+1}}$$

$$= \sum_{n=1}^{\infty} \frac{(-1)^n (2n+1)(2n)x^{2n+1}}{n!(n+1)!2^{2n+1}} + \sum_{n=0}^{\infty} \frac{(-1)^n (2n+1)x^{2n+1}}{n!(n+1)!2^{2n+1}} - \sum_{n=1}^{\infty} \frac{(-1)^n x^{2n+1}}{(n-1)!n!2^{2n-1}}$$

$$- \sum_{n=0}^{\infty} \frac{(-1)^n x^{2n+1}}{n!(n+1)!2^{2n+1}}$$

$$= \frac{x}{2} - \frac{x}{2} + \sum_{n=1}^{\infty} (-1)^n \left[\frac{(2n+1)(2n) + (2n+1) - (n)(n+1)2^2 - 1}{n!(n+1)!2^{2n+1}} \right] x^{2n+1} = 0$$

(b) $J_0'(x) = \sum_{n=1}^{\infty} \frac{(-1)^n (2n)x^{2n-1}}{2^{2n}(n!)^2} = \sum_{n=0}^{\infty} \frac{(-1)^{n+1} 2(n+1)x^{2n+1}}{2^{2n+2}((n+1)!)^2}$

$$= - \sum_{n=0}^{\infty} \frac{(-1)^n x^{2n+1}}{2^{2n+1}(n+1)!n!} = -J_1(x)$$

60. $\frac{|\sin nx|}{n^2} \leq \frac{1}{n^2}$ so $\sum_{n=1}^{\infty} \frac{\sin nx}{n^2}$ converges by the Comparison Test.

$\frac{d}{dx}\left[\frac{\sin nx}{n^2} \right] = \frac{\cos nx}{n}$, so when $x = 2k\pi$ (k an integer) $\sum_{n=1}^{\infty} f_n'(x)$

$= \sum_{n=1}^{\infty} \frac{\cos 2kn\pi}{n} = \sum_{n=1}^{\infty} \frac{1}{n}$ which diverges (harmonic series).

$f_n''(x) = -\sin nx$ so $\sum_{n=1}^{\infty} f_n''(x) = - \sum_{n=1}^{\infty} \sin nx$ which will converge only

if $\sin nx = 0$, or $x = k\pi$ (k an integer).

Section 10.10

Exercises 10.10

2. $(1+x)^{-3} = \sum_{n=0}^{\infty} \begin{bmatrix} -3 \\ n \end{bmatrix} x^n = 1 + \sum_{n=1}^{\infty} \frac{(-1)^n 3 \cdot 4 \cdot 5 \cdots (n+2)x^n}{n!}$ with R=1.

4. $(1+x^2)^{1/3} = \displaystyle\sum_{n=0}^{\infty} \begin{bmatrix} 1/3 \\ n \end{bmatrix} x^{2n} = 1 + \dfrac{x^2}{3} + \dfrac{\begin{bmatrix}\frac{1}{3}\end{bmatrix}\begin{bmatrix}-\frac{2}{3}\end{bmatrix}}{2!} x^4 + \dfrac{\begin{bmatrix}\frac{1}{3}\end{bmatrix}\begin{bmatrix}-\frac{2}{3}\end{bmatrix}\begin{bmatrix}-\frac{5}{3}\end{bmatrix}}{3!} x^6 + \cdots$

$= 1 + \dfrac{x^2}{3} + \displaystyle\sum_{n=2}^{\infty} \dfrac{(-1)^{n-1} 2 \cdot 5 \cdot 8 \cdots (3n-4) x^{2n}}{3^n \, n!}$ with R=1.

6. $(2+x)^{-1/2} = \dfrac{1}{\sqrt{2}}\left[1 + \dfrac{x}{2}\right]^{-1/2} = \dfrac{\sqrt{2}}{2} \displaystyle\sum_{n=0}^{\infty} \begin{bmatrix} -1/2 \\ n \end{bmatrix} \begin{bmatrix} \dfrac{x}{2} \end{bmatrix}^n$

$= \dfrac{\sqrt{2}}{2}\left[1 + \begin{bmatrix}-\frac{1}{2}\end{bmatrix}\begin{bmatrix}\frac{x}{2}\end{bmatrix} + \dfrac{\begin{bmatrix}-\frac{1}{2}\end{bmatrix}\begin{bmatrix}-\frac{3}{2}\end{bmatrix}}{2!}\begin{bmatrix}\frac{x}{2}\end{bmatrix}^2 + \cdots\right]$

$= \dfrac{\sqrt{2}}{2}\left[1 + \displaystyle\sum_{n=1}^{\infty} \dfrac{(-1)^n 1 \cdot 3 \cdot 5 \cdots (2n-1) x^n}{2^{2n} \, n!}\right]$ with $\left|\dfrac{x}{2}\right| < 1$ so $|x| < 2$ and R=2.

8. $(4+x)^{3/2} = 8\left[1 + \dfrac{x}{4}\right]^{3/2} = 8 \displaystyle\sum_{n=0}^{\infty} \begin{bmatrix} 3/2 \\ n \end{bmatrix} \begin{bmatrix} \dfrac{x}{4} \end{bmatrix}^n$

$= 8\left[1 + \begin{bmatrix}\frac{3}{2}\end{bmatrix}\begin{bmatrix}\frac{x}{4}\end{bmatrix} + \dfrac{\begin{bmatrix}\frac{3}{2}\end{bmatrix}\begin{bmatrix}\frac{1}{2}\end{bmatrix}}{2!}\begin{bmatrix}\frac{x}{4}\end{bmatrix}^2 + \dfrac{\begin{bmatrix}\frac{3}{2}\end{bmatrix}\begin{bmatrix}\frac{1}{2}\end{bmatrix}\begin{bmatrix}-\frac{1}{2}\end{bmatrix}}{3!}\begin{bmatrix}\frac{x}{4}\end{bmatrix}^3 + \cdots\right]$

$= 8 + 3x + \displaystyle\sum_{n=2}^{\infty} \dfrac{(3)(1)(-1)\cdots(5-2n) x^n}{8^{n-1} \, n!}$ with $\left|\dfrac{x}{4}\right| < 1$ so $|x| < 4$ and R=4.

10. $(1+(-x^3))^{-1/2} = \displaystyle\sum_{n=0}^{\infty} \begin{bmatrix} -1/2 \\ n \end{bmatrix} (-x^3)^n = 1 + \begin{bmatrix}-\frac{1}{2}\end{bmatrix}(-x^3) + \dfrac{\begin{bmatrix}-\frac{1}{2}\end{bmatrix}\begin{bmatrix}-\frac{3}{2}\end{bmatrix}}{2!}(-x^3)^2 + \cdots$

$= 1 + \displaystyle\sum_{n=1}^{\infty} \dfrac{1 \cdot 3 \cdot 5 \cdots (2n-1) x^{3n}}{2^n \, n!}$ so $\dfrac{x^2}{\sqrt{1-x^3}} = x^2 + \displaystyle\sum_{n=1}^{\infty} \dfrac{1 \cdot 3 \cdot 5 \cdots (2n-1) x^{3n+2}}{2^n \, n!}$

with R=1.

12. $\sqrt[5]{x-1} = -(1+(-x))^{1/5} = -\displaystyle\sum_{n=0}^{\infty} \begin{bmatrix} 1/5 \\ n \end{bmatrix} (-x)^n$

$= -\left[1 + \dfrac{1}{5}(-x) + \dfrac{\begin{bmatrix}\frac{1}{5}\end{bmatrix}\begin{bmatrix}-\frac{4}{5}\end{bmatrix}}{2!}(-x)^2 + \dfrac{\begin{bmatrix}\frac{1}{5}\end{bmatrix}\begin{bmatrix}-\frac{4}{5}\end{bmatrix}\begin{bmatrix}-\frac{9}{5}\end{bmatrix}}{3!}(-x)^3 + \cdots\right]$

$= -1 + \dfrac{x}{5} + \displaystyle\sum_{n=2}^{\infty} \dfrac{4 \cdot 9 \cdots (5n-6) x^n}{5^n \, n!}$ with R=1.

14. (a) $(1+x^2)^{-1/2} = \displaystyle\sum_{n=0}^{\infty} \begin{bmatrix} -1/2 \\ n \end{bmatrix} x^{2n} = 1 + \displaystyle\sum_{n=1}^{\infty} \dfrac{(-1)^n 1 \cdot 3 \cdot 5 \cdots (2n-1) x^{2n}}{2^n \, n!}$

(b) $\sinh^{-1}x = \int \dfrac{dx}{\sqrt{1+x^2}} = C + x + \displaystyle\sum_{n=1}^{\infty} \dfrac{(-1)^n 1 \cdot 3 \cdot 5 \cdots (2n-1)x^{2n+1}}{2^n\, n!\, (2n+1)}$, but $C=0$

since $\sinh^{-1}0 = 0$ so $\sinh^{-1}x = x + \displaystyle\sum_{n=1}^{\infty} \dfrac{(-1)^n 1 \cdot 3 \cdot 5 \cdots (2n-1)x^{2n+1}}{2^n\, n!\, (2n+1)}$, $R=1$.

16. (a) $(8+x)^{1/3} = 2\left[1 + \dfrac{x}{8}\right]^{1/3} = 2 \displaystyle\sum_{n=0}^{\infty} \begin{bmatrix} 1/3 \\ n \end{bmatrix} \left[\dfrac{x}{8}\right]^n$

$= 2\left[1 + \dfrac{1}{3}\left[\dfrac{x}{8}\right] + \dfrac{\left[\dfrac{1}{3}\right]\left[-\dfrac{2}{3}\right]}{2!}\left[\dfrac{x}{8}\right]^2 + \dfrac{\left[\dfrac{1}{3}\right]\left[-\dfrac{2}{3}\right]\left[-\dfrac{5}{3}\right]}{3!}\left[\dfrac{x}{8}\right]^3 + \cdots\right]$

$= 2\left[1 + \dfrac{x}{24} + \displaystyle\sum_{n=2}^{\infty} \dfrac{(-1)^{n-1} 2 \cdot 5 \cdots (3n-4)x^n}{24^n\, n!}\right]$

(b) $(8 + 0.2)^{1/3} = 2\left[1 + \dfrac{0.2}{24} - \dfrac{(0.2)^2}{24^2} + \dfrac{2 \cdot 5(0.2)^3}{24^3 3!} - \cdots\right]$

$\approx 2\left[1 + \dfrac{0.2}{24} - \dfrac{(0.2)^2}{24^2}\right]$ since $\dfrac{2 \cdot 5(0.2)^3}{24^3 3!} \approx 0.000001$, so $\sqrt[3]{8.2} \approx 2.0165$.

18. (a) $(1+(-x))^{-3} = \displaystyle\sum_{n=0}^{\infty} \begin{bmatrix} -3 \\ n \end{bmatrix}(-x)^n = 1 + (-3)(-x) + \dfrac{(-3)(-4)}{2!}x^2 +$

$\dfrac{(-3)(-4)(-5)(-x)^3}{3!} + \cdots = \displaystyle\sum_{n=0}^{\infty} \dfrac{3 \cdot 4 \cdot 5 \cdots (n+2)}{n!}x^n = \displaystyle\sum_{n=0}^{\infty} \dfrac{(n+1)(n+2)}{2}x^n \Rightarrow$

$(x+x^2)(1+(-x))^{-3} = \displaystyle\sum_{n=0}^{\infty} \dfrac{(n+1)(n+2)}{2}x^{n+1} + \displaystyle\sum_{n=0}^{\infty} \dfrac{(n+1)(n+2)}{2}x^{n+2}$

$= x + \displaystyle\sum_{n=2}^{\infty} \left[\dfrac{n(n+1)}{2} + \dfrac{(n-1)n}{2}\right]x^n = x + \displaystyle\sum_{n=2}^{\infty} n^2 x^n = \displaystyle\sum_{n=1}^{\infty} n^2 x^n$, $-1 < x < 1$.

(b) Setting $x = \dfrac{1}{2}$ in the last series above gives the required

series, so $\displaystyle\sum_{n=1}^{\infty} \dfrac{n^2}{2^n} = \dfrac{1/2 + (1/2)^2}{(1 - 1/2)^3} = 6$.

20. (a) $(1+x^3)^{-1/2} = \displaystyle\sum_{n=0}^{\infty} \begin{bmatrix} -1/2 \\ n \end{bmatrix} x^{3n} = 1 + \displaystyle\sum_{n=1}^{\infty} \dfrac{(-1)^n 1 \cdot 3 \cdot 5 \cdots (2n-1)x^{3n}}{2^n\, n!}$

(b) The coefficient of x^9 in the above series will be $\dfrac{f^{(9)}(0)}{9!}$, so

$\dfrac{f^{(9)}(0)}{9!} = \dfrac{(-1)^3 1 \cdot 3 \cdot 5}{2^3\, 3!} \Rightarrow f^{(9)}(0) = -\dfrac{9! \cdot 5}{8 \cdot 2} = -113{,}400$.

Exercises 10.11

2. $f(x) = x^3 - 1$ $f(1) = 0$

    $f'(x) = 3x^2$ $f'(1) = 3$

    $f''(x) = 6x$ $f''(1) = 6$

    $f^{(3)}(x) = 6$ $f^{(3)}(1) = 6$

$$T_3(x) = \sum_{n=0}^{3} \frac{f^{(n)}(1)}{n!}(x-1)^n = 0 + 3(x-1) + \frac{6(x-1)^2}{2!} + \frac{6(x-1)^3}{3!}$$

$$= 3(x-1) + 3(x-1)^2 + (x-1)^3$$

4. $f(x) = \cos x$ $f(\frac{2\pi}{3}) = -\frac{1}{2}$

    $f'(x) = -\sin x$ $f'(\frac{2\pi}{3}) = -\frac{\sqrt{3}}{2}$

    $f''(x) = -\cos x$ $f''(\frac{2\pi}{3}) = \frac{1}{2}$

    $f^{(3)}(x) = \sin x$ $f^{(3)}(\frac{2\pi}{3}) = \frac{\sqrt{3}}{2}$

    $f^{(4)}(x) = \cos x$ $f^{(4)}(\frac{2\pi}{3}) = -\frac{1}{2}$

$$T_4(x) = \sum_{n=0}^{4} \frac{f^{(n)}(2\pi/3)}{n!}(x-2\pi/3)^n$$

$$= -\frac{1}{2} - \frac{\sqrt{3}}{2}(x-\frac{2\pi}{3}) + \frac{1}{4}(x-\frac{2\pi}{3})^2 + \frac{\sqrt{3}}{12}(x-\frac{2\pi}{3})^3 - \frac{1}{48}(x-\frac{2\pi}{3})^4$$

6. $f(x) = \tan x$ $f(\frac{\pi}{4}) = 1$

    $f'(x) = \sec^2 x$ $f'(\frac{\pi}{4}) = 2$

    $f''(x) = 2\sec^2 x \tan x$ $f''(\frac{\pi}{4}) = 4$

    $f^{(3)}(x) = 4\sec^2 x \tan^2 x + 2\sec^4 x$ $f^{(3)}(\frac{\pi}{4}) = 16$

    $f^{(4)}(x) = 8\sec^2 x \tan^3 x + 16\sec^4 x \tan x$ $f^{(4)}(\frac{\pi}{4}) = 80$

$$T_4(x) = \sum_{n=0}^{4} \frac{f^{(n)}(\pi/4)}{n!}(x-\pi/4)^n$$

$$= 1 + 2(x-\frac{\pi}{4}) + 2(x-\frac{\pi}{4})^2 + \frac{8}{3}(x-\frac{\pi}{4})^3 + \frac{10}{3}(x-\frac{\pi}{4})^4$$

8. $f(x) = e^x \cos 2x$ $f(0) = 1$

    $f'(x) = e^x(\cos 2x - 2\sin 2x)$ $f'(0) = 1$

    $f''(x) = e^x(-3\cos 2x - 4\sin 2x)$ $f''(0) = -3$

    $f^{(3)}(x) = e^x(-11\cos 2x + 2\sin 2x)$ $f^{(3)}(0) = -11$

$$T_3(x) = \sum_{n=0}^{3} \frac{f^{(n)}(0)}{n!} x^n = 1 + x - \frac{3}{2}x^2 - \frac{11}{6}x^3$$

10. $f(x) = x^{-1/3}$ $\qquad\qquad$ $f(8) = \frac{1}{2}$

$f'(x) = -\frac{1}{3}x^{-4/3}$ $\qquad\qquad$ $f'(8) = -\frac{1}{48}$

$f''(x) = \frac{4}{9}x^{-7/3}$ $\qquad\qquad$ $f''(8) = \frac{1}{288}$

$f^{(3)}(x) = -\frac{28}{27}x^{-10/3}$ $\qquad\qquad$ $f^{(3)}(8) = -\frac{7}{6912}$

$$T_3(x) = \sum_{n=0}^{3} \frac{f^{(n)}(8)}{n!}(x-8)^n = \frac{1}{2} - \frac{1}{48}(x-8) + \frac{1}{576}(x-8)^2 - \frac{7}{41472}(x-8)^3$$

12. $f(x) = \sec x$ $\qquad\qquad$ $f(\frac{\pi}{3}) = 2$

$f'(x) = \sec x \tan x$ $\qquad\qquad$ $f'(\frac{\pi}{3}) = 2\sqrt{3}$

$f''(x) = \sec x \tan^2 x + \sec^3 x$ $\qquad\qquad$ $f''(\frac{\pi}{3}) = 14$

$f^{(3)}(x) = \sec x \tan^3 x + 5\sec^3 x \tan x$ $\qquad$ $f^{(3)}(\frac{\pi}{3}) = 46\sqrt{3}$

$$T_3(x) = \sum_{n=0}^{3} \frac{f^{(n)}(\pi/3)}{n!}(x-\frac{\pi}{3})^n = 2 + 2\sqrt{3}(x-\frac{\pi}{3}) + 7(x-\frac{\pi}{3})^2 + \frac{23\sqrt{3}}{3}(x-\frac{\pi}{3})^3$$

14. $f(x) = x^{-1}$ $\qquad\qquad$ $f(1) = 1$

$f'(x) = -x^{-2}$ $\qquad\qquad$ $f'(1) = -1$

$f''(x) = 2x^{-3}$ $\qquad\qquad$ $f''(1) = 2$

$f^{(3)}(x) = -6x^{-4}$ $\qquad\qquad$ $f^{(3)}(1) = -6$

$T_1(x) = 1 - (x-1) = 2 - x$

$T_2(x) = 1-(x-1)+(x-1)^2 = x^2-3x+3$

$T_3(x) = 1-(x-1)+(x-1)^2-(x-1)^3$

$\qquad = -x^3+4x^2-6x+4$

16. (a) Using the information of Exercise 14, and $f^{(4)}(x) = 24x^{-5}$, we

see that $\frac{1}{x} = 1 - (x-1) + (x-1)^2 - (x-1)^3 + R_3(x)$ with $R_3(x) =$

$\frac{24z^{-5}}{4!}(x-1)^4 = \frac{(x-1)^4}{z^5}$ where z is between 1 and x.

(b) $0.8 \leq x \leq 1.2 \Rightarrow |x-1| \leq 0.2$ and $z^5 > (0.8)^5 \Rightarrow |R_3(x)| < \dfrac{(0.2)^4}{(0.8)^5}$

< 0.005.

18. $f(x) = \cos x$ $\qquad\qquad f(\frac{\pi}{3}) = \frac{1}{2}$

$f'(x) = -\sin x$ $\qquad\qquad f'(\frac{\pi}{3}) = -\frac{\sqrt{3}}{2}$

$f''(x) = -\cos x$ $\qquad\qquad f''(\frac{\pi}{3}) = -\frac{1}{2}$

$f^{(3)}(x) = \sin x$ $\qquad\qquad f^{(3)}(\frac{\pi}{3}) = \frac{\sqrt{3}}{2}$

$f^{(4)}(x) = \cos x$ $\qquad\qquad f^{(4)}(\frac{\pi}{3}) = \frac{1}{2}$

$f^{(5)}(x) = -\sin x$

(a) $\cos x = \frac{1}{2} - \frac{\sqrt{3}}{2}(x-\frac{\pi}{3}) - \frac{1}{4}(x-\frac{\pi}{3})^2 + \frac{\sqrt{3}}{12}(x-\frac{\pi}{3})^3 + \frac{1}{48}(x-\frac{\pi}{3})^4 + R_4(x)$

where $R_4(x) = \dfrac{-\sin z}{5!}(x-\frac{\pi}{3})^5$ and z is between x and $\frac{\pi}{3}$.

(b) $0 \leq x \leq \frac{2\pi}{3} \Rightarrow |x-\frac{\pi}{3}| < \frac{\pi}{3} \Rightarrow |R_4(x)| < \dfrac{1 \cdot (\pi/3)^5}{5!} \approx 0.0105$

20. $f(x) = (1+x^2)^{1/3}$ $\qquad\qquad f(0) = 1$

$f'(x) = \frac{2x}{3}(1+x^2)^{-2/3}$ $\qquad\qquad f'(0) = 0$

$f''(x) = \frac{2}{3}(1-x^2/3)(1+x^2)^{-5/3}$ $\quad f''(0) = \frac{2}{3}$

$f^{(3)}(x) = \dfrac{8x^3-72x}{27(1+x^2)^{8/3}}$

(a) $\sqrt[3]{1+x^2} = 1 + \dfrac{x^2}{3} + R_2(x)$ where $R_2(x) = \dfrac{8z^3-72z}{3! \, 27(1+z^2)^{8/3}} x^3$ with z

between 0 and x. (b) $1+z^2 > 1$ and $|z| < |x| \leq 0.5$, so $|R_2(x)| <$

$\dfrac{8(0.5)^3+72(0.5)}{3! \; 27 \cdot 1}(0.5)^3 \approx 0.0285$ (using the Triangle Inequality).

[Or: $|R_2(x)| = \dfrac{|8z(z^2-9)|}{3! \, 27(1+z^2)^{8/3}} |x|^3 \leq \dfrac{8(0.5)(9)}{6 \cdot 27 \cdot 1} = \dfrac{1}{36} < 0.028$]

22. $f(x) = \ln \cos x$ $\qquad\qquad f(0) = 0$

$f'(x) = -\tan x$ $\qquad\qquad f'(0) = 0$

$f''(x) = -\sec^2 x$ $\qquad\qquad f''(0) = -1$

$f^{(3)}(x) = -2 \sec^2 x \tan x$ $\qquad f^{(3)}(0) = 0$

$f^{(4)}(x) = -4 \sec^2 x \tan^2 x - 2 \sec^4 x$

(a) $\ln \cos x = \dfrac{-x^2}{2} + R_3(x)$ where $R_3(x) =$

$\frac{1}{4!}(-4 \sec^2 z \tan^2 z - 2 \sec^4 z)x^4$ with z between 0 and x.

(b) $|R_3(x)| < \frac{1}{12}\left[2 \sec^2\left[\frac{\pi}{4}\right] \tan^2\left[\frac{\pi}{4}\right] + \sec^4\left[\frac{\pi}{4}\right]\right]\left[\frac{\pi}{4}\right]^4$ (since both sec

and tan are increasing functions on $[0,\frac{\pi}{4}]$), so $|R_3(x)| < 0.2537$.

24. (a) Clearly $f^{(2n)}(0) = 1$ and $f^{(2n+1)}(0) = 0$. So cosh x =

$1 + \frac{x^2}{2} + \frac{x^4}{24} + R_5(x)$ where $R_5(x) = \frac{f^{(6)}(z)}{6!}x^6$ with $0 < |z| < |x|$.

(b) $|R_5(x)| = \left|\frac{\cosh z}{6!} x^6\right| < \frac{\cosh(1)}{6!} \approx 0.00214$

26. $f(x) = \ln x$ $\qquad\qquad\qquad\qquad$ $f(4) = \ln 4$

$f'(x) = x^{-1}$ $\qquad\qquad\qquad\qquad$ $f'(4) = \frac{1}{4}$

$f''(x) = -x^{-2}$ $\qquad\qquad\qquad\qquad$ $f''(4) = \frac{-1}{16}$

$f^{(3)}(x) = 2x^{-3}$ $\qquad\qquad\qquad\qquad$ $f^{(3)}(4) = \frac{1}{32}$

$f^{(4)}(x) = -6x^{-4}$

(a) $\ln x = \ln 4 + \frac{1}{4}(x-4) - \frac{1}{32}(x-4)^2 + \frac{1}{192}(x-4)^3 + R_3(x)$ where

$R_3(x) = \frac{-6z^{-4}}{4!}(x-4)^4$ with z between x and 4.

(b) $3 \le x \le 5 \Rightarrow |x-4| \le 1$ and $z > 3 \Rightarrow 1/z^4 < 1/3^4$, so

$|R_3(x)| < \frac{6}{4!\,3^4} = \frac{1}{324} \approx 0.0031$

28. $e^x = 1 + x + \frac{x^2}{2!} + \frac{x^3}{3!} + \ldots + \frac{x^n}{n!} + R_n(x)$ where $R_n(x) = \frac{e^z}{(n+1)!}x^{n+1}$

where z is between 0 and x. $|R_5(\frac{1}{3})| < \frac{2}{6!}\left[\frac{1}{3}\right]^6$ since $e^z < e^{1/3} <$

$8^{1/3} = 2$, so $|R_5(\frac{1}{3})| < \frac{1}{262440} < 0.00005$ so $\sqrt[3]{e} \approx \sum_{n=0}^{5} \frac{(1/3)^n}{n!} \approx 1.3956$.

30. $f(x) = \sqrt{x}$, $f'(x) = \frac{1}{2}x^{-1/2}$, $f''(x) = -\frac{1}{4}x^{-3/2}$, $f'''(x) = \frac{3}{8}x^{-5/2}$ $\Rightarrow$ $\sqrt{x}$

$= 2 + \frac{x-4}{4} - \frac{(x-4)^2}{64} + R_2(x)$, where $R_2(x) = \frac{f^{(3)}(z)}{3!}(x-4)^3$ and z lies

between 4 and x. $|R_2(x)| = \left|\frac{3(x-4)^3}{3!\,8z^{5/2}}\right|$ so $z > 4 \Rightarrow |R_2(4.08)| <$

$\frac{(0.08)^3}{16 \cdot 4^{5/2}} = 0.000001$ and $\sqrt{4.08} \approx 2 + \frac{0.08}{4} - \frac{(0.08)^2}{64} = 2.0199$.

32. It is far easier to use the Maclaurin series (Example 10.9.9):
    $\arctan x = x - \dfrac{x^3}{3} + \dfrac{x^5}{5} - \dfrac{x^7}{7} + \cdots$. With $x = 0.5$ this is an
    alternating series and $\dfrac{(0.5)^9}{9} < 0.00022$, so
    $\arctan(0.5) \approx (0.5) - \dfrac{(0.5)^3}{3} + \dfrac{(0.5)^5}{5} - \dfrac{(0.5)^7}{7} \approx 0.4635$.

34. $\cos x = \displaystyle\sum_{n=0}^{\infty} \dfrac{(-1)^n x^{2n}}{(2n)!}$ so $\cos(0.4) = 1 - \dfrac{(0.4)^2}{2} + \dfrac{(0.4)^4}{24} + R_4(0.4)$
    where $R_4(x) = \dfrac{\cos z}{5!}x^5$ with z between 0 and x. $\left| R_4(0.4) \right| < \dfrac{1 \cdot (0.4)^5}{5!}$
    $\approx 0.000085 < 0.0001$, so $\cos(0.4) \approx 1 - \dfrac{(0.4)^2}{2} + \dfrac{(0.4)^4}{24} \approx 0.9211$.

36. $\sin x = x - \dfrac{x^3}{3!} + \dfrac{x^5}{5!} + R_5(x)$ where $R_5(x) = \dfrac{\cos z}{6!}x^6$ so $\left| R_5(\dfrac{\pi}{12}) \right| <$
    $\dfrac{(\pi/12)^6}{6!} \approx 0.0000004$ and $\sin(\pi/12) \approx \dfrac{\pi}{12} - \dfrac{(\pi/12)^3}{6} + \dfrac{(\pi/12)^5}{120} \approx$
    0.25882.

38. Using our answer to Exercise 18, above, we see that (since 69°
    corresponds to $\dfrac{\pi}{3} + \dfrac{\pi}{20}$ in radians) $\cos 69^{\circ} = \dfrac{1}{2} - \dfrac{\sqrt{3}}{2}\left[\dfrac{\pi}{20}\right] - \dfrac{1}{4}\left[\dfrac{\pi}{20}\right]^2 +$
    $\dfrac{\sqrt{3}}{12}\left[\dfrac{\pi}{20}\right]^3 + \dfrac{1}{48}\left[\dfrac{\pi}{20}\right]^4 + R_4\left[\dfrac{23\pi}{60}\right]$ where $R_4\left[\dfrac{23\pi}{60}\right] = \dfrac{-\sin z}{5!}\left[\dfrac{\pi}{20}\right]^5$ and z is
    between $\dfrac{23\pi}{60}$ and $\dfrac{\pi}{3}$. So $\left| R_4\left[\dfrac{23\pi}{60}\right] \right| < \dfrac{1}{5!}\left[\dfrac{\pi}{20}\right]^5 \approx 0.0000008 < 0.000005$,
    and $\cos 69^{\circ} \approx \dfrac{1}{2} - \dfrac{\sqrt{3}}{2}\left[\dfrac{\pi}{20}\right] - \dfrac{1}{4}\left[\dfrac{\pi}{20}\right]^2 + \dfrac{\sqrt{3}}{12}\left[\dfrac{\pi}{20}\right]^3 + \dfrac{1}{48}\left[\dfrac{\pi}{20}\right]^4 \approx 0.35837$.

40. $R_5(x) = \dfrac{-\cos z}{6!}x^6$ and we want $\left| R_5(x) \right| = \left| \dfrac{-\cos z}{6!}x^6 \right| < 0.005$. Since
    $\left| \dfrac{-\cos z}{6!}x^6 \right| \leq \dfrac{x^6}{6!}$ this will be true if $\dfrac{x^6}{6!} < .005 \Longleftrightarrow x^6 < 3.6 \Rightarrow$
    $\left| x \right| < 1.238$.

42. $R_n(x) = \dfrac{f^{(n+1)}(z)}{(n+1)!}(x - \dfrac{\pi}{4})^{n+1}$ with z between $\dfrac{\pi}{4}$ and x. But since
    $f^{(n+1)}(z)$ is $\pm\sin z$ or $\pm\cos z$, $\left| f^{(n+1)}(z) \right| \leq 1$, so $\left| R_n(x) \right| \leq$
    $\dfrac{\left| x - \pi/4 \right|^{n+1}}{(n+1)!} \to 0$ as $n \to \infty$ by 10.57, so $\lim\limits_{n \to \infty} \left| R_n(x) \right| = 0$ and the given
    series must converge to $\sin x$ by Theorem 10.56.

44. Since the same estimate for $\left| R_n(x) \right|$ is obtained in this case as in
    the case for $\sinh x$ (Exercise 43), the same argument will apply.

46. $T_n(x) = f(c) + \dfrac{f'(c)}{1!}(x-c) + \dfrac{f''(c)}{2!}(x-c)^2 + \ldots + \dfrac{f^{(n)}(c)}{n!}(x-c)^n$. Let

$0 \leq m \leq n$. Then $T_n^{(m)}(x) = m!\dfrac{f^{(m)}(c)}{m!}(x-c)^0 +$

$(m+1)(m)\cdots(2)\dfrac{f^{(m+1)}(c)}{(m+1)!}(x-c)^1 + \ldots +$

$n(n-1)\cdots(n-m+1)\dfrac{f^{(n)}(z)}{(n)!}(x-c)^{n-m}$ so $T_n^{(m)}(c) = \dfrac{m!f^{(m)}(c)}{m!} = f^{(m)}(c)$.

48. We must show that f equals its Taylor series expansion on I; i.e.
we must show that $\lim\limits_{n \to \infty} |R_n(x)| = 0$. For $x \in I$, $|R_n(x)| =$

$\left|\dfrac{f^{(n+1)}(z)}{(n+1)!}(x-c)^{n+1}\right| \leq \dfrac{M \cdot R^{n+1}}{(n+1)!} \to 0$ as $n \to \infty$ by 10.57.

Chapter 10 Review

Review Exercises for Chapter 10

2. $\lim\limits_{n \to \infty} (5-(0.9)^n) = 5 - 0 = 5$. Convergent.

4. $\left\{\dfrac{n}{\ln n}\right\}$ diverges, since $\lim\limits_{x \to \infty} \dfrac{x}{\ln x} \overset{H}{=} \lim\limits_{x \to \infty} \dfrac{1}{1/x} = \infty$.

6. $\left\{\dfrac{\sin n}{n}\right\}$ converges, since $-\dfrac{1}{n} \leq \dfrac{\sin n}{n} \leq \dfrac{1}{n}$ and $\pm\dfrac{1}{n} \to 0$ as $n \to \infty$, so
$\lim\limits_{n \to \infty} \dfrac{\sin n}{n} = 0$ by the Squeeze Theorem.

8. $\left\{\dfrac{(-10)^n}{n!}\right\}$ converges, since $\dfrac{10^n}{n!} = \dfrac{10\cdot10\cdot10\cdots10}{1\cdot 2\cdot 3\cdots10}\cdot\dfrac{10\cdot10\cdots10}{11\cdot12\cdots n} \leq$
$10^{10}\left[\dfrac{10}{11}\right]^{n-10} \to 0$ as $n \to \infty$, so $\lim\limits_{n \to \infty} \dfrac{(-10)^n}{n!} = 0$ (Squeeze Theorem).

[Or use (10.57).]

10. Let $a_n = \dfrac{n+n^2}{n+n^4}$ and $b_n = \dfrac{1}{n^2}$. Then $\lim\limits_{n \to \infty} \dfrac{a_n}{b_n} = \lim\limits_{n \to \infty} \dfrac{n^4+n^3}{n^4+n} = 1 > 0$, so
since $\sum\limits_{n=1}^{\infty} b_n$ converges $(p=2>1)$, $\sum\limits_{n=1}^{\infty}\dfrac{n+n^2}{n+n^4}$ converges also by the Limit
Comparison Test.

12. $\lim\limits_{n \to \infty} \left|\dfrac{a_{n+1}}{a_n}\right| = \dfrac{1}{3}\lim\limits_{n \to \infty}\left[\dfrac{n+1}{n}\right]^2 = \dfrac{1}{3}$ so series converges by Ratio Test.

14. $\lim\limits_{n \to \infty} \left[\dfrac{n-1}{n}\right]^{1/2} = 1$ so series diverges by the Test for Divergence.

16. $f(x) = \dfrac{1}{x(\ln x)^2}$ is continuous, positive and decreasing on $[2, \infty)$, so

    we can use the Integral Test. $\displaystyle\int_2^\infty \dfrac{dx}{x(\ln x)^2} = \lim\limits_{t \to \infty} \dfrac{-1}{\ln x}\Big]_2^t = \dfrac{1}{\ln 2}$ so

    the series converges.

18. If $f(x) = \dfrac{\ln x}{\sqrt{x}}$ then $f'(x) = \dfrac{2 - \ln x}{2x^{3/2}} < 0$ for $x > e^2$ so $\{a_n\}$ is

    eventually decreasing, and since $\lim\limits_{n \to \infty} \dfrac{\ln n}{\sqrt{n}} = 0$ (use l'Hospital's

    Rule), the series converges by the Alternating Series Test.

20. Use the Limit Comparison Test with $a_n = \dfrac{\sqrt{n+1} - \sqrt{n-1}}{n} =$

    $\dfrac{2}{n(\sqrt{n+1} + \sqrt{n-1})}$ [rationalizing the numerator] and $b_n = \dfrac{1}{n^{3/2}}$. $\lim\limits_{n \to \infty} \dfrac{a_n}{b_n}$

    $= \lim\limits_{n \to \infty} \dfrac{2\sqrt{n}}{\sqrt{n+1} + \sqrt{n-1}} = 1$, so $\displaystyle\sum_{n=1}^\infty b_n$ convergent $(p = \tfrac{3}{2} > 1)$ $\Rightarrow$ $\displaystyle\sum_{n=1}^\infty a_n$ converges.

22. $\displaystyle\sum_{n=1}^\infty \dfrac{1}{n(n+3)} = \sum_{n=1}^\infty \left[\dfrac{1}{3n} - \dfrac{1}{3(n+3)}\right]$. $\quad s_n = \displaystyle\sum_{i=1}^n \left[\dfrac{1}{3i} - \dfrac{1}{3(i+3)}\right] =$

    $\dfrac{1}{3} + \dfrac{1}{6} + \dfrac{1}{9} - \dfrac{1}{3(n+1)} - \dfrac{1}{3(n+2)} - \dfrac{1}{3(n+3)}$, so $\displaystyle\sum_{n=1}^\infty \dfrac{1}{n(n+3)} = \lim\limits_{n \to \infty} s_n$

    $= \dfrac{1}{3} + \dfrac{1}{6} + \dfrac{1}{9} = \dfrac{11}{18}$.

24. This is a geometric series which converges whenever $|\ln x| < 1 \Rightarrow$

    $-1 < \ln x < 1 \Rightarrow e^{-1} < x < e$.

26. (a) $\lim\limits_{n \to \infty} \left|\dfrac{a_{n+1}}{a_n}\right| = \lim\limits_{n \to \infty} \dfrac{(n+1)^{n+1}(2n)!}{(2n+2)! \; n^n} = \lim\limits_{n \to \infty} \left[1 + \dfrac{1}{n}\right]^n \dfrac{1}{2(2n+1)} = e \cdot 0 = 0$

    < 1 so the series converges by the Ratio Test.

    (b) The series of (a) is convergent so $\lim\limits_{n \to \infty} a_n = 0$ by Theorem 10.17.

28. $\lim\limits_{n \to \infty} \left|\dfrac{u_{n+1}}{u_n}\right| = 3x^2 \lim\limits_{n \to \infty} \dfrac{n+1}{n+2} = 3x^2 < 1$ for convergence $\Rightarrow$ $|x| < \dfrac{1}{\sqrt{3}}$ so

    $R = \dfrac{1}{\sqrt{3}}$. If $x = \pm\dfrac{1}{\sqrt{3}}$ the series is $\displaystyle\sum_{n=1}^\infty \dfrac{(-1)^n}{n+1}$ which converges by the

    Alternating Series Test, so interval of convergence is $\left[-\dfrac{1}{\sqrt{3}}, \dfrac{1}{\sqrt{3}}\right]$.

30. $\lim\limits_{n\to\infty} \sqrt[n]{|u_n|} = \lim\limits_{n\to\infty} \dfrac{x+1}{n} = 0$ for all x so $R = \infty$ and $I = (-\infty, \infty)$.

32. $\lim\limits_{n\to\infty} \left|\dfrac{u_{n+1}}{u_n}\right| = \lim\limits_{n\to\infty} \dfrac{(2n+2)(2n+1)}{(n+1)(n+1)}|x| = 4|x| < 1$ to converge, so $R = \dfrac{1}{4}$.

34. $f(x) = \cos x \qquad\qquad\qquad f\left(\dfrac{\pi}{3}\right) = \dfrac{1}{2}$

$f'(x) = -\sin x \qquad\qquad\quad f'\left(\dfrac{\pi}{3}\right) = -\dfrac{\sqrt{3}}{2}$

$f''(x) = -\cos x \qquad\qquad\quad f''\left(\dfrac{\pi}{3}\right) = -\dfrac{1}{2}$

$f^{(3)}(x) = \sin x \qquad\qquad\quad f^{(3)}\left(\dfrac{\pi}{3}\right) = \dfrac{\sqrt{3}}{2}$

$f^{(4)}(x) = \cos x \qquad\qquad\quad f^{(4)}\left(\dfrac{\pi}{3}\right) = \dfrac{1}{2}$

$$\cos x = \sum_{n=0}^{\infty} \frac{(-1)^n (x - \pi/3)^{2n}}{2\,(2n)!} + \sum_{n=0}^{\infty} \frac{(-1)^{n+1}\sqrt{3}(x - \pi/3)^{2n+1}}{2\,(2n+1)!}$$

36. $(1-x^2)^{1/2} = \sum\limits_{n=0}^{\infty} \binom{1/2}{n}(-x^2)^n = 1 - \dfrac{x^2}{2} - \sum\limits_{n=2}^{\infty} \dfrac{1\cdot 3\cdot 5\cdots(2n-3)x^{2n}}{2^n\, n!}$, $R=1$.

38. $e^x = \sum\limits_{n=0}^{\infty} \dfrac{x^n}{n!} \Rightarrow xe^{2x} = \sum\limits_{n=0}^{\infty} \dfrac{x(2x)^n}{n!} = \sum\limits_{n=0}^{\infty} \dfrac{2^n x^{n+1}}{n!}$, $R=\infty$.

40. $10^x = e^{x\ln 10} = \sum\limits_{n=0}^{\infty} \dfrac{\ln^n 10\cdot x^n}{n!}$, $R=\infty$.

42. $(1-3x)^{-5} = \sum\limits_{n=0}^{\infty} \binom{-5}{n}(-3x)^n = 1 + \sum\limits_{n=1}^{\infty} \dfrac{5\cdot 6\cdots(n+4)\cdot 3^n x^n}{n!}$, $|3x| < 1$ so $R = \dfrac{1}{3}$.

44. $(1-x^4)^{1/2} = \sum\limits_{n=0}^{\infty} \binom{1/2}{n}(-x^4)^n = 1 - \dfrac{x^4}{2} - \sum\limits_{n=2}^{\infty} \dfrac{1\cdot 3\cdot 5\cdots(2n-3)x^{4n}}{2^n\, n!}$ so

$\displaystyle\int_0^1 (1-x^4)^{1/2}dx = x - \dfrac{x^5}{10} - \sum\limits_{n=2}^{\infty} \dfrac{1\cdot 3\cdot 5\cdots(2n-3)x^{4n+1}}{2^n\, n!\,(4n+1)}\Bigg]_0^1$

$= 1 - \dfrac{1}{10} - \dfrac{1}{72} - \dfrac{3}{624} - \dfrac{15}{6528} - \dfrac{105}{80640} - \dfrac{945}{1152000} - \dfrac{10395}{18708480} - \cdots$

≈ 0.874

46. $\ln(1-x) = -x - \dfrac{x^2}{2} - \dfrac{x^3}{3} - \cdots - \dfrac{x^n}{n} + R_n(x)$ with $R_n(x) = \dfrac{-n!(1-z)^{n+1}}{(n+1)!}x^{n+1}$

$= -\dfrac{(1-z)^{n+1}}{n+1}x^{n+1}$ where z is between 0 and x. $|R_2(0.05)| < \dfrac{1}{3}(0.05)^3$

≈ 0.00004, so $\ln(0.95) = \ln(1 - 0.05) \approx -(0.05) - \dfrac{(0.05)^2}{2} \approx 0.0513$.

48. $f(x) = \sec x$ $f(0) = 1$

$f'(x) = \sec x \tan x$ $f'(0) = 0$

$f''(x) = \sec x \tan^2 x + \sec^3 x$ $f''(0) = 1$

$f^{(3)}(x) = \sec x \tan^3 x + 5\sec^3 x \tan x$

$\sec x = 1 + \dfrac{x^2}{2} + R_2(x)$ where $R_2(x) = \dfrac{\sec z \tan^3 z + 5\sec^3 z \tan z}{3!} x^3$

with z between 0 and x. If $0 < z < \dfrac{\pi}{6}$, $1 < \sec z < \dfrac{2}{\sqrt{3}}$ and

$0 < \tan z < \dfrac{1}{\sqrt{3}}$ so $|R_2(x)| < \dfrac{2/9 + 40/9}{6}\left[\dfrac{\pi}{6}\right]^3 \approx 0.1117$.

50. Let $f(x) = \displaystyle\sum_{m=0}^{\infty} a_m x^m$ and $g(x) = e^{f(x)} = \displaystyle\sum_{n=0}^{\infty} b_n x^n$. Then

$g'(x) = \displaystyle\sum_{n=0}^{\infty} nb_n x^{n-1}$, so nb_n occurs as the coefficient of x^{n-1}.

But also $g'(x) = e^{f(x)} f'(x) = \left[\displaystyle\sum_{n=0}^{\infty} b_n x^n\right]\left[\displaystyle\sum_{m=0}^{\infty} m a_m x^{m-1}\right]$

$= (b_0 + b_1 x + b_2 x^2 + \cdots + b_{n-1} x^{n-1} + \cdots)(a_1 + 2a_2 x + 3a_3 x^2 + \cdots + na_n x^{n-1} + \cdots)$

so the coefficient of x^{n-1} is

$$a_1 b_{n-1} + 2a_2 b_{n-2} + 3a_3 b_{n-3} + \cdots + na_n b_0 = \sum_{i=1}^{n} i a_i b_{n-i}$$

Therefore $nb_n = \displaystyle\sum_{i=1}^{n} i a_i b_{n-i}$